Fundamentals of Electronics: AC Circuits

Fundamentals of
Electronics: AC Circuits

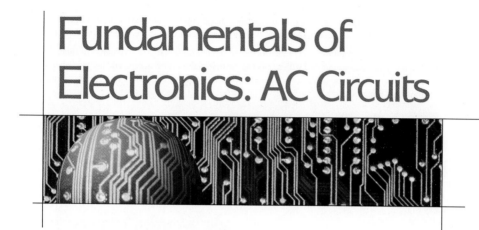

David L. Terrell

Delmar Publishers

an International Thomson Publishing company I(T)P®

Albany • Bonn • Boston • Cincinnati • Detroit • London • Madrid
Melbourne • Mexico City • New York • Pacific Grove • Paris • San Francisco
Singapore • Tokyo • Toronto • Washington

Cover Design: Nicole Reamer

Delmar Staff
Publisher: Michael A. McDermott
Acquisitions Editor: Gregory L. Clayton
Developmental Editor: Michelle Ruelos Cannistraci
Senior Project Editor: Christopher Chien
Production Manager: Larry Main

Art Director: Nicole Reamer
Marketing Manager: Kitty Kelly
Marketing Coordinator: Paula Collins
Editorial Assistant: Amy E. Tucker

Dedication

To Linda, my best friend, whose talents, wit, and charm are without end.

For more information, contact:

Delmar Publishers
3 Columbia Circle, Box 15015
Albany, New York 12212-5015

International Thomson Publishing Europe
Berkshire House
168-173 High Holborn
London, WC1V7AA
United Kingdom

Thomas Nelson Australia
102 Dodds Street
South Melbourne,
Victoria, 3205 Australia

Nelson Canada
1120 Birchmont Road
Scarborough, Ontario
M1K 5G4, Canada

ITE Spain/Paraninfo
Calle Magallanes, 25
28015-Madrid, Espana

International Thompson Editores
Seneca 53
Colonia Polanco
11560 Mexico D. F. Mexico

ITP Southern Africa
Building 18, Constantia Square
138 Sixteenth Road
P.O. Box 2459
Halfway House
1685 South Africa

International Thomson Publishing Asia
60 Albert Street
#15-01 Albert Complex
Singapore 189969

International Thomson Publishing Japan
Hirakawa-cho Kyowa Building, 3F
2-2-1 Hirakawa-cho, Chiyoda-ku,
Tokyo 102, Japan

3 4 5 6 7 8 9 10 XXX 05 04 03 02

Library of Congress Cataloging-in-Publication Data
Terrell, David L.
    Fundamentals of electronics (DC/AC circuits) / David Terrell.
      p. cm.
    Includes index.
    ISBN 0-8273-5340-5
    1. Electronics. I. Title.
TK7816.T42 1998   98-44678
621.381—dc21   CIP

CONTENTS

preface

Introduction

This fundamental electronics text covers dc and ac circuits, passive components, circuit analysis, and troubleshooting. It is designed as a core text for electronics courses in community colleges, technical institutes, and vocational/technical schools. The material can be presented in a two-semester or two-quarter sequence covering dc and ac circuits.

In today's job market, it is no longer adequate for a technician to be "exposed" to an array of topics in electronics. Rather, an entry-level technician is expected to demonstrate a practical knowledge of important skills and concepts. One primary objective of this book is to present the material in such a way that the student learns the true foundations of electronics (e.g., Ohm's and Kirchhoff's Laws) early in the sequence of topics. Then, subsequent concepts such as numerical circuit analysis are not only easier to master because they are based on familiar tools, but the coverage of the advanced material inherently reviews those previously-learned concepts that form the key building blocks for effective learning. Unlike many other texts, this book is designed specifically to be used by a student. The conversational writing style used throughout the book conveys technical concepts in terms that can be readily visualized and understood by students. For example, when introducing the various units of measure for magnetic quantities, and how these quantities interact, the author contrasts the analysis of magnetic circuits with the previously learned analysis of electrical circuits. Contrasts, similarities, and analogies are used frequently in the book to tie new material to more familiar material that is already known to the student. For example, some aspects of passive filter circuits (Chapter 18) are viewed as voltage divider circuits, which have been used extensively in earlier chapters.

Teaching Philosophy

One very important belief that permeates this text is that if the knowledge and skills being presented are to be truly practical and ultimately valuable to the student, they must be acquired as an aggregate of electronics knowledge. That is, each new principle, technique, or fact must fit naturally and logically into the student's growing knowledge base. If subjects are presented as independent, standalone topics, then memorization tends to replace learning. While either method may produce adequate grades in an academic environment, only applied, integrated learning (as opposed to rote memorization) can be expected to produce a graduate with skills that will support a lifetime of continued learning. Additionally, a graduate who has integrated knowledge understands the bigger picture with reference to electronics. This understanding can provide a significant edge for an entry-level technician during interviews with potential employers.

One example of how this belief is manifest in the text is the fact that Ohm's and Kirchhoff's Laws are presented early in the text and provide the basis for nearly all subsequent analyses. Where practical, each new circuit type or analysis technique is introduced in terms of previously mastered material, so it fits naturally into the student's knowledge base.

Like no other text available, *Fundamentals of Electronics: DC/AC Circuits* will help students learn and understand faster and better. An important teaching principle practiced within the text is formally called the multipass, multilevel learning system. During the first pass, each new type of circuit is presented from a qualitative, nonmathematical viewpoint. This initial pass develops vocabulary and provides perspective on how the new skills compare with previously mastered subjects. One or more subsequent passes provide the numerical analysis aspects of the circuit. However, since the overall behavior of the circuit has already been mastered, the numerical analysis is much less confusing. This enables students to achieve greater depths of learning in the same or an even shorter time period than conventional methods would require.

Following are some brief examples to illustrate this teaching philosophy:

- Positive identification of series, parallel, series-parallel, and complex circuits is mastered before even the simplest series circuit is analyzed numerically.
- When numerical analyses for series and for parallel circuits are introduced, the overall voltage and current characteristics of the circuit are presented first. Second, circuit analysis based on Ohm's and Kirchhoff's Laws is discussed in a completely specified circuit (i.e., all component values are known). A subsequent pass then presents the numerical analysis of partially specified series and parallel circuits.
- In a similar manner, the topic of series-parallel circuits relies heavily on the concepts and computational strategies discussed with reference to series and parallel circuits.

This same underlying teaching strategy extends to include discussions on magnetism and electromagnetics. The student first learns qualitative concepts (e.g., what factors affect the value of voltage induced into a wire as it passes through a magnetic field, and what relationship–direct or inverse–these factors have). Subsequently, the numerical analysis of magnetic circuits is presented, but the student already has the vision needed to conceptualize the overall problem and the knowledge needed to judge the "reasonableness" of an answer. Without this important sequence of learning, students often compute absurd answers to problems, but are unable to detect the error. Instructors frequently hear the defensive comment, "But that's what the calculator said!"

Overall Organization

Fundamentals of Electronics: DC/AC Circuits contains 18 chapters. The book begins with a brief overview of electronics, an introduction to atomic structure, and a discussion of technical notation. The student is then introduced to various electronic components and electrical quantities that form the basis for further studies. Vocabulary building is an important part of a student's initial efforts.

Identification of all circuit types is then presented *before* a detailed mathematical analysis is made of any circuit type. Thus, a student is able to readily classify a circuit as series, parallel, series-parallel, or complex before learning to compute circuit values in even a basic series circuit. This simple step goes a long way toward reducing student confusion and increasing student success when more formal circuit analyses are presented.

In-depth analysis of series, parallel, series-parallel, and complex circuits then follows. The more intense numerical procedures are preceded by introductory discussions to clarify principles and to help students grasp the important concepts before becoming focused on intricate calculations. The introductory discussions provide the student with an intuitive or qualitative understanding of circuit or device operation; subsequent numerical analyses provide the technical depth required to support subsequent studies in advanced electronics courses. This sequence increases the student's ability to judge the reasonableness of mathematical results, and greatly strengthens his or her practical knowledge of the subject.

Kirchhoff's Voltage Law is presented as an integral part of series circuit analysis, and Kirchhoff's Current Law is presented as an integral part of parallel circuit analysis. Both of these laws and Ohm's Law are then used as the basis for most subsequent analyses. It is believed that if a student has a genuine command of these basic laws as they apply to circuit analysis, that student is armed with tools that will streamline learning throughout his or her career.

The DC portion of the text (Chapters 1 through 10) concludes with discussions on power sources, wire and cable, DC test equipment, and magnetism and electromagnetism. The magnetism topics include both qualitative and numerical analyses of magnetic circuits. Even here, however, the numerical computations are strongly rooted in previously studied topics such as Ohm's Law and series circuit analysis.

The AC portion of the book (Chapters 11 through 18) begins with the generation of AC and defines the various characteristics, values, and relationships associated with sine waves. Inductance and *RL* circuits are presented before capacitance and *RC* circuits. There is considerable disagreement (even within the same school) about the "best" sequence for these important topics. These two general subject areas consisting of Chapters 12 through 15 can be presented in a different sequence if the instructor so chooses. Thus, the expected sequence of Chapters 12, 13, 14, and 15 could be altered to the sequence of Chapters 14, 15, 12, and 13 if the instructor prefers to introduce capacitance and *RC* circuits prior to inductance and *RL* circuits. Depending on the intended depth of coverage, it might be necessary to present complex-number operations separately, since this subject is currently introduced as part of the *RL* circuits chapter. In either case, *RLC* circuits (Chapter 16) follows naturally. Both intuitive characteristics and numerical analyses of resonant and nonresonant *RLC* circuits are presented.

Transformers and mutual inductance are presented in Chapter 17. Again, the important sequence of intuitive introduction based on previous learning followed by more rigorous numerical computations is employed.

The book concludes with a discussion of passive filter circuits. This may be taught as a standalone chapter. Alternatively, an instructor may successfully teach the various filter circuits presented in Chapter 18 as isolated applications used to illustrate the principles discussed in the *RL*, *RC*, and *RLC* circuit chapters.

Chapter Format

Each chapter consists of the following sections:

- **Objectives** start off each chapter and identify the main areas to be discussed and the main skills to be acquired in the chapter. The general format of behavioral objectives is used, but with the stringent requirements on verbiage relaxed to simplify their expressions. The chapter objectives can be a powerful tool to guide the student's progress through the chapter, and to clarify the answer to the otherwise prevalent question in the student's mind, "What do I really need to know?".
- **Key Terms** are listed at the opening of each chapter. They are boldfaced and are defined with their first use in the text.
- **Examples and Solutions** guide students through step-by-step procedures to solve problems. Each discussion of a new analytical procedure is followed by one or more detailed examples that illustrate the steps in the solution.

Key Terms are listed at the opening of each chapter. They are boldfaced and defined with their first use in the text.

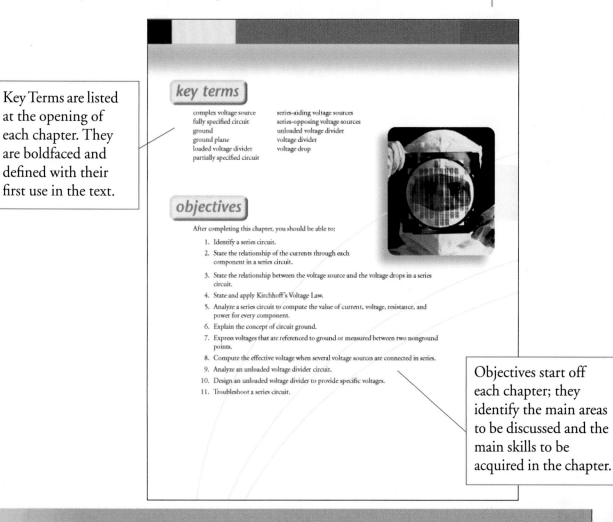

key terms

complex voltage source	series-aiding voltage sources
fully specified circuit	series-opposing voltage sources
ground	unloaded voltage divider
ground plane	voltage divider
loaded voltage divider	voltage drop
partially specified circuit	

objectives

After completing this chapter, you should be able to:

1. Identify a series circuit.
2. State the relationship of the currents through each component in a series circuit.
3. State the relationship between the voltage source and the voltage drops in a series circuit.
4. State and apply Kirchhoff's Voltage Law.
5. Analyze a series circuit to compute the value of current, voltage, resistance, and power for every component.
6. Explain the concept of circuit ground.
7. Express voltages that are referenced to ground or measured between two nonground points.
8. Compute the effective voltage when several voltage sources are connected in series.
9. Analyze an unloaded voltage divider circuit.
10. Design an unloaded voltage divider to provide specific voltages.
11. Troubleshoot a series circuit.

Objectives start off each chapter; they identify the main areas to be discussed and the main skills to be acquired in the chapter.

preface

- **Practice Problems** allow students to solve problems on their own and to reinforce important concepts. Answers to practice problems follow for immediate feedback. The combination of discussion, example, and practice exposes the student to a "Here's how you do it"–"Now watch me do it"–"OK, now you do it" learning sequence.

Examples and Solutions guide students with step-by-step procedures to solve problems

Art consists of four-color illustrations, schematics, and photos.

Practice Problems allow students to solve problems on their own and reinforce important concepts.

Key Points are highlighted in the margin to reinforce essential concepts.

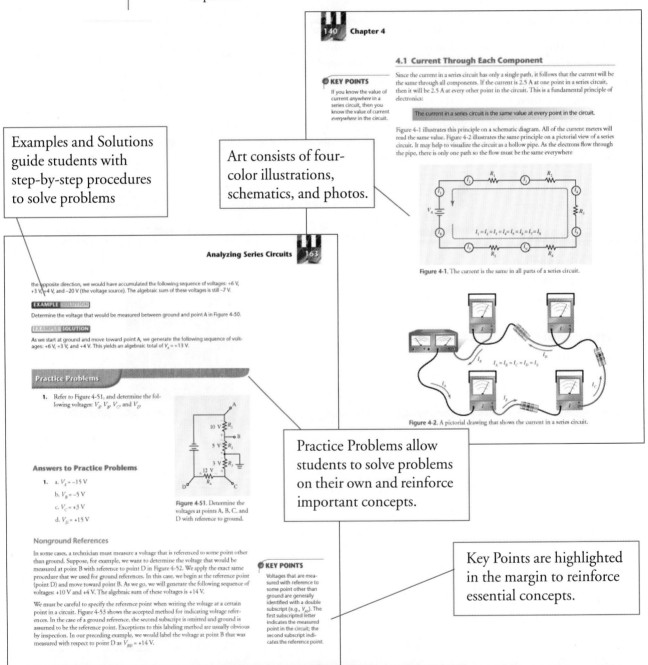

140 Chapter 4

4.1 Current Through Each Component

KEY POINTS

If you know the value of current *anywhere* in a series circuit, then you know the value of current *everywhere* in the circuit.

Since the current in a series circuit has only a single path, it follows that the current will be the same through all components. If the current is 2.5 A at one point in a series circuit, then it will be 2.5 A at every other point in the circuit. This is a fundamental principle of electronics:

> The current in a series circuit is the same value at every point in the circuit.

Figure 4-1 illustrates this principle on a schematic diagram. All of the current meters will read the same value. Figure 4-2 illustrates the same principle on a pictorial view of a series circuit. It may help to visualize the circuit as a hollow pipe. As the electrons flow through the pipe, there is only one path so the flow must be the same everywhere

Figure 4-1. The current is the same in all parts of a series circuit.

Figure 4-2. A pictorial drawing that shows the current in a series circuit.

Analyzing Series Circuits   163

the opposite direction, we would have accumulated the following sequence of voltages: +6 V, +3 V, –4 V, and –20 V (the voltage source). The algebraic sum of these voltages is still –7 V.

EXAMPLE SOLUTION

Determine the voltage that would be measured between ground and point A in Figure 4-50.

EXAMPLE SOLUTION

As we start at ground and move toward point A, we generate the following sequence of voltages: +6 V, +3 V, and +4 V. This yields an algebraic total of $V_A = +13$ V.

Practice Problems

1. Refer to Figure 4-51, and determine the following voltages: V_A, V_B, V_C, and V_D.

Answers to Practice Problems

1. a. $V_A = -15$ V
   b. $V_B = -5$ V
   c. $V_C = +3$ V
   d. $V_D = +15$ V

Figure 4-51. Determine the voltages at points A, B, C, and D with reference to ground.

Nonground References

In some cases, a technician must measure a voltage that is referenced to some point other than ground. Suppose, for example, we want to determine the voltage that would be measured at point B with reference to point D in Figure 4-52. We apply the exact same procedure that we used for ground references. In this case, we begin at the reference point (point D) and move toward point B. As we go, we will generate the following sequence of voltages: +10 V and +4 V. The algebraic sum of these voltages is +14 V.

We must be careful to specify the reference point when writing the voltage at a certain point in a circuit. Figure 4-53 shows the accepted method for indicating voltage references. In the case of a ground reference, the second subscript is omitted and ground is assumed to be the reference point. Exceptions to this labeling method are usually obvious by inspection. In our preceding example, we would label the voltage at point B that was measured with respect to point D as $V_{BD} = +14$ V.

KEY POINTS

Voltages that are measured with reference to some point other than ground are generally identified with a double subscript (e.g., V_{BD}). The first subscripted letter indicates the measured point in the circuit; the second subscript indicates the reference point.

- **Key Points** are highlighted in the margin to reinforce essential concepts so the learner has immediate capsulation of the most important points in a particular section. These also serve as an excellent review tool, since they effectively summarize the more critical topics. If a particular key point remains unclear, the student can refer to the adjacent discussion for further details and clarification.

Troubleshooting and Circuit Analysis Tables help students organize circuit analysis problems.

Exercise Problems provide self-check and review questions at the end of each section.

Chapter Summaries highlight the most important topics in the chapter.

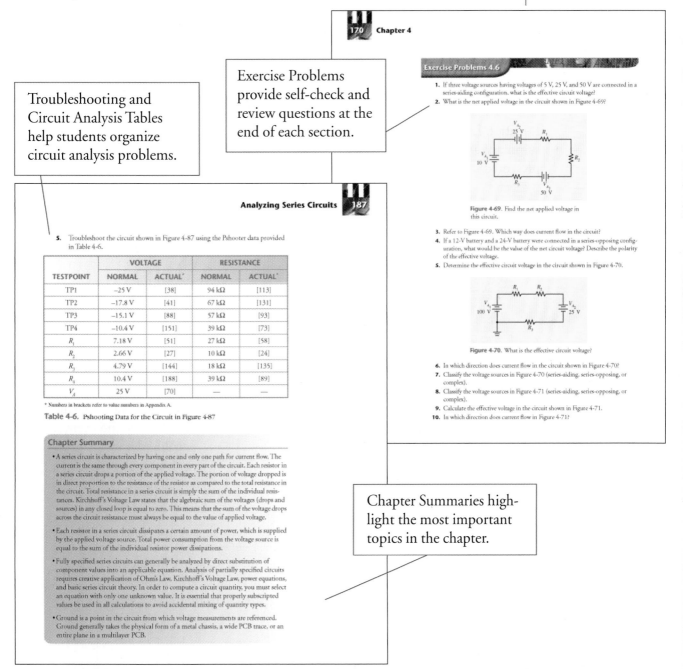

170 Chapter 4

Exercise Problems 4.6

1. If three voltage sources having voltages of 5 V, 25 V, and 50 V are connected in a series-aiding configuration, what is the effective circuit voltage?
2. What is the net applied voltage in the circuit shown in Figure 4-69?

Figure 4-69. Find the net applied voltage in this circuit.

3. Refer to Figure 4-69. Which way does current flow in the circuit?
4. If a 12-V battery and a 24-V battery were connected in a series-opposing configuration, what would be the value of the net circuit voltage? Describe the polarity of the effective voltage.
5. Determine the effective circuit voltage in the circuit shown in Figure 4-70.

Figure 4-70. What is the effective circuit voltage?

6. In which direction does current flow in the circuit shown in Figure 4-70?
7. Classify the voltage sources in Figure 4-70 (series-aiding, series-opposing, or complex).
8. Classify the voltage sources in Figure 4-71 (series-aiding, series-opposing, or complex).
9. Calculate the effective voltage in the circuit shown in Figure 4-71.
10. In which direction does current flow in Figure 4-71?

Analyzing Series Circuits 187

5. Troubleshoot the circuit shown in Figure 4-87 using the Pshooter data provided in Table 4-6.

TESTPOINT	VOLTAGE NORMAL	VOLTAGE ACTUAL*	RESISTANCE NORMAL	RESISTANCE ACTUAL*
TP1	−25 V	[38]	94 kΩ	[113]
TP2	−17.8 V	[41]	67 kΩ	[131]
TP3	−15.1 V	[88]	57 kΩ	[93]
TP4	−10.4 V	[151]	39 kΩ	[73]
R_1	7.18 V	[51]	27 kΩ	[58]
R_2	2.66 V	[27]	10 kΩ	[24]
R_3	4.79 V	[144]	18 kΩ	[135]
R_4	10.4 V	[188]	39 kΩ	[89]
V_A	25 V	[70]	—	—

* Numbers in brackets refer to value numbers in Appendix A.

Table 4-6. Pshooting Data for the Circuit in Figure 4-87

Chapter Summary

- A series circuit is characterized by having one and only one path for current flow. The current is the same through every component in every part of the circuit. Each resistor in a series circuit drops a portion of the applied voltage. The portion of voltage dropped is in direct proportion to the resistance of the resistor as compared to the total resistance in the circuit. Total resistance in a series circuit is simply the sum of the individual resistances. Kirchhoff's Voltage Law states that the algebraic sum of the voltages (drops and sources) in any closed loop is equal to zero. This means that the sum of the voltage drops across the circuit resistance must always be equal to the value of applied voltage.

- Each resistor in a series circuit dissipates a certain amount of power, which is supplied by the applied voltage source. Total power consumption from the voltage source is equal to the sum of the individual resistor power dissipations.

- Fully specified series circuits can generally be analyzed by direct substitution of component values into an applicable equation. Analysis of partially specified circuits requires creative application of Ohm's Law, Kirchhoff's Voltage Law, power equations, and basic series circuit theory. In order to compute a circuit quantity, you must select an equation with only one unknown value. It is essential that properly subscripted values be used in all calculations to avoid accidental mixing of quantity types.

- Ground is a point in the circuit from which voltage measurements are referenced. Ground generally takes the physical form of a metal chassis, a wide PCB trace, or an entire plane in a multilayer PCB.

preface

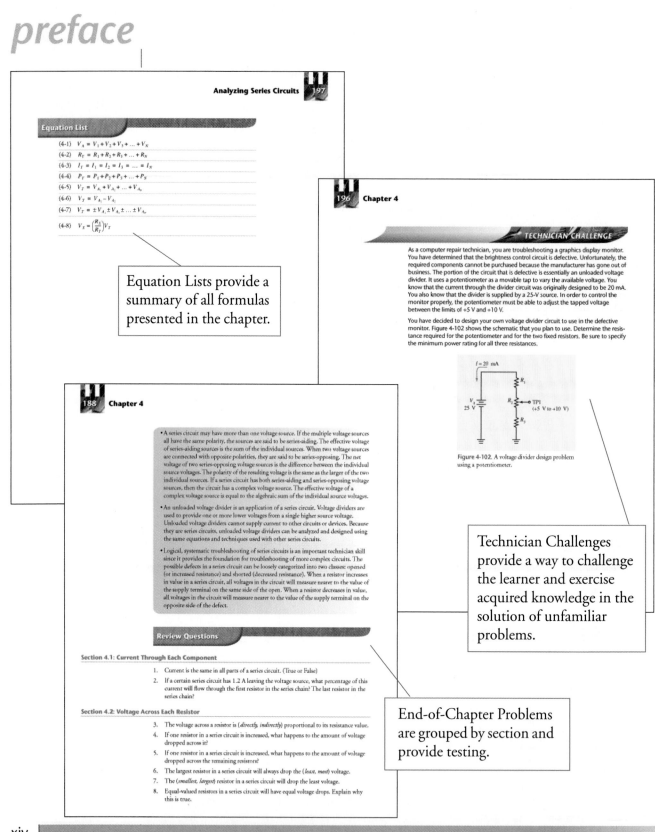

Equation Lists provide a summary of all formulas presented in the chapter.

Technician Challenges provide a way to challenge the learner and exercise acquired knowledge in the solution of unfamiliar problems.

End-of-Chapter Problems are grouped by section and provide testing.

- **Summaries** at the end of each chapter highlight the most important topics in the chapter. This can be a valuable study resource for a student.
- **End-of-Chapter Problems** are grouped by section to enable quick referencing of related discussions in the body of the chapter. The large number of available problems permits considerable flexibility based on the needs of the learner.
- **Equation Lists** provide a collection of all of the equations formally introduced within a given chapter. They provide a quick reference tool during homework assignments or when referencing material in a previous chapter.

Important Features

There are numerous unique features incorporated throughout the book to help stimulate critical thinking, problem solving, troubleshooting and circuit analysis skills.

- **Technician Challenge**. This feature provides a way to challenge the learner and to exercise acquired knowledge in the solution of unfamiliar problems. All of the Technician Challenge problems can be solved by applying the principles and methods presented in the particular chapter or preceding chapters. However, in many cases, they are tough enough to interest even the most accomplished students.
- **Use of Mathematics.** A brief look through the text will quickly reveal that mathematics is an integral part of this text, just as it is an integral part of electronics. However, the mathematics is not used to introduce a subject, nor is it generally used to explain circuit operation. Rather, an effort is made to give the student a solid intuitive understanding of a circuit or component's operation or behavior *before* the introduction of rigorous calculations. The mathematics simply provides a tool for the next level of analysis.

  There is debate as to whether calculations involving polar and rectangular coordinates should be included in an introductory electronics text. In this text, the use of complex numbers to represent circuit quantities and the associated conversions is presented in the text; however, the inclusion appears in key areas only (e.g., numerical analysis of series-parallel *RL* and *RC* circuits). These sections can be skipped in the classroom, if desired.

  Network theorems is another area of debate. This text presents all of the relevant theorems in a single chapter, which may be omitted if desired. However, since each of eight theorems is presented as a separate section within the chapter, instructors may select those areas that are most valuable to their particular classroom. The step-by-step procedures and examples provided in the chapter also make self-study a viable alternative.

- **Circuit Analysis Tables.** Solution matrices or tables are an integral part of detailed circuit analysis procedures for all basic circuit configurations. This is a powerful teaching tool that helps students organize circuit analysis problems and quickly contrast known quantities with unknown quantities for a given problem.

preface

- **Applied Technology.** Applied Technology sections illustrate how textbook concepts relate to practical applications outside the classroom. In each case, one or more applications are described that utilize the components, circuits, or principles discussed in the chapter. This helps the student appreciate the value of the material being studied by seeing the relationship to real applications.

- **Troubleshooting Exercises.** A great number of electronics students initially come to school with the belief that they are going to learn to "fix" anything that has a wire coming out of the back. In principle, they do, but in practice students rarely feel or believe that they can really troubleshoot a circuit. A majority of the chapters in this text include a section on troubleshooting.

  The troubleshooting sections address three important areas: application of relevant test equipment, the development of a logical and systematic procedure, and troubleshooting practice. Of course, there is no substitute for the troubleshooting of actual defective equipment, but the PShooter exercises presented in this text require the student to utilize many of the same skills that would be required in an actual troubleshooting environment. These skills include test equipment selection, testpoint selection, measurement interpretation, schematic interpretation, and minimization of the number of circuit checks.

  PShooter exercises consist of a schematic diagram with numbered testpoints. Each problem is accompanied by a table that lists the normal values (i.e., values with no defect) for each component and each testpoint in the circuit. Also associated with each measurable point are a series of numerical codes indicating the actual values of circuit quantities such as voltage, current, and resistance that are present with the defect in the circuit. The student chooses a testpoint and a measurement type. The associated code number is then used to look up the actual measured value in a table in the appendix of the book. A student should strive to make as few measurements as possible to develop a systematic troubleshooting procedure in preference to a simple sequence of guesses. While either method may ultimately locate the defect, the student is shown why only a systematic procedure is conducive to long-term success in the field.

  The author also conveys important techniques that represent practicalities in a business environment. Examples include minimizing the soldering/desoldering of surface-mount components on an expensive circuit board, the discarding and subsequent replacement of suspected surface-mounted capacitors even if they are found to be good, and the value of in-circuit ohmmeter tests.

The Learning Package

The complete ancillary package was developed to achieve two goals:

1. To assist students in learning essential information needed to succeed to in the exciting field of electronics.
2. To assist instructors in planning and implementing their instructional programs for the most efficient use of time and other resources.

For The Student

Lab Manual–A lab manual is available to support *Fundamentals of Electronics: DC/AC Circuits*. The 54 experiments are closely related to the material presented in the text. Emphasis is placed on practical applications of theory and development of practical technician skills. The experiments are designed to promote student thinking. Cognitive skills are developed as the student progresses through the projects. Step-by-step procedures are minimized in preference to equivalent procedures, which provide flexibility, allow room for creativity, and demand authentic application of the principles presented in the text. The projects are also designed to provide the instructor with quick but effective means for determining learning success in each key area.

Order #: 0-8273-5342-1

Troubleshooting DC/AC Circuits with Electronics Workbench (with enclosed Circuits Data Disk)–This workbook teaches students how to troubleshoot circuits with the help of Electronics Workbench®. Students learn how to make measurements just as they would in an actual electronics lab. They replace components, test results, and observe effects on circuit operation, via a powerful computer-based learning tool.

Order #: 0-7668-1133-6

For The Instructor

Instructor's Guide –This comprehensive Instructor's Guide provides answers from the text and lab manual along with instructional strategies, sample course schedules, and transparency masters.

Order #: 0-8273-5341-3

Instructor's Teaching System (ITS)–An innovative Teaching System composed of tools that are designed to correlate, reinforce each other, and provide synergy, but can also be used individually. This binder of educational tools includes:

- Instructor's Guide
- e.resource™–Available all on one CD-ROM, this custom-designed teaching resource acts as an organizer and launch pad for all of the following applications:

   Computerized Testbank–Over 1,500 questions that provide mix-and-match capabilities for designing test for any phase of training.

   Electronic Gradebook–Tracks student performance, prints student progress reports, organizes assignments, and more, to simplify administrative tasks.

   On-line Testing–This is a feature of the computerized testbank that allows exams to be administered on-line via a school network or standalone PC.

PowerPoint Lecture Outline–Provides customizable teaching outlines for every chapter in the textbook. Graphics from the Image Library or your own can be imported to create individualized classroom presentations.

Image Library–Selected color illustrations from the textbook provide the instructor with another means of promoting student understanding. The Image Library allows the instructor to display or print images for classroom presentations.

• **Circuits Data Disk**–Diskette includes circuits from the textbook created in Electronics Workbench® to be used in conjunction with the accompanying troubleshooting workbook. Instructors may copy and distribute to students free of charge.

User Documentation–Additional print material provides information, instruction, and teaching hints on how to use all of the tools together for maximum benefit.

ITS Order #: 0-7668-0655-3

Electronics into the Future: Circuit Fundamentals CD–*Electronics into the Future* is a new CD-Based Interactive Learning product that is the perfect technology accompaniment to your DC/AC Circuits text or as a standalone learning tool. This full multimedia product includes animation, video, and troubleshooting. Interactive, interesting, innovative–it is a great way to visualize and understand electronics concepts!

Network version Order #: 0-7668-0657-X
Student version Order #: 0-7668-0659-6

Online Companion™–This text has a companion website, which will have high appeal to both educators and students. Features include:

• Technology Updates
• Internet Activities
• Periodic Discussion Forums
• Ask the Author: Frequently Asked Questions
• Comprehensive listing of links to electronics industry and educational sites
• Instructors Resources
• Periodic RealAudio® broadcasts from author and contributors on new technology and educational strategies in electronics.
• Free Internet-based online syllabus through Thomson's World Class Course.
• Come visit our site at **www.electronictech.com**

Technology

Electronics Workbench

New to this edition are optional Electronics Workbench® projects. In the accompanying *Troubleshooting DC/AC Circuits with Electronics Workbench®* workbook, circuits are selected from the textbook and are built using Electronics Workbench®. Students learn how to make measurements as they would in the lab. Students replace components and then test the results to see how the changes affect the operation on the circuits. This is all done on a computer.

Using Electronics Workbench® to learn electronics still permits the learner to solve a problem in student-sized steps, yet gives a deeper understanding of the subject. The teaching of electronics has changed because today's students have much more to learn in the same or less time. Application of a powerful yet intuitive learning tool like Electronics Workbench® is essential so students can master all the important concepts and skills in the time available.

This provides a new and exciting dimension to learning electronics by providing 'live' circuits. The troubleshooting strategies used in the computer simulation are the same as those used with physical circuits in the lab. Circuits are provided on a diskette included in this package. The workbook coupled with Electronics Workbench insures that learning how to troubleshoot is swift and effective.

Electronics into the Future: Circuit Fundamentals CD

Electronics into the Future is a new interactive CD-ROM-based product from Delmar that is the perfect technology accompaniment to your DC/AC circuits text or as a stand-alone learning tool.

Electronics into the Future offers your students, and you as an instructor, a wide range of multimedia presentations and interactive simulations designed to develop and clarify important concepts in electronics.

Electronics into the Future puts the power of nonlinear learning technology in your and your students' hands. As a classroom learning tool, *Electronics into the Future* gives you the power to use technology to illustrate difficult concepts. As a standalone learning tool, *Electronics into the Future* enables students to learn theory and troubleshooting from interactive practical applications.

FEATURES:

- Available in either student or network version
- Contains six interactive modules featuring elements such as: presentation video (with practical application video opening and exposition circuit modeling of a practical example), Interactive Conceptualization, Troubleshooting, and much more.

  The content modules will cover the following topics: fundamental quantities, Ohm's law, power, series circuits, parallel circuits, series-parallel circuits, network theorems (Kirchhoff's, superposition, Thevenin's), and magnetism and electromagnetism.
- Mathematics for Electronics content module. This model can be accessed as a standalone module and is linked logically into each content module.

preface

- Recognizing that Troubleshooting is one of the key learning objectives for students in DC/AC Circuits, special emphasis is placed on Troubleshooting. *Electronics into the Future* has circuits for troubleshooting that were created in Electronics Workbench®.

- *Electronics into the Future* can launch the student edition of Electronics Workbench®. The network version allows instructors to add links to their own Electronics Workbench® files.

  Runs in an easy-to-navigate browser environment.

  Includes free copy of Netscape Navigator® and Microsoft Internet Explorer®.

- Please visit our web site at www.electronictech.com for more details and a demonstration. Please contact your sales representative for a full demonstration and for pricing details.

Acknowledgments

The Author and Delmar Publishers would like to extend their appreciation to the following reviewers who evaluated the textbook at different stages of development and provided valuable comments to publishing the best quality textbook:

John Avakian, College of San Mateo

R. Gary Bennett, Bryant & Stratton

Edward L. Bowling, Johnston Community College

Mike Brandt, Western Dakota Vo-Tech

Mel Bratley, Skagit Valley Community College

Dick Bridgeman, DeVry Institute of Technology

Kelley M. Brumley

Bruce Bush, Albuquerque Technical–Vocational Institute

William Campbell, Bay Area Vocational Technical School

John H. Carpenter, Sandhills Community College

Ron Craig, DeVry Institute of Technology

Donnin Custer, Western Iowa Tech

Joe Etminan, Rock Valley College

David Fridenmaker, ITT Technical Institute

John Giancola, DeVry Institute of Technology

Thomas Giasomo, Bryant & Stratton

Randy Goldsmith, Southeast Community College

Jim Hallam, Spokane Community College

John Edward Hart, DeVry Institute of Technology

Dr. Gaby Hawat, Valencia Community College

Timothy Haynes, Haywood Community College

David Heiserman, SweetHaven Publishing Services

William Hill, DeVry Institute of Technology

Robert S. Hockman, Texas State Technical College

Mark Hughes, Orangeburg-Calhoun Technical College

Wade Jung, ITT Technical Institute

Marc Kalis, Winona Technical College

Peter Kerckhoff, DeVry Institute of Technology

Stephen Kuchler, Ivy Tech

James R. Mallory, Rochester Institute of Technology

Brent Meyers, Oakland Community College

Dave Miller, New Hampshire Technical Institute

Shayan Mirabi, ITT Technical Institute

Donald Montgomery, ITT Technical Institute

Patrick O'Connor, DeVry Institute of Technology

Jeff Rankinen, Pennsylvania College of Technology

Jim Rhodes, Trident Technical College

Gus Rummel, Central Texas College

Gary Saylor, Crowder College

Allan Souder, Seneca College

George Sweiss, DeVry Institute of Technology

Ken Teel, ITT Technical Institute

Dale Willett, Lansing Community College

preface

The Author would like to thank many people and companies who provided photographs, physical components, and technical literature to help make this text representative of the most current technologies. The following individuals deserve special appreciation for their efforts on this project:

Denise Anderson, NEC Technologies (Golin-Harris Communications, Inc.), Chicago, IL

Robert K. Beachler, Altera Corporation, San Jose, CA

Derek Brooke, PREM Magnetics Incorporated, Johnsburg, IL

Linda Capcara, Motorola, Inc., Phoenix, AZ

Baldev Chaudhari, SMEC (Surface Mountable Electronic Components), Austin, TX

Linda Chocholka, Technipower, Danbury, CT

DeVry Institutes of Technology

Trisha Di Diego, LeCroy Corporate Headquarters, Chestnut Ridge, NY

Chris Dunlap, Murata Erie North America, Inc., Smyrna, GA

Greg Elmore, Maxtec International Corporation, Chicago, IL

Claude Forter, Fair-Rite Products Corporation, Wallkill, NY

Karl Grubb, Potter and Brumfield, Princeton, NJ

Kim Hall, Duracell Inc., Bethel, CT

Angie Hatfield, Motorola, Inc., Phoenix, AZ

Robyn L. Hensel, Meunier Electronic Supply, Indianapolis, IN

Roslyn Howard, IRC, Inc., Boone, NC

Johansen Manufacturing Corporation (John E. Deimel Company), Northfield, IL

Bryan Johnson, GE Medical Systems, Milwaukee, WI

Terri Johnson, Mallory (North American Capacitor Company), Indianapolis, IN

Dr. Kenneth Keenan, The Keenan Corporation, Pinellas Park, FL

Mary Levitt, AVX Corporation, New York, NY

Matt Maready, Ledtronics, Torrance, CA

Jane Marks, Deltrol Controls, Milwaukee, WI

Mike Morone, Meunier Electronic Supply, Indianapolis, IN

Julie Nusom, Tektronix, Inc., Wilsonville, OR

Darwa Renshaw, IDEC Corporation, Sunnyvale, CA

Janet Roberts, MicroSim Corporation, Irvine, CA

Will Rodgers, Florida Power Corporation, St. Petersburg, FL

Joan Roy, Leader Instruments Corporation, Hauppauge, NY

Loren Santow, Chicago, IL

Keith Schopp, Eveready Battery Company, Inc., St. Louis, MO

Craig Skarpiak, Andrew Corporation, Orland Park, IL

Ted Suever, Triplett Corporation, Bluffton, OH

Joan Sykes, Hewlett-Packard Company, Atlanta, GA

Robert S. Waselewski, Tampa Electric Company, Tampa, FL

Chris Willson, Cornell-Dubilier, Pickens, SC

alternation

asymmetrical waveform

cycle

fundamental frequency

harmonic frequency

period

periodic waveform

root-mean-square

slip rings

symmetrical waveform

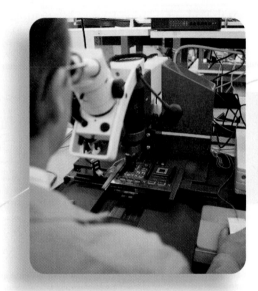

objectives

After completing this chapter, you should be able to:

1. Explain how a sinusoidal waveform can be generated.

2. Describe the relationship between frequency and period of a sine wave.

3. Compute any of the following voltage or current values for a given sine wave: peak, peak-to-peak, average, rms, instantaneous at a specified angle.

4. Discuss the meaning of phase when referencing sinusoidal waveforms.

5. Analyze resistive ac circuits.

6. Use an oscilloscope to make the following sinusoidal measurements: voltage, frequency, and period

Alternating Voltage and Current

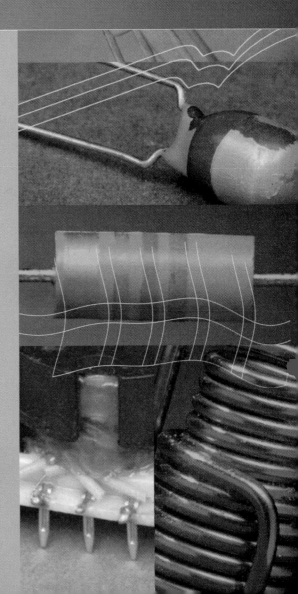

Alternating current and voltage is critical to the operation of nearly all practical electronic devices. The 120 volts supplied to your home by the power company, the signal voltages that cause music from your stereo, the radio waves that allow radio and television transmission, the radar waves used in speed detectors, the ultrasonic waves used in burglar alarms, and the telemetry signals used to communicate with a satellite are all examples of alternating current and voltage.

11.1 Generation of Alternating Voltage

A direct voltage or current (dc) has a certain value and a certain polarity. It remains relatively constant indefinitely. By contrast, an alternating voltage or current (ac) varies in both amplitude and polarity. To better appreciate these important characteristics of an alternating voltage or current, let us see how these voltages may be produced.

Rectangular Waveshapes

Figure 11-1 illustrates a very simple way to produce an alternating voltage. When the switch in Figure 11-1(a) is in position A, a positive voltage (with reference to ground) is applied to the resistor. V_{A_1} is essentially connected across the resistor. These times are labeled in Figure 11-1(b). When the switch is moved to position B, V_{A_2} is connected across the resistor, and a negative voltage (with reference to ground) can be measured. These times are also labeled in Figure 11-1(b). The horizontal axis of the graph is measured in time (e.g., seconds). Clearly, the rate at which the switch is moved between positions determines the duration of each voltage polarity interval on the graph.

Figure 11-2 shows the graph (called a **waveform**) of a voltage (or current, since $I = V/R$ and R is constant) that might be produced by the circuit shown in Figure 11-1. Several important characteristics of alternating voltages are labeled.

Note that the waveform in Figure 11-2 is repetitious and consists of a continuing series of **cycles.** The time required for one complete cycle is called the **period** of the waveform. A period consists of two opposite polarity **alternations.** The lengths of the positive and negative alternations are not necessarily the same, but the combined length is always equal to the period of the waveform. If the positive and negative alternations are equal, the waveform is said to be **symmetrical.** Waveforms with unequal alternations are called **asymmetrical.** If the cycles of the waveform are continuous (regardless of symmetry), the waveform is said to be **periodic.**

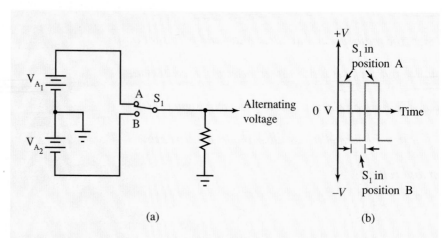

Figure 11-1. A simple way to produce alternating voltage.

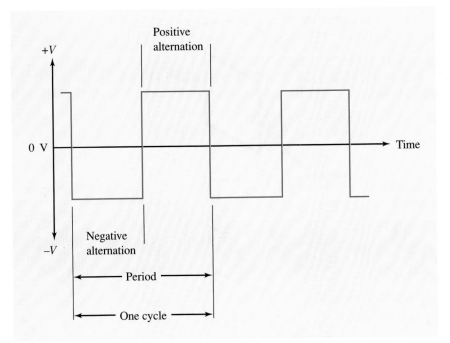

Figure 11-2. Some important characteristics of alternating waveforms.

A waveform like the one shown in Figure 11-2, which makes abrupt changes in polarity, is called a digital signal, a rectangular waveform, a square wave (if symmetrical), a pulse, or other similar classification. You will learn additional characteristics of this type waveform when you study digital electronics.

Sinusoidal Waveshapes

Figure 11-3 shows a loop of wire being rotated in a magnetic field. This is the basis of an ac generator or alternator. When we studied dc generators in Chapter 10, we saw how a segmented commutator and brush assembly is used to connect the rotating conductor to the external circuitry. In a similar manner, the **slip rings** and brushes in Figure 11-3 perform the task of making a continuous electrical connection to the rotating conductor. As shown in Figure 11-3, each end of the rotating loop is connected to a slip ring. The slip rings are mounted on the shaft that supports the rotating loop. Each of the slip rings is a continuous ring of smooth metal. The spring-loaded brushes slide along the surface of the slip rings as the conductor assembly rotates.

Figure 11-3 also shows a graph that plots the magnitude and polarity of the voltage that is produced as the conductor loop rotates. The first position shown in Figure 11-3(a) is labeled as 0°. Here, the conductors are moving parallel to the flux lines, so no voltage is generated. The graph shows 0 V at 0°. The sketch in Figure 11-3(b) shows the conductor as it passes directly across the pole faces of the magnet. In this case, the conductor is cutting a maximum number of flux lines and produces a maximum voltage. The left-hand rule for induction can be used to confirm the polarity of induced voltage. Since the conductor has moved one-fourth of a complete rotation, we label this as the 90° point. The graph shows that we have a maximum induced voltage at this point.

KEY POINTS

When a loop of wire is rotated at a constant speed in a magnetic field, a sinusoidal waveform of voltage is induced into the wire.

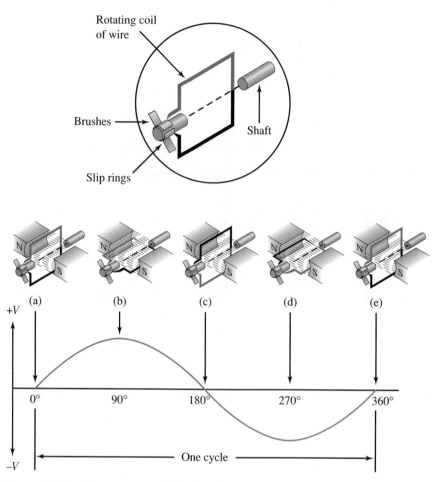

Figure 11-3. Construction of a basic alternator.

In Figure 11-3(c), the coil has reached the halfway point, and the conductors are once again moving parallel to the magnetic flux lines. No voltage is induced. This is shown graphically as the 180° point. Figure 11-3(d) shows the conductors moving across the pole faces and generating maximum voltage. Realize, however, that each of the conductors is moving across the opposite pole face from that shown in Figure 11-3(b). Thus, we would expect an opposite polarity of induced voltage. This expectation is labeled as the 270° point on the graph, and can easily be confirmed with the left-hand rule for induction.

Finally, Figure 11-3(e) shows the conductor back in its original position. The relative movement of the conductor and magnetic field is again zero, so no voltage is induced. This is identified as the 360° point on the graph. The graph clearly shows that the voltage varies continuously in amplitude and periodically changes polarity. Although the horizontal axis of the graph in Figure 11-3 is labeled in degrees of rotation, it could just as easily be labeled in units of time. That is, if the conductor is rotated at a given speed, then it will take a definite amount of time to make a full 360° rotation. A practical alternator, as with a practical dc generator, requires the combined output from many rotating loops of wire to produce usable levels of voltage.

KEY POINTS

The positive and negative alternations of a sinusoidal waveform are equal in time and amplitude.

Figure 11-4 shows two full cycles of alternating voltage with several important points labeled. A period is the time required for one full cycle. As with a rectangular wave, a

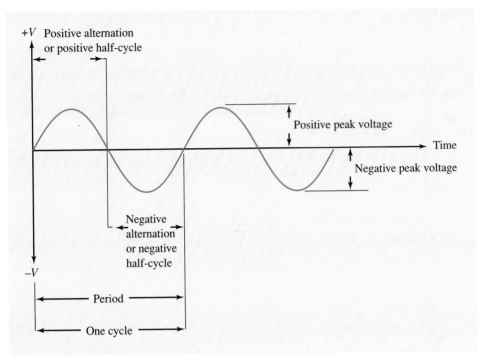

Figure 11-4. A basic sinusoidal waveform.

period consists of two opposite polarity alternations. Each alternation is also called a half-cycle. A waveform like that shown in Figure 11-4 is called a sine wave, or more generally a sinusoidal waveform. The two half-cycles of a sinusoidal waveform are identical except for their opposite polarities. Each half cycle has a maximum value called the peak value.

Function Generators

Figure 11-5 shows a function generator (also generically called a signal generator). This is a common item of test equipment used by electronic technicians. Nearly all function generators are capable of producing fundamental waveforms such as sine waves and rectangular waveforms.

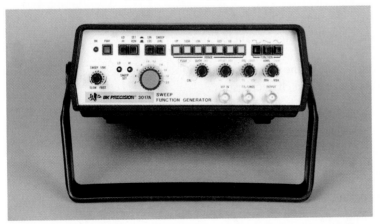

Figure 11-5. A representative function generator. (Courtesy of B&K Precision)

Some function generators can produce many other waveshapes, including arbitrary waveforms that can be programmed by the technician. In addition to selecting a particular waveshape, a technician can also adjust the voltage, symmetry, and time characteristics of the waveforms.

Exercise Problems 11.1

1. Match each of the labeled points on the waveform in Figure 11-6 to the following list of waveform characteristics:

   - positive alternation _____ A _____
   - negative alternation _____ & D _____
   - period _____ E _____
   - time axis _____ C _____
   - voltage or current axis _____ B _____

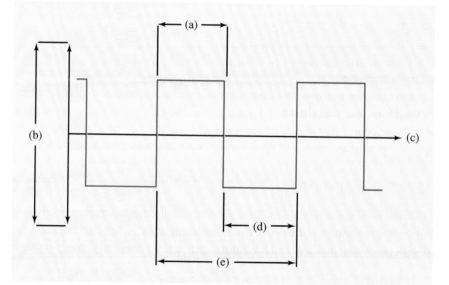

Figure 11-6. Identify the labeled areas.

2. Match each of the labeled points on the waveform in Figure 11-7 to the following list of waveform characteristics:

   - positive half-cycle _____ A _____
   - positive peak _____ F _____
   - negative peak _____ G _____
   - negative half-cycle _____ C _____
   - period _____ B _____
   - time axis _____ E _____
   - voltage or current axis _____ D _____

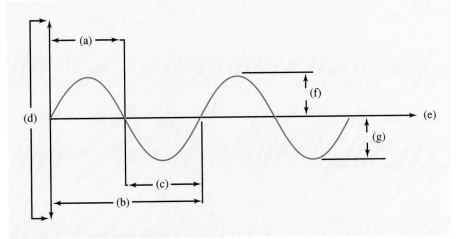

Figure 11-7. Identify the labeled areas.

11.2 Characteristics of Sine Waves

We examined some of the basic characteristics of sine waves in the previous section. We are now ready to examine these basic characteristics more closely and to identify other important characteristics that distinguish one sine wave from another. It is important to understand that the following characteristics apply to the sine waveshape itself. The sine wave may represent voltage, current, or another parameter.

Period

We have seen that the period of a sine wave is the time required for one full cycle of the waveform to occur. The measurement of a period does not have to begin at zero degrees. That is,

> The period of a sine wave is the time from any given point on the cycle to the same point on the following cycle.

The period is measured in time (t), and in most cases, it is measured in seconds (i.e., s, ms, μs, ns, ps).

EXAMPLE SOLUTION

Determine the period for the sine wave shown in Figure 11-8.

EXAMPLE **SOLUTION**

We measure the time from any point on one cycle to the same point on the following cycle. Suppose we started at the 0° point on the first cycle ($t = 0$). The 0° point on the next cycle starts at 2.0 ms. Therefore, the period is 2.0 ms – 0 ms = 2.0 ms.

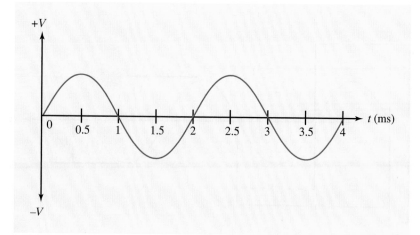

Figure 11-8. What is the period of this sine wave?

EXAMPLE SOLUTION

Determine the period for the sine wave shown in Figure 11-9.

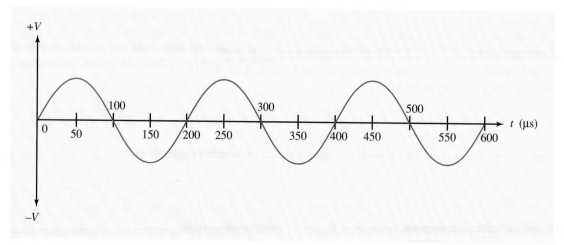

Figure 11-9. What is the period for this sine wave?

EXAMPLE **SOLUTION**

Let's measure the time between two consecutive 90° points. The first 90° point occurs at $t = 50$ μs. The 90° point on the next cycle occurs at $t = 250$ μs. The period is the difference between these two times, or $t = 250$ μs $- 50$ μs $= 200$ μs. Always subtract the smaller time value from the larger. A negative period has no meaning.

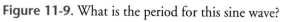

Practice Problems

1. What is the period for the sine wave shown in Figure 11-10?

2. Determine the period of the sine wave shown in Figure 11-11.

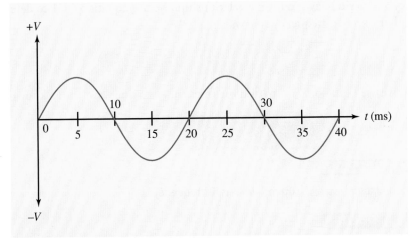

Figure 11-10. What is the period of this sine wave?

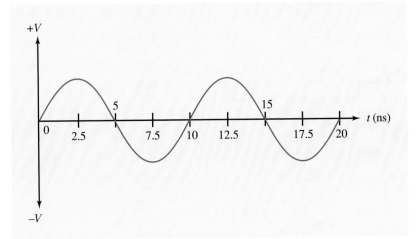

Figure 11-11. Determine the period of this sine wave.

Answers to Practice Problems

1. 20 ms   **2.** 10 ns

Frequency

The frequency of a sine wave (or any other periodic waveform) is the number of complete cycles in one second. In the case of the simple alternator (Figure 11-3), frequency (number of cycles per second) is equivalent to the speed of the alternator (revolutions per second). This is because each complete revolution produces one complete sine wave cycle.

Frequency (f) is measured in hertz (Hz). One hertz corresponds to one cycle per second. In fact, frequency used to be expressed in units of cycles per second. Usable frequencies range from less than 1 Hz (although 15 to 20 Hz is a more common low-frequency end) to frequencies over 50 billion hertz (50 GHz).

○ KEY POINTS

Frequency is measured in hertz and indicates the number of cycles that occur in one second.

Frequency and period have an inverse relationship. We use Equation 11-1 to determine the period of a known-frequency sine wave.

$$t = \frac{1}{f} \qquad\qquad (11\text{-}1)$$

Similarly, we use Equation 11-2 to find the frequency of a sine wave with a known period.

$$f = \frac{1}{t} \qquad\qquad (11\text{-}2)$$

EXAMPLE SOLUTION

If the period of a sine wave is 100 ms, what is its frequency?

EXAMPLE **SOLUTION**

We apply Equation 11-2 as follows:

$$f = \frac{1}{t}$$

$$= \frac{1}{100 \text{ ms}} = 10 \text{ Hz}$$

EXAMPLE SOLUTION

What is the period of a 250-MHz sine wave?

EXAMPLE **SOLUTION**

We apply Equation 11-1 as follows:

$$t = \frac{1}{f}$$

$$= \frac{1}{250 \text{ MHz}} = 4 \text{ ns}$$

Frequency-to-period and period-to-frequency conversions are especially easy with an electronic calculator. Simply enter the known quantity and press the reciprocal button (1/x).

Practice Problems

1. What is the period of a 10-kHz sine wave?
2. What is the frequency of a sine wave that has a period of 80 μs?
3. Find the period of a 4-GHz sine wave.
4. What frequency corresponds to a period of 175 ms?
5. One sine wave has a period of 3 ms, and another has a period of 6 ms. Which one has the higher frequency?

Answers to Practice Problems

1. 100 μs   2. 12.5 kHz

3. 250 ps **4.** 5.7 Hz

5. The shorter period (3 ms) has the higher frequency (333.3 Hz).

Peak Value

We briefly discussed the peak sine wave value in an earlier section. It is the maximum voltage on a sine wave. By inspection of a sine wave graph, we can conclude several things about the peak value of a sine wave:

- Peak voltage occurs at two different points in the cycle.
- One peak point is positive, while the other is negative.
- The positive peak occurs at 90°.
- The negative peak occurs at 270°.
- The positive and negative peaks have equal magnitudes (opposite polarities).

EXAMPLE SOLUTION

If a sine wave has a value of +10 V (V_1) as it passes through the 90° point on the cycle, what voltage (V_2) will it have as it passes through the 270° point?

EXAMPLE **SOLUTION**

The 90° and 270° points correspond to the positive and negative peaks, respectively. These two points have equal magnitudes, but opposite polarities. Thus, we would expect the sine wave to have a value of $V_2 = -V_1 = -10$ volts as it passes through the 270° point.

Note the use of lowercase letters to represent instantaneous voltages. Instantaneous voltages are values that occur at a specific instant in time. This measurement is discussed more completely in a later section. Throughout the remainder of this text we will use lowercase letters to represent instantaneous values of alternating voltage and current, and uppercase letters for other values. This is an accepted practice in industry.

Practice Problems

1. If a certain sine wave of current has a negative peak of −1.5 A, what is its positive peak current value?

Answers to Practice Problems

1. 1.5 A

Average Value

The average value of any measured quantity is determined by summing all of the intermediate values and then dividing by the number of intermediate values. In the case of a sine wave, we need to consider two conditions: the average value for a full cycle, and the average value of a half-cycle.

AVERAGE VALUE OF A FULL SINE WAVE

The sine wave shown in Figure 11-12 has seventeen labeled points. If we measured the voltage at these seventeen points, added the values together, and then divided by 17, we could get an estimate of the average value for the full sine wave. It would only be an estimate, since we did not use an infinite number of points.

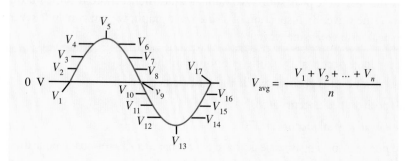

Figure 11-12. Determination of the average value of a sine wave.

Nevertheless, by inspection of Figure 11-12, we can see that no matter how many equally distributed points we choose, there will be as many positive values as there are negative values. Further, every positive value will have a corresponding negative value. For example, the positive values V_3 and V_5 in Figure 11-12 correspond to the negative values V_{11} and V_{13}, respectively. If we add equal positive and negative values together, we will always get zero. Therefore, we can conclude the following about the average value of a sine wave:

> A full cycle of any sine wave has an average value of zero.

This is an important consideration when troubleshooting amplifier circuits.

Practice Problems

1. What is the average value of a full sine wave that has a +100-V peak value?
2. What is the average value of a full sine wave with a negative peak of 3 V and a frequency of 10 MHz?
3. If the period of a certain sine wave is 5 ms, what is the average value for a full cycle?
4. What is the average value of a full sine wave if the peak value is 2.4 A?

Answers to Practice Problems

1. Zero   2. Zero

3. Zero   4. Zero

AVERAGE VALUE FOR ONE HALF-CYCLE

If we sum the voltage at a number (ideally an infinite number) of points in a single half-cycle of a sine wave and then divide by the number of sampled points, we can find the average value for one half-cycle. You can perform this calculation in the laboratory, by measuring a large number of points on a sine wave and then dividing by the number of points. However, since a sine wave has a consistent shape, higher mathematics can be used to prove the following relationships:

$$V_{avg} = 0.637 \, V_P \qquad (11\text{-}3)$$

and

$$I_{avg} = 0.637 \, I_P \qquad (11\text{-}4)$$

where V_P and I_P are the peak voltage and current values. Of course, current is still directly proportional to voltage in a given circuit as described by Ohm's Law.

EXAMPLE SOLUTION

What is the average value for one half-cycle of a sine wave that has a peak voltage of 100 V?

EXAMPLE **SOLUTION**

We apply Equation 11-3 as follows:

$$V_{avg} = 0.637 \, V_P$$
$$= 100 \text{ V} \times 0.637 = 63.7 \text{ V}$$

Since the average value of a single half-cycle provides a more meaningful result in most cases than the average value of a full sine wave, it is customary to interpret the expression "average value of a sine wave" to mean average value of a half-cycle. While this may be technically incorrect, it is very common throughout industry. As a technician, it is important that you understand this interpretation. For the remainder of this text, will shall interpret V_{avg}, I_{avg}, and so on to mean the average of one half-cycle, unless otherwise stated.

Practice Problems

1. Compute the average value (V_{avg}) for a sine wave with a peak value of 20 V.
2. Find V_{avg} for a sine wave with a peak value of 150 mV.
3. What is the average voltage (V_{avg}) for a 1,000-V peak sine wave?
4. Compute I_{avg} for a sine wave with a 150 μA peak current.

Answers to Practice Problems

1. 12.74 V   **2.** 95.55 mV

3. 637 V   **4.** 95.55 μA

rms Value

One of the most important characteristics of a sine wave is its rms or effective value. The rms value describes the sine wave in terms that can be compared to an equivalent dc voltage. Figure 11-13(a) shows a 10-V$_{rms}$ sine wave voltage source connected to a resistor. The resistor dissipates power in the form of heat. Figure 11-13(b) illustrates that a 10-V$_{dc}$ source will produce the same amount of heat in the resistor. That is,

> The rms value of a sine wave produces the same heating effect in a resistance as an equal value of dc.

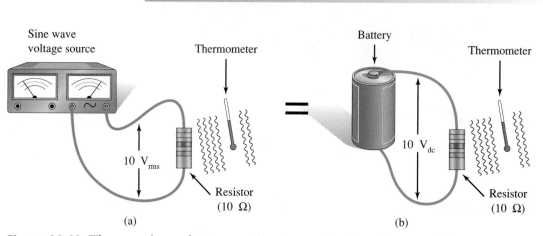

Figure 11-13. The rms voltage of a sine wave has the same heating effect as a similar dc voltage source.

The abbreviation rms stands for **root-mean-square**. For a given sine wave, we can take a large number (ideally an infinite number) of voltage values, square each value, sum our squared values together, divide by the number of points to get the average or mean squared value, and then extract the square root to get the rms value. Fortunately, higher mathematics can be used to derive Equation 11-5 and Equation 11-6, which describe the rms value of a sine wave in terms of its peak values.

$$V_{rms} = 0.707\ V_P \qquad (11\text{-}5)$$

and

$$I_{rms} = 0.707\ I_P \qquad (11\text{-}6)$$

EXAMPLE SOLUTION

What is the rms value of a sine wave that has a 25-V peak?

EXAMPLE **SOLUTION**

We apply Equation 11-5 as follows:

$$V_{rms} = 0707\ V_P$$
$$= 0.707 \times 25\ V = 17.68\ V$$

EXAMPLE SOLUTION

What peak value of a sine wave is required to produce the same heating effect as a 48-V battery pack?

EXAMPLE **SOLUTION**

Since the rms value of a sine wave produces the same heating effect as dc, we know that our sine wave will have an rms value of 48 V. We compute the peak voltage by applying Equation 11-5.

$$V_{\text{rms}} = 0.707 \ V_P, \text{ or}$$

$$V_P = \frac{V_{\text{rms}}}{0.707}$$

$$= \frac{48 \ V}{0.707} = 67.89 \ V$$

This latter calculation is used so often that it is generally remembered as separate equations.

$$V_P = \frac{V_{\text{rms}}}{0.707} = 1.414 \ V_{\text{rms}} \qquad (11\text{-}7)$$

and

$$I_P = \frac{I_{\text{rms}}}{0.707} = 1.414 \ I_{\text{rms}} \qquad (11\text{-}8)$$

It is important to note that most ac voltmeters—both digital and analog—are calibrated to display the rms value of the measured ac voltage. Further, most ac voltmeters only respond accurately to sinusoidal waveforms.

Peak-to-Peak Value

Figure 11-14 illustrates another measurement that can be used to describe a sine wave. The peak-to-peak voltage or current value of a sine wave is the difference between the two peak values. We can express this mathematically with Equations 11-9 and 11-10.

$$V_{PP} = 2 \ V_P \qquad (11\text{-}9)$$

and

$$I_{PP} = 2 \ I_P \qquad (11\text{-}10)$$

KEY POINTS

Peak-to-peak voltage is the difference between the positive and negative peak values. Its value is simply $2 \times V_p$.

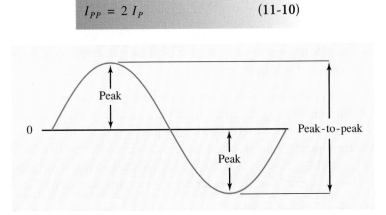

Figure 11-14. The peak-to-peak value of a sine wave is equal to the difference between the two peak values.

EXAMPLE SOLUTION

What is the peak-to-peak current of a sine wave that has a 750-mA peak current?

EXAMPLE **SOLUTION**

We apply Equation 11-10 as follows:

$$I_{PP} = 2 I_P$$
$$= 2 \times 750 \text{ mA} = 1.5 \text{ A}$$

Practice Problems

1. If a sine wave has a peak voltage of 500 mV, what is its peak-to-peak value?
2. What is the peak-to-peak voltage of a sine wave that has a peak value of 12 V?
3. If the peak-to-peak voltage of a sine wave is 150 V, what is its peak voltage?

Answers to Practice Problems

1. 1.0 V   2. 24 V   3. 75 V

> **KEY POINTS**
>
> The peak-to-peak measurement is useful to characterize a sine wave, but it is important to remember that the peak-to-peak voltage value never actually exists at any given instant in time.

It is important to note that the value of peak-to-peak voltage never really exists as a measurable voltage at some point in time. Recall that the horizontal axis of a sine wave graph can be marked off in units of time. This means that the positive and negative peaks of the sine wave do not occur at the same exact time. Therefore, as stated in an earlier section, the highest voltage or current of a sine wave is its peak value. The peak-to-peak value is mathematically twice the peak value, *but it does not exist as a measurable voltage at some instant in time.* It is, however, an important way to describe a sine wave. It is also the easiest value to interpret with an oscilloscope, since the scope display can show voltages that occur at different times.

Phase

> **KEY POINTS**
>
> In-phase waveforms go through the corresponding points on the sine waves at the same time. Out-of-phase waveforms do not pass through corresponding points at the same time.

Phase is a relative term that is used to compare two or more sine waves that have the same frequency. When two sine waves are in phase, the various points on one sine wave (e.g., 0°, 90°, 180°, and so on) occur at exactly the same time as the corresponding points on the second sine wave. When two sine waves are out of phase, the corresponding points of the two sine waves occur at different times.

Figure 11-15 shows one method to help you understand phase relationships. Here, two identical alternators are rotating at exactly the same speed. They will produce two identical sine waves. However, one of the alternators is one-quarter turn ahead of the other one. Therefore, the corresponding points of the two resulting sine waves will occur at different times. This is illustrated in Figure 11-15(b). We say that the two sine waves are out of phase. In the case shown in Figure 11-15(b), we can say the two sine waves are 90° out of phase.

In order to describe the relative order of two out-of-phase waveforms, we use the terms leading and lagging. A waveform that has a leading phase of 45° is simply 45° ahead of another waveform. That is, any given point on the leading waveform occurs one-eighth

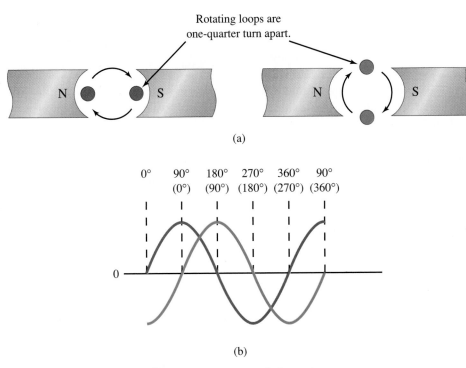

(a)

(b)

Figure 11-15. Corresponding points on out-of-phase sine waves occur at different times.

(45°/360°) of a cycle before the corresponding point of the second waveform. If we prefer, we can refer to the second waveform as lagging by 45°. We will further examine the use of the terms leading and lagging in Chapter 12.

ANGULAR MEASUREMENTS

There are two ways to express the angular measurements of a sine wave. We have already seen how degrees can be used to describe a particular point on a sine wave. A sine wave of voltage passes through 0 V at 0°, 180°, and 360°. Similarly, it has maximum positive and negative values at 90° and 270°, respectively. While it is mathematically correct to express angles larger than 360°, it is not generally done, since anything beyond 360° has a corresponding point on a previous cycle that is between 0° and 360°.

Angles can also be expressed in radians. One radian (rad) corresponds to 57.3°. As a technician, you should be able to perform calculations with either unit of measurement.

DEGREE-TO-RADIAN CONVERSION

We can express an angle given in degrees as an equivalent angle measured in radians by applying Equation 11-11.

$$\text{radians} = \frac{\text{degrees}}{57.3°} \qquad (11\text{-}11)$$

KEY POINTS

Phase is expressed as an angular measurement and can be measured in degrees or radians.

This can also be expressed as

$$radians = degrees\left(\frac{\pi}{180°}\right)$$

where π (the Greek letter pi) represents the approximate value of 3.1416. Scientific calculators have a π button. Pressing it automatically enters the value of 3.141... into your calculation.

EXAMPLE SOLUTION

Express the 30° point of a sine wave as an equivalent number of radians.

EXAMPLE **SOLUTION**

We apply Equation 11-11 as follows:

$$radians = \frac{degrees}{57.3°}$$

$$= \frac{30°}{57.3°} \approx 0.52 \text{ rad}$$

Practice Problems

1. 45° is the same as _____ radians.
2. 350° is the same as _____ radians.
3. 270° is the same as _____ radians.
4. 90° is the same as _____ radians.
5. 180° is the same as _____ radians.

Answers to Practice Problems

1. 0.785 or $\pi/4$ 2. 6.11   3. 4.7 or $3\pi/2$

4. 1.57 or $\pi/2$ 5. 3.14 or π

RADIAN-TO-DEGREE CONVERSION

If an angle is expressed in radians, we can convert it to an equivalent angle expressed in degrees by applying Equation 11-12.

$$degrees = radians \times 57.3° \qquad (11\text{-}12)$$

This can also be expressed as

$$degrees = radians\left(\frac{180°}{\pi}\right)$$

EXAMPLE SOLUTION

If a certain point on a sine wave is at 3.5 rad, express the same point in degrees.

We apply Equation 11-12 as follows:

$$\text{degrees} = \text{radians} \times 57.3°$$
$$= 3.5 \text{ rad } (57.3°) = 200.55°$$

Practice Problems

1. 2.5 rad is equivalent to _____ degrees.
2. 6.2827 rad is equivalent to _____ degrees.
3. 4 rad is equivalent to _____ degrees.
4. 1.75 rad is equivalent to _____ degrees.
5. 5.25 rad is equivalent to _____ degrees.

Answers to Practice Problems

1. 143.3   2. 360.2   3. 229.2

4. 100.3   5. 300.8

Instantaneous Value

As a sine wave progresses through its cycle, we can express the voltage (or current) at any instant in time as the instantaneous voltage (or current). Thus, for example, the instantaneous voltage of a sine wave is zero at 0°. Similarly, a sine wave with a 10-V peak amplitude, will have an instantaneous voltage of +10 V at 90° and –10 V at 270°. Equations 11-13 and 11-14 give us a way to determine the instantaneous value of a sine wave at any given angle.

$$v = V_P \sin\theta \qquad\qquad (11\text{-}13)$$

and

$$i = I_P \sin\theta \qquad\qquad (11\text{-}14)$$

where the lowercase v and i are used to represent instantaneous voltage and current values, θ is the angle, and sin is the trigonometric sine function.

The sine function is easily found on a scientific calculator by keying in the given angle (θ) and pressing the SIN button. Most scientific calculators can be configured to work in either degrees or radians. They will have a key labeled DRG, RAD, DEG, or other similar identification. Be sure your calculator is in the correct mode for the units of angular measurement you are using. A later section provides additional guidance in calculator operation.

> **KEY POINTS**
>
> The voltage at any specific instant in time is called the instantaneous voltage.

What is the instantaneous voltage at the 45° point of a sine wave with a peak voltage of 10 V?

EXAMPLE SOLUTION

We apply Equation 11-13 as follows:

$$v = V_P \sin\theta$$
$$= 10 \text{ V} \times \sin 45°$$
$$= 10 \text{ V} \times 0.7071 = 7.071 \text{ V}$$

EXAMPLE SOLUTION

If the peak current of a sine wave is 500 μA, what is the instantaneous current at 3.75 rad?

EXAMPLE SOLUTION

We apply Equation 11-14 as follows:

$$i = I_P \sin\theta$$
$$= 500 \text{ μA} \times \sin 3.75 \text{ rad}$$
$$= 500 \text{ μA} \times (-0.572) = -286 \text{ μA}$$

The negative current value, as with negative direct current values, simply means the current is going in the opposite direction from a positive current.

EXAMPLE SOLUTION

What is the peak voltage of a sine wave that has an instantaneous voltage of –25 V at 225°?

EXAMPLE SOLUTION

We apply Equation 11-13 as follows:

$$v = V_P \sin\theta, \text{ or}$$
$$V_P = \frac{v}{\sin\theta}$$

CONVERT FROM	CONVERT TO				
	PEAK	**PEAK TO PEAK**	**rms**	**INSTANTANEOUS**	**AVERAGE**
Peak	—	$V_{PP} = 2 V_P$	$V_{rms} = 0.707 V_P$	$v = V_P \sin\theta$	$V_{avg} = 0.637 V_P$
Peak to Peak	$V_P = \dfrac{V_{PP}}{2}$	—	$V_{rms} = \dfrac{V_{PP}}{2.828}$	$v = 0.5 V_{PP} \sin\theta$	$V_{avg} = 0.318 V_{PP}$
rms	$V_P = 1.414 V_{rms}$	$V_{PP} = 2.828 V_{rms}$	—	$v = \dfrac{V_{rms} \sin\theta}{0.707}$	$V_{avg} = 0.9 V_{rms}$
Instantaneous	$V_P = \dfrac{v}{\sin\theta}$	$V_{PP} = \dfrac{2v}{\sin\theta}$	$V_{rms} = \dfrac{0.707 v}{\sin\theta}$	—	$V_{avg} = \dfrac{0.637 v}{\sin\theta}$
Average	$V_P = \dfrac{V_{avg}}{0.637}$	$V_{PP} = 1.274 V_{avg}$	$V_{rms} = 1.1 V_{avg}$	$v = \dfrac{V_{avg} \sin\theta}{0.637}$	—

Table 11-1. Voltage Conversion Summary

$$= \frac{-25\ \text{V}}{\sin 225°}$$

$$= \frac{-25\ \text{V}}{-0.707} = 35.36\ \text{V}$$

Practice Problems

1. What is the instantaneous voltage of a sine wave at 30°, if its peak voltage is 500 V?

2. Compute the instantaneous voltage of sine wave at 2.8 rad, if its peak voltage is 200 mV.

3. Determine the maximum current value in a circuit that has a sinusoidal current with an instantaneous value of 740 mA at 1.6 rad.

4. What is the peak current in a circuit that has a sinusoidal current wave with an instantaneous current of 1.2 A at 50°?

Answers to Practice Problems

1. 250 V   2. 67 mV

3. 740.3 mA   4. 1.57 A

Time and Frequency Domains

All electronic signals can be viewed from either of two perspectives: time domain and frequency domain. It is useful to have a conceptual view of how these two domains interact.

TIME DOMAIN

We think of a time-domain signal as one whose instantaneous voltage changes over time. An oscilloscope, for example, displays the instantaneous values of a waveform as they change with time. We say an oscilloscope is a time-domain instrument.

FREQUENCY DOMAIN

We can also analyze an electronic signal in terms of its frequency content. That is, any given waveform can be shown to be composed of one or more sinusoidal signals at specific frequencies and amplitudes. A spectrum analyzer can be used to measure the frequency content of a waveform. We say that a spectrum analyzer is a frequency-domain instrument.

Converting between the time and frequency domains is well defined but requires advanced mathematics techniques. There are also many computer programs available that can make these conversions.

HARMONICS

Any repetitive, nonsinusoidal waveform in the time domain can be shown to be composed of a **fundamental frequency** and some combination of **harmonic frequencies.** The fundamental frequency is the basic frequency of the waveform as determined by the period of the waveform. Harmonic frequencies are exact multiples of the fundamental frequency. Both fundamental and harmonic frequency components of the original waveform have sinusoidal characteristics in the time domain.

A frequency component of a waveform that is exactly twice the fundamental frequency is called the second harmonic. The third and fourth harmonic frequencies occur at three and four times the frequency of the fundamental, respectively. The first, third, fifth, and seventh harmonics, and so on are collectively called **odd harmonics.** Similarly, the second, fourth, sixth, and eighth harmonics are collectively called the **even harmonics.**

Now let us consider a specific example. Figure 11-16 illustrates that a square wave in the time domain corresponds to a mixture of the fundamental and the odd harmonic frequencies. Figure 11-16(a) shows the fundamental and the third and fifth harmonics. Figure 11-16(b) shows the algebraic sum of the three sine waves shown in Figure 11-16(a). Clearly, a rectangular waveform is starting to form. Figures 11-16(c) and (d) illustrate the effects of adding additional harmonic frequencies. The more harmonics we include, the more nearly the result resembles a square wave. A perfect square wave would have an infinite number of odd harmonics. The lower frequencies are primarily responsible for the flat, horizontal portions of the square wave. The higher harmonic frequencies contribute to the steepness of the rising and falling edges. Although the square wave is a selected example, any periodic nonsinusoidal waveform in the time domain can be decomposed into the fundamental and some combination of harmonics in the frequency domain.

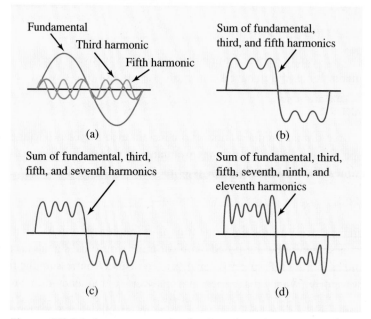

Figure 11-16. A square wave in the time domain corresponds to a mixture of the fundamental and odd harmonic frequencies in the frequency domain.

EXAMPLE SOLUTION

What is the third harmonic of a 1 kHz sine wave?

EXAMPLE SOLUTION

The third harmonic is three times the frequency of the fundamental, or

$$f_3 = 3 \times 1.0 \text{ kHz} = 3.0 \text{ kHz}$$

Practice Problems

1. What is the second harmonic frequency if the fundamental frequency is 2.5 MHz?
2. List the first four harmonics of a 25-MHz waveform.
3. List the first three odd harmonics of a 100-MHz sine wave.
4. List the first three even harmonics of a 250-MHz waveform.

Answers to Practice Problems

1. 5 MHz
2. 50 MHz, 75 MHz, 100 MHz, 125 MHz
3. 300 MHz, 500 MHz, 700 MHz
4. 500 MHz, 1,000 MHz, 1,500 MHz

Exercise Problems 11.2

1. If the frequency of a sine wave is 100 kHz, what is its period?
2. What is the period of the 60-Hz sinusoidal power supplied to your home by the power company?
3. If a sine wave has a period of 10 μs, what is its frequency?
4. A sine wave with a period of 2 ms has a frequency of _____ .
5. The positive peak of a sine wave occurs at _____ degrees.
6. The maximum negative voltage of a sine wave occurs at _____ radians.
7. A sine wave has a peak value of 150 A. Find its average value (I_{avg}).
8. If the average value (V_{avg}) of a sine wave is 35 V, what is its peak value?
9. What is the rms value for a sine wave with a 200-V peak?
10. What is the rms voltage for a sine wave with an average value of 12 V?
11. If a sine wave has a peak value of 25 V, what is its peak-to-peak value?
12. How much dc voltage is required to provide the same heating effect as a sine wave with a 200-V peak-to-peak amplitude?
13. What is the instantaneous voltage of a sine wave at 55° if its value at 90° is 100 V?
14. What is the peak voltage of a sine wave whose instantaneous voltage is –20 V at 300°?
15. A phase angle of 150° corresponds to _____ radians.
16. An angle of 2.5 rad is the same as an angle of _____ degrees.

11.3 Working with Phasors

Technicians frequently have to solve problems that involve phase relationships of one or more sinusoidal waveforms. It is very difficult to sketch sinusoidal curves accurately, but we need an accurate method of analyzing sinusoidal waveforms. Phasors provide us with a convenient way to represent sinusoidal waveforms and simplify many calculations.

Phasor Diagrams

KEY POINTS

The length of the phasor represents peak voltage, the angle of the phasor with respect to the horizontal axis corresponds to the instantaneous phase angle of the sine wave, and the distance from the end of the phasor to the horizontal axis represents the instantaneous voltage of the sine wave.

Figure 11-17 shows a phasor diagram. The phasor itself consists of a vector or "arrow" that can be rotated around a central point. The length of the phasor corresponds to the peak value of the sine wave. The angle of the phasor (θ) relative to the right-most horizontal axis corresponds to the angle of the sine wave. Finally, the distance from the point of the phasor to the horizontal axis represents the instantaneous voltage at the specified angle.

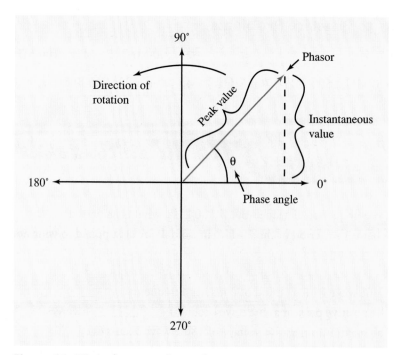

Figure 11-17. A phasor can be used to represent a sinusoidal quantity.

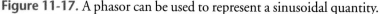

Figure 11-18(a) shows a phasor diagram for a particular sine wave. What is the peak value of the sine wave? What is the instantaneous voltage?

EXAMPLE **SOLUTION**

The peak voltage is represented on a phasor diagram by the length of the phasor. In the case shown in Figure 11-18, the peak voltage is 100 V. In Figure 11-18(b), we have drawn a horizontal dotted line from the point of the phasor to the vertical axis. The point of intersection is the instantaneous voltage. In this case, the instantaneous voltage is 50 V.

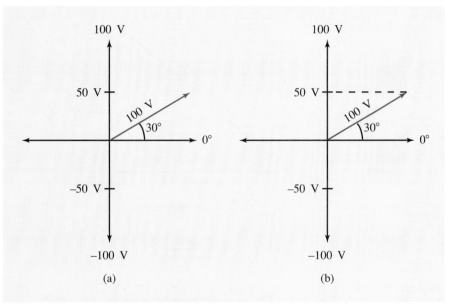

Figure 11-18. An example phasor diagram.

If the angle were not given, we could find it with a protractor. However, our accuracy would be limited by the preciseness of the phasor sketch. This would be tedious and inaccurate. Thus, we need yet a better way to calculate phasor values.

Right-Triangle Relationships

Figure 11-19 shows a phasor diagram. We have drawn a dotted line from the point of the phasor to the horizontal axis. This forms a triangle. Side "a" is a portion of the horizontal axis. Side "b" corresponds to the instantaneous voltage of the sine wave. Side "c" represents the peak voltage of the sine wave. The angle of the sine wave is represented by θ. A triangle drawn in this way will always have a right angle (90°), where the dotted line from the phasor point intersects the horizontal axis. Solution of problems involving triangles requires application of a branch of mathematics called trigonometry. Fortunately, the right-triangle calculations required to solve phasor problems are a well-defined subset of trigonometry. You do not have to understand all there is to know about trigonometry to solve these problems.

Figure 11-20(a) shows a right triangle with the sides labeled according to standard practice. The hypotenuse is always the longest side and is across from the right angle. Angle θ is used to represent the phase of a sine wave. The other two sides are named according to their relationship to θ. That is, the adjacent side is adjacent (i.e., forms one side of the angle) to θ, and the opposite side is opposite (i.e., across the triangle from) θ.

There are three basic equations that we must know in order to solve basic phasor problems.

$$\sin\theta = \frac{\text{opposite side}}{\text{hypotenuse}} \quad \text{(11-15)}$$

$$\cos\theta = \frac{\text{adjacent side}}{\text{hypotenuse}} \quad \text{(11-16)}$$

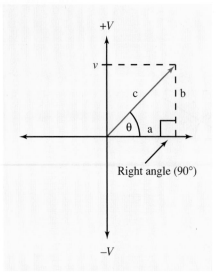

Figure 11-19. Phasor calculations are based on right-triangle calculations

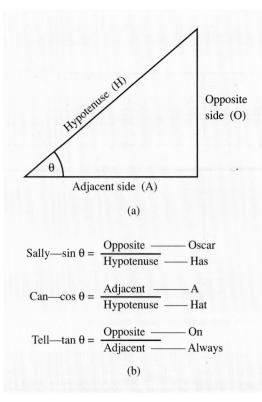

(a)

Sally—$\sin \theta = \dfrac{\text{Opposite}}{\text{Hypotenuse}}$ ——— Oscar / Has

Can—$\cos \theta = \dfrac{\text{Adjacent}}{\text{Hypotenuse}}$ ——— A / Hat

Tell—$\tan \theta = \dfrac{\text{Opposite}}{\text{Adjacent}}$ ——— On / Always

(b)

Figure 11-20. A right triangle with standard labels (a) and a memory aid (b).

$$\tan \theta = \frac{\text{opposite side}}{\text{adjacent side}} \qquad (11\text{-}17)$$

KEY POINTS

Phasor calculations are based on three basic trigonometric functions: sine, cosine, and tangent.

Sin, cos, and tan are basic functions (sine, cosine, and tangent) that are easily computed by your calculator. Equations 11-15, 11-16, and 11-17 are important relationships that will be used extensively in subsequent chapters. They should be committed to memory. Figure 11-20(b) shows a memory aid that is popular among technicians. Some technicians have different words, but basically the first letter in the expression "**S**ally **C**an **T**ell **O**scar **H**as **A** **H**at **O**n **A**lways" corresponds to the words **S**ine, **C**osine, **T**angent, **O**pposite, **H**ypotenuse, and **A**djacent. If you remember the phrase, then you can quickly construct the three equations.

Calculator Operation

KEY POINTS

Values for each of the trigonometric functions are easily found with a scientific calculator.

There are several functions of your calculator that have not been required in the preceding chapters. We will, however, use them extensively in the following chapters, and you will certainly need to use them as a technician in industry. The trigonometric functions are of immediate interest to us. You might want to view the trigonometric function values as a code. Every angle has a corresponding numeric code called the sine (sin) of the angle. Each angle has a different code called the cosine (cos) of the angle. Finally, for every angle, there is a coded numerical value called the tangent (tan) of the angle. Scientific calculators have built-in look-up tables that allow you to determine the function values (or codes) for any given angle. Think of your calculator as your encoder/decoder device. You key in an angle.

Your calculator gives you a corresponding code. Alternatively, you can key in a coded value and the calculator will produce the value of the corresponding angle.

TRIGONOMETRIC FUNCTIONS

A scientific calculator will compute the sin, cos, and tan functions by simply keying in the value and pressing the appropriate button. The sine of an angle is computed when the SIN button is pressed. The cosine is found by pressing the COS button. And, finally, the tangent of an angle can be calculated by using the TAN button.

Many scientific calculators can work with angles expressed in either degrees or radians. Be certain that your calculator is in the degree mode, if your angles are expressed in degrees. Similarly, you must put your calculator in the radian mode, if you want to enter the angle values as radians.

[EXAMPLE SOLUTION**]**

Find the value of cos θ, when θ = 55°.

[EXAMPLE **SOLUTION]**

The key sequence required to obtain the value of a trigonometric function is the same for a standard engineering calculator or an RPN calculator. It consists of keying in the angle and pressing the appropriate function key. We must also ensure that the calculator is in the correct mode. Figure 11-21 shows a typical key sequence for the given problem. You should get a result of 0.5736. If your calculator produces an answer of 0.0221, then it is in the radian mode instead of the degree mode. Some calculators have the sin, cos, and tan functions as second, or shifted, functions. In these cases, you will need to press the "2nd" function key to invoke the cos function.

| 5 | 5 | COS |

Figure 11-21.
A typical key sequence to compute cos 55°.

[EXAMPLE SOLUTION**]**

Find the value of tan θ, when θ = 2.75 rad.

[EXAMPLE **SOLUTION]**

Put your calculator into the radian mode. Look for a DRG or RAD button or consult your calculator manual. Figure 11-22 shows a typical key sequence. Your calculator should produce a result of –0.4129. If you get 0.048 for an answer, then your calculator is in the degree mode.

| 2 | · | 7 | 5 | TAN |

Figure 11-22.
A typical key sequence to compute tan 2.75 rad.

Practice Problems

Find the value of each of the following functions:

1. cos 28° = _____
2. sin 3.6 rad = _____
3. tan 150° = _____
4. sin 20° = _____
5. tan 175° = _____

6. tan 5 rad = _____
7. cos 1.8 rad = _____
8. sin 3.75 rad = _____
9. cos 200° = _____
10. sin 90° = _____

Answers to Practice Problems

1.	0.883	**6.**	–3.381
2.	–0.443	**7.**	–0.227
3.	–0.577	**8.**	–0.572
4.	0.342	**9.**	–0.94
5.	–0.087	**10.**	1

INVERSE TRIGONOMETRIC FUNCTIONS

KEY POINTS

Each of the basic functions has a corresponding inverse function: arcsin, arccos, and arctan.

There will be many times that we know the sine, cosine, or tangent of an angle, but we do not know the angle itself. That is, we known the "code," but we don't know the original angle. The sine, cosine, and tangent operations are called functions. The corresponding opposite (or decoding) operations are the arcsin, arccos, and arctan. These are called the inverse trigonometric functions. You can think of "arc" as meaning "angle whose." Thus, the expression arcsin 0.2 can be interpreted as "angle whose sine is 0.2."

EXAMPLE SOLUTION

We know the sine of an angle is 0.5. What is the size of the angle in degrees?

EXAMPLE SOLUTION

We need to find the angle whose sine is 0.5. That is, we need to find arcsin 0.5. First, we check to be sure our calculator is in the degree mode. Then, we key in the value of 0.5 and press the inverse sine button. In many cases, the inverse sine function is a second or shifted function of the sine key. You may have to press the "2nd" then the sine key to invoke the arcsin function. Some calculators label the inverse trigonometric functions as $\sin^{-1}$, $\cos^{-1}$, and $\tan^{-1}$. Again, they are probably shifted functions. Another alternative labeling used on some calculators is ASIN, ACOS, and ATAN. Figure 11-23 shows a typical key sequence. You should get a result of 30°. If you get an answer of 0.524, then your calculator is in the radian mode.

Figure 11-23.
A typical calculator key sequence to compute arcsin 0.5.

Practice Problems

Find the value of the following inverse functions.

1.	arcsin 0.7 = _____		**6.**	arctan –0.577 = _____
2.	arccos –0.633 = _____		**7.**	arcsin –0.174 = _____
3.	arctan 0.466 = _____		**8.**	arccos 0.259 = _____
4.	arcsin 0.0872 = _____		**9.**	arctan –0.7 = _____
5.	arccos –1 = _____		**10.**	arcsin 0.2 = _____

Answers to Practice Problems

1.	44.4° or 0.78 rad	**3.**	24.99° or 0.44 rad
2.	129.27° or 2.26 rad	**4.**	5° or 0.087 rad

5. 180° or 3.14 rad   **8.** 74.99° or 1.31 rad

6. −29.98° or −0.52 rad   **9.** −34.99° or −0.611 rad

7. −10.02° or −0.175 rad   **10.** 11.54° or 0.2 rad

Phasor Calculations

In later chapters, we will use phasor calculations extensively to analyze circuits that contain inductors and/or capacitors. For now, however, let us concentrate on using the sine, cosine, and tangent functions and their inverse functions to solve right-triangle problems and basic sine wave phase problems.

EXAMPLE SOLUTION

Figure 11–24 shows a phasor diagram with known values for the peak and instantaneous voltages. Calculate the angle θ.

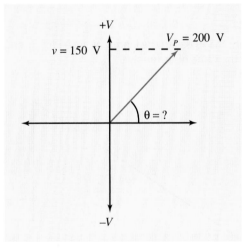

Figure 11-24. Find the angle θ.

EXAMPLE **SOLUTION**

In Figure 11-25, we have extended a vertical line from the phasor tip to the horizontal axis. This makes a right triangle. As long as we know the value of any two sides or at least one side and one of the smaller angles, we can find the rest by using Equations 11-15 through 11-17. In the present case, we know the hypotenuse and the opposite side. We can use Equation 11-15 to find the sine of the angle.

$$\sin\theta = \frac{\text{opposite side}}{\text{hypotenuse}}$$

$$\sin\theta = \frac{150 \text{ V}}{200 \text{ V}} = 0.75$$

If we know the sine of an angle, then the arcsin function will give us the value of the angle in degrees or radians.

$$\theta = \text{arcsin } 0.75$$

$$\theta = 48.59° \text{ or } 0.848 \text{ rad}$$

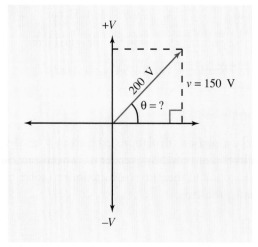

Figure 11-25. Form a right triangle and solve for θ.

Figure 11-26 shows a right triangle with the length of two sides given. Find the length of the remaining side, and find the value of the angle θ.

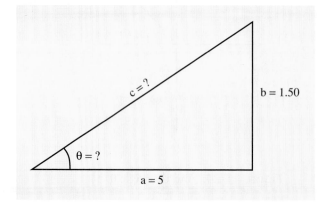

Figure 11-26. Find the angle θ and the length of side c.

EXAMPLE **SOLUTION**

Recall that if we know any two sides, we can find all other missing values. In this case, we know the adjacent side (a) and we know the opposite side (b). We can use Equation 11-17 to find the tangent of angle θ.

$$\tan\theta = \frac{\text{opposite side}}{\text{adjacent side}}$$

$$\tan\theta = \frac{1.5}{5} = 0.3$$

The arctan function will give us the actual value of the angle.

$$\theta = \arctan 0.3$$

$$\theta = 16.7° \text{ or } 0.29 \text{ rad}$$

We can use Equation 11-15 to determine side c (the hypotenuse).

$$\sin \theta = \frac{\text{opposite side}}{\text{hypotenuse}}$$

$$\text{hypotenuse} = \frac{\text{opposite side}}{\sin \theta} = \frac{1.5}{0.2873} = 5.22$$

Practice Problems

1. Find the length of side c and the value of angle θ in Figure 11-27.

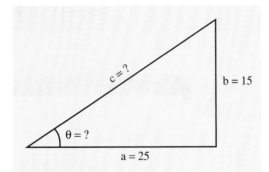

Figure 11-27. Find the missing values.

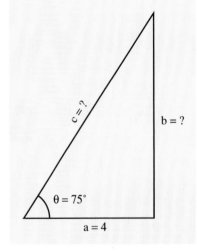

Figure 11-28.
Find the missing values.

2. Find the lengths of sides b and c in Figure 11-28.
3. Determine the lengths of sides a and c in Figure 11-29.

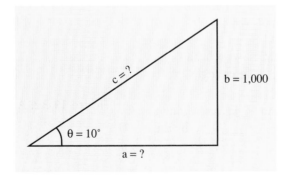

Figure 11-29. Find the missing values.

4. Calculate the value of θ in Figure 11-30.

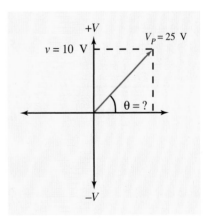

Figure 11-30.
What is the value of θ?

5. Find the value of θ in Figure 11-31.

Answers to Practice Problems

1. θ = 30.96° or 0.54 rad
c = 29.16

2. b = 14.93
c = 15.46

3. a = 5,671.28
c = 5,758.77

4. 23.58° or 0.412 rad

5. −26.74° or −0.467 rad

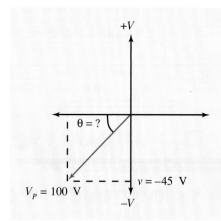

Figure 11-31. What is the value of θ?

Exercise Problems 11.3

1. Figure 11-32 shows a phasor diagram for a sine wave. What is the peak value of the sine wave?

2. What is the instantaneous voltage of the sine wave represented by the phasor diagram in Figure 11-32?

3. The longest side of a right triangle is called the _____ .

4. A right triangle always has a _____ -degree angle.

5. The sine of an angle can be found by dividing the _____ by the _____ .

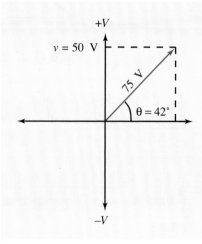

Figure 11-32. A phasor diagram.

6. Compute the following values:

   a. cos 100°   **b.** tan 27°   **c.** sin 278°
   d. cos 1.2 rad   **e.** tan 4.8 rad   **f.** sin 2.9 rad

7. Determine the following angles and express in degrees:

   a. arccos 0.6   **b.** arcsin 0.09   **c.** arctan 11
   d. arcsin 0.91   **e.** arccos 0.91   **f.** arctan 30

8. Determine the following angles and express in radians:
   a. arccos 0.54   b. arcsin 0.04   c. arctan 9
   d. arcsin 0.95   e. arccos 0.95   f. arctan 26

9. What is the value of θ (in degrees) in Figure 11-33?
10. Find the length of side a in Figure 11-33.

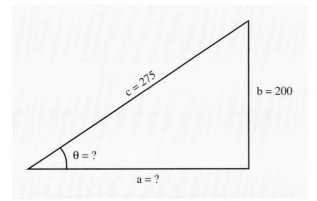

Figure 11-33. Find the missing values.

11.4 Resistive ac Circuit Analysis

Circuits composed of resistors and supplied by an ac voltage source can be analyzed with Ohm's and Kirchhoff's Laws. You must be careful, however, that you use the correct values. For example, if you want to find peak current, then use peak voltage in your calculations. If you want to find the rms voltage drop across a resistor, then use the rms value of current. For most purposes, power dissipation is computed using rms values of voltage and/or current. Although peak and average power are also useful computations for some applications (e.g., power supply circuits, antenna calculations, speaker design), unless specifically noted, power calculations in the remainder of the text will refer to rms values.

KEY POINTS

Analysis problems for ac resistive circuits may be simple or complex, but the method of solution is similar to that used to analyze dc resistive networks.

EXAMPLE SOLUTION

Figure 11-34 shows a simple series circuit composed of an ac source and a single resistor. Find the peak current in the circuit and the power dissipated in the resistor.

EXAMPLE SOLUTION

Since the value of the voltage source is given as a peak voltage, we can apply Ohm's Law directly to determine peak current.

$$I_P = \frac{V_P}{R}$$

$$= \frac{10 \text{ V}}{2 \text{ k}\Omega} = 5 \text{ mA}$$

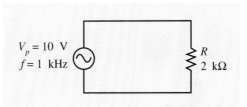

Figure 11-34. An ac circuit for analysis.

KEY POINTS

Although peak and average power calculations are important for some applications, the remainder of this text will concentrate on power dissipations using rms values of voltage and current.

We can use any of the power formulas to compute power, but we will need to use rms values of voltage and/or current. Let's use the $P = V^2/R$ formula. First, we will need to find the rms value of voltage.

$$V_{rms} = 0.707 \; V_P$$
$$= 0.707 \times 10 \text{ V} = 7.07 \text{ V}$$

We can now compute power dissipation.

$$P = \frac{V^2}{R}$$
$$= \frac{(7.07 \text{ V})^2}{2 \text{ k}\Omega} = 24.99 \text{ mW}$$

EXAMPLE SOLUTION

Figure 11-35 shows a series-parallel circuit with an ac source. Complete Table 11-2 with reference to this circuit.

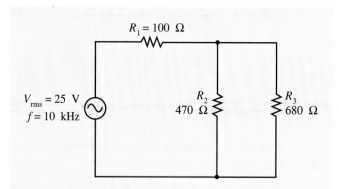

Figure 11-35. Analyze this circuit.

	VOLTAGE				CURRENT			
	V_P	V_{PP}	V_{rms}	V_{avg}	I_P	I_{PP}	I_{rms}	I_{avg}
R_1								
R_2								
R_3								
Total								

Table 11-2. Values for Figure 11-35

EXAMPLE SOLUTION

As with most circuit analysis problems, there are many ways to solve the problem. Let's begin by simplifying the circuit and sketching intermediate schematics. First, we note that R_2 and R_3 are in parallel. We can replace them with an equivalent resistance having a value of

$$R_{2,3} = \frac{R_2 R_3}{R_2 + R_3}$$

$$= \frac{470 \ \Omega \times 680 \ \Omega}{470 \ \Omega + 680 \ \Omega} = 277.9 \ \Omega$$

This step is shown in Figure 11-36. We can now find the total circuit resistance by combining the series resistances of R_1 and $R_{2,3}$.

$$R_T = R_1 + R_{2,3}$$

$$= 100 \ \Omega + 277.9 \ \Omega = 377.9 \ \Omega$$

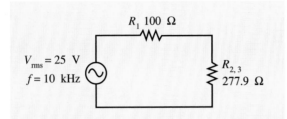

Figure 11-36. Simplification of the circuit shown in Figure 11-35.

The result at this point is shown in Figure 11-37.

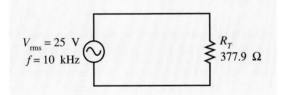

Figure 11-37. An equivalent circuit for Figure 11-35.

As a next step, let's compute the various voltage values for the applied voltage (V_T). V_{rms} is given. From this, we can find the others. We find V_p by using Equation 11-7.

$$V_{T(P)} = 1.414 V_{T(rms)}$$

$$= 1.414 \times 25 \ V = 35.35 \ V$$

We use Equation 11-9 to compute V_{pp}.

$$V_{T(PP)} = 2 V_{T(P)}$$

$$= 2 \times 35.35 \ V = 70.7 \ V$$

Finally, we can compute the average value by applying Equation 11-3.

$$V_{T(avg)} = 0.637 V_{T(P)}$$

$$= 0.637 \times 35.35 \ V = 22.52 \ V$$

This completes the first four boxes on the bottom row of Table 11-2. Since we know all forms of the applied voltage, and we know the value of total resistance, we can complete the lower row of Table 11-2 by using Ohm's Law. We find I_p as follows:

$$I_{T(P)} = \frac{V_{T(P)}}{R_T}$$

$$= \frac{35.35 \text{ V}}{377.9 \text{ }\Omega} = 93.54 \text{ mA}$$

Similarly, we compute I_{pp} as

$$I_{T(PP)} = \frac{V_{T(PP)}}{R_T}$$

$$= \frac{70.7 \text{ V}}{377.9 \text{ }\Omega} = 187.1 \text{ mA}$$

I_{rms} is computed as

$$I_{T(rms)} = \frac{V_{T(rms)}}{R_T}$$

$$= \frac{25 \text{ V}}{377.9 \text{ }\Omega} = 66.16 \text{ mA}$$

And we compute the total average value as

$$I_{T(avg)} = \frac{V_{T(avg)}}{R_T}$$

$$= \frac{22.52 \text{ V}}{377.9 \text{ }\Omega} = 59.59 \text{ mA}$$

If we wanted to compute total power dissipation, we could use any of the basic power formulas along with the relevant value of total current, voltage, or resistance.

We have computed everything we can with Figure 11-37, so let us move back to Figure 11-36 and continue. First, we note that total current also flows through R_1. This observation immediately gives us the values for all the R_1 currents in Table 11-2. We can find the voltages across R_1 as follows:

$$V_{1(P)} = I_{1(P)}R_1 = 93.54 \text{ mA} \times 100 \text{ }\Omega = 9.354 \text{ V}$$

$$V_{1(PP)} = I_{1(PP)}R_1 = 187.1 \text{ mA} \times 100 \text{ }\Omega = 18.71 \text{ V}$$

$$V_{1(rms)} = I_{1(rms)}R_1 = 66.16 \text{ mA} \times 100 \text{ }\Omega = 6.616 \text{ V}$$

$$V_{1(avg)} = I_{1(avg)}R_1 = 59.59 \text{ mA} \times 100 \text{ }\Omega = 5.959 \text{ V}$$

This completes the first row of answers in Table 11-2.

Kirchhoff's Law can be used to determine the various voltages across the $R_{2,3}$ resistance as follows:

$$V_{2,3(P)} = V_{T(P)} - V_{1(P)} = 35.35 \text{ V} - 9.354 \text{ V} = 26 \text{ V}$$

$$V_{2,3(PP)} = V_{T(PP)} - V_{1(PP)} = 70.7 \text{ V} - 18.71 \text{ V} = 51.99 \text{ V}$$

$$V_{2,3(rms)} = V_{T(rms)} - V_{1(rms)} = 25 \text{ V} - 6.616 \text{ V} = 18.38 \text{ V}$$

$$V_{2,3(avg)} = V_{T(avg)} - V_{1(avg)} = 22.52 \text{ V} - 5.959 \text{ V} = 16.56 \text{ V}$$

Because resistors R_2 and R_3 are in parallel, they will have the same voltages across them. Therefore, we can use the values for $V_{2,3}$ in both R_2 and R_3 rows of Table 11-2. This leaves only the current for R_2 and R_3 to be calculated. For this, we must move to Figure 11-35. There are many ways to calculate these currents. Let us use Ohm's Law for the R_2 calculations and Kirchhoff's Current Law for the R_3 calculations. The calculation for the R_2 currents are

$$I_{2(P)} = \frac{V_{2(P)}}{R_2} = \frac{26 \text{ V}}{470 \text{ } \Omega} = 55.32 \text{ mA}$$

$$I_{2(PP)} = \frac{V_{2(PP)}}{R_2} = \frac{51.99 \text{ V}}{470 \text{ } \Omega} = 110.6 \text{ mA}$$

$$I_{2(rms)} = \frac{V_{2(rms)}}{R_2} = \frac{18.38 \text{ V}}{470 \text{ } \Omega} = 39.11 \text{ mA}$$

$$I_{2(avg)} = \frac{V_{2(avg)}}{R_2} = \frac{16.56 \text{ V}}{470 \text{ } \Omega} = 35.23 \text{ mA}$$

Using Kirchhoff's Current Law for the R_3 current gives us the following results:

$$I_{3(P)} = I_{T(P)} - I_{2(P)} = 93.54 \text{ mA} - 55.32 \text{ mA} = 38.22 \text{ mA}$$

$$I_{3(PP)} = I_{T(PP)} - I_{2(PP)} = 187.1 \text{ mA} - 110.6 \text{ mA} = 76.5 \text{ mA}$$

$$I_{3(rms)} = I_{T(rms)} - I_{2(rms)} = 66.16 \text{ mA} - 39.11 \text{ mA} = 27.05 \text{ mA}$$

$$I_{3(avg)} = I_{T(avg)} - I_{2(avg)} = 59.59 \text{ mA} - 35.23 \text{ mA} = 24.36 \text{ mA}$$

The completed solution matrix is shown in Table 11-3.

	VOLTAGE (V)				CURRENT (mA)			
	V_P	V_{PP}	V_{rms}	V_{avg}	I_P	I_{PP}	I_{rms}	I_{avg}
R_1	9.354	18.71	6.616	5.959	93.54	187.1	66.16	59.59
R_2	26	51.99	18.38	16.56	55.32	110.6	39.11	35.23
R_3	26	51.99	18.38	16.56	38.22	76.5	27.05	24.36
Total	35.35	70.7	25	22.52	93.54	187.1	66.16	59.59

Table 11-3. Completed Solution Matrix for Figure 11-35

Exercise Problems 11.4

1. Complete a solution matrix similar to Table 11-3 for the circuit shown in Figure 11-38.

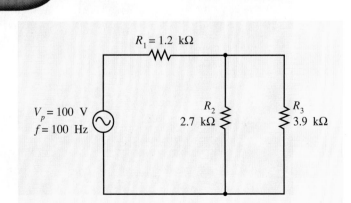

Figure 11-38. Complete a solution matrix for this circuit.

2. Refer to Figure 11-39 and complete a solution matrix similar to Table 11-3.

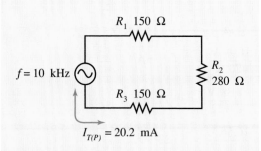

Figure 11-39. Complete a solution matrix for this circuit.

11.5 Applied Technology: Alternating Voltage Applications

There is an endless array of applications that rely on alternating voltage and current. The following sections provide a brief sampling of applications in several frequency ranges.

60-Hz Power Distribution

Undoubtedly, the most common application of alternating voltage is the 60-Hz power distribution that is supplied by power companies throughout the United States. The voltage is initially produced by alternators at such places as Hoover Dam near Las Vegas, Nevada. In the case of Hoover Dam, the alternators are rotated by the force of water as the Colorado River flows past the dam. Other power-generating plants use coal or nuclear power to produce steam, which ultimately provides the mechanical energy needed to spin the alternators. Figure 11-40 shows an alternator used to generate commercial power.

Figure 11-40. A 60-Hz alternator used for generation of commercial power. (Courtesy of Tampa Electric Company)

The voltage is initially generated at a level of several thousand volts. Near the power station, it is increased to several hundred thousand volts for long-distance transmission. Once the power has reached your neighborhood, it is again reduced to several thousand volts for local distribution. Finally, at a point just outside your home, the voltage is lowered to 220 V and routed into your house. At the service entrance (fuse or breaker box) in your house, the voltage is tapped off at a 120-V level for most appliances and lights, while the full 220 V is available for larger equipment such as air conditioners and electric dryers.

It may surprise you to learn that 120 V is an ideal rms value. (The peak voltage is nearly 170 V.) The actual rms voltage may change significantly throughout the day. It may be less than 100 V or higher than 130 V at certain times depending on the load demands and the capabilities of your power company.

The frequency is nominally 60 Hz and is established by the speed of the alternators. The frequency does vary slightly throughout the day. However, it is carefully compensated, so that the long-term average is very nearly 60 Hz. Many electrical and electronic devices (e.g., clocks and turntables) use the 60-Hz frequency as a time reference.

In most cases, transmission of 60-Hz energy is restricted to conductive wires and cables. No substantial energy is intentionally radiated at 60 Hz. Additional information regarding the transmission of 60-Hz power is presented in Chapter 17.

Sound Waves

Sound waves are made up of sinusoidal pressure changes in the air. We use sound waves in electronics for things like microphones and speakers. Sound also plays an important role in computers. Nearly all computers emit a "beep" to alert the user to an error. Some computers create and play music. Many industrial applications utilize sound as an audible annunciator to attract the operator's attention.

The frequency range for audible sound is from about 15 to 20 Hz on the low-frequency end to about 15 kHz to 20 kHz on the high-frequency end of the range. Sound waves travel through air at about 1,130 ft per second. This is roughly 1 ms per foot.

Ultrasonic Waves

Ultrasonic waves, like sound waves, are pressure changes in the air or other material. Ultrasonic applications include burglar alarms, range finders, and nondestructive inspection (NDI) equipment. In these cases, the ultrasonic sound is emitted by a transducer (equivalent of a speaker). It travels outward, reflects off objects (e.g., a burglar), and returns to a receiving transducer (like a microphone). Figure 11-41 illustrates this echo principle.

Some applications (e.g., a range finder on a camera) simply measure the amount of time that it takes the ultrasonic wave to travel from the "speaker" to the object and back to the "microphone." Since the waves travel at 1,130 feet per second, we can easily compute the distance to the object.

Other applications rely on a detected frequency difference between the transmitted and received signal. When the reflecting object is stationary, the received frequency is the same as the transmitted frequency. If the object is moving toward or away from the transmitter/receiver, then the received signal will be higher or lower, respectively, than the transmitted

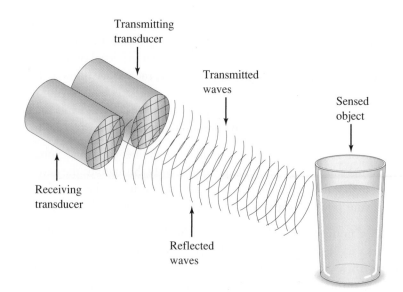

Figure 11-41. An ultrasonic receiver can detect an echo bounced off a sensed object.

signal. This shift in frequency is known as the doppler effect. This is the same phenomenon that causes the sound of a rapidly approaching train or race car to sound like a higher frequency. As the train or car passes you, the frequency drops to a much lower value.

Many medical electronics applications use ultrasonic frequencies. Ultrasound imaging systems can effectively "see" inside the body without the dangers associated with x rays. Ultrasonics are also used by oral hygienists to clean your teeth. Figure 11-42 shows a medical application for ultrasonics.

Ultrasonic energy travels through air at about 1,130 feet per second. The frequency range is from about 25 kHz to several hundreds of kilohertz.

Figure 11-42. An ultrasound machine used to view inside a human body. (Courtesy of GE Medical Systems)

Radio Waves

Radio, or electromagnetic, waves are used by a wide array of electronic devices. The most obvious applications include radio and television broadcasts. Other common applications include microwave communications links, satellite communications, and a variety of radar applications. Radio frequencies are also used for navigation. A small handheld receiver can intercept signals from a satellite and locate any spot in the world within a few feet.

Microwave ovens use radio frequencies. Other radio-frequency (rf) devices are used in industry to heat metal, melt plastic, and dry plywood. A similar device can be used to induce an artificial fever in a human.

Radio waves are transmitted from an antenna and travel through the air at very nearly the speed of light. The waves travel at about 300×10^6 meters per second, or 186,000 miles per second. Unlike sound waves, which are high- and low-pressure regions moving through the air, rf waves are electromagnetic. The moving wave has characteristics of both magnetic fields and electrostatic fields. The frequency range for electromagnetic radio waves begins below 20 Hz and extends into the hundreds of gigahertz. Figure 11-43 shows an antenna used for transmission of electromagnetic waves.

Figure 11-43. A radio-frequency antenna used to transmit electromagnetic energy. (Courtesy of Andrew Corporation)

1. Would a 10-Hz signal probably be referred to as ultrasonic?
2. The highest rf wave is about 100 MHz. (True or False)
3. Electromagnetic waves travel through the air at 1,130 feet per second. (True or False)

11.6 Oscilloscope Fundamentals

A previous chapter discussed oscilloscope operation as it applied to dc measurements. In this section, we will discuss the use of an oscilloscope for ac measurements. In particular, we will see how to use a scope to measure period, frequency, and voltage of a sine wave.

Voltage Measurements

Measurement of ac voltage on an oscilloscope consists of observing the amount of vertical deflection and multiplying by the setting of the vertical sensitivity control. Most modern scopes have internal microprocessors that automatically interpret the average, peak, peak-to-peak, and rms values of a measured wave. The values are displayed on the oscilloscope screen as text. Figure 11-44 shows a scope presentation with on-screen text of measured values.

Some less sophisticated scopes require the technician to measure and interpret the voltage manually. As a technician, you should be capable of operating any type of scope. It is best to learn on a basic scope with few automatic operations. If you later encounter a more sophisticated scope that has automatic measurements, then it will be easy to operate. On the other hand, if you only know how to operate a scope with automatic measurement capability, then you will be unable to operate a more basic scope.

KEY POINTS

An oscilloscope can directly measure peak-to-peak voltage and period. Once these two values are known, a technician can calculate the peak, rms, and average voltages and the frequency by applying basic sine wave equations.

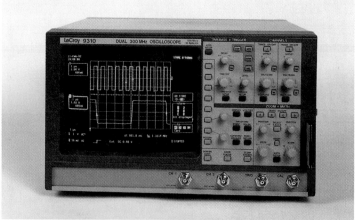

Figure 11-44. An oscilloscope with on-screen display of measured values. (Courtesy of LeCroy Corporation, Chestnut Ridge, NY)

Figure 11-45 illustrates how to measure the peak-to-peak voltage of a sine wave. The setting of the horizontal and triggering controls of the scope are not critical, but they should be adjusted to provide a stable display that includes at least one full cycle of the measured wave. If you prefer, you can slow the horizontal sweep down to the point where there are so many cycles on the screen that they appear as a solid band. It doesn't matter, so long as you can accurately determine the amplitude of the peaks.

The vertical gain control should be adjusted to provide the maximum deflection that still allows the entire sine wave to be viewed on the screen. The more deflection you have, the more accurate your measurement can be. The measurement itself consists of counting the number of divisions between the extreme negative peak and the extreme positive peak. The vertical position control can be used to move the displayed waveform into a more convenient position. In most cases, if the negative peak is placed directly on one of the horizontal graticule lines, then it is easier to determine the amount of deflection. Otherwise (as pictured in Figure 11-45), both peaks will appear in the middle portion of a division, making it more difficult to count divisions.

Once you have determined the number of divisions of vertical deflection, you simply multiply this number by the setting of the vertical gain (or sensitivity) control. This is expressed by Equation 11-18.

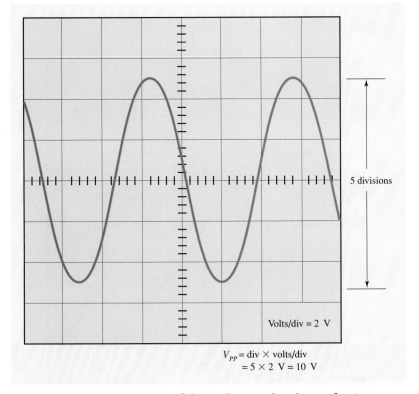

Figure 11-45. Measurement of the peak-to-peak voltage of a sine wave.

$$V_{PP} = \text{No. of vertical divisions} \times \text{volts per division} \qquad (11\text{-}18)$$

In the case pictured in Figure 11-45, we have five divisions of deflection, and the vertical gain control is set for 2 volts/division. The peak-to-peak voltage of the sine wave is computed as

$$V_{PP} = \text{No. of vertical divisions} \times \text{volts per division}$$
$$= 5 \text{ divisions} \times 2 \text{ V/division} = 10 \text{ V}$$

Practice Problems

1. Measure the peak-to-peak voltage of the sine wave in Figure 11-46.
2. What is the peak-to-peak voltage of the sine wave in Figure 11-47?
3. Determine the peak-to-peak voltage of the sine wave in Figure 11-48.

Answers to Practice Problems

1. 20 V

2. 60 mV

3. 0.36 V

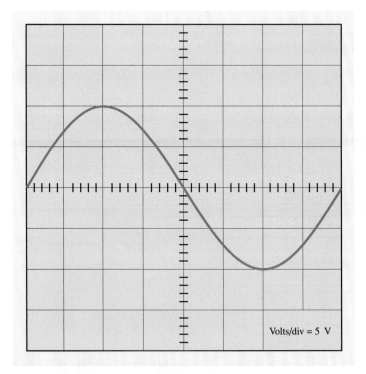

Figure 11-46. Measure peak-to-peak voltage.

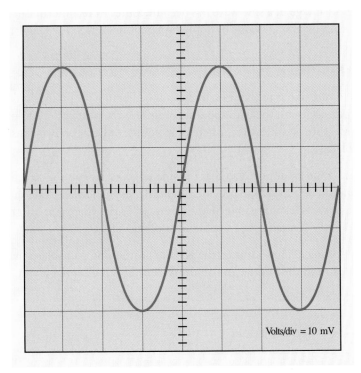

Figure 11-47. What is the peak-to-peak voltage of this sine wave?

Volts/div = 10 mV

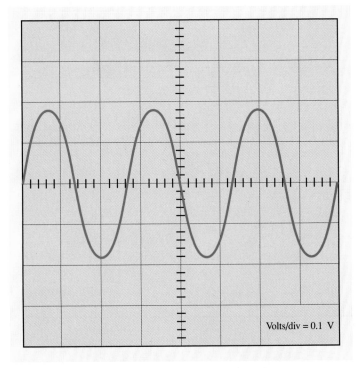

Figure 11-48. Determine the peak-to-peak voltage.

Volts/div = 0.1 V

Once the peak-to-peak voltage of a sine wave has been measured, a technician can readily determine the peak, rms, or average value by applying Equations 11-3, 11-5, and 11-9.

Period Measurements

To measure the period of a sine wave, we essentially count the number of divisions between any point on a cycle and the corresponding point on the next cycle. It is usually most convenient to measure between the zero-crossing points, or between two consecutive peaks of the same polarity.

The vertical controls should be adjusted so that the sine wave nearly fills the screen. The triggering controls should be adjusted to provide a stable display. The sweep rate should be adjusted to provide as few cycles as possible on the screen as long as there is at least one full cycle visible. Figure 11-49 illustrates the measurement of period.

In Figure 11-49, the technician has adjusted the vertical positioning control, so that the sine wave is centered around the middle line on the screen. This is essential if you plan to

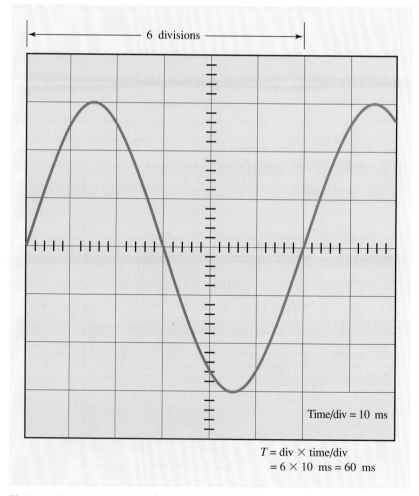

Time/div = 10 ms

$$T = \text{div} \times \text{time/div}$$
$$= 6 \times 10 \text{ ms} = 60 \text{ ms}$$

Figure 11-49. Measuring the period of a sine wave.

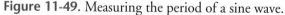

measure between the zero-crossing points. The period is determined by counting the number of divisions between corresponding zero-crossing points on two consecutive half-cycles, and multiplying this number by the setting of the sweep rate control. This is expressed by Equation 11-19.

$$t = \text{No. of horizontal divisions} \times \text{sweep rate} \qquad \textbf{(11-19)}$$

In the case shown in Figure 11-49, the horizontal distance between the two corresponding zero-crossing points is 6 divisions. The sweep rate is set for 10 ms per division. The period is determined with Equation 11-19.

$$t = \text{No. of horizontal divisions} \times \text{sweep rate}$$
$$= 6 \text{ divisions} \times 10 \text{ ms/division} = 60 \text{ ms}$$

Figure 11-50 shows an alternate way to measure period. Here, the technician is measuring the time between two consecutive positive peaks. In this case, the waveform does not have to be centered on the screen. The period of the sine wave shown in Figure 11-50 is determined by applying Equation 11-19.

$$t = \text{No. of horizontal divisions} \times \text{sweep rate}$$
$$= 4.5 \text{ divisions} \times 100 \text{ μs/division} = 450 \text{ μs}$$

Either of the preceding methods provides better results when the vertical gain is set to provide a large vertical deflection. In the case of measuring between zero-crossing points,

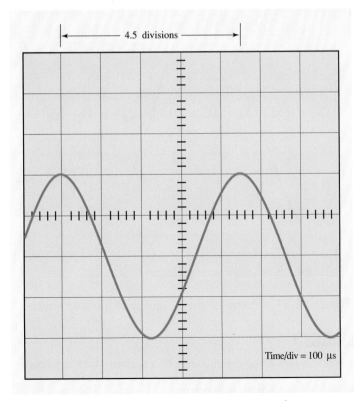

Figure 11-50. An alternate way to measure period.

maximum accuracy can be obtained when the vertical deflection is adjusted to extend beyond the limits of the screen. This makes the zero-crossing points on the wave appear more vertical and well-defined. The technician must be very certain that the trace is centered when this method is used. When measuring between two peaks, increased vertical amplitude makes the peaks appear sharper. It is easier to pinpoint the exact peak. If you are measuring between the positive peaks, it is all right for the negative peaks to extend off the screen.

Frequency Measurements

An oscilloscope does not measure frequency directly, unless it has a built-in micropro-cessor to perform automatic measurements. Without automatic measurements, the tech-nician must measure period, as described in the preceding section. Then Equation 11-2 must be applied to determine the frequency.

EXAMPLE SOLUTION

What is the frequency of the sine wave shown in Figure 11-51?

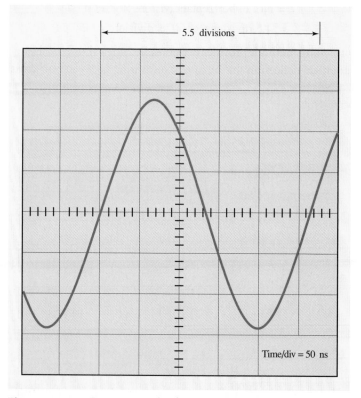

Figure 11-51. Determine the frequency of this sine wave.

EXAMPLE **SOLUTION**

The period of the sine wave can be determined with Equation 11-19 as follows:

$$t = \text{No. of horizontal divisions} \times \text{sweep rate}$$
$$= 5.5 \text{ div} \times 50 \text{ ns/div} = 275 \text{ ns}$$

The frequency can now be computed by applying Equation 11-2.

$$f = \frac{1}{t}$$

$$= \frac{1}{275 \text{ ns}} = 3.636 \text{ MHz}$$

Exercise Problems 11.6

1. Determine the following values for the sine wave pictured in Figure 11-52.

    a. peak-to-peak voltage **b.** average voltage **c.** rms voltage
    d. frequency **e.** period

2. Measure the following values on the waveform displayed in Figure 11-53.

    a. peak-to-peak voltage **b.** average voltage **c.** rms voltage
    d. frequency **e.** period

3. Determine the following values for the sine wave pictured in Figure 11-54.

    a. peak-to-peak voltage **b.** average voltage **c.** rms voltage
    d. frequency **e.** period

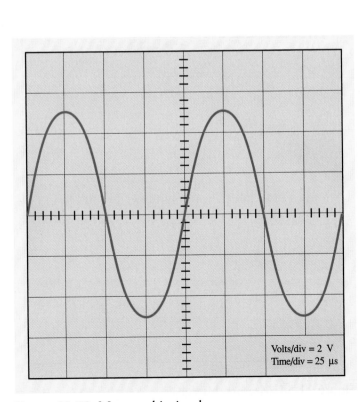

Volts/div = 2 V
Time/div = 25 µs

Figure 11-52. Measure this signal.

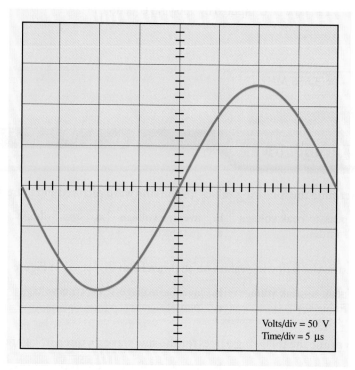

Figure 11-53. Measure this waveform.

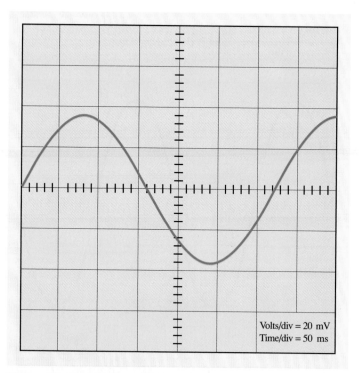

Figure 11-54. Measure this signal.

Chapter Summary

- Alternating voltage and current is at the heart of a vast majority of electronic applications. A sinusoidal voltage continuously varies in amplitude and periodically reverses polarity. A sinusoidal current continuously varies in amplitude and periodically changes direction. Sinusoidal waveforms consist of a series of repetitious cycles. The time for one cycle is called the period of the waveform. Frequency describes how many full cycles occur in a one-second interval. Each cycle is composed of two half-cycles with opposite polarities. Sine waves can be generated by an alternator or electronically (e.g., a function generator). If the durations of the two half-cycles are equal (as in a sine wave), the waveform is said to be symmetrical. An asymmetrical waveform has unequal half-cycles.

- The highest instantaneous voltage or current point on a sine wave is called the peak. Each sine wave has a positive and a negative peak. The average value of a full sine wave is zero, since it is positive as long as it is negative. As a general practice, the term average, when used to describe sine waves, refers to the average of one half-cycle. The average voltage is $0.637 \times V_p$. The root-mean-square (rms) voltage of a sine wave describes the heating effect of the waveform. It takes an amount of dc equal to the rms value of a sine wave to produce the same amount of heat in a resistance. The rms voltage is equal to $0.707 \times V_p$. The peak-to-peak voltage does not actually exist as an instantaneous value, but it is useful to describe the sine wave. It is always equal to twice the peak value.

- The phase of a sine wave describes an angular point on the wave at a specific time. Zero and 180 degrees coincide to the zero-crossing points of the sine wave. The peak values occur at 90° and 270°. If two sine waves are in phase, then the corresponding points of the two waveforms occur at the same time. Out-of-phase sine waves have corresponding points occurring at different times.

- Phase angle can be expressed in degrees or radians. One radian is equal to 57.3°. Either unit of measure is easy to use with a scientific calculator.

- The instantaneous voltage of a sine wave varies with each instant in time. For a given peak amplitude, the instantaneous voltage depends on the instantaneous phase of the sine wave. More specifically, $v = V_p \sin \theta$.

- A phasor diagram is a pictorial representation of the instantaneous phase in a sine wave. It can also show the phase relationships between multiple sine waves. The length of a phasor arrow represents the peak voltage of a sine wave. The distance of the arrowhead from the horizontal axis represents the instantaneous voltage of the sine wave. Finally, the angle formed by the phasor and the horizontal axis corresponds to the instantaneous phase of the sine wave.

- Phasor calculations are based on right-triangle calculations. A technician should be able to compute the sine, cosine, and tangent functions of an angle. Each of these functions also has a corresponding inverse function (arcsin, arccos, and arctan).

- Resistive circuits with an ac source are analyzed in a manner consistent with the dc analysis presented in previous chapters. Care must be exercised to ensure that corresponding voltages and currents are used (e.g., rms voltage with rms current).

- Applications that utilize alternating voltage and current are virtually endless. New applications are being created continuously. The applications can be grossly categorized according to frequency of operation. The frequency of alternating voltages and currents used in electronics extends from subaudio to well over 100 GHz.

- An oscilloscope can be used to measure period. The technician must compute frequency. The oscilloscope can be used to measure peak-to-peak voltage. The technician generally computes peak, average, and rms values. Many scopes have an internal microprocessor that automatically computes sine wave values and displays them on the scope screen.

Review Questions

Section 11.1: Generation of Alternating Voltage

1. The time required to complete a full cycle of alternating voltage is called the _____ .

2. How many alternations are required to make one full cycle?

3. If the positive and negative half-cycles of an alternating voltage are equal, the waveform is (*symmetrical, asymmetrical*).

4. If the cycles of a waveform are continuous, the waveform is said to be _____ .

5. What is another name for an ac generator?

6. Slip rings are segmented like a commutator on a dc generator. (True or False)

7. Why are the brushes on an alternator spring loaded?

8. When a looped conductor is rotated at a constant speed in a magnetic field, a sinusoidal wave is produced. What conductor position corresponds to zero degrees on the sine wave?

9. The maximum instantaneous value of a sine wave is called the _____ voltage.

10. What type of test equipment can generate sine waves, rectangular waves, and waves of other shapes?

Section 11.2: Characteristics of Sine Waves

11. What is the basic unit of measurement for the period of a sine wave?

12. What sine wave quantity describes how many cycles occur in a one-second interval?

13. What is the basic unit of measurement for the frequency of a sine wave?

14. If the period of a certain sine wave is 2.5 ms, what is its frequency?

15. What is the frequency of a sine wave that has a period of 75 ns?

16. A sine wave with a period of 100 ns has a higher frequency than a sine wave with a period of 100 ms. (True or False)

17. What is the period of a 5-MHz sine wave?

18. If the frequency of a certain sine wave is 2.5 GHz, what is its period?

19. What is the period of a 60-Hz sine wave?

20. What is the period of a 550-kHz sine wave?

21. How many times does a peak occur during one cycle of a sine wave?

22. The positive peak of a sine wave occurs at 180°. (True or False)

23. The negative peak of a sine wave occurs at 270°. (True or False)

24. If a sine wave has a positive peak current of 2.75 A, what is its negative peak value?

25. What is the average value of a *full cycle* of a sine wave, if the peak voltage is 10 V?

26. What is the average value of a *full sine wave,* if the peak voltage is 1,000 V?

27. What is the average value (V_{avg}) of a sine wave with a peak voltage of 25 V?

28. If the average value of a sine wave is 108 V, what is its peak value?

29. It takes an amount of dc equal to the average value of a sine wave to cause the same heat in a resistance. (True or False)

30. If a sine wave has a peak-to-peak current value of 10 A, what is its rms value?

31. What is the rms value of a sine wave that has a 150-mV average value?

32. What is the peak voltage of a sine wave that has a 200-μV rms value?

33. What is the peak-to-peak voltage of a 10-V peak sine wave?

34. Which sine wave would cause the most heat in a resistor?
    a) 10 V_{pp} b) 10 V_{rms} c) 10 V_{avg} d) 10 V_p

35. Angular measurement of a sine wave can be expressed in _____ or _____ .

36. When the corresponding points on two similar frequency sine waves occur at different times, we say the sine waves are (*in, out*) of _____ .

37. If the instantaneous phase of a certain sine wave is 45° and the peak voltage is 100 V, what is the instantaneous voltage?

38. A phase angle of 2 rad is the same as a phase angle of _____ degrees.

39. A phase angle of 35° is the same as a phase angle of _____ radians.

40. A 100° angle can be expressed as an angle of _____ radians.

41. A 5-rad angle can be expressed as a _____ -degree angle.

42. What is the instantaneous voltage of a sine wave at 25° if its peak voltage is 30 V?

43. What is the instantaneous voltage of a sine wave at 105° if the rms voltage is 100 V?

44. What is the peak voltage of a sine wave that has an instantaneous voltage of 10 V at 1.2 rad?

45. If a sine wave at 3 rad has an instantaneous voltage of 120 V, what is its peak-to-peak value?

46. What is the frequency of the fifth harmonic of a 75-MHz waveform?

47. Seventy-five megahertz is the _____ harmonic frequency of a 25-MHz fundamental.

Section 11.3: Working with Phasors

48. The length of a phasor represents the _____ voltage of a sine wave.

49. The phase of a sine wave is represented on a phasor diagram by the angle between the phasor and the vertical axis. (True or False)

50. The distance of the phasor tip from the horizontal axis represents the _____ voltage of a sine wave.

51. The longest side of a right triangle is called the _____ .

52. The cosine of an angle in a right triangle is obtained by dividing the _____ by the _____ .

53. If the _____ in a right triangle is divided by the _____ , the result is a number that is the tangent of the angle.

54. If you know the tangent of an angle, how do you find the angle itself?

55. If you know the cosine of an angle, how do you find the angle itself?

56. What is the sine of a 35° angle?

57. What is the sine of a 3.2-rad angle?

58. What is the tangent of a 23° angle?

59. What is the cosine of a 1.6-rad angle?

60. If the tangent of an angle is 5.6, what is the angle in degrees?

61. If the tangent of an angle is 4.25, what is the size of the angle in radians?

62. Refer to Figure 11-55. What is the length of side a?

63. What is the length of side b in Figure 11-55?

64. What is the value of θ in Figure 11-56?

65. What is the length of side c in Figure 11-56?

66. What is the peak voltage of the sine wave represented in Figure 11-57?

67. What is the instantaneous voltage of the sine wave represented in Figure 11-57?

68. What is the instantaneous voltage of the sine wave represented in Figure 11-58?

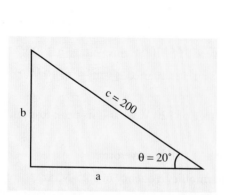

Figure 11-55. A right-triangle problem.

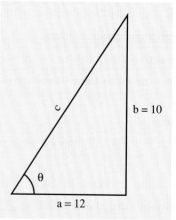

Figure 11-56. A right-triangle problem.

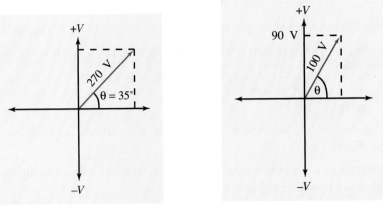

Figure 11-57. A phasor diagram.

Figure 11-58. A phasor diagram.

69. What is the phase angle of the sine wave represented in Figure 11-58?

70. Compute the value of arccos 0.6 and express in radians.

71. Express the value of arcsin 0.8 in degrees.

72. The value of arctan 20 corresponds to _____ degrees.

Section 11.4: Resistive ac Circuit Analysis

Refer to Figure 11-59 for Questions 73–77.

73. What is the peak current?

74. What is the power dissipation in the resistor?

75. What is the average value of input voltage?

76. What is the peak-to-peak input voltage?

77. What is the instantaneous current at 50°?

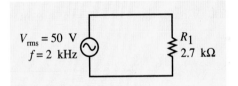

Figure 11-59. Analyze this circuit.

Refer to Figure 11-60 for Questions 78–87.

78. What is the total resistance?

79. What is the total rms current?

80. What is the peak voltage across R_1?

81. What is the average current through R_4?

82. What is the peak-to-peak voltage across R_2?

83. What is the rms current through R_3?

84. What is the total average current?

85. What is the total average current over a full cycle?

86. What is the total power dissipation?

87. What is the rms current through R_4?

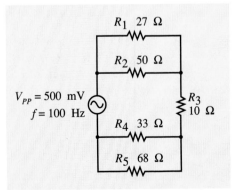

Figure 11-60. Analyze this circuit.

Section 11.5: Applied Technology: Alternating Voltage Applications

88. What is the frequency of the power distribution network in the United States?

89. When the power used in your home is first generated, it is a much lower voltage. (True or False)

90. The nominal value of voltage available at the wall sockets in your home is about 108 V average.

91. Sound and ultrasonic waves both travel through air at about 1,130 feet per second. (True or False)

92. What is the name of the effect that explains the frequency shift in an ultrasonic system when the reflecting object is moving?

93. An ultrasonic transmitter transducer is like a _____ in an audio system.

94. An ultrasonic receiver transducer is like a _____ in an audio system.

95. Radio frequency waves travel through air at approximately _____ meters per second.

96. Radio waves move through the air as high- and low-pressure changes. (True or False)

97. Radio waves are called electromagnetic waves. (True or False)

98. It is possible to have radio waves at least as high as 2,000 MHz. (True or False)

Section 11.6: Oscilloscope Fundamentals

99. What is the period of the sine wave shown in Figure 11-61?

100. What is the rms voltage of the sine wave shown in Figure 11-61?

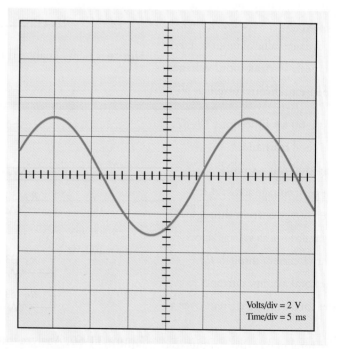

Volts/div = 2 V
Time/div = 5 ms

Figure 11-61. Interpret this display.

101. What is the frequency of the sine wave shown in Figure 11-62?

102. What is the peak voltage of the sine wave shown in Figure 11-62?

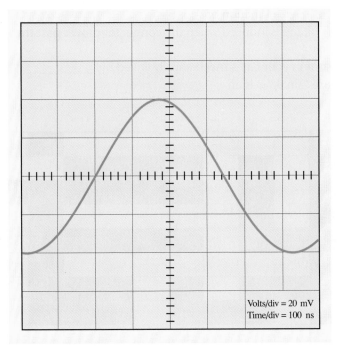

Volts/div = 20 mV
Time/div = 100 ns

Figure 11-62. Interpret this display.

TECHNICIAN CHALLENGE

Following is a crossword puzzle with entries that are related to the material presented in this chapter. It will give you one more opportunity to recall the facts and terms learned in this chapter.

ACROSS:

1. A unit of angular measurement.
8. One of the factors that determine the instantaneous voltage of a sine wave.
11. A type of current that is steady and flows in one direction.
12. The name of a 90° angle.
13. $0.637\ V_p$.
14. The longest side of a right triangle.
15. A point in an ac circuit where the current splits.
16. $0.707\ V_p$.

DOWN:

1. The "r" in rms.
2. A unit of angular measurement.
3. Alternating current.

4. Arccos is the inverse function of _____ .
5. A way to produce alternating voltage.
6. One positive alternation + one negative half-cycle.
7. Arctan is the inverse function of _____ .
8. Maximum voltage is induced when the conductor moves past the _____ in an alternator.
9. The alternator in your car is mechanically linked by _____ .
10. In the phrase "sin θ," θ is an _____ .

Equation List

(11-1)　$t = \dfrac{1}{f}$

(11-2)　$f = \dfrac{1}{t}$

(11-3)　$V_{avg} = 0.637\, V_P$

(11-4)　$I_{avg} = 0.637\, I_P$

(11-5)　$V_{rms} = 0.707\, V_P$

(11-6)　$I_{rms} = 0.707\, I_P$

(11-7)　$V_P = \dfrac{V_{rms}}{0.707} = 1.414\, V_{rms}$

(11-8)　$I_P = \dfrac{I_{rms}}{0.707} = 1.414\, I_{rms}$

(11-9)　$V_{PP} = 2\, V_P$

(11-10)　$I_{PP} = 2\, I_P$

(11-11)　$radians = \dfrac{degrees}{57.3°}$

(11-12)　$degrees = radians \times 57.3°$

(11-13)　$v = V_P \sin\theta$

(11-14)　$i = I_P \sin\theta$

(11-15)　$\sin\theta = \dfrac{opposite\ side}{hypotenuse}$

(11-16)　$\cos\theta = \dfrac{adjacent\ side}{hypotenuse}$

(11-17)　$\tan\theta = \dfrac{opposite\ side}{adjacent\ side}$

(11-18)　$V_{PP} = No.\ of\ vertical\ divisions \times volts\ per\ division$

(11-19)　$t = No.\ of\ horizontal\ divisions \times sweep\ rate$

choke   inductive reactance
copper loss Q
eddy currents   skin effect
effective series resistance (*ESR*)

objectives

After completing this chapter, you should be able to:

1. List six factors that affect electromagnetic induction.

2. State Faraday's and Lenz's Laws regarding electromagnetic induction.

3. List the factors that affect the value of an inductor.

4. Name and describe at least six types of inductors.

5. Determine the total inductance of a circuit having inductors connected in series, parallel, series-parallel, or in a complex configuration.

6. Contrast the effects of an inductor in an ac versus a dc circuit.

7. State the factors that determine the inductive reactance of an inductor.

8. Calculate the inductive reactance of an inductor in a given circuit.

9. Calculate the total inductive reactance of a circuit having multiple inductive reactances connected in series, parallel, series-parallel, or in a complex configuration.

10. Calculate the Q of a coil.

11. State the phase relationship between current and voltage in an inductive circuit.

12. Explain the power dissipation of an ideal inductance.

13. Identify possible reasons for power loss in a nonideal inductance.

14. Explain how to identify defects in an inductor.

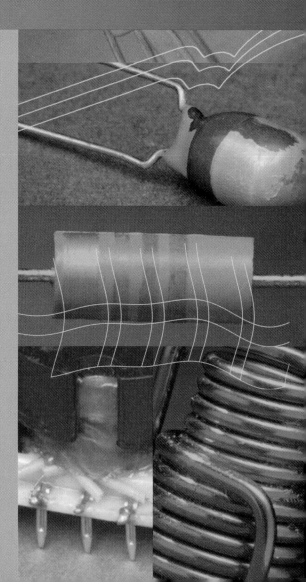

12

Inductance and Inductive Reactance

Inductors, like resistors, are a fundamental building block of electronic circuits. Like resistors, inductors tend to impede current flow. Unlike resistors, however, the opposition offered by inductors is different for dc and ac circuits. Inductors are also called coils or **chokes.** *The latter term comes from the use of some inductors to suppress (i.e., choke out) undesired frequencies. The basis for understanding the effects of an inductor in an electronic circuit lies in the understanding of electromagnetic induction.*

12.1 Electromagnetic Induction

Figure 12-1 illustrates the basic principle of electromagnetic induction. Here, two coils are wound on a common core. The core is a material with a high permeability, so the flux lines are more concentrated. One of the coils is connected to an alternating current source. As the current changes continuously, so does the magnetic flux within the core. Since a significant percentage of this flux is common to the second coil, the turns of the second coil will be intercepted by the changing flux lines. You will recall that when a conductor is cut by moving magnetic flux, a voltage is induced. Figure 12-1 shows that a voltage can be measured in the second coil, even though there is only a magnetic connection to the first coil. The process of inducing a voltage into a conductor with a changing magnetic field is called electromagnetic induction.

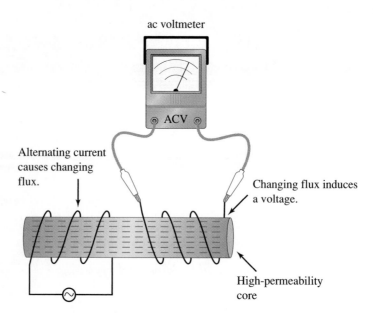

Figure 12-1. A demonstration of electromagnetic induction.

Review of Factors Affecting Induction

In a previous chapter, we discussed the factors that determine the amount and polarity of induced voltage. The factors are:

- field strength
- rate of relative motion
- angle of relative motion
- number of turns on the conductor
- direction of relative motion
- polarity of the magnetic field

These factors are illustrated in Figure 12-2.

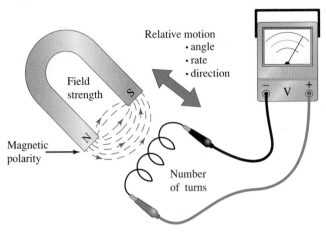

Figure 12-2. Factors that affect electromagnetic induction.

FIELD STRENGTH

The amount of induced voltage is directly proportional to the strength of the magnetic field. A stronger field produces more voltage.

RATE OF RELATIVE MOTION

In order to induce a voltage, there must be relative motion between the magnetic flux and the conductor. The conductor can move through the flux (as in a generator), or the changing flux can cut through the conductor (as illustrated in Figure 12-1). In either case, the amount of induced voltage is directly proportional to the rate of relative motion. If the conductor and flux are moving toward or away from each other faster, then a higher voltage will be induced.

ANGLE OF RELATIVE MOTION

If the conductor moves parallel to the flux lines, then it will not be intercepted by the flux and no induction will occur. If the conductor moves at right angles to the flux (cuts directly through it), then maximum interception of flux occurs, and the maximum voltage will be induced.

NUMBER OF TURNS IN THE CONDUCTOR

We can form the conductor into a coil to increase the amount of induced voltage. As the coiled inductor moves through the magnetic flux, each turn of the coil will have an induced voltage. The individual voltages are additive. Thus, the amount of induced voltage is directly proportional to the number of turns on the coil.

DIRECTION OF RELATIVE MOTION

The direction of flux interception determines the polarity of induced voltage. If the flux periodically increases and decreases (i.e., moves in both directions), then it will induce both polarities of voltage into a nearby conductor.

POLARITY OF MAGNETIC FIELD

The polarity of the magnetic field is the second factor that determines the polarity of induced voltage. If the polarity of the field is changed, then the polarity of the induced voltage will change.

Faraday's Law

Michael Faraday found that moving a magnet through a coil of wire produced a voltage in the coil. In 1831, he formally documented what we call Faraday's Law. In short, Faraday's Law states the following:

> When a coil of wire is intercepted by a magnetic field, a voltage is induced into the coil that is directly proportional to the number of turns on the coil and directly proportional to the rate of change of flux relative to the coil.

Lenz's Law

When current flows in a wire, it causes a magnetic field to be formed around the wire. If the wire is formed into a coil, then the magnetic field becomes concentrated and magnetic poles are formed. We already know that the polarity of induced voltage (or current in a closed circuit) is determined by the polarity of the magnetic field and the relative direction of motion. Lenz's Law describes the relationship of induced current polarity to the polarity of the moving magnetic field that caused the current. Lenz's Law can be summarized as follows:

> When a current is induced in a coil by a changing magnetic field, the current creates a second magnetic field. The magnetic field produced by the current has a polarity that opposes the changes in the original magnetic field.

This important principle is illustrated in Figure 12-3. In Figure 12-3(a), the north pole of a magnet is approaching a coil. An induced current flows in the coil such that a magnetic field that opposes the motion of the moving field is produced. In the case shown in Figure 12-3(a), the coil forms a north pole on the end nearest the approaching north pole. The two fields now oppose the relative motion.

Figure 12-3(b) illustrates the effects when the magnet is moved away from the coil. Since the field is moving in the opposite direction, we would expect an opposite polarity to be induced in the coil. As shown in Figure 12-3(b), the resulting current flow causes a magnetic field that opposes the motion of the original magnetic field. In the case shown in Figure 12-3(b), the induced current causes a south pole to form nearest the departing north pole. The unlike poles tend to attract, which retards the movement of the departing field.

Inductors

An inductor is essentially a coil of wire. When current flows through the turns of an inductor, a magnetic field is produced around each turn. If the current is changing, then the magnetic

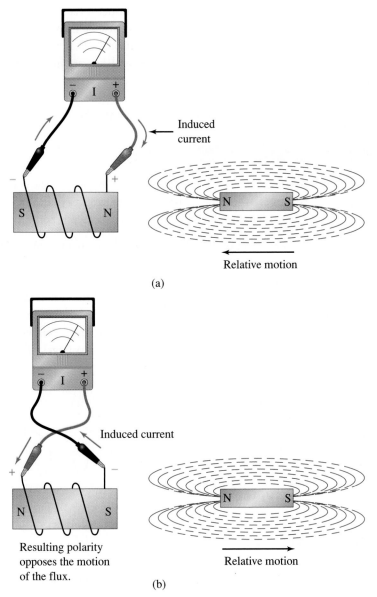

(a)

(b)

Figure 12-3. An illustration of Lenz's Law.

field will change. Any change in the magnetic field associated with one turn in the coil will produce a voltage (induced voltage) in the other turns of the coil as the flux lines intersect the wire. Thus, any change in current produces a change in flux which, according to Faraday's Law, causes an induced voltage in each turn of the coil. Further, Lenz's Law tells us that the polarity of induced voltage in each turn will be such that it opposes the original change in current. This is a very important concept that describes the basic behavior of an inductor.

> When current changes in an inductor, a voltage is induced in the turns of the inductor that opposes the initial change in the current.

The key word here is *change*. If, for example, a certain inductor had a very high—but steady—current, then there would be a very strong magnetic field around the coil. But there would be no induced voltage, since the field is stationary (i.e., not changing). If, by contrast, a current changes in an inductor, then there can be a very high value of induced voltage. The value of induced voltage is, according to Faraday's Law, determined by the number of turns and by how quickly the current (and therefore the flux) changes. Many technicians prefer to state the behavior of an inductor yet another way:

> An inductor opposes a change in current.

This is a simple but important concept. An inductor does not oppose the actual flow of current. It opposes any changes in current. Thus, if the current tries to increase or decrease, the inductor will oppose the changing current and will try to keep it constant.

Figure 12-4 illustrates the net effect of the self-induced voltage in an inductor that has a changing current flowing through it. In Figure 12-4(a), the voltage source is increasing, which causes an increase in current through the coil. However, the increasing current causes a changing flux. As the magnetic field builds out around the coil, it induces a voltage into the turns of the coil. As illustrated in Figure 12-4(a), the polarity of the induced voltage opposes the current change. Thus, the net increase in current will be less, since the effective voltage in the circuit is less (remember series-opposing voltages subtract).

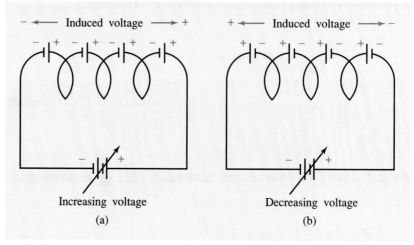

Figure 12-4. The self-induced voltage in an inductor opposes any changes in current.

Figure 12-4(b) shows the results when the current (same polarity) is decreased. As the current decreases, the magnetic field begins to collapse. As it collapses, a voltage is induced into the turns of the coil. But, the field is moving in the opposite direction from that shown in Figure 12-4(a), so the induced voltage polarity will also be opposite. As you can see from Figure 12-4(b), the induced voltage is now series-aiding with the applied voltage. This tends to compensate for or oppose or retard the decrease in current.

The property of an inductor that allows it to exhibit the characteristics just described is called inductance (L). Inductance is measured in henries (H). More specifically, if the current through an inductor changes at the rate of one ampere per second and causes one volt of induced voltage, then the inductor has a value of one henry.

Factors Affecting Inductance

The inductance of a coil is determined by the physical characteristics of the coil and the magnetic characteristics of the core. Let's examine each of these individually.

NUMBER OF TURNS

Each turn of the coil has an induced voltage. Intuitively, we know that more turns must produce more inductance. In fact, the amount of inductance is directly proportional to the square of the number of turns on the coil. If, for example, we increased the number of turns on a coil by a factor of 4, then the inductance would increase by 4^2 or 16 times. This is illustrated in Figure 12-5.

Figure 12-5(a) shows a coil with 10 turns and an inductance of 100 μH. In Figure 12-5(b), the number of turns has been increased to 50. This factor-of-5 increase produces an increase of 5^2 or 25 times in the inductance. Thus, the inductance of the coil shown in Figure 12-5(b) is 2,500 μH. This computation assumes that no other factors were changed.

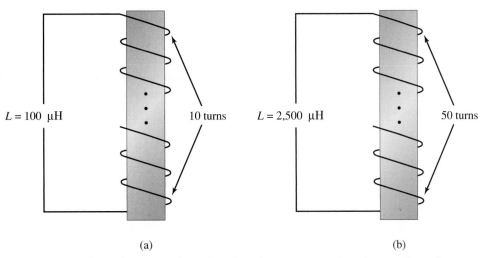

(a) (b)

Figure 12-5. The inductance of a coil is directly proportional to the number of turns squared.

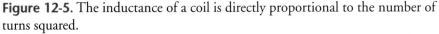

Practice Problems

1. If the number of turns on a 10-mH coil is tripled, what will be the new value of inductance?

2. If the turns on a coil are increased from 25 to 65 turns, how much does the inductance increase?

3. If a technician removes half of the turns from a 100-turn coil, what happens to the value of inductance in the coil?

Answers to Practice Problems

1. 90 mH   2. Inductance increases 6.76 times.

3. Inductance reduces to one-fourth its original value.

LENGTH OF THE MAGNETIC CIRCUIT

This characteristic of a coil is easy to discuss, but very complex to calculate. In general, the longer the magnetic path, the lower the inductance of a coil. This is illustrated in Figure 12-6.

In Figure 12-6(a), the average length of the magnetic circuit is 26 cm. In Figure 12-6(b), the magnetic path length has been increased to 56 cm. Since the path length is longer in Figure 12-6(b), the inductance will be proportionally less. In particular, the magnetic path length has increased by 56 cm/26 cm, or a factor of 2.15. This will produce a reduction in the inductance of the coil by a factor of 1/2.15 or 46.5%.

Accurate computation of the magnetic path length for a solenoid is much more complex. The portion of the path within the coil is easily computed as the length of the core, or in the case of an air-core solenoid, the length of the coil itself. However, the portion of the complete magnetic path outside of the coil is not clearly defined. Its computation requires advanced mathematics.

CROSS-SECTIONAL AREA OF THE COIL

The size of the turns on a coil has a direct effect on the amount of inductance exhibited by the coil. Figure 12-7 illustrates the effects on inductance caused by a change in the cross-sectional area of the coil.

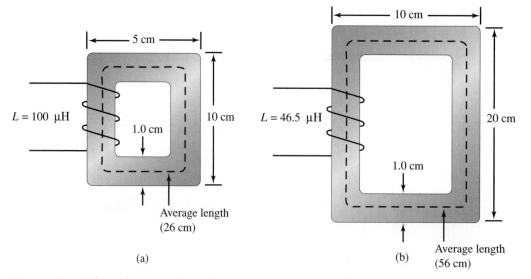

Figure 12-6. The inductance of a coil is inversely proportional to the length of the magnetic circuit.

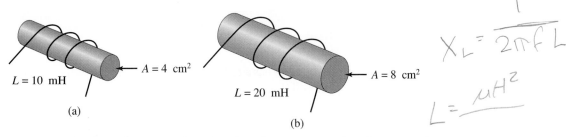

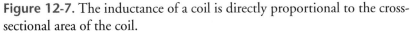

$X_L = \dfrac{1}{2\pi f L}$

$L = \mu H^2$

Figure 12-7. The inductance of a coil is directly proportional to the cross-sectional area of the coil.

In Figure 12-7(a), the coil has a cross-sectional area of 4 cm² and has an inductance of 10 mH. In Figure 12-7(b), the cross-sectional area of the coil is doubled (with all other factors constant). This increased area causes the inductance to double to 20 mH.

Practice Problems

1. If the cross-sectional area of a coil is increased by a factor of five, what happens to the value of inductance?
2. If the cross-sectional area of a coil is reduced to one-tenth its original size, what effect does this change have on the value of inductance for the coil?
3. The inductance of a coil is (*directly, inversely*) proportional to the cross-sectional area of the coil.

Answers to Practice Problems

1. Inductance increases to five times the original inductance.
2. Inductance decreases to one-tenth the original inductance.
3. directly

PERMEABILITY OF THE CORE

Recall that flux density is directly proportional to the permeability of a material. If we increase the permeability of the core material for a coil, we will produce a corresponding increase in flux density. Thus, a given change in current will now produce a larger change in flux. The increased flux changes create higher values of self-induced voltage in the turns of the coil. This, of course, translates to increased inductance in the coil. This is illustrated in Figure 12-8.

Figure 12-8(a) shows an air-core coil with an inductance of 1.0 μH. Figure 12-8(b) shows the same coil with a ferrite core inserted. The ferrite shown has a relative permeability of 2,000. Thus, the inductance will be increased by a factor of 2,000. The inductance in Figure 12-8(b) is 2,000 μH. Most technicians know intuitively that iron- or ferrite-core coils have a much higher inductance than air-core coils.

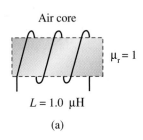

Air core

$\mu_r = 1$

$L = 1.0\ \mu H$

(a)

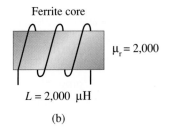

Ferrite core

$\mu_r = 2{,}000$

$L = 2{,}000\ \mu H$

(b)

Figure 12-8. The inductance of a coil is directly proportional to the permeability of the core material.

Practice Problems

1. The core of a 50-μH coil has a relative permeability of 500. What happens to the inductance of the coil if it is wound on a core having a relative permeability of 5,000?

2. If the core of a 10-mH coil is changed from a material with a relative permeability of 4,000 to one with a relative permeability of 1,000, what will happen to the inductance of the coil?

Answers to Practice Problems

1. Inductance increases to 500 μH.   2. Inductance decreases to 2.5 mH.

All of the factors discussed that affect inductance can be used in an equation to compute inductance. Equation 12-1 describes their relationships to inductance.

$$L = \mu\frac{N^2 A}{l} \qquad (12\text{-}1)$$

where L is the inductance in henries, μ is the absolute permeability of the core, N is the number of turns, A is the cross-sectional area of the coil in square meters, and l is the length of the magnetic circuit in meters.

Since the permeability of most materials used by technicians is given as a relative permeability, this expression can also be written as Equation 12-2, by applying Equation 10-5.

$$L = \mu_r \times 1.257 \times 10^{-6} \times \frac{N^2 A}{l} \qquad (12\text{-}2)$$

where L is the inductance in henries, μ_r is the relative permeability of the core, N is the number of turns, A is the cross-sectional area of the coil in square meters, and l is the length of the magnetic circuit in meters.

Equations 12-1 and 12-2 show some very important relationships, but they produce only approximations of the true inductance of a coil. There are many nonideal effects, plus the poorly defined characteristics of the complete magnetic circuit, that make an accurate prediction of inductance very difficult to achieve. However, Equations 12-1 and 12-2 are fairly accurate for single-layer, air-core coils whose diameters are no more than one-tenth the coil length. For many technicians, the real value of Equation 12-1 or Equation 12-2 lies in the simple expression of relationships.

KEY POINTS

The inductance of an inductor or coil is determined by the:

- Physical dimensions of the coil
- Number of turns on the coil
- Permeability of the core material

The inductance is:

- Inversely proportional to the length of the magnetic path
- Directly proportional to the cross-sectional area of the coil, the permeability of the core material, and the square of the number of turns on the coil

Exercise Problems 12.1

1. A changing current in one coil can produce a voltage in a nearby coil through a process called _____ _____.

2. The amount of induced voltage in a conductor is _____ proportional to the strength of the moving magnetic field.

3. The polarity of induced voltage is determined by the number of turns on the coil. (True or False)

4. The angle of relative motion between a conductor and a magnetic field affects the amount of induced voltage. (True or False)

5. An inductor opposes any changes in current. (True or False)

6. Inductance is measured in _____.

7. The symbol for inductance is _____.

8. H is the abbreviation for _____.

9. If the number of turns on an inductor is increased from 100 to 300, the inductance of the coil will (*increase, decrease*) by a factor of _____.

10. If 25 turns are removed from a 100-turn coil, what is the effect on inductance?

11. If the cross-sectional area of a coil is made five times larger, what will happen to the inductance of the coil?

12. If the magnetic path length of a torroidal inductor is made shorter, what happens to the inductance of the coil?

13. If the permeability of the core material for a particular coil is changed from a relative permeability of 500 to a relative permeability of 15,000, what is the effect on inductance?

12.2 Self-Induction

In the preceding section we briefly discussed self-induction. When a changing current flows through the windings of a coil, a changing magnetic field is produced around the turns of the coil. This changing magnetic field intercepts the other turns on the coil and induces a voltage in them. This voltage is induced by a process called self-induction. Lenz's Law tells us that the polarity of self-induced voltage will be such that it opposes the initial current change. Faraday's Law tells us that the magnitude of the self-induced voltage will be determined by the number of turns on the coil and by the rate of change of flux. The rate of change of flux is determined by the rate of change of current. Now let us examine how various waveshapes of current affect the value of induced voltage in an inductor.

Effect of a Ramp Current

Figure 12-9(a) shows an inductor being driven by a current source. The amplitude of the current varies continuously. First, it slowly ramps from −1 mA to +1 mA during times t_1 and t_2. Then, it changes steadily, but more quickly, from +1 mA to −1 mA during times t_3 and t_4. The cycle then repeats.

As shown in Figure 12-9(b), the inductor voltage is constant as long as the rate of change of current is constant. The polarity of the self-induced voltage is not dependent on the polarity (i.e., direction) of current flow, but rather the direction of change. During the time period t_1, the value of current is steadily decreasing from −1 mA to zero. The polarity of the inductor voltage opposes this decrease. During time interval t_2, the current is increasing in the opposite direction. Note the polarity of the inductor is still the same in order to oppose this increase.

KEY POINTS

If a current ramp is applied to an inductor, the value of self-induced voltage is constant, since the rate of change of current is constant.

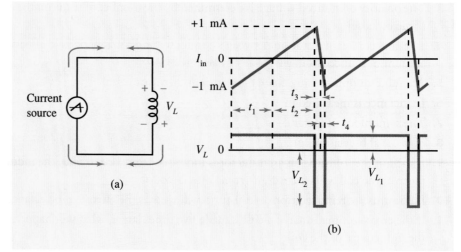

Figure 12-9. An inductor driven by a ramp current source generates a rectangular waveform of self-induced voltage.

A similar situation occurs on the other portion of the cycle. At the beginning of time t_3, the current stops increasing and begins to decrease toward zero. The inductor opposes this change. As you can see in Figure 12-9(b), the polarity of the self-induced voltage changes at the beginning of time t_3. During time t_3, the current decays steadily toward zero. The inductor voltage remains constant, since the rate of change of current is constant. During t_4, the current is building up in the opposite direction. The polarity of the inductor again opposes this increase.

The rate of change of current is greater during times t_3 and t_4 in Figure 12-9(b). This causes a greater value of self-induced voltage. Compare the magnitudes of V_{L_1} and V_{L_2} in Figure 12-9(b). You are encouraged to study Figure 12-9 and the preceding discussion carefully until you full appreciate what is being demonstrated. The very heart of inductor behavior is being shown.

Effect of a Step Current

Figure 12-10 shows an inductor connected to a current source capable of making sudden changes in value. The current changes from zero to +1 mA in a very short (but not zero) time period. Since this represents a very high rate of change of current, the inductor develops a substantial value of self-induced voltage that opposes the increasing current. This is shown in Figure 12-10(b) at time t_1.

Once the current reaches its 1-mA level, it is constant. Since the associated flux is no longer changing, there can be no induced voltage. So, between times t_1 and t_2 in Figure 12-10(b), the inductor has no self-induced voltage.

At time t_2 in Figure 12-10(b), the current changes rapidly from 1 mA to zero. During this brief period, the inductor experiences a high rate of change of flux, and therefore produces a relatively high value of self-induced voltage. Also note the polarity of induced voltage is opposite, since it is opposing a decreasing current.

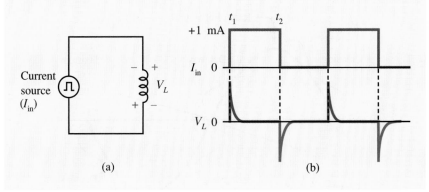

Figure 12-10. An inductor driven by a current source that makes sudden current changes.

There is no scale on the voltage graph in Figure 12-10(b), but it is important to note the value of self-induced voltage can easily reach thousands of volts for a modest current change. We will learn to compute specific values of induced voltage in a later section.

Effect of a Sine Wave Current

When we apply a sine wave of current to an inductive circuit, the coil behaves in the same manner as previously described. That is, it generates a self-induced voltage whose polarity opposes any change in current, and whose magnitude is determined by the rate of change of flux.

First, let us examine a sine wave of current more closely, by studying Figure 12-11. Recall that the magnitude of self-induced voltage in a coil is proportional to the rate of change in current. When the sine wave of current reaches its 90° and 270° points, the instantaneous rate of change of current is zero. For example, between the 0° and 90° points on the sine wave, the current is increasing, but its rate of increase slows as it approaches 90°. As the current wave passes through 90°, the rate of change passes through zero. Between 90° and 180° on the sine wave, the current is decreasing toward zero. As it approaches zero, it is decreasing, but it is changing the most rapidly. As the current wave passes through zero (at the 180° point), it changes direction and begins increasing between the 180° and 270° points.

Since induced voltage is directly proportional to the rate of change of voltage, we would expect maximum induced voltage at the 0° and 180° points on the current wave, since the current is changing most rapidly at these points. Similarly, we would expect no induced voltage at the 90° and 270° points on the current wave, since the rate of change of current is zero at these points.

Now let us consider the polarity of induced voltage. The direction of change (i.e., increasing or decreasing) changes as we pass through 90° and 270°. Thus, we would expect the polarity of induced voltage to change at these same points. The direction of current changes as it passes through zero, but so does the direction of change, so we will expect no change in the polarity of induced voltage at the 0° and 180° points on the current wave.

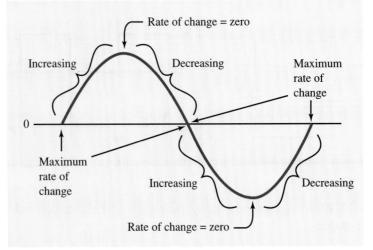

Figure 12-11. Analysis of a sine wave.

Figure 12-12(a) shows a coil driven by a sinusoidal current source. Figure 12-12(b) shows the relationship between current and voltage in the circuit. Note that the induced voltage is maximum at the points where the sine wave of current has the highest rates of change (0° and 180°). The induced voltage is zero when the rate of change of current is zero (90° and 270° on the current wave). Also note that the induced voltage changes polarity as the current wave passes through 90° and 270°. It is at these points that the current direction remains the same, but the direction of change is opposite.

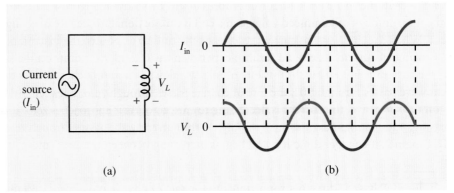

Figure 12-12. Current and voltage are 90° out of phase in an inductor.

General Equation for Self-Induced Voltage

Regardless of the specific waveshape of current through an inductor, the self-induced voltage will be directly proportional to the value of inductance and the rate of change of current flow through the inductor. This is summarized by Equation 12-3.

$$V_L = L\frac{\Delta i}{\Delta t} = L\frac{di}{dt} \qquad (12\text{-}3)$$

where the lowercase *d* or the Greek letter delta (Δ) represents the phrase "a change in," *L* is the value of inductance, *i* is the amount of current change, and *t* is the time during which the current change occurred.

EXAMPLE SOLUTION

If the current through a 100-μH inductor changes by 100 mA in a 10-ms period, what is the value of voltage across the inductor?

EXAMPLE **SOLUTION**

We apply Equation 12-3 as follows:

$$V_L = L\frac{di}{dt}$$

$$= 100 \ \mu\text{H} \times \frac{100 \ \text{mA}}{10 \ \text{ms}}$$

$$= 1.0 \ \text{mV}$$

Practice Problems

1. Determine the voltage developed across a 10-mH coil, if the current through it changes by 500 mA in a 100-μs period.
2. What is the value of self-induced voltage when the current changes at the rate of 100 A/s through a 250-mH inductor?
3. What rate of change of current is required to produce 500 mV across a 5-H inductor?

Answers to Practice Problems

1. 50 V   2. 25 V   3. 100 mA/s

Exercise Problems 12.2

1. Refer to Figure 12-13. Draw the waveshape of self-induced voltage that will be developed by the inductor.

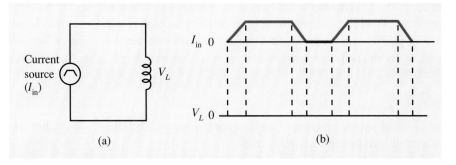

Figure 12-13.
What is the wave-shape of V_L?

2. The maximum rate of change on a sine wave occurs at the _____ and _____ points.

3. The minimum rate of change on a sine wave occurs at the _____ and _____ points.

12.3 Types of Inductors

Fixed inductor

Adjustable inductor

Figure 12-14.
Generic schematic symbols for a fixed and an adjustable inductor.

All inductors are similar in certain respects. They all possess inductance. They all generate a self-induced voltage in direct proportion to the rate of change of current. And the polarity of self-induced voltage will always oppose any changes in current. There are many different types of inductors, however, and they vary dramatically in value, primary application, and their physical appearance.

Inductors can be categorized into two classes: fixed and adjustable (variable). Figure 12-14 shows the schematic symbols for these two general classes of inductors.

Inductors can also be classified by the type of core material used. Some, but not all, manufacturers indicate the type of core material by using a slightly modified schematic symbol. We will examine several types of inductors in the following paragraphs. Variations to the generic schematic symbol will be shown where appropriate.

Air Core

KEY POINTS

An inductor can be made to be fixed or adjustable.

Probably the simplest type of inductor is an air-core coil. Figure 12-15(a) shows a picture of a commercial air-core inductor. An air-core coil is represented by the standard schematic symbol, Figure 12-15(b).

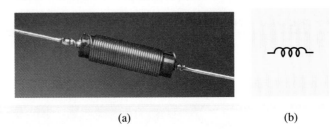

(a)   (b)

Figure 12-15. (a) An air-core coil and (b) its schematic symbol.

KEY POINTS

Inductors can be classed according to their core material: iron, ferrite, powdered iron, and air.

If the wire used to wind the coil is very stiff, then no support is needed for the coil, and it can be self-supporting. In many cases, however, the wire is not sufficiently rigid to support itself. In these cases, a coil form is used to support the coil winding. The coil form may be made of cardboard, plastic, or other nonconductive, nonmagnetic material. As long as the material has a relative permeability of near unity, then the coil is considered to have an air core.

Iron Core

Figure 12-16(a) shows a picture of an iron-core inductor. The schematic symbol for an iron-core coil is shown in Figure 12-16(b).

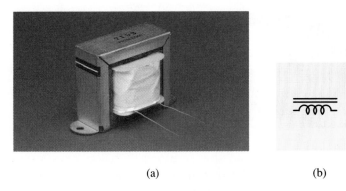

(a)   (b)

Figure 12-16. (a) An iron-core inductor and (b) its schematic symbol.

In most cases, the iron core is made of several laminated layers of thin iron sheets. Each metal sheet is electrically insulated from the other sheets by a thin coating of varnish and iron oxide. The layers of insulation have no significant effect on the overall magnetic characteristics of the core, but they greatly increase the electrical resistance of the core. This reduces core losses and is described in more detail in a later section.

Iron-core inductors are generally used for low-frequency applications in the audio range. They are easily recognized by their physical size, weight, and general appearance.

Powdered-Iron Core

Individual granules of iron can be individually coated with an insulative material and then pressed into a solid pellet that can be used as the core of a small inductor. The iron granules provide the high permeability needed to obtain the desired values of inductance. The insulative material makes the electrical resistance of the core very high to reduce power losses in the core. Many powdered-iron core inductors are adjustable. The powdered-iron slug is threaded and can be screwed in and out of the coil. As the core is inserted further, the inductance of the coil increases. This type of coil is generally used for radio frequencies.

Ferrite Core

A ferrite is a ceramic material that provides very high values of permeability, but has a high electrical resistance. From a user's point of view, there is little physical difference between a ferrite core and a powdered-iron core inductor. Figure 12-17 shows a typical ferrite core (or powdered-iron core) inductor along with the schematic symbol. Ferrite core inductors are used from frequencies in the low kilohertz to frequencies in the hundreds of megahertz.

Ferrite Beads as Inductors

Ferrite beads are also available in a wide array of sizes and material types. A ferrite bead has a hole (or holes) through which a wire or leaded component may be inserted. (Note: Some beads are sold with the wire already inserted.) The presence of the bead adds series inductance to the wire. The bead also adds resistance to the circuit.

KEY POINTS

Ferrite beads can also be used as inductors at some frequencies. The ferrite bead can be slipped over either a wire or the lead of another component. It acts like a series resistance and a series inductance.

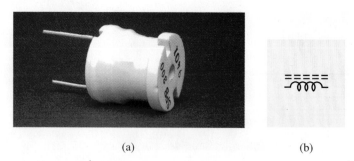

(a) (b)

Figure 12-17. (a) A ferrite (or powdered-iron) core inductor and (b) its schematic symbol.

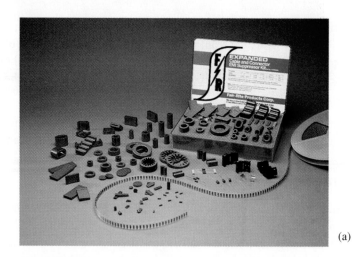

(a)

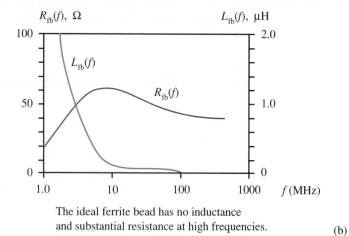

The ideal ferrite bead has no inductance and substantial resistance at high frequencies.

(b)

Figure 12-18. (a) Ferrite beads are available in many different styles. (Courtesy of Fair-Rite Products Corporation) (b) The inductance and resistance of the ferrite material varies with frequency. (© TKC, Pinellas Park, FL)

Figure 12-18(a) shows an assortment of ferrite beads. Surface-mount ferrite beads are also shown. The exact behavior of the ferrite bead is largely dependent on frequency. The graph in Figure 12-18(b) shows that the inductance and resistance of the bead vary greatly with frequency. It is important to note that although the bead is slipped over the wire (even an insulated wire in some cases), the bead's inductance and resistance characteristics appear as if they were in series with the inserted wire. The frequency characteristics shown in Figure 12-18(b) are only representative. Exact performance varies considerably with the specific type of ferrite material.

Ferrite beads find extensive use in high-frequency circuits. They are also widely used in personal and handheld computers to suppress unwanted emissions that might otherwise interfere with nearby radio and television reception.

Molded Inductors

Figure 12-19 shows a molded inductor. Some molded inductors are easily confused with a resistor, since they may have a similar appearance and both have color-coded values. Manufacturers generally put a double-width band on inductors to distinguish them from resistors.

Figure 12-19. A molded inductor.

> **KEY POINTS**
>
> Molded inductors often look like color-coded resistors. The presence of a double-width band identifies the component as an inductor.

The color-coded bands (or dots in some cases) for a molded inductor are interpreted in much the same way as resistor color codes. There are, however, three major differences. First, the double-width band is not included as part of the color-coded value. Second, the value of the inductor is given in microhenries. Third, a gold band can serve one of two different purposes. If it appears as the last band, it indicates a 5% tolerance, similar to a resistor tolerance. If, however, the gold band appears in a position other than the tolerance position, it represents a decimal point.

EXAMPLE SOLUTION

What is the value of the molded inductor shown in Figure 12-20?

EXAMPLE SOLUTION

The wide silver band identifies the component as an inductor. The value is decoded as follows:

Figure 12-20. What is the value of this inductor?

red—2; gold—decimal point; violet—7; tolerance—10%. The component is a 2.7-μH inductor with a 10% tolerance.

EXAMPLE SOLUTION

Determine the value of the component shown in Figure 12-21.

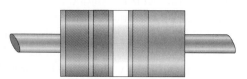

EXAMPLE **SOLUTION**

The wide band identifies the component as a molded inductor. Its value is decoded as follows:

orange—3; white—9; gold—5%. The component is a 39-μH inductor with a 5% tolerance.

Figure 12-21. What is the value of this component?

Practice Problems

1. Determine the values for each of the components shown in Figure 12-22.

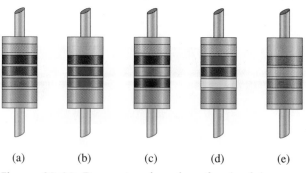

(a)　(b)　(c)　(d)　(e)

Figure 12-22. Determine the value of each of these components.

Answers to Practice Problems

1. **a.** 270 μH ± 5%
    b. 560 μH
    c. 180 μH ± 5%
    d. 475 μH ± 5%
    e. 2.2 μH

Surface-Mount

Figure 12-23 shows a picture of a surface-mount inductor. Except for the small physical size and the absence of leads, a surface-mount inductor functions like any other inductor. Because of their small size, they require care when soldering and desoldering them on a printed circuit board. Surface-mount inductors are often too small to print or color code the value. If the inductor has no apparent markings, then the technician must use an inductance meter to measure the value of inductance, or locate the value on a schematic diagram.

KEY POINTS

Surface-mount inductors have no leads and are soldered directly to pads on a printed circuit board.

Figure 12-23. A surface-mount inductor is commonly used in high-density printed circuit boards.

Exercise Problems 12.3

1. Iron-core inductors are generally used for frequencies in excess of 100 MHz. (True or False)
2. How is a decimal point indicated on a molded inductor?
3. What is the purpose of the double-width color band on a molded inductor?
4. What is the value of a molded inductor that has the following color bands: a wide brown band, followed by blue, gray, and silver bands?
5. What is the value of a molded inductor that has the following color bands: a wide silver band, followed by red, gold, red, and silver bands?

12.4 Multiple Circuit Inductances

Any time two or more inductances are used near each other, there exists a possibility that the expanding and contracting magnetic field from one inductor will intercept the windings of another inductor. This complicates analysis, since the voltage induced by the external inductor may be in or out of phase with the self-induced voltage of the inductor. In either case, however, the effective value of inductance is altered.

For the purposes of this chapter, we shall assume that there is no interaction of magnetic fields between multiple inductors. This is a valid assumption in most cases where two or more physical coils are being considered. Chapter 17 discusses the case where there is magnetic interaction between two or more inductors.

Series Inductors

Figure 12-24 shows three inductors connected in series. Each inductor responds to changes in the common series current. The self-induced voltages all act to oppose any changes in current. The combined inductance of series-connected inductors is the simple sum of the individual inductors. This is expressed in Equation 12-4.

> **KEY POINTS**
>
> As long as the magnetic fields from the various inductors do not interact, series and parallel combinations of inductors can be combined using the same basic procedures used with resistors.

> **KEY POINTS**
>
> The total inductance of series-connected coils is found by summing the individual inductances.

Chapter 12

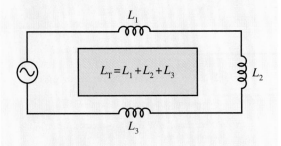

Figure 12-24. Series-connected inductors combine like series resistors.

$$L_T = L_1 + L_2 + L_3 + \dots + L_N \qquad (12\text{-}4)$$

This equation is not valid if any of the coils are magnetically linked.

EXAMPLE SOLUTION

If $L_1 = 10\ \mu H$, $L_2 = 50\ \mu H$ and $L_3 = 25\ \mu H$ in Figure 12-24, what is the total circuit inductance?

EXAMPLE **SOLUTION**

We apply Equation 12-4 as follows:

$$\begin{aligned} L_T &= L_1 + L_2 + L_3 \\ &= 10\ \mu H + 50\ \mu H + 25\ \mu H \\ &= 85\ \mu H \end{aligned}$$

Practice Problems

1. What is the combined inductance if four 10-μH coils are connected in series?
2. If a 150-μH and a 250-μH inductor are connected in series, what is the total inductance?
3. How much inductance must be connected in series with a 20-mH inductor to have a total inductance of 45 mH?

Answers to Practice Problems

1.   40 μH   2.   400 μH   3.   25 mH

The total inductance of several parallel-connected coils is found using the reciprocal formula.

Parallel Inductors

Figure 12-25 shows three parallel-connected inductors. Since the total current divides among the various inductors, any given inductor experiences less than the total change in current. The self-induced voltage for a given inductor will be correspondingly smaller than

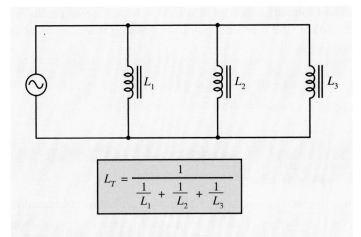

Figure 12-25. Parallel-connected inductors combine like parallel resistors.

if the total current change were applied to the coil. As with parallel-connected resistors, the total inductance is found by using a reciprocal formula:

$$L_T = \frac{1}{\frac{1}{L_1} + \frac{1}{L_2} + \frac{1}{L_3} + \ldots + \frac{1}{L_N}} \qquad (12\text{-}5)$$

As you might expect, the combined inductance of parallel-connected inductors is always less than the smallest individual inductance.

EXAMPLE SOLUTION

If $L_1 = 80$ mH, $L_2 = 50$ mH and $L_3 = 35$ mH in Figure 12-25, what is the total circuit inductance?

EXAMPLE **SOLUTION**

We apply Equation 12-5 as follows:

$$L_T = \frac{1}{\frac{1}{L_1} + \frac{1}{L_2} + \frac{1}{L_3}}$$

$$= \frac{1}{\frac{1}{80 \text{ mH}} + \frac{1}{50 \text{ mH}} + \frac{1}{35 \text{ mH}}}$$

$$= 16.37 \text{ mH}$$

It would be helpful to realize that the shortcut equations for parallel resistors can also be applied to parallel inductances. For example, Equation 12-6 can be used to find the combined inductance of several (N) parallel-connected inductors that all have the same (L) value.

$$L_T = \frac{L}{N} \qquad (12\text{-}6)$$

where L is the common inductance value and N is the number of parallel-connected inductances. Equation 12-7 is another useful relationship that computes the total inductance of two coils in parallel.

$$L_T = \frac{L_1 L_2}{L_1 + L_2} \qquad (12\text{-}7)$$

Practice Problems

1. What is the total inductance if five 25-mH chokes are connected in parallel?
2. If a 10-μH and a 45-μH coil are connected in parallel, what is the total inductance?
3. What is the total inductance if a 5-mH, a 25-mH, and a 10-mH inductor are connected in parallel?

Answers to Practice Problems

1. 5 mH   2. 8.18 μH   3. 2.94 mH

Other Network Configurations

Although not required for most practical applications, inductors can be connected in series-parallel or complex configurations. The total inductance for these networks can be found using the same basic procedures that are used for series-parallel and complex combinations of resistors. This method of analysis is not valid if any of the coils are magnetically coupled to each other.

Exercise Problems 12.4

1. What is the total inductance of the circuit shown in Figure 12-26?

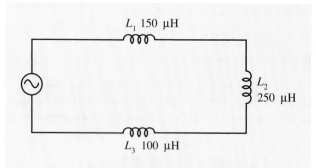

Figure 12-26. Find total inductance.

2. What is the value of L_3 in Figure 12-27?

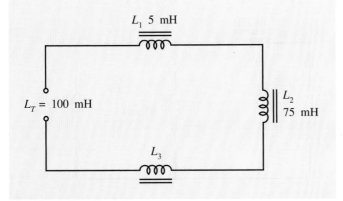

Figure 12-27. What is the inductance of L_3?

3. Find the total inductance of the circuit in Figure 12-28.

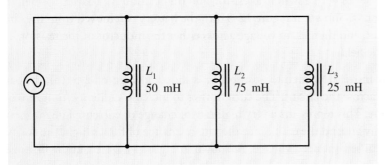

Figure 12-28. Find the total inductance of this circuit.

4. Determine the value of L_2 in Figure 12-29.

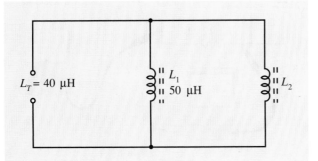

Figure 12-29. What is the value of L_2?

5. Compute the total inductance for the circuit shown in Figure 12-30.

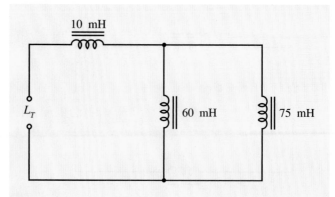

Figure 12-30. Find the total inductance of this circuit.

12.5 Inductance in DC Circuits

Now let us examine the behavior of an inductor in a dc circuit. Figure 12-31(a) shows an inductor in series with a switch, a resistor, and (in position A) a battery. When the switch is in position B, as shown in Figure 12-31(a), the battery is removed from the circuit. There is no current, and there is no voltage across either the inductor or the resistor. The coil has no magnetic field.

Now, if we move the switch to position A, as shown in Figure 12-31(b), the battery is connected across the circuit. The current tries to increase suddenly from zero to some higher value. This represents a very high rate of change of current. The magnetic field will build rapidly around the coil. Since the rate of change of flux is high, the coil will have a high value of self-induced voltage. As shown in Figure 12-31(b), at the first instant the self-induced voltage in the coil will be 12 V. Additionally (according to Lenz's Law), the

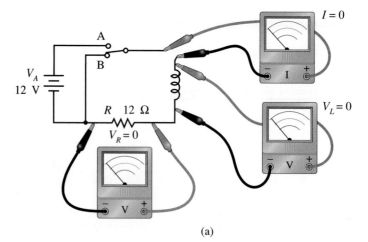

(a)

Figure 12-31. The response of an inductive circuit to a switched dc source.

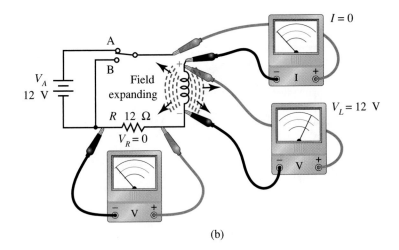

(b)

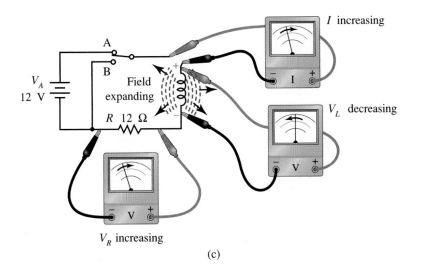

(c)

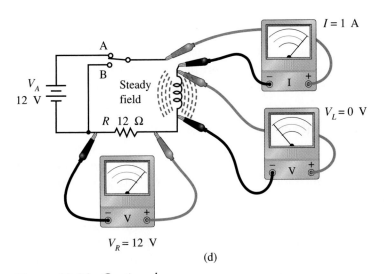

(d)

Figure 12-31. *Continued*

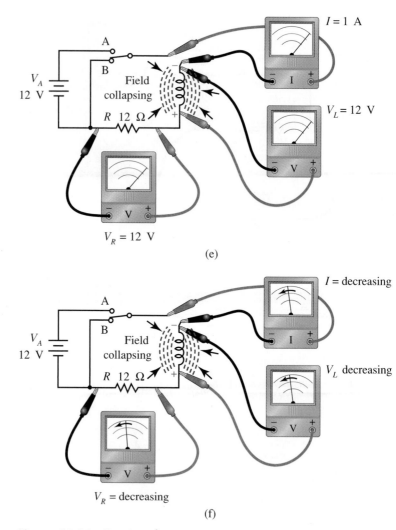

Figure 12-31. *Continued*

polarity will be such that it opposes the current increase. Now at the first instant, the 12 V of self-induced voltage completely opposes the 12 V of the battery to yield a net circuit voltage of zero. Thus, at this first instant, there is no current in the circuit and no voltage across the resistor.

Figure 12-31(c) shows the circuit a few moments after the battery was connected. The rate of expansion of the magnetic field is decreasing, so the self-induced voltage is also decreasing. Since the inductor voltage is offering less opposition to the battery voltage, the current continues to increase. Since the current flows through the resistor, its voltage will also be increasing.

Eventually, the current will stop increasing and the magnetic field will stop expanding. This condition is shown in Figure 12-31(d). The magnetic field is at its maximum level, but it is stationary. Therefore, no voltage is induced into the windings of the coil. At this point, the inductor is nothing more than a coiled piece of wire. It drops no voltage and offers no opposition to current. As shown in Figure 12-31(d), the full supply voltage is across the resistor, and the current is determined by Ohm's Law. This condition will exist as long as the switch remains in position A.

Figure 12-31(e) shows the circuit condition at the instant the switch is moved back to position B. With the power source disconnected, the field of the inductor will begin to collapse. As it does, it will induce a voltage into the windings of the coil. Because the flux is now moving in the opposite direction, the induced voltage will be of the opposite polarity. The coil is now acting as a voltage source, and it (momentarily) keeps the current flowing at the same 1-A value. As indicated in Figure 12-31(e), the current remains the same for the first instant, as does the resistor voltage. The inductor voltage, as shown in Figure 12-31(e), is −12 V. (Note that the negative sign merely indicates that the polarity is opposite from that previously shown).

Figure 12-31(f) shows the circuit conditions a few moments after the switch was moved back to position B. Here, the magnetic field is continuing to collapse, but its rate of collapse is decreasing as the field dissipates. Consequently, the voltage induced into the coil is also decreasing. Since the voltage produced by the coil is the only source of voltage in the circuit at this time, then the resistor voltage and the current will also be decaying at the same rate. Eventually, the magnetic field will completely collapse. At this time, there will be no voltage or current in the circuit, and we will return to the conditions depicted in Figure 12-31(a).

In Chapter 13, you will learn how to calculate the amount of time it takes for the magnetic field to build to maximum or to decay to zero. For now, it is important for you to understand the following points:

- When a direct current is switched through a coil, the self-induced voltage is maximum at the first instant and prevents any current flow.
- As the magnetic field builds out around the coil, the self-induced voltage slowly drops and the current through the circuit slowly rises.
- Once the magnetic field becomes stable (limited by the circuit resistance or the magnetic saturation of the core), then there is no self-induced voltage across the coil. The circuit current is strictly limited by the circuit resistance. The inductor has no effect on current flow.
- When an attempt is made to abruptly reduce the direct current through an inductor to zero, the magnetic field around the inductor begins to collapse. At the first instant, the induced voltage is adequate to keep the same value of current flowing through the circuit. The coil acts as a voltage source as it returns energy to the circuit. As the magnetic field decays, the self-induced voltage and the circuit current decrease toward zero.
- It takes a definite amount of time for the current to change from one value to another. The inductor prevents any abrupt current changes.

The fourth item in the preceding list describes an inductor characteristic that allows us to produce a high voltage from a lower battery voltage. Figure 12-32 shows a circuit similar to the one previously discussed, with the addition of R_2. Figure 12-32(a) shows the circuit condition after the magnetic field has had time to fully expand. The circuit is stable with a current of 1 A.

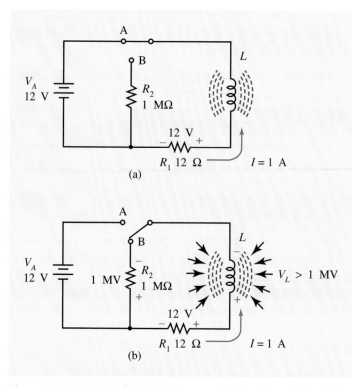

Figure 12-32. An inductor can create a high voltage from a low battery voltage.

Figure 12-32(b) shows the circuit at the first instant after the switch is moved to position B. You will recall that the collapsing inductor field generates enough self-induced voltage to keep the current constant for a moment. Note, however, that the resistance of the circuit is now in excess of 1 MΩ. When 1 A flows through R_2, it generates one million volts! So what is the source for this high voltage? Since R_2 is so large, the current tries to decrease abruptly when the switch is moved to position B. This high rate of change of current produces a high rate of change of flux, which causes a high self-induced voltage. In the present case, the self-induced voltage will be in excess of one million volts!

This same principle is used in the ignition system of an automobile to provide the high voltage needed to arc across the spark gap in the spark plugs. The automobile only has a 12-V dc source, but the spark plugs require several thousand volts to arc across the gap and ultimately ignite the fuel vapor.

Exercise Problems 12.5

1. What determines the amount of self-induced voltage across an inductor when used in a dc circuit?

2. Explain how it is possible to obtain a high voltage from a low-voltage battery.

12.6 Inductance in ac Circuits

When an inductor is used in a circuit that has a sinusoidal current, the self-induced voltage is also sinusoidal. The self-induced voltage always has a polarity that opposes any changes in current. The magnitude of the self-induced voltage is determined by the rate of change of current through the inductor. Since the maximum rate of change for a sine wave of current occurs at the 0° and 180° points, these are the points that correspond to maximum inductor voltage.

Inductive Reactance

The self-induced voltage in an inductor is constantly changing if the current through the inductor is sinusoidal. However, the polarity of the induced voltage always opposes the changing current. This opposition results in a lower value of current than would otherwise flow. The opposition to a sinusoidal alternating current flow presented by an inductor is called **inductive reactance**. It is measured in ohms. The generic symbol for reactance is X. Inductive reactance is represented by the symbol X_L.

FACTORS AFFECTING INDUCTIVE REACTANCE

Anything that affects the value of self-induced voltage in the inductor will affect its inductive reactance. Thus, we would expect the number of turns on the coil, permeability of the core, rate of change of current, and other such factors to be related to inductive reactance. They are. However, we can group all the factors such as physical coil character- istics and magnetic core characteristics together, since they collectively determine the value of inductance. That is, by referring to the value of inductance, we are inherently referring to all of the physical and magnetic factors. We can account for the rate of change of current factor by referring to the frequency of the current or voltage in the inductor. Equation 12-8 provides us with a direct method for computing the inductive reactance of an inductor:

$$X_L = 2\pi f L \qquad (12\text{-}8)$$

EXAMPLE SOLUTION

How much inductive reactance is provided by a 10-mH coil when operated at a frequency of 25 kHz?

EXAMPLE SOLUTION

We apply Equation 12-8 as follows:

$$X_L = 2\pi f L$$
$$= 6.28 \times 25 \text{ kHz} \times 10 \text{ mH}$$
$$= 1.57 \text{ k}\Omega$$

EXAMPLE SOLUTION

What frequency causes a 100-μH inductor to present an inductive reactance of 5 kΩ?

EXAMPLE SOLUTION

We apply Equation 12-8 as follows:

$$X_L = 2\pi f L, \text{ or}$$

$$f = \frac{X_L}{2\pi L}$$

$$= \frac{5 \text{ k}\Omega}{6.28 \times 100 \text{ μH}}$$

$$= 7.96 \text{ MHz}$$

Practice Problems

1. Calculate the inductive reactance provided by a 33-μH coil at a frequency of 2.5 MHz.
2. Determine the value of inductance needed to produce an inductive reactance of 1.5 kΩ when operated at a frequency of 250 kHz.
3. Compute the inductive reactance of a 200-mH inductor, if it is operated at a frequency of 1.2 kHz.
4. What frequency causes a 500-mH inductor to have an inductive reactance of 470 Ω?

Answers to Practice Problems

1. 518.1 Ω   2. 955.4 μH   3. 1.51 kΩ   4. 149.7 Hz

OHM'S LAW WITH X_L

Inductive reactance is measured in ohms, and it offers opposition to current flow much like a resistance does. All of the relationships between voltage, current, and resistance described by Ohm's Law are equally applicable to sinusoidal inductive circuits. That is,

$$V_L = I_L X_L \tag{12-9}$$

$$I_L = \frac{V_L}{X_L} \tag{12-10}$$

$$X_L = \frac{V_L}{I_L} \tag{12-11}$$

EXAMPLE SOLUTION

Refer to Figure 12-33. What is the rms value of current flowing in the circuit?

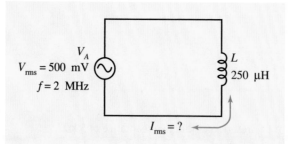

V_A
$V_{rms} = 500 \text{ mV}$
$f = 2 \text{ MHz}$

L
250 μH

$I_{rms} = ?$

Figure 12-33. How much current flows in this circuit?

EXAMPLE SOLUTION

First, we need to determine the inductive reactance in the circuit. We can apply Equation 12-8.

$$X_L = 2\pi f L$$
$$= 6.28 \times 2 \text{ MHz} \times 250 \text{ }\mu\text{H}$$
$$= 3.14 \text{ k}\Omega$$

Now, we can apply Ohm's Law (Equation 12-10) to find the value of current.

$$I = \frac{V_L}{X_L}$$
$$= \frac{500 \text{ mV}}{3.14 \text{ k}\Omega} = 159.2 \text{ }\mu\text{A}$$

Since the voltage was given as an rms value, the computed current is also an rms value.

Practice Problems

1. Calculate the value of rms current for the circuit shown in Figure 12-34.

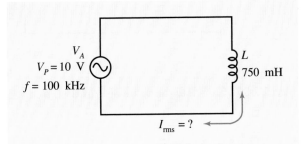

Figure 12-34. Find the rms current in this circuit.

2. What is the value of peak-to-peak current for the circuit shown in Figure 12-35?

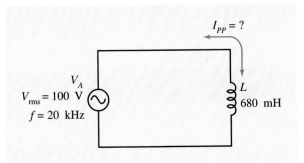

Figure 12-35. Find the value of I_{PP}.

3. What is the peak value of voltage applied to the circuit shown in Figure 12-36?

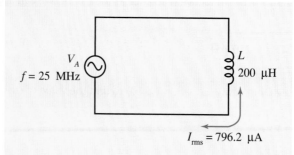

Figure 12-36. Find the peak voltage in this circuit.

4. What is the value of the inductor in the circuit shown in Figure 12-37?

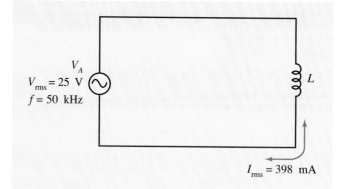

Figure 12-37. Calculate the value of L in this circuit.

Answers to Practice Problems

  1.   15.01 μA   **2.**   3.31 mA   **3.**   35.35 V   **4.**   200 μH

INDUCTIVE REACTANCES IN SERIES

⊙ **KEY POINTS**

Series inductive reactances combine like series resistances.

When the individual inductive reactances of two or more series-connected inductors are known, the total inductive reactance can be found by summing the individual reactances. This is expressed by Equation 12-12.

$$X_{L_T} = X_{L_1} + X_{L_2} + X_{L_3} + \ldots + X_{L_N} \quad (12\text{-}12)$$

EXAMPLE SOLUTION

Determine the total inductive reactance for the circuit shown in Figure 12-38.

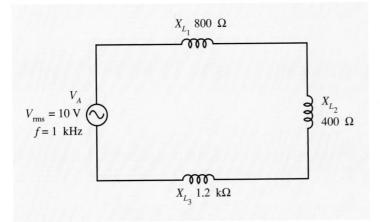

Figure 12-38. What is the value of X_{L_T} in this circuit?

We apply Equation 12-12 as follows:

$$X_{L_T} = X_{L_1} + X_{L_2} + X_{L_3}$$
$$= 800 \ \Omega + 400 \ \Omega + 1.2 \ k\Omega = 2.4 \ k\Omega$$

Practice Problems

1. What is the total inductive reactance (X_{L_T}) in the circuit shown in Figure 12-39?
2. What is the value of X_{L_2} in Figure 12-40?
3. What is the total inductive reactance if 5 coils are connected in series and each coil has a 2.5-kΩ reactance?
4. What happens to the value of inductive reactance in a circuit if the frequency is increased?

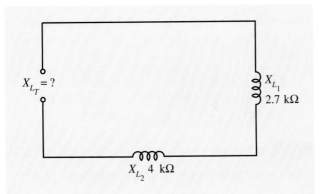

Figure 12-39. Find the value of X_{L_T}.

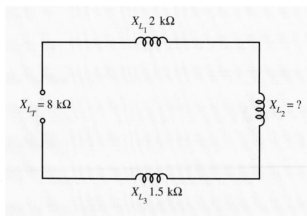

Figure 12-40. Find the value of X_{L_2}.

5. What happens to the value of inductive reactance in a circuit if the applied voltage is increased?

6. What happens to the value of inductive reactance in a circuit if the value of inductance is increased?

Answers to Practice Problems

1. 6.7 kΩ

2. 4.5 kΩ

3. 12.5 kΩ

4. Inductive reactance increases.

5. Inductive reactance stays the same.

6. Inductive reactance increases.

INDUCTIVE REACTANCES IN PARALLEL

When inductive reactances are connected in parallel, the total inductive reactance is less than the smallest individual reactance. The exact value can be computed with the reciprocal formula (Equation 12-13).

$$X_{L_T} = \frac{1}{\dfrac{1}{X_{L_1}} + \dfrac{1}{X_{L_2}} + \dfrac{1}{X_{L_3}} + \dots + \dfrac{1}{X_{L_N}}} \quad (12\text{-}13)$$

EXAMPLE SOLUTION

What is the total inductive reactance for the circuit shown in Figure 12-41?

EXAMPLE SOLUTION

We apply the reciprocal formula (Equation 12-13) as follows:

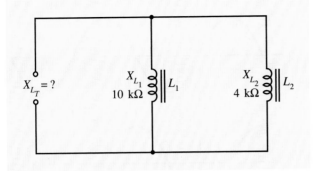

Figure 12-41. Find the total inductive reactance in this circuit.

$$X_{L_T} = \cfrac{1}{\cfrac{1}{X_{L_1}} + \cfrac{1}{X_{L_2}}}$$

$$= \cfrac{1}{\cfrac{1}{10\ k\Omega} + \cfrac{1}{4\ k\Omega}} = 2.86\ k\Omega$$

Practice Problems

1. What is the total inductive reactance if 2 coils having reactances of 27 kΩ and 68 kΩ are connected in parallel?
2. What is the total inductive reactance if 4 coils are connected in parallel and each coil has a reactance of 100 Ω?
3. What value of inductive reactance must be used to parallel a 10-kΩ inductive reactance, if the total reactance must be 2,000 Ω.

Answers to Practice Problems

1. 19.33 kΩ   **2.** 25 Ω   **3.** 2.5 kΩ

Phase Relationships

You will recall from a previous discussion that the voltage across an inductor is proportional to the rate of change of current through the inductor. If the current waveform is a sine wave, then it follows that the points of highest self-induced voltage will coincide with the 0° and 180° points of the current waveform, since these points have the highest rate of change. Similarly, there will be no self-induced voltage as the current wave passes through the 90° and 270° points, since the rate of change of current at these points is zero. These relationships lead to the waveforms shown in Figure 12-42.

As you can see from the waveforms in Figure 12-42(b), the voltage peaks coincide with the points of maximum rate of change of current. Similarly, the zero-crossing points of

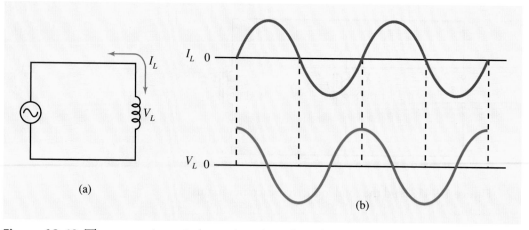

Figure 12-42. The current in an inductor lags the voltage by 90°.

the voltage waveform coincide with the peaks (minimum rate of change) of the current waveform.

Both current and voltage waveforms are sinusoidal, but the voltage waveform is 90° out of phase with the current waveform. That is, the current and voltage peaks do not occur at the same time. More specifically, the voltage waveform leads (i.e., is ahead of) the current waveform by 90°. Alternatively, we may say the current waveform lags (i.e., is behind) the voltage waveform.

This is a very important characteristic of inductors. Let's state it as a rule.

> The sinusoidal voltage across an inductor will always lead the sinusoidal current by 90°.

Exercise Problems 12.6

1. What is the inductive reactance offered by a 10-mH coil when the applied frequency is 175 kHz?
2. Calculate the frequency at which a 250-μH coil has an inductive reactance of 100 Ω.
3. Which coil will have the highest reactance at a particular frequency: 100 μH or 100 mH?
4. Inductive reactance is (*directly, inversely*) proportional to frequency.
5. Inductive reactance is (*directly, inversely*) proportional to inductance.
6. If 10 V$_{rms}$ at 25 MHz is applied to a 500-μH coil, how much rms current will flow?
7. What is the peak voltage across a 33-mH inductor if 100 mA of current flow at a frequency of 200 kHz?
8. What size inductor is needed to provide 2.5 kΩ of inductive reactance when supplied by a 100-MHz source?

9. If the sine wave of current in an inductor is passing through 150°, what angle is the inductor voltage passing through at this same time?

10. If the voltage across an inductor is at its 45° point, at what point is the current wave?

12.7 Q of an Inductor

Although the primary purpose of an inductor is to provide inductance (or inductive reactance), a practical inductor also adds resistance to the circuit. The ratio of inductive reactance (the desired quantity) to the resistance (the undesired quantity) is called the quality of the coil. The symbol for quality is Q. Since Q is a simple ratio, it has no units of measurement. The computation of a coil's Q is accomplished with Equation 12-14.

$$Q = \frac{X_L}{ESR} \qquad (12\text{-}14)$$

where X_L is the inductive reactance of the coil and ESR is the effective series resistance of the coil. The ESR of the coil is more complex than the simple dc resistance of the wire itself. It is actually a summation of several coil losses that collectively dissipate heat. This combined apparent resistance is called the coil's effective series resistance, or ESR. We will discuss the various components that make up the ESR in a subsequent section. Figure 12-43 illustrates the way the ESR appears to the external circuitry.

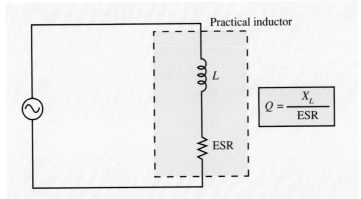

Figure 12-43. A practical inductor also adds resistance to the circuit in the form of an effective series resistance, or ESR.

EXAMPLE SOLUTION

What is the Q of a 250-mH coil that has an ESR of 100 Ω when operated at a frequency of 3 kHz?

EXAMPLE **SOLUTION**

First, we compute the inductive reactance of the coil with Equation 12-8.

$X_L = 2\pi f L$

$\quad = 6.28 \times 3 \text{ kHz} \times 250 \text{ mH}$

$\quad = 4.71 \text{ k}\Omega$

Next, we compute the Q of the coil by applying Equation 12-14.

$$Q = \frac{X_L}{ESR}$$

$$= \frac{4.71 \text{ k}\Omega}{100 \ \Omega} = 47.1$$

Although the Q of a coil is a calculable numeric quantity, technicians often speak of Q in relative terms. Generally, a coil with a Q of less than ten is called a low-Q coil. Similarly, if a coil has a Q of over 100, it is usually called a high-Q coil.

Both factors (X_L and ESR) of Q are frequency-dependent. Therefore, Q is frequency dependent. The Q of a coil must be specified at a particular operating or test frequency. At frequencies well below the optimum operating range, the Q decreases due to a falling X_L. At frequencies substantially higher than the optimum operating range, the Q decreases due to the increase in ESR.

Practice Problems

1. What is the Q of a coil that has an inductive reactance of 600 Ω and an ESR of 27 Ω?

2. Would a coil that has an ESR of 5 Ω and an inductive reactance of 100 Ω, generally be classified as a high-Q coil?

3. What is the most ESR a 33-mH coil can have, if it is to have a Q of at least 40 at a frequency of 100 kHz?

Answers to Practice Problems

1. 22.22　　**2.** No　　**3.** 518.1 Ω

Power Dissipation

A perfect inductor dissipates no power (i.e., generates no heat). Figure 12-44 helps explain why an ideal inductor dissipates no power.

Figure 12-44(a) shows an ideal (i.e., ESR = 0) inductor connected to an ac source. Figure 12-44(b) illustrates the resulting current, voltage, and power dissipation waveforms. The current and voltage waveforms are 90° out of phase as discussed in a previous section. The power dissipation waveform (P_L) was constructed by using the power formula $P = VI$. That is, if we multiply the instantaneous voltage and current values at many points on the voltage and current curves, we will obtain the results shown in Figure 12-44(b) as P_L. Clearly, the power dissipation curve has a frequency that is twice the applied frequency. Of more immediate interest, however, are the polarities of the power dissipation curve and the average value.

During times when the power dissipation curve is positive, the inductor is taking energy from the circuit. This occurs while the magnetic field is expanding around the coil (i.e., the current is increasing). During times when the current is decreasing (between 90° and

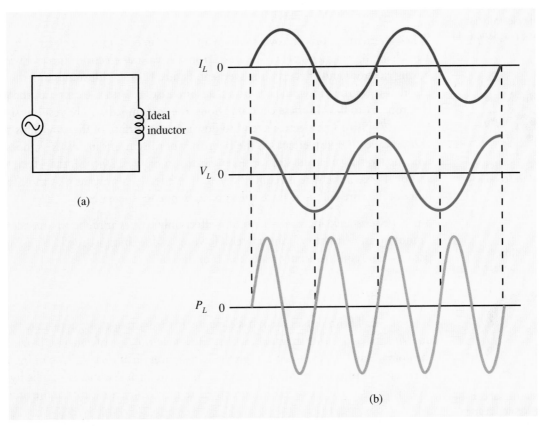

Figure 12-44. An ideal inductor dissipates no power.

180° and between 270° and 360° on the current wave), the magnetic field is collapsing. This actually generates a voltage and returns power to the circuit. These times are indicated in Figure 12-44(b) as a negative power curve. So, half of the time the inductor is taking energy from the circuit where it is stored in the magnetic field. The other half of the time, the energy stored in the magnetic field is returned to the circuit. The net power loss is zero.

Inductor Losses

A practical inductor has a nonzero ESR, which causes a positive power dissipation. The ESR of a coil is made up of several losses. Some of the losses occur in the coil winding, while others occur in the core of the coil. Let's examine each of them individually.

LOSS DUE TO WIRE RESISTANCE

The copper wire used to wind the inductor has a definite amount of ohmic resistance. You will recall from our discussion of conductors in Chapter 8, that the resistance of a wire is directly proportional to its length and inversely proportional to its cross-sectional area. Both of these factors affect the resistance of the coil wire and, therefore, the Q of the coil. Loss due to the resistance of the wire is called **copper loss** or I^2R loss. It is not frequency dependent.

⊙ **KEY POINTS**

A practical coil has a number of power losses that appear as a resistance in series with the coil winding. This apparent resistance is called the effective series resistance, or *ESR*, of the coil.

⊙ **KEY POINTS**

Winding losses include the power dissipated by the ohmic resistance of the wire used to wind the coil and the increase in effective wire resistance due to skin effect.

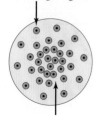

Each moving electron has a surrounding magnetic field.

Flux density is highest in the center of the conductor.

(a)

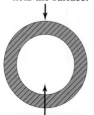

Current flows near the surface.

There is no substantial current flowing in the central regions of the conductor.

(b)

Figure 12-45.
Skin effect reduces the effective cross-sectional area of a wire.

● **KEY POINTS**

Skin effect describes the condition where high-frequency currents tend to flow near the surface of a conductor, making the solid wire appear to be a hollow tube.

● **KEY POINTS**

Skin effect causes the effective cross-sectional area of the wire to decrease, which increases the effective resistance of the wire.

LOSS DUE TO SKIN EFFECT

When alternating current flows through an inductor, each moving electron has an associated changing magnetic field. The fields from the various electrons interact with neighboring electrons and affect their movement. Figure 12-45(a) illustrates that the cumulative flux density of the individual electron fields increases toward the center of the wire. When electrons try to flow in these central regions, they are impeded. The result is shown in Figure 12-45(b). The electrons tend to flow near the surface of the wire. This phenomenon is called the **skin effect.** As the frequency of the current increases, so does its tendency to flow near the surface. As indicated in Figure 12-45(b), the effective cross-sectional area of the wire is reduced due to skin effect. This means that the effective resistance of the wire will increase as the applied frequency increases.

Since the resistance increase due to skin effect only occurs at higher frequencies, you cannot measure it with an ohmmeter. However, it does increase the ESR and power dissipation of the coil. It also decreases the Q of the coil.

HYSTERESIS LOSS

You will recall from our study of basic magnetic theory that a magnetic material has domains that align with external magnetic fields. In the case of a magnetic-core inductor, the domains in the core must realign themselves every half cycle. This requires energy and the energy must come from the ac source. As the frequency is increased, the hysteresis loss also increases, since the domain-switching energy is being consumed more often.

As discussed in Chapter 10, the degree of hysteresis loss for a particular material is indicated by the area of its hysteresis loop. Cores for inductors are generally made from a material that has a high permeability, but a narrow hysteresis loop.

EDDY-CURRENT LOSS

When a changing magnetic field intersects a conductor, it induces a voltage in the conductor. The induced voltage can cause current to flow. We know from the basic power formula ($P = VI$) that there must be an associated power dissipation.

When the changing magnetic field of an inductor cuts through the magnetic core, it can induce a voltage in the core, if the core is conductive. Many materials that are highly magnetic are also conductive. Since the core is relatively large, different potentials are induced into different regions of the core at any instant in time. This causes current to flow from one point in the core to another. However, since the flux pattern is continually changing, so does the specific current paths within the core. Currents induced into the core of an inductor are called **eddy currents.** They are essentially circulating currents whose paths are dynamic, but they do draw energy from the power source. Figure 12-46 illustrates the formation of eddy currents in the core of an inductor.

We can reduce the power dissipation due to eddy currents by using a high-resistance core. This is one advantage of a ferrite or powdered-iron core. These materials provide high permeability, but they also have a high ohmic resistance. This limits the magnitude of the eddy currents. Eddy currents increase with higher frequencies, since the voltage induced into the core material increases.

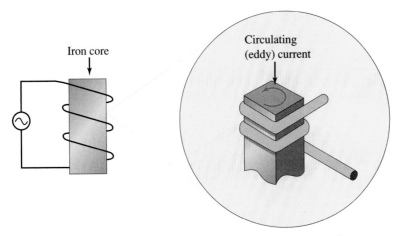

Figure 12-46. Eddy currents flow in the conductive core of an inductor.

● **KEY POINTS**

Hysteresis loss results from the energy that is required to cause realignment of the domains in the core every half-cycle.

● **KEY POINTS**

Hysteresis losses increase with frequency.

● **KEY POINTS**

Hysteresis loss is reduced by selecting a material with a narrow hysteresis loop.

You will recall from an earlier section that iron-core coils normally use a laminated core. The core consists of thin sheets of core material separated with an insulative coating. This allows the core to provide the high permeability needed to obtain high values of inductance, but the insulative barriers keep the eddy current losses to a minimum.

Exercise Problems 12.7

1. A coil with a Q of 8 could be classified as a (*high, low*)-Q coil.
2. If the ESR of a coil increases, the Q _____.
3. Eddy currents are unaffected by frequency. (True or False)
4. Hysteresis loss is unaffected by frequency. (True or False)
5. Skin effect is unaffected by frequency. (True or False)
6. Copper loss is unaffected by frequency. (True or False)
7. What is the Q of a 10-mH coil that has an ESR of 75 Ω when it is operated at a frequency of 25 kHz?
8. Q is unaffected by frequency. (True or False)
9. If a certain coil has an inductive reactance of 22 kΩ and an ESR of 1.5 kΩ, what is the Q of the coil?
10. What can be done to minimize losses due to eddy currents?

● **KEY POINTS**

Eddy currents are circulating currents within the core of the coil. They flow because of the voltage induced into the core by the changing magnetic flux of the windings.

● **KEY POINTS**

Eddy currents can be reduced by using a laminated core, a powdered-iron core, or a ferrite core, since each of these cores has a higher electrical resistance than a solid iron core.

12.8 Troubleshooting Inductors

Since an inductor is nothing more than a wire wrapped around a core, there are only three defects that are probable. An open in the coil winding is probably the most common malfunction. Figure 12-47 illustrates the use of an ohmmeter to detect the open winding. If the winding is open, the ohmmeter will indicate infinite (∞) resistance.

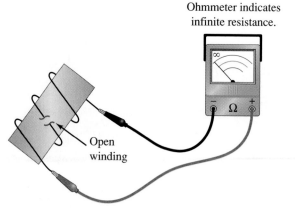

Ohmmeter indicates
infinite resistance.

Open
winding

Figure 12-47. An open coil has infinite resistance.

When an ohmmeter is used to check the condition of a good coil, the meter will indicate the resistance of the wire. This varies with the type of coil being considered. It can be less than one ohm or as high as several thousand ohms. As a technician, you should measure and record the normal resistances of coils used in circuits you are expected to troubleshoot. That way, you can contrast the resistance values of suspected coils with those of known good coils.

Figure 12-48 shows another possible defect that can occur in a multilayer coil. Here, the insulation between two adjacent turns has disintegrated, allowing the windings to short together. This effectively shorts out or bypasses a portion of the coil. Depending on the location of the short and the method of winding the coil, the short may only bypass a single turn, or it may bypass a significant portion of the inductor. A shorted coil is sometimes very difficult to detect with an ohmmeter. The ohmmeter will read a value of coil resistance that is less than the normal value for the coil. However, since the normal value may only be one or two ohms, a typical ohmmeter may not absolutely identify shorted turns.

Windings usually become shorted as a direct result of overheating or internal arcing. In either case, the short may be accompanied by physical clues such as discoloration of the coil, visible melting of the insulation, or a characteristic, pungent odor.

Figure 12-49 shows a test instrument that technicians use to measure the value of inductance in a coil. If a significant number of turns in the coil are shorted, or if the coil is open,

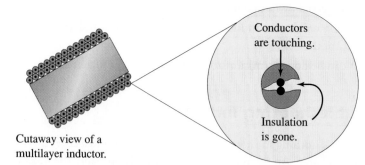

Conductors
are touching.

Insulation
is gone.

Cutaway view of a
multilayer inductor.

Figure 12-48. Adjacent turns on a multilayer coil can become shorted if the insulation breaks down.

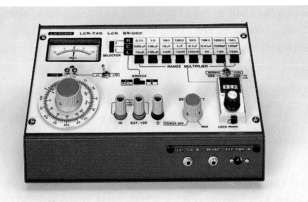

Figure 12-49. An inductance meter measures the actual value of an inductor. It can be used to detect opens or shorts in the coil winding. (Courtesy of Leader Instruments Corporation)

then the inductance meter will easily and quickly identify the defect. For accurate measurements in most circuits, at least one lead of the inductor must be removed from the circuit while it is being measured.

The final defect that is likely to occur in coils is similar to the case of shorted windings. If the coil overheats, the insulation that separates the winding from the metallic core can break down. This allows the coil winding to contact the conductive core material. In the case of iron-core coils, this is generally a catastrophic failure, since the core is often connected directly to the chassis ground of the equipment. This means that the current that would ordinarily flow through the coil is bypassed directly to ground. Additionally, the short to ground effectively bypasses the inductive reactance of the coil, which may allow a substantial current to flow.

An ohmmeter can be used to detect a winding that is shorted to the core. Figure 12-50 illustrates this technique. Figure 12-50(a) shows that a good coil will have an infinite

KEY POINTS

An inductance meter provides a good way to measure the inductance of a coil and thereby determine its condition.

KEY POINTS

An ohmmeter can detect a winding that has shorted to the core.

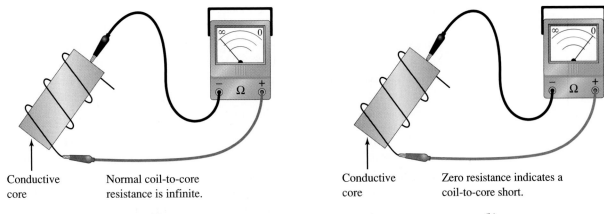

Conductive core	Normal coil-to-core resistance is infinite.

Conductive core	Zero resistance indicates a coil-to-core short.

(a)   (b)

Figure 12-50. (a) An ohmmeter can distinguish between a normal coil winding and (b) a winding that is shorted to the core.

resistance (at least higher than a typical ohmmeter will read) between the coil winding and the metallic core. If the winding shorts to the core, as shown in Figure 12-50(b), then an ohmmeter check will easily detect this condition by indicating zero ohms.

Exercise Problems 12.8

1. If the resistance of a coil winding measures infinity, and the normal value is 500 Ω, what is the most likely defect?
2. If the normal resistance of a coil is 500 Ω, but it measures 300 Ω, what is the most likely defect?
3. What is the normal ohmmeter indication for a good coil when measuring the resistance between the winding and the core?

Chapter Summary

• When current flows through a conductor, it creates a magnetic field around the conductor. If the current is changing, then the magnetic field will be changing. If a changing magnetic field intercepts a conductor, a voltage will be induced into the inductor by a process known as electromagnetic induction.

• When the magnetic field of a coil intercepts the turns of the same coil, the induced voltage is called a self-induced voltage. The value of the self-induced voltage is determined by the strength of the magnetic field, the rate of change of flux, the angle of flux cutting, and the number of turns in the coil. These factors are summarized in Faraday's Law. The polarity of the induced voltage is determined by the direction of the changing magnetic field (i.e., expanding or contracting) and the polarity of the field. According to Lenz's Law, the polarity of the induced voltage will always oppose the change in current. That is, the inductor works to keep the current from changing (i.e., increasing or decreasing).

• Inductance (L) is measured in henries (H). One henry will produce a self-induced voltage of one volt when its current changes at the rate of one ampere per second. The value of inductance for a particular coil is determined by its physical characteristics: number of turns, length of the magnetic circuit, cross-sectional area, and permeability of the core. The inductance of a coil is inversely proportional to the length of the magnetic circuit. It is directly proportional to all other factors.

• Since the value of self-induced voltage in a coil is dependent on the rate of change of current through the coil, the waveshape of self-induced voltage may differ from the waveshape of current. That is, the value of self-induced voltage is dependent on the rate of change of current, but it is unaffected by the absolute value of current. When a sine wave is applied to an inductor, the waveshapes of both voltage and current are sinusoidal, but they are 90° out of phase with each other. More specifically, the voltage waveform leads the current waveform by 90° in a pure inductance.

- There are many different kinds of inductors. They are generally classified as fixed or variable. They can also be classified by the type of material used for the core. Examples include air-core, iron-core, and ferrite-core. A ferrite bead can be added to a wire or the lead of a component to add inductance and resistance to the circuit. The resistance and inductance of the bead appear as series elements to the circuit. Both inductors and ferrite beads are available as surface-mount devices.

- When inductors are combined in series, parallel, or another configuration and not linked magnetically, the total inductance can be found with the same general procedures used to combine resistances. Series inductances add together to form the total inductance. The total inductance of parallel inductances can be computed with the reciprocal formula.

- When inductors are used in dc circuits, there is no effect except when the current value changes. The inductor tends to oppose any changes in current, and may develop substantial voltages, if the current changes quickly.

- When inductors are used in ac circuits, they also oppose changes in current. However, since the current is changing continuously, we express this opposition as inductive reactance. Inductive reactance (X_L) is measured in ohms. It varies directly with the applied frequency and the value of inductance.

- Multiple values of inductive reactance connected in series, parallel, or other configurations, may be combined in much the same manner as resistances, provided there is no magnetic coupling between the various inductors. Additionally, Ohm's Law can be applied to inductive circuits in much the same way as it applies to resistive circuits. Inductive reactance is substituted for resistance in the Ohm's Law equations.

- An ideal inductor has no resistance. It offers only inductance to the circuit. A practical inductor has several forms of power loss, which manifest as a series resistance. This apparent resistance is called the effective series resistance, or ESR of the coil. A portion of the ESR is contributed by the winding itself: copper loss and skin effect. The remaining portion of the ESR is due to losses in the core of the inductor: hysteresis loss and eddy currents. Copper loss is unaffected by frequency. The other factors that make up the ESR are frequency dependent.

- The quality, or Q, of a coil indicates how ideal a coil is. Q is computed as the ratio of inductive reactance to ESR. Since both of these factors are frequency dependent, the Q of a coil is specified at a particular frequency.

- Since an ideal coil has no resistance, it dissipates no power. Energy that is taken from the circuit during one portion of the cycle is returned to the circuit during a subsequent time period. A practical inductor dissipates power in the ESR of the coil.

- A technician can use an inductance meter or an ohmmeter to locate defects in a coil. The normal resistance of a coil winding should be known in advance by the technician. If the resistance of a suspected coil is substantially less than the normal value, then one or more turns of the coil could be shorted. If the coil winding measures infinity, then the coil has an open winding. Finally, the windings of a coil may short to the core. An ohmmeter can detect this condition.

Review Questions

Section 12.1: Electromagnetic Induction

1. When a conductor passes through a magnetic field, the induced voltage is (*directly, inversely*) proportional to field strength.

2. If the relative rate of motion between a conductor and a magnetic field is increased, the induced voltage will (*increase, decrease*).

3. When a conductor moves parallel to the magnetic lines of force, (*minimum, maximum*) voltage is induced.

4. When a conductor moves perpendicular to the magnetic lines of force, (*minimum, maximum*) voltage is induced.

5. If the number of turns on a coil that is being moved through a magnetic field is increased, what happens to the value of induced voltage?

6. Name two factors that determine the polarity of the voltage that will be induced into a conductor that is moving through a magnetic field.

7. According to Faraday's Law, the amount of induced voltage is directly proportional to the rate of change of flux. (True or False)

8. According to Faraday's Law, the amount of induced voltage is directly proportional to the number of turns on a coil. (True or False)

9. The polarity of self-induced voltage in a coil always (*aids, opposes*) the initial current change.

10. Which current would receive the greatest opposition from a 100-mH inductor: a 10-μA current at a frequency of 25 MHz or a 10-A current from a dc source?

11. Inductors oppose a _____ in current.

12. The value of an inductor is inversely proportional to the number of turns on the inductor. (True or False)

13. If the number of turns on an inductor is doubled, what happens to the value of inductance?

14. If the length of the magnetic circuit in a coil is increased, what happens to the value of inductance?

15. If the cross-sectional area of a coil is increased, what happens to the value of inductance?

16. The inductance of a coil is directly proportional to the cross-sectional area of the winding. (True or False)

17. If the number of turns on an inductor is increased by three, but the cross-sectional area of the coil is reduced to one-third of its original size, what happens to the value of inductance?

18. If the relative permeability of the core material in a coil is increased by a factor of ten, what will happen to the value of inductance?

19. The inductance of a coil is directly proportional to the permeability of the core. (True or False)

Section 12.2: Self-Induction

20. Briefly define the term *self-induction*.

21. Describe the voltage waveform across an inductor during times when the rate of change of current through the coil is constant.

22. Explain why a sudden change in current values through a coil produces high voltage.

23. When a sine wave of current flows through an inductor, the maximum value of induced voltage occurs at the _____ and _____-degree points on the current wave.

24. What points on a sine wave correspond to the minimum rate of change?

Section 12.3: Types of Inductors

25. Draw the schematic symbol for a fixed inductor.

26. Draw the schematic symbol for a variable inductor.

27. A coil wound on a nonmagnetic core is generally called a(n) _____-core inductor.

28. Iron-core transformers are generally used at frequencies in excess of 25 MHz. (True or False)

29. The permeability of a powdered-iron core is (*higher, lower*) than the permeability of an air core.

30. The ohmic resistance of a powdered-iron core is (*low, high*).

31. Powdered-iron core coils are generally used for frequencies below 100 Hz. (True or False)

32. A ferrite bead adds both _____ and _____ to a circuit.

33. The opposition to current flow offered by a ferrite bead varies with frequency. (True or False)

34. Molded inductors are often color coded. Their values are assumed to be in

    _____.

35. What is the value of a molded inductor that has the following color bands: silver (wide), gray, red, silver?

36. What is the value of a molded inductor that has the following color bands: silver, red, gold, violet, gold?

37. What is the primary advantage of a surface-mount inductor over a leaded inductor?

Section 12.4: Multiple Circuit Inductances

38. What is the total inductance of three 100-mH coils that are series-connected?

39. If a 25-μH coil is connected in series with a 50-μH coil, what is the total inductance in the circuit?

40. If the total inductance of three series-connected coils is 250 μH, and two of the coils have values of 50 μH and 75 μH, what is the value of the third coil?

41. How much inductance must be connected in series with 830 mH to obtain a total inductance of 1.2 H?

42. The total inductance of series-connected coils is always (*smaller, larger*) than the largest individual coil.

43. The total inductance of parallel-connected coils is always (*smaller, larger*) than the smallest individual coil.

44. What is the total inductance of four parallel-connected 100-µH coils?

45. If L_1, L_2, and L_3 have values of 40 mH, 50 mH, and 200 mH, respectively, and are parallel-connected, what is the total circuit inductance?

46. What value of inductance must be connected in parallel with a 50-µH inductor to obtain a total circuit inductance of 15 µH?

47. What is the total inductance for the circuit shown in Figure 12-51?

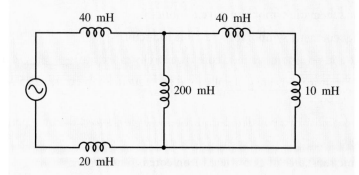

Figure 12-51. What is the total inductance in this circuit?

Section 12.5: Inductance in DC Circuits

48. When direct current is switched into a coil, the self-induced voltage is (*minimum, maximum*) at the first instant.

49. When direct current passes through a coil and the circuit has had time to stabilize, the self-induced voltage across the coil is zero. (True or False)

50. An inductor has no effect on direct current unless it changes values. (True or False)

51. An inductor prevents abrupt changes in the current in a dc circuit. (True or False)

Section 12.6: Inductance in AC Circuits

52. If an inductor has a sinusoidal waveform of current, what is the waveform of voltage?

53. Inductive reactance is unaffected by frequency of operation. (True or False)

54. Inductive reactance is directly proportional to the value of inductance. (True or False)

55. What is the inductive reactance of a 75-mH coil when operated at a frequency of 150 kHz?

56. What frequency causes a 2.5-mH coil to present an inductive reactance of 130 Ω?

57. What is the inductive reactance of a 20-mH coil at a frequency of 5.6 MHz?

58. Inductive reactance is measured in _____.

59. What is the value of rms current in the circuit shown in Figure 12-52?

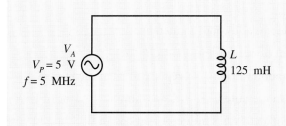

Figure 12-52. Find the rms current in this circuit.

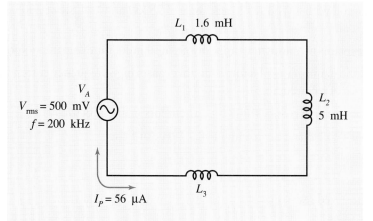

Figure 12-53. Determine the value of L_3.

60. What is the value of L_3 in Figure 12-53?

61. What is the value of X_{L_3} in Figure 12-53?

62. What is the value of peak-to-peak voltage across L_2 in Figure 12-53?

63. What is the value of rms voltage across L_1 in Figure 12-53?

64. If three inductive reactances of 30 kΩ each are connected in series, what is the total inductive reactance?

65. If three inductive reactances of 30 kΩ each are connected in parallel, what is the total inductive reactance?

66. What is the total inductive reactance if 47 kΩ of inductive reactance are connected in parallel with 20 kΩ of inductive reactance?

67. If a sine wave of current flowing through an inductor is passing through its 90° point, at what point is the voltage wave across the inductor?

68. Current through an inductor (*leads, lags*) the voltage across the inductor by _____ degrees.

69. The voltage across an inductor (*leads, lags*) the current through the inductor by _____ degrees.

70. The maximum sinusoidal current through an inductor does not occur at the same time as its maximum voltage. (True or False)

Section 12.7: Q of an Inductor

71. A practical inductor adds both inductance and _____ to the circuit.

72. What is the unit of measurement for Q?

73. What does the abbreviation ESR represent when used to describe an inductor?

74. A technician can measure ESR with an ohmmeter. (True or False)

75. What is the Q of a 100-mH inductor that has an ESR of 100 Ω when operated at a frequency of 12 kHz?

76. If a 10-μH coil has an ESR of 7 Ω at a frequency of 2.5 MHz, what is its Q?

77. Would a coil with an inductive reactance of 25 kΩ and an ESR of 200 be considered a low-Q coil?

78. Briefly explain in your own words why an ideal inductor dissipates no power.

79. What is the name of the phenomenon that causes high-frequency current to flow near the surface of a conductor?

80. Name two ways to reduce the eddy-current loss in an inductor.

81. The Q of a coil changes with frequency. (True or False)

Section 12.8: Troubleshooting Inductors

82. If the measured resistance of a coil is 1.5 Ω and the normal value is 4.5 Ω, what is a possible defect?

83. If an ohmmeter check of the winding in an iron-core inductor indicates infinite resistance, is the coil good?

84. What is the normal value of resistance that should be measured between the winding of a coil and its metallic core?

TECHNICIAN CHALLENGE

Figure 12-54 shows the schematic diagram of a circuit that can be used as an electric fence charger. Electric fences are often used to keep farm animals and pets restricted to a particular area. If an animal touches the electric fence, it receives a harmless, but memorable, electric shock. The circuit operates from 12 Vdc, but it provides high-voltage to the fence.

Study the circuit shown in Figure 12-54 carefully to determine how it works. Then, accomplish the following:

- Write a complete theory of operation to describe how the circuit works. This description will be used in the service manual for the charger.
- State the purpose of every component.
- If practical, build the circuit in the laboratory to verify its operation. You can replace the one-second timer with a manually operated switch. Inductor L_1 should be as large as practical. (You might use the coil from another relay or a winding on a transformer, if no large inductors are available.)

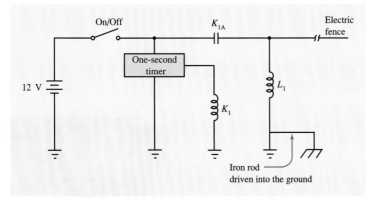

Figure 12-54. A circuit for an electric fence charger.

Equation List

(12-1) $L = \mu \dfrac{N^2 A}{l}$

(12-2) $L = \mu_r \times 1.257 \times 10^{-6} \times \dfrac{N^2 A}{l}$

(12-3) $V_L = L\dfrac{\Delta i}{\Delta t} = L\dfrac{di}{dt}$

(12-4) $L_T = L_1 + L_2 + L_3 + \ldots + L_N$

(12-5) $L_T = \dfrac{1}{\dfrac{1}{L_1} + \dfrac{1}{L_2} + \dfrac{1}{L_3} + \ldots + \dfrac{1}{L_N}}$

(12-6) $L_T = \dfrac{L}{N}$

(12-7) $L_T = \dfrac{L_1 L_2}{L_1 + L_2}$

(12-8) $X_L = 2\pi f L$

(12-9) $V_L = I_L X_L$

(12-10) $I_L = \dfrac{V_L}{X_L}$

(12-11) $X_L = \dfrac{V_L}{I_L}$

(12-12) $X_{L_T} = X_{L_1} + X_{L_2} + X_{L_3} + \ldots + X_{L_N}$

(12-13) $X_{L_T} = \dfrac{1}{\dfrac{1}{X_{L_1}} + \dfrac{1}{X_{L_2}} + \dfrac{1}{X_{L_3}} + \ldots + \dfrac{1}{X_{L_N}}}$

(12-14) $Q = \dfrac{X_L}{\text{ESR}}$

key terms

admittance
apparent power
differentiator
impedance
integrator

power factor
reactive power
susceptance
true power

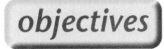

objectives

After completing this chapter, you should be able to:

1. Use both polar and rectangular notation to calculate the following quantities in a series, parallel, or series-parallel *RL* circuit:

   admittance
   apparent power
   component currents
   component voltages
   phase angle between total
      voltage and total current

   power factor
   reactive power
   total current
   total impedance
   true power

   The calculations will include both polar and rectangular notation.

2. Draw a phasor diagram to represent a given series or parallel *RL* circuit.

3. Express circuit quantities in either polar or rectangular form.

4. State and apply the Pythagorean theorem.

5. Calculate the *RL* time constant of an *RL* circuit.

6. State the general requirements for *RL* differentiator and integrator circuits.

7. Determine the approximate pulse response of an *RL* circuit.

8. Name at least two applications that utilize *RL* circuits.

9. Explain the relationship between and calculate the values of the following quantities: true power, apparent power, reactive power, power factor.

13

Resistive-Inductive Circuit Analysis

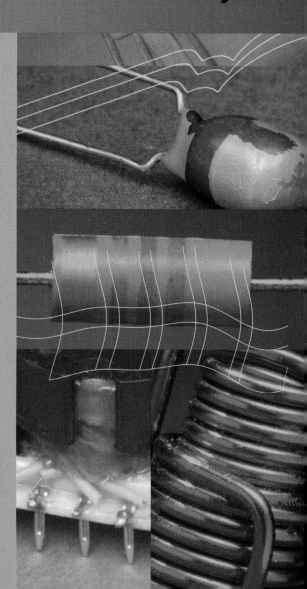

When resistance (R) and inductance (L) are combined in the same circuit, we refer to it as an RL circuit. As you might expect, the characteristics of the circuit lie between those of a pure resistive or a pure inductive circuit. The various components that make up the circuit may be connected as series, parallel, series-parallel, or complex. The basic principles that have been emphasized in previous chapters such as Ohm's Law and Kirchhoff's Laws will still apply, but we need to include the concept of phase relationships.

13.1 Series *RL* Circuits with Sinusoidal Currents

Let us begin by learning some of the basic characteristics of series *RL* circuits. We will consider a few mathematical relationships, but will defer most computations until a later section. Figure 13-1 shows a series *RL* circuit consisting of one resistor and one inductor. Let's examine some basic characteristics of this circuit configuration.

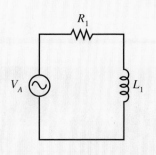

Figure 13-1. A simple series *RL* circuit.

Series *RL* Circuit Characteristics

CURRENT

Since we are considering a series circuit, we know that the current will be the same in all parts of the circuit. If we knew, for example, that the current through L_1 was 150 mA, then we would immediately know the value of current through R_1 and through the source. This important principle is true in any series circuit. It is illustrated in Figure 13-2.

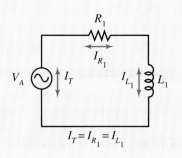

Figure 13-2. The current is the same through all components in a series *RL* circuit.

VOLTAGE DROPS

We recall from Ohm's Law that the voltage across a component is determined by its resistance (or reactance) and the value of current flowing through it. Since current is the same in all parts of a series *RL* circuit, the various components will have voltage drops that are proportional to the resistance or reactance values. Those with higher resistances or reactances will drop more voltage than components with smaller resistances or reactances. This is illustrated in Figure 13-3.

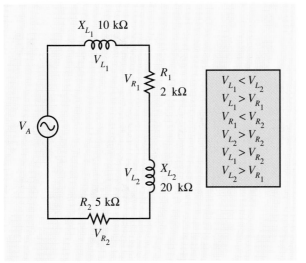

Figure 13-3. Component voltage drops in a series *RL* circuit are proportional to their resistance or reactance values.

PHASE RELATIONSHIPS

We can easily predict the phase relationships in a series *RL* circuit by applying what we already know. Consider these three facts:

- Current is the same in all parts of the circuit at all times.
- Current and voltage are in phase in a resistance.
- Current lags voltage by 90° in an inductance.

As shown in Figure 13-4, the voltage waveforms across the two inductors will have the same phase (they lead the common current by 90°). The inductor voltage waveforms will be 90° out of phase with the resistor voltage waveforms. Specifically, the inductor voltages will lead the resistor voltages by 90°. Finally, we would expect the two resistor voltage waveforms to be in phase with each other.

POWER FACTOR

The **power factor** of a circuit is a dimensionless (no units of measure) quantity that describes the phase relationship between total current and total voltage. A later section will show that the power factor is numerically equal to the cosine of the phase angle. This means that it has numeric values that range between zero and one.

A power factor of one or unity indicates a zero-degree phase relationship between current and voltage. That is, the circuit is purely resistive. Under these conditions, all power that

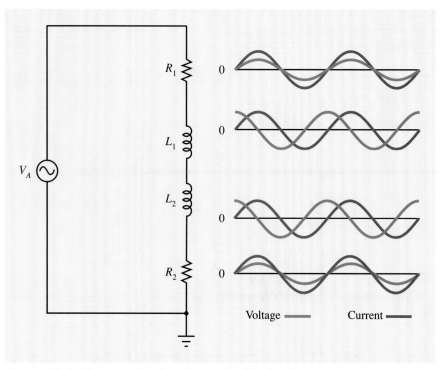

Figure 13-4. Phase relationships in a series *RL* circuit.

leaves the source is transferred to the load and converted to another form of energy (e.g., heat in a resistor, mechanical energy in a motor, heat and light energy in a lamp, and so on). A power factor of zero indicates a purely reactive circuit. In this case, energy leaves the source and is temporarily stored in the reactive component. During a later portion of the ac cycle, energy is returned from the reactive component to the source. Thus, energy moves back and forth between the source and the external circuit, but it is not converted to another more useful form. In most cases, we want the energy to be transformed to provide useful work. The power factor gives us a numerical measure of how much of the energy is actually being transformed and how much is being returned to the source.

IMPEDANCE

We know that the total opposition to current flow in a series resistive circuit is found by adding the individual resistances in the circuit. Similarly, we determine total inductive reactance in a series circuit by adding together the individual inductive reactance values. This same concept extends to include series *RL* circuits, but we have to consider one additional point—phase.

First, the total opposition to current flow in a circuit consisting of both resistance and reactance is called **impedance.** As you would expect, it is measured in ohms. We use the letter *Z* to represent impedance. Thus, we might describe the total opposition to current (impedance) of a particular circuit by saying $Z = 12.5$ kΩ.

Impedance in a series *RL* circuit is computed by adding the individual resistance and inductive reactance values using phasor addition. This is the same concept as simple addition, but it accounts for the fact that the instantaneous opposition to current flow depends on the phase of the current (i.e., the instantaneous rate of change of current). We will examine phasor addition in a subsequent section.

SUSCEPTANCE

Recall that the reciprocal of a pure resistance is conductance (G). This is a measurement of the ease with which current flows through a resistance. **Susceptance** (B) is a comparable quantity of a pure reactance. We can express it formally with Equation 13-1.

$$B = \frac{1}{X_L} \qquad (13\text{-}1)$$

Susceptance, like conductance, is measured in siemens (S).

KEY POINTS

Just as conductance is the reciprocal of resistance, susceptance is the reciprocal of reactance.

EXAMPLE SOLUTION

What is the susceptance of a 10-mH inductor when it is operating at a frequency of 100 kHz?

EXAMPLE **SOLUTION**

We will apply Equation 13-1, but first we need to compute the value of inductive reactance.

$$X_L = 2\pi f L$$
$$= 6.28 \times 100 \text{ kHz} \times 10 \text{ mH} = 6.28 \text{ k}\Omega$$

Now we can apply Equation 13-1.

$$B = \frac{1}{X_L}$$
$$= \frac{1}{6.28 \text{ k}\Omega} = 159.2 \text{ } \mu\text{S}$$

Practice Problems

1. What is the susceptance of a coil that has a 25-kΩ reactance?
2. How much susceptance will a 100-μH coil have, if it is operated at a frequency of 2.5 MHz?
3. At what frequency must a 75-μH inductor be operated in order to have a susceptance of 5 μS?

Answers to Practice Problems

1. 40 μS   2. 636.9 μS   3. 424.6 MHz

ADMITTANCE

Conductance (G) and susceptance (B) are the reciprocals of pure resistance and pure reactance. Both conductance and susceptance are measured in siemens. When the circuit has a

KEY POINTS

Conductance (G), susceptance (B), and admittance (Y) are all measured in siemens (S).

○ KEY POINTS

Admittance is the recip-
rocal of impedance.

combination of resistance and reactance, we express its total opposition to current flow as impedance. The reciprocal of impedance is called **admittance** (Y). It is also measured in siemens. We can express it formally as Equation 13-2.

$$Y = \frac{1}{Z} \qquad\qquad (13\text{-}2)$$

EXAMPLE SOLUTION

What is the admittance of a series RL circuit that has a 10-kΩ impedance?

EXAMPLE **SOLUTION**

We apply Equation 13-2 as follows:

$$Y = \frac{1}{Z} = \frac{1}{10\ \text{k}\Omega} = 100\ \mu\text{S}$$

Circuit Simplification

○ KEY POINTS

If a series RL circuit has multiple resistances and/or inductances, we can simplify the circuit by combining the individual resistances into a single resistance. We can combine the individual inductances into a single equivalent inductance.

We can simplify a series RL circuit such as the one shown in Figure 13-5 by combining the various resistances into an equivalent resistance and by combining the various inductances (assuming no magnetic linkage) into a single equivalent inductance. We use our previously discussed equations for each of these simplification steps.

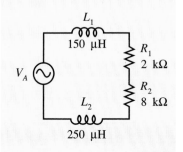

Figure 13-5. An unsimplified RL circuit.

EXAMPLE SOLUTION

Simplify the RL circuit shown in Figure 13-5.

EXAMPLE **SOLUTION**

First, we combine the resistances as follows:

$$R_T = R_1 + R_2$$
$$= 2\ \text{k}\Omega + 8\ \text{k}\Omega = 10\ \text{k}\Omega$$

Next we combine the series inductances in a similar manner:

$$L_T = L_1 + L_2$$
$$= 150\ \mu\text{H} + 250\ \mu\text{H} = 400\ \mu\text{H}$$

The simplified circuit is shown in Figure 13-6. It consists of a single equivalent resistance and a single equivalent inductance. It should be noted that we can further simplify this circuit by adding (phasor addition) the equivalent resistance and the equivalent inductance to obtain the overall impedance of the circuit. We shall discuss this final simplification step momentarily.

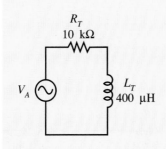

Figure 13-6. The equivalent circuit for the original circuit shown in Figure 13-5.

Practice Problems

1. Draw the equivalent circuit for the *RL* circuit shown in Figure 13-7.

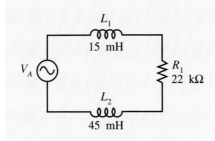

Figure 13-7. Simplify this circuit.

2. Draw the equivalent circuit for the *RL* circuit shown in Figure 13-8.

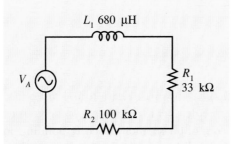

Figure 13-8. Simplify this circuit.

3. Simplify the circuit shown in Figure 13-9.

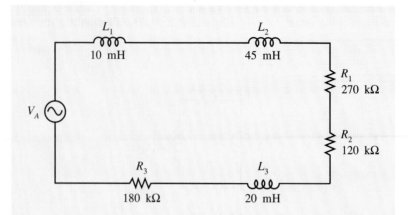

Figure 13-9. Simplify this circuit.

Answers to Practice Problems

1.

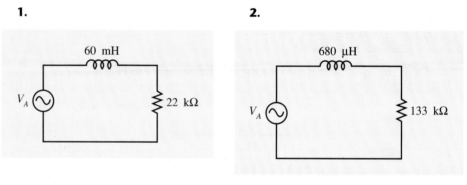

2.

3.

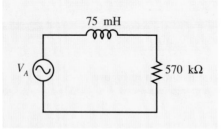

Phasor Representation

Let us now take a closer look at the phase relationships in a series *RL* circuit. As we proceed, it is important to remember that the term *phase* refers to time. That is, if two sinusoidal waveforms are out of phase, then the corresponding points occur at different times. Technicians use phasor diagrams to help visualize the phase relationships in a circuit.

VOLTAGE PHASORS

As previously noted, the voltage waveforms across the components in a series *RL* circuit are not all in phase. The current waveforms, however, must be identical, since the instantaneous current is the same in all parts of a series circuit. For this reason, we shall use current as the reference phasor when sketching phasor diagrams for series circuits. The voltage phasors will be drawn relative to the reference phasor.

EXAMPLE SOLUTION

Draw a phasor diagram to represent the circuit shown in Figure 13-10.

EXAMPLE SOLUTION

First, we sketch the reference phasor (current). As shown in Figure 13-11, it is customary to draw the reference phasor extending horizontally to the right. The relative lengths of the current and voltage phasors are not critical. It is, for example, impossible to discuss the relative magnitudes of 100 V and 100 A. They have different units and cannot be compared. For clarity, however, we normally make the reference phasor longer than any others.

Next, we can add a phasor representing the voltage drop across the series resistance. Since voltage and current are in phase through a resistance, we will sketch the resistor voltage phasor (V_{R_1}) in the same direction as our current phasor (*I*). As previously mentioned, its length relative to the reference phasor is not critical.

Finally, we add the phasor to represent the inductive voltage (V_{L_1}). We know that inductor voltage leads current by 90°, so we will draw the inductive voltage phasor 90° ahead (more counterclockwise) of the current phasor. The resistive voltage and inductive voltage phasors have common units (volts). Therefore, we can indicate their relative magnitudes on the phasor diagram. In the present case, we shall make the V_{L_1} phasor (20 V) twice as long as the V_{R_1} phasor (10 V).

We can also indicate the phase angle and magnitude of the applied voltage. We can do this graphically by simply completing a parallelogram where V_{R_1} and V_{L_1} are two of the sides and the axes of the graph are the other two sides. The phasor sum is represented by the diagonal of the parallelogram. As shown in Figure 13-11, the diagonal is drawn from the origin to the opposite side of the parallelogram.

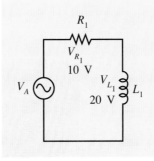

Figure 13-10. Draw the phasors for this circuit.

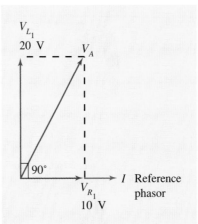

Figure 13-11. A phasor diagram for the circuit in Figure 13-10.

PHASOR ADDITION

When you first learned how to add numbers, you restricted yourself to positive integers. Later you extended your skills to include fractions and decimals. Later studies further extended your scope to include algebraic addition, which allowed you to sum positive and negative numbers. We will now extend your addition skills even more to include phasor addition. This will allow us to add two quantities that are out of phase.

Figure 13-12 illustrates the three basic levels of addition as they might apply to a summation of mechanical forces. In Figure 13-12(a), the two forces are in the same direction. They can be combined with simple arithmetic addition. Figure 13-12(b) is more complex. Here, the forces are acting in opposite directions. Summation of the forces requires algebraic addition to account for the signed numbers. Finally, Figure 13-12(c) shows the two forces pulling at a right angle to each other. Summation of these right-angle forces requires vector addition. This is numerically equivalent to phasor addition.

Arithmetic addition: Total force = force 1 + force 2

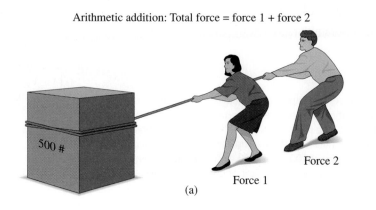

(a)

Algebraic addition: Total force = force 1 + (−force 2)
= force 1 − force 2

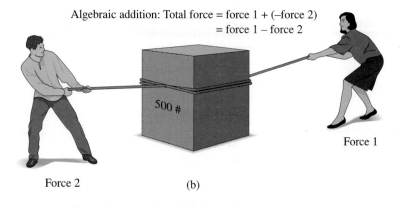

(b)

Vector (phasor) addition: Total force = $\sqrt{(\text{force } 1)^2 + (\text{force } 2)^2}$

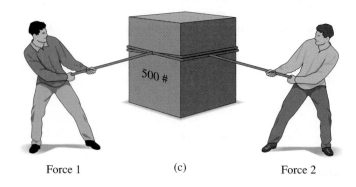

(c)

Figure 13-12. A mechanical analogy showing addition of forces.

As shown in Figure 13-12(c), right-angle forces are combined by finding the square root of the sum of the squares of the individual forces. This stems from a basic theorem in right-angle trigonometry called the Pythagorean theorem.

In the case of a series *RL* circuit, we know the inductive and resistive voltages are 90° out of phase. We also know that the total voltage in a series circuit is equal to the sum of the voltage drops. This leads us to Equation 13-3 for determining the applied voltage in a series *RL* circuit.

$$V_T = V_A = \sqrt{V_R^2 + V_L^2} \qquad (13\text{-}3)$$

Note that V_T and V_A are both commonly used to represent total or applied voltage.

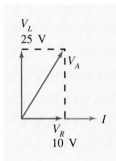

Figure 13-13.
Find the value of applied voltage in this circuit.

EXAMPLE SOLUTION

Find the value of applied voltage for the circuit shown in Figure 13-13.

EXAMPLE **SOLUTION**

The phasor diagram for this circuit is shown in Figure 13-14. We compute the value of applied voltage by applying Equation 13-3 as follows:

$$V_A = \sqrt{(V_L)^2 + (V_R)^2}$$
$$= \sqrt{(25 \text{ V})^2 + (10 \text{ V})^2}$$
$$= \sqrt{625 + 100} = \sqrt{725} \approx 26.93 \text{ V}$$

You can check your calculations by applying the following rule:

> The result of phasor addition will always be greater than either individual phasor but less than the arithmetic sum of the two phasors.

Figure 13-14. Phasor diagram for the circuit shown in Figure 13-13.

EXAMPLE SOLUTION

Determine the value of resistor voltage for the circuit shown in Figure 13-15.

EXAMPLE **SOLUTION**

The phasor diagram for this circuit is shown in Figure 13-16. We find V_R by applying Equation 13-3 as follows:

$$V_A = \sqrt{(V_L)^2 + (V_R)^2}, \text{ or}$$
$$V_A^2 = ((V_L)^2 + (V_R)^2), \text{ or}$$
$$(V_R)^2 = (V_A)^2 - (V_L)^2; \text{ therefore}$$
$$V_R = \sqrt{(V_A)^2 - (V_L)^2}$$
$$= \sqrt{(10 \text{ V})^2 - (5 \text{ V})^2}$$
$$= \sqrt{100 - 25} = \sqrt{75} \approx 8.66 \text{ V}$$

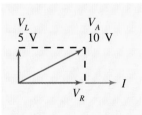

Figure 13-15.
Find the voltage across the resistor in this circuit.

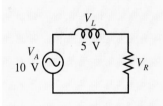

Figure 13-16. Phasor diagram for the circuit shown in Figure 13-15.

CALCULATOR SEQUENCES

One possible set of calculator button sequences for phasor addition is shown in Figures 13-17 and 13-18 for standard and RPN engineering calculators, respectively.

$$a = 5$$
$$b = 7$$
$$c = \sqrt{5^2 + 7^2} \cong 8.6$$

Figure 13-17. Calculator sequence for phasor addition on a standard engineering calculator.

$$a = 5$$
$$b = 7$$
$$c = \sqrt{5^2 + 7^2} \cong 8.6$$

Figure 13-18. Calculator sequence for phasor addition on a RPN engineering calculator.

Practice Problems

1. Determine the value of applied voltage for the circuit shown in Figure 13-19.
2. What is the value of V_A in Figure 13-20?
3. Find the resistor voltage in Figure 13-21.

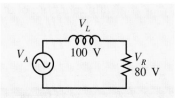

Figure 13-19. Find the applied voltage.

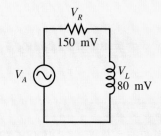

Figure 13-20. Determine V_A in this circuit.

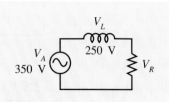

Figure 13-21. What is the resistor voltage?

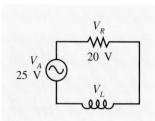

Figure 13-22. Determine the inductor voltage.

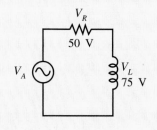

Figure 13-23. Find the total applied voltage in this circuit.

4. What is the voltage drop across the inductor in Figure 13-22?

5. What is the total (i.e., applied) voltage in Figure 13-23?

Answers to Practice Problems

1. 128.1 V   **2.** 244.9 V   **3.** 170 mV

4. 15 V   **5.** 90.14 V

IMPEDANCE PHASORS

The voltage drops across the components in a series circuit are directly proportional to their relative resistances and reactances. Therefore, the impedance phasor diagram is identical (except for labels) to the voltage phasor diagram. Additionally, we can compute impedance of the series RL circuit by adding (phasor addition) the individual resistance and reactance. This is reflected in Equation 13-4.

$$Z = \sqrt{R^2 + X_L^2} \qquad (13\text{-}4)$$

EXAMPLE SOLUTION

Draw the impedance phasor diagram and determine the total impedance for the circuit shown in Figure 13-24.

EXAMPLE SOLUTION

The phasor diagram is shown in Figure 13-25. We compute impedance with Equation 13-4 as follows:

$$Z = \sqrt{R^2 + X_L^2}$$
$$= \sqrt{(10 \text{ k}\Omega)^2 + (20 \text{ k}\Omega)^2}$$
$$= \sqrt{500 \times 10^6} \approx 22.36 \text{ k}\Omega$$

Since our result is larger than either individual phasor and less than their arithmetic sum, we have some assurance that our calculation is correct.

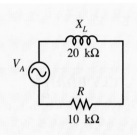

Figure 13-24. Draw the impedance phasor diagram for this circuit.

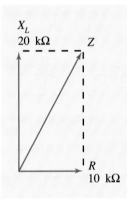

Figure 13-25. Phasor diagram for the circuit shown in Figure 13-24.

Practice Problems

1. Draw the impedance phasor diagram and compute total impedance for the series RL circuit shown in Figure 13-26.

2. What is the total impedance in a series RL circuit that has 82 kΩ of inductive reactance and 47 kΩ of resistance?

3. How much resistance must be connected in series with 10 kΩ of inductive reactance to produce a total impedance of 15 kΩ?

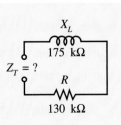

Figure 13-26. Find the impedance in this circuit.

Answers to Practice Problems

1.   **2.** 94.5 kΩ   **3.** 11.18 kΩ

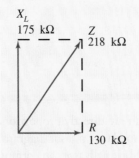

POWER PHASORS

We know from discussions in Chapter 12 that a purely inductive circuit dissipates no power. During one portion of the cycle, power is stored in the inductor's magnetic field. The power is returned to the circuit during the remaining portion of the cycle.

In a series *RL* circuit then, we must be concerned with two different types of power. The most obvious power is that dissipated by the resistance in the circuit. This can be computed with any one of the basic power formulas (e.g., $P = I^2R$) and is measured in watts. We refer to this as **real power** or **true power.**

The power that is taken from and subsequently returned to the circuit by the inductance is called **reactive power.** Reactive power is measured in volt-amperes-reactive (VAR).

Total power in a series *RL* circuit can be found by summing (phasor addition) the reactive and true power components. Total power in an *RL* circuit is called **apparent power.** Apparent power is measured in volt-amperes (VA). Figure 13-27 shows a power phasor diagram for a series *RL* circuit. Note the phasor positions.

We shall consider additional power relationships in a later section, but we can already express total or apparent power as the phasor sum of the true power and reactive power components. This phasor sum is given by Equation 13-5.

$$P_A = \sqrt{P_T{}^2 + P_R{}^2} \qquad (13\text{-}5)$$

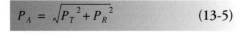
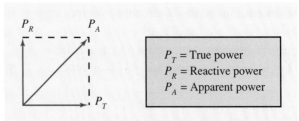

Figure 13-27. A power phasor diagram.

EXAMPLE SOLUTION

A series *RL* circuit has 10 VAR of reactive power and 10 W of true power. What is the value of apparent power in the circuit?

EXAMPLE SOLUTION

We apply Equation 13-5 as follows:

$$P_A = \sqrt{P_T{}^2 + P_R{}^2}$$
$$= \sqrt{(10 \text{ W})^2 + (10 \text{ VAR})^2}$$
$$= \sqrt{200} = 14.14 \text{ VA}$$

Note the phasor sum is larger than either individual phasor but is less than the arithmetic sum.

Practice Problems

1. What is the apparent power in a series *RL* circuit if the true power is 120 W and the reactive power is 95 VAR?

2. What is the apparent power in a series *RL* circuit that has a resistive power dissipation of 250 mW and a reactive power of 100 mVAR?

3. How much power is dissipated by the resistance in a series *RL* circuit if the apparent power is 20 VA and the reactive power is 15 VAR?

4. What is the reactive power in a series *RL* circuit if the apparent power is 9 mVA and the resistive power is 5 mW?

Answers to Practice Problems

1. 153.1 VA   2. 269.3 mVA   3. 13.23 W   4. 7.48 mVAR

Exercise Problems 13.1

1. What can be said about the relative current through the various components in a series *RL* circuit?

2. If the current through the resistance in a series *RL* circuit is 100 mA, how much current flows through the inductance?

3. If the total current in a series *RL* circuit is 2.75 A, how much current flows through the circuit inductance?

4. Refer to Problem 3. How much current flows through the circuit resistance?

5. The voltage drops in a series *RL* circuit must be summed using _____ _____ to compute the total circuit voltage.

6. The voltage across the resistance in a series *RL* circuit is (*in, out*) of phase with the current.

7. The voltage across the inductance in a series *RL* circuit is (*in, out*) of phase with the current.

8. The total current in a series *RL* circuit is out of phase with the applied voltage by an angle that is between zero and ninety degrees. (True or False)

9. If a certain series *RL* circuit has an 8.2-kΩ resistor and a 12-kΩ inductive reactance, what is the value of the circuit impedance?

10. How much resistance must be connected in series with a 250-Ω inductive reactance to produce a total circuit impedance of 400 Ω?

11. A circuit consists of a 10-kΩ, a 5-kΩ, and a 25-kΩ resistor connected in series with two 25-mH coils. Draw the simplified circuit.

12. Draw the simplified circuit for a series *RL* circuit that consists of three 150-kΩ resistors in series with four 100-μH inductors.

13. Draw a voltage phasor diagram to represent the circuit shown in Figure 13-28.

14. Refer to Figure 13-28. What is the value of applied voltage?

15. Draw an impedance phasor diagram to represent the circuit shown in Figure 13-29.

16. Compute the total circuit impedance for the circuit shown in Figure 13-29.

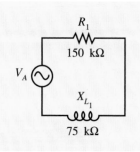

Figure 13-28. A series *RL* circuit.

17. If the voltage across the resistance in a series *RL* circuit is 18 V and the applied voltage is 25 V, what is the voltage drop across the inductance?

18. The unit of measure for apparent power is _____ .

19. The unit of measure for true power is _____ .

20. Apparent power in a series *RL* circuit can be found by summing the true power and the _____ power using phasor addition.

21. The unit of measure for admittance is _____ .

22. The unit of measure for susceptance is _____ .

23. What is the susceptance of a coil that has 25 kΩ of reactance?

24. What is the admittance of a circuit that has an impedance of 275 kΩ?

Figure 13-29.
A series *RL* circuit.

13.2 Parallel *RL* Circuits with Sinusoidal Currents

Now let us learn some of the basic characteristics and relationships found in a parallel *RL* circuit. Figure 13-30 shows two resistors that are in parallel with two inductors. Since all of the components are in parallel, we can classify this circuit as a parallel circuit.

Parallel *RL* Circuit Characteristics
VOLTAGE DROPS

Since every component in a parallel *RL* circuit is connected directly across the voltage source, we know that all components will have identical voltage drops. This is consistent with what we know about resistive parallel circuits.

KEY POINTS

Every component in a parallel *RL* circuit has exactly the same value of voltage.

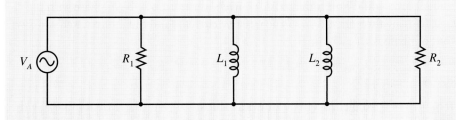

Figure 13-30. A basic parallel *RL* circuit.

PHASE RELATIONSHIPS

We can easily predict the phase relationships in a parallel *RL* circuit by applying what we already know. Consider these three facts:

- Voltage is the same across all components in the circuit.
- Current and voltage are in phase in a resistance.
- Current lags voltage by 90° in an inductance.

As shown in Figure 13-31, the voltage waveforms across all components will have the same phase. The current waveforms through the inductors will be 90° out of phase with the circuit voltage waveforms. Specifically, the inductor currents will lag the circuit voltage by

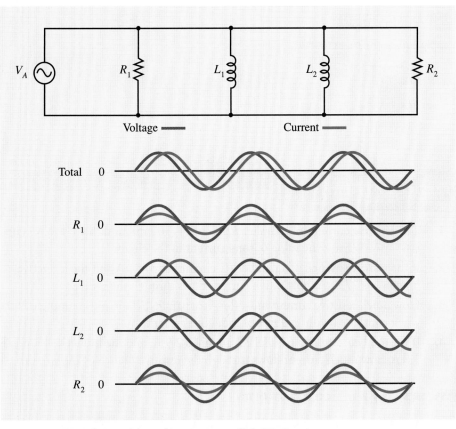

Figure 13-31. Phase relationships in a parallel *RL* circuit.

90°. Finally, we would expect the resistor current waveforms to be in phase with the circuit voltage. We can also conclude that the resistive currents and the inductive currents will be 90° out of phase with each other.

CURRENT

> **KEY POINTS**
>
> Each branch of a parallel *RL* circuit has a value of current determined by the applied voltage and by the amount of opposition (resistance or reactance) to current in that branch.

Each branch of a parallel *RL* circuit draws a value of current that is determined by the applied voltage and the resistance or reactance of the branch (Ohm's Law). The current in a given branch is unaffected by the value of currents in other branches.

As with a resistive parallel circuit, the individual branch currents in a parallel *RL* circuit are summed to find total current (Kirchhoff's Current Law). However, since the currents are 90° out of phase with each other, we must sum them using phasor addition. We know, then, that the total current will be greater than any individual branch current, but it will be less than the arithmetic sum of the branch currents. Equation 13-6 expresses this summation more formally.

> **KEY POINTS**
>
> Branch currents may be summed (Kirchhoff's Current Law) to find total current. However, since the inductive currents and the resistive currents are 90° out of phase, they must be summed using phasor addition.

$$I_T = \sqrt{I_R{}^2 + I_L{}^2} \qquad (13\text{-}6)$$

EXAMPLE SOLUTION

Compute the total current in a parallel *RL* circuit if the resistive branch has 3.5 A of current and the inductive branch has 5.25 A.

EXAMPLE **SOLUTION**

We apply Equation 13-6 as follows:

$$I_T = \sqrt{I_R{}^2 + I_L{}^2}$$
$$= \sqrt{(3.5 \text{ A})^2 + (5.25 \text{ A})^2}$$
$$\approx 6.31 \text{ A}$$

Practice Problems

1. The resistive current in a parallel *RL* circuit is 100 mA and the inductive current is 65 mA. What is the value of total current in the circuit?
2. If the resistive branch of a parallel *RL* circuit has 375 μA and the inductive branch has 275 μA, how much current flows through the source?
3. How much resistive current must flow in a parallel *RL* circuit to produce 200 mA when combined with 150 mA of inductive current?
4. If the total current in a parallel *RL* circuit is 2.9 A, and the inductive branch has 1.8 A, how much current flows through the resistive branch of the circuit?

Answers to Practice Problems

1. 119.3 mA   2.   465 μA   3.   132.3 mA   4.   2.27 A

IMPEDANCE

Since the current in a parallel *RL* circuit is greater than any individual branch current, it follows that total circuit impedance must be less than any individual branch resistance or reactance. This is consistent with what we learned about resistive parallel circuits. Computation of the value of circuit impedance is somewhat different, however, since the currents for the resistive and reactive branches are 90° out of phase. We will learn to compute impedance in a later paragraph.

SUSCEPTANCE AND ADMITTANCE

The characteristics of a parallel *RL* circuit have the same definitions as discussed for series circuits.

Circuit Simplification

The various resistances in a multiresistor parallel *RL* circuit can be combined as in a simple resistive parallel circuit. Similarly, the various branch inductances (assuming no magnetic linkage) can be combined as we did with a purely inductive parallel circuit. The result of these two simplifications produces an equivalent circuit having a single resistance and a single inductance in parallel with the voltage source.

EXAMPLE SOLUTION

Draw the equivalent circuit for the parallel *RL* circuit shown in Figure 13-32.

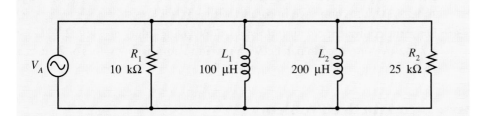

Figure 13-32. Simplify this circuit.

EXAMPLE **SOLUTION**

First, we combine the parallel resistors using any of the methods discussed for parallel resistive circuits. Let's select the product-over-the-sum method.

$$R_T = \frac{R_1 R_2}{R_1 + R_2}$$
$$= \frac{10\ k\Omega \times 25\ k\Omega}{10\ k\Omega + 25\ k\Omega}$$
$$\approx 7.14\ k\Omega$$

Similarly, we combine the parallel inductors as we did with purely inductive parallel circuits. For variety, let's select the reciprocal method.

$$L_T = \cfrac{1}{\cfrac{1}{L_1} + \cfrac{1}{L_2}}$$

$$= \cfrac{1}{\cfrac{1}{100\ \mu H} + \cfrac{1}{200\ \mu H}}$$

$$\approx 66.7\ \mu H$$

These results are summarized in Figure 13-33.

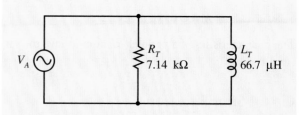

Figure 13-33. An equivalent circuit for the original circuit shown in Figure 13-32.

Practice Problems

1. Draw the equivalent circuit if three resistors having values of 10 kΩ, 22 kΩ, and 27 kΩ are connected in parallel with a 50-mH inductor.

2. Draw the equivalent circuit if three inductors having values of 275 μH, 100 μH, and 330 μH are connected in parallel with a 3.9-kΩ resistor.

3. Draw the equivalent circuit if three resistors having values of 5 kΩ, 2.7 kΩ, and 4.7 kΩ are connected in parallel with two inductors having values of 25 mH and 75 mH.

Answers to Practice Problems

1. **2.** **3.**

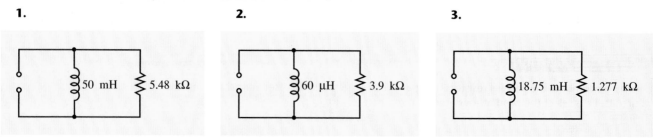

Phasor Representation

There are two types of phasor diagrams that are particularly useful when analyzing parallel *RL* circuits: current phasors and power phasors.

CURRENT PHASORS

The current phasor diagram for a parallel *RL* circuit will seem sensible, if we consider the following facts that we already know:

- The branch currents in a parallel circuit must be summed to find the total current (Kirchhoff's Current Law).
- The resistive branch currents and the inductive branch currents are 90° out of phase.
- Voltage is the same for all components in a parallel circuit.

We will always use voltage as the reference phasor when working with parallel circuits, because voltage is common to all components. Refer to Figure 13-34 as we determine the positions of the remaining phasors.

We know that current and voltage are always in phase in a resistive circuit. Therefore, the phasor representing resistive current will be drawn in the same relative position as voltage on our phasor diagram. Inductive current, by contrast, is 90° out of phase with the voltage. In particular, the current lags the voltage by 90°. Our phasor diagram must show this relationship, so we sketch the inductive current phasor 90° behind (clockwise) the voltage or reference phasor.

Finally, as shown in Figure 13-34, we can complete the parallelogram and sketch the diagonal, which represents the phasor sum of the two current phasors. Since the current phasors represent branch currents, the phasor sum will represent the total current in the circuit (Kirchhoff's Current Law).

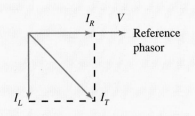

Figure 13-34. Current phasor diagrams for parallel circuits use voltage as the reference phasor.

Draw a current phasor diagram to represent the parallel *RL* circuit shown in Figure 13-35.

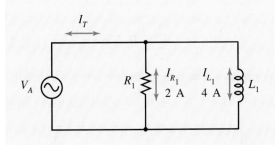

Figure 13-35. Draw a current phasor diagram for this circuit.

EXAMPLE SOLUTION

First, we draw our reference phasor representing circuit voltage. Next, we sketch the resistive current phasor (2 A) in the same relative position as the reference phasor, since current and

> **KEY POINTS**
>
> Current phasors are drawn using voltage as the reference phasor. The phasor representing resistive current is aligned with the voltage or reference phasor. The phasor representing inductive current is drawn 90° behind (clock-wise) the voltage or reference phasor. Completion of the phasor parallelogram for the inductive and resistive current phasors produces a phasor (diagonal of the parallelogram) that represents total current.

voltage are in phase through a resistive circuit. Next, we sketch the inductive current phasor (4 A), such that it lags 90° behind the reference phasor, because current lags voltage by 90° in an inductive circuit. Finally, we complete the parallelogram, as shown in Figure 13-36, and compute the value of I_T using Equation 13-6.

$$I_T = \sqrt{I_R^2 + I_L^2}$$
$$= \sqrt{(2 \text{ A})^2 + (4 \text{ A})^2}$$
$$\approx 4.47 \text{ A}$$

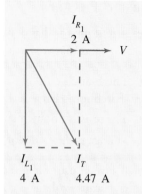

Figure 13-36. A current phasor diagram for the circuit shown in Figure 13-35.

Practice Problems

1. Draw a current phasor diagram for the circuit shown in Figure 13-37. Be sure to compute the value of total current.

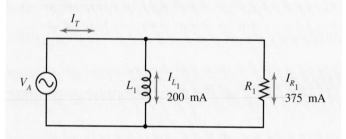

Figure 13-37. Draw a current phasor diagram for this circuit.

2. Draw a current phasor diagram for the circuit shown in Figure 13-38.

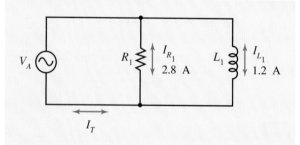

Figure 13-38. Draw a current phasor diagram for this circuit.

3. Simplify the circuit shown in Figure 13-39 by combining similar currents. Then draw the current phasor diagram and compute total current.

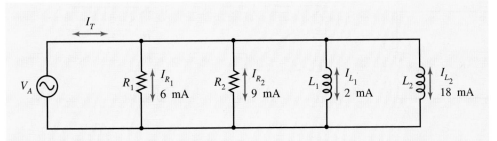

Figure 13-39. Simplify this circuit and draw a current phasor diagram.

Answers to Practice Problems

1.

2.

3.

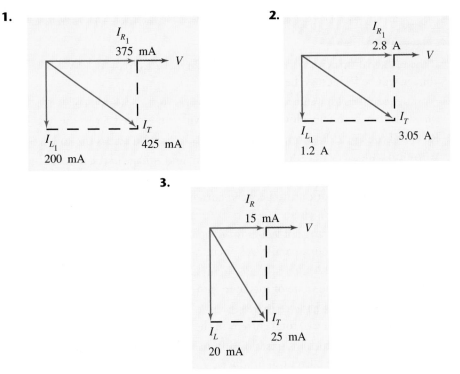

POWER PHASORS

You will recall from our previous study of resistive circuits, that power calculations are the same whether the circuit is series, parallel, or more complex. This same relationship holds true for *RL* circuits.

In a parallel *RL* circuit, then, we are interested in the values of true power, reactive power, and apparent power. The meaning and relationships of these powers were discussed with reference to series *RL* circuits and will not be repeated here.

The power phasors for a parallel *RL* circuit are drawn in the same relative positions as the current phasors. Figure 13-40 shows a representative power phasor diagram for a parallel *RL* circuit.

KEY POINTS

Power phasors can be used to represent the values of true power, reactive power, and apparent power in a parallel *RL* circuit. The definitions and relationships of these powers is similar to those discussed for series *RL* circuits.

KEY POINTS

Power phasors for parallel *RL* circuits are drawn in the same relative positions as the current phasors.

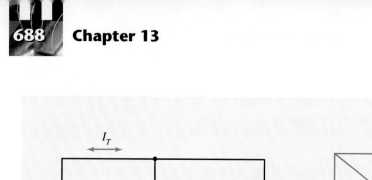

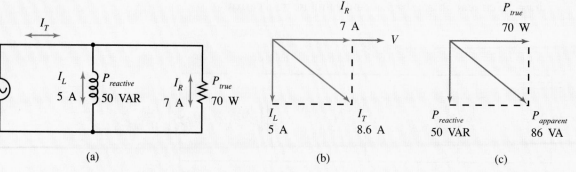

Figure 13-40. A parallel *RL* circuit with corresponding current and power phasor diagrams.

Exercise Problems 13.2

1. If the voltage drop across the resistance in a parallel *RL* circuit is 10 V, how much voltage will be felt across the inductance?

2. A certain parallel *RL* circuit consists of a 100-Ω resistor, a 350-mH coil, and a 25-V sinusoidal power source. How much voltage will be measured across the resistor?

3. Refer to Problem 2. How much voltage will be measured across the coil?

4. What is the phase relationship between current and voltage in the resistive branch of a parallel *RL* circuit?

5. What is the phase relationship between current and voltage in the inductive branch of a parallel *RL* circuit?

6. What is the possible range of values for the phase relationship between total current and total voltage in a parallel *RL* circuit?

7. If the resistive current in a parallel *RL* circuit is 120 mA and the inductive current is 225 mA, what is the value of total current in the circuit?

8. If a parallel *RL* circuit has a resistive current of 3.7 A and an inductive current of 1.8 A, what is the value of total current in the circuit?

9. How much resistive current must flow in a parallel *RL* circuit in order to combine with 3 A of inductive current to produce 5 A of total current?

10. The total current in a parallel *RL* circuit is 390 mA. The resistive branch current is 175 mA. Calculate the value of inductive branch current.

11. The total impedance in a parallel *RL* circuit is (*smaller, larger*) than any individual branch resistance or reactance.

12. Simplify the circuit shown in Figure 13-41.

13. Combine similar values in Figure 13-42 to simplify the circuit.

14. What quantity is used as the reference phasor for a current phasor diagram representing a parallel *RL* circuit?

15. The total current in a parallel *RL* circuit can be computed by simple arithmetic addition of the individual branch currents. (True or False)

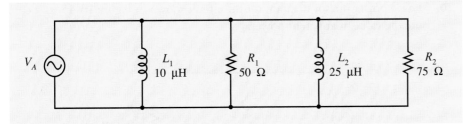

Figure 13-41. Simplify this circuit.

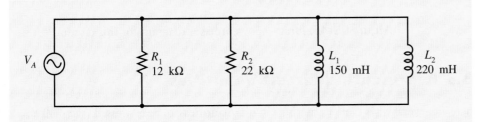

Figure 13-42. Simplify this circuit.

16. Kirchhoff's Current Law applies to parallel RL circuits, but the currents must be combined using _____ _____ .

17. Draw a current phasor diagram for the circuit shown in Figure 13-43.

18. Calculate the value of total current in Figure 13-43.

19. Draw a current phasor diagram for the circuit shown in Figure 13-44.

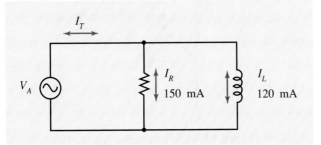

Figure 13-43. Draw a current phasor diagram for this circuit.

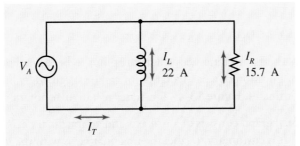

Figure 13-44. Draw a current phasor diagram for this circuit.

20. Draw a power phasor diagram for the circuit shown in Figure 13-45, and compute the value of apparent power.

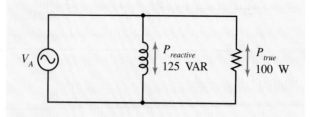

Figure 13-45. Draw a power phasor diagram for this circuit.

13.3 Representing Circuit Quantities

There are several ways that alternating circuit quantities can be expressed. We shall employ two common methods that are used by technicians: polar and rectangular notation. Further, we will concentrate on developing a knowledge of these notations that can be directly applied to the solution of circuit analysis problems.

Regardless of the notation used, we must have a way to represent the value of a phasor. Figure 13-46 illustrates the general requirement of a notation system.

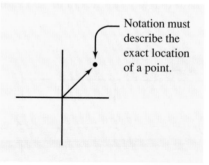

Figure 13-46. The requirements of a notation system for representing phasors.

Rectangular Notation

The rectangular method of notation considers the point to be located on a two-dimensional graph. Location of a particular point can be specified by listing the two corresponding coordinates. Figure 13-47 illustrates rectangular notation.

The two-dimensional graph consists of a real axis and an imaginary axis (sometimes called the reactance axis). It is customary to label the imaginary axis with the letter j. Mathematicians label the imaginary axis with the letter i, but technicians prefer to use j to avoid

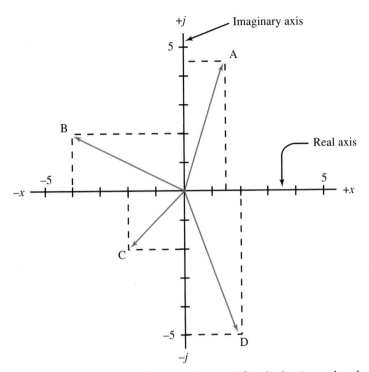

Figure 13-47. Rectangular notation specifies the horizontal and vertical coordinates of a given point.

confusion with the letter i, which is used to represent current. In either case, each axis has a positive and negative region. The horizontal scale is positive on the right half, and the vertical scale is positive on the upper half. A point is identified by specifying the coordinates of the point. We always list the horizontal coordinate first, and we preface the vertical coordinate with a lowercase j. The letter j is often called the j-operator and implies a 90° phase relationship.

EXAMPLE SOLUTION

Write the rectangular notation to describe each of the points shown in Figure 13-47.

EXAMPLE SOLUTION

Point A in Figure 13-47 can be described by the horizontal coordinate of 1.5 and the vertical coordinate of 4.5. We write this as 1.5 + j4.5. Similarly, point B can be described as –4 + j2, since it is 4 units to the left and 2 units up. Point C is 2 units to the left (negative) and 2 units down (negative), so we describe it as –2 – j2. Finally, point D is 2 units to the right (positive) and 5 units down (negative). We describe it as 2 – j5.

It is important to note that rectangular notation is used to represent a point on a graph. For our purposes, this point corresponds to the tip of a phasor. The phasor may represent current, voltage, impedance, or power. Thus, we might have a voltage (V_1) expressed as $V_1 = +25 + j42$ V, or perhaps a current (I_3) written as $I_3 = -6 + j2.5$ A.

Practice Problems

1. Write the rectangular notation for each of the current phasors shown in Figure 13-48.

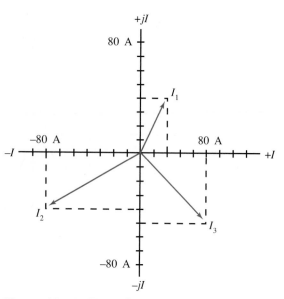

Figure 13-48. Write the rectangular notation to describe each of these phasors.

2. Write the rectangular notation to describe each of the voltage phasors shown in Figure 13-49.

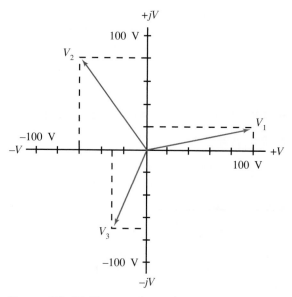

Figure 13-49. Express these phasors using rectangular notation.

3. Express each of the power phasors shown in Figure 13-50 in their rectangular form.

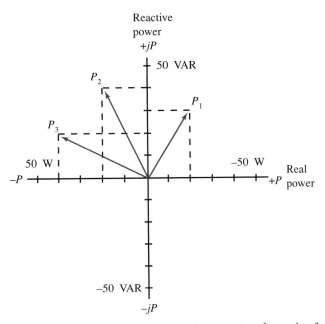

Figure 13-50. Write the rectangular notation for each of these phasors.

Answers to Practice Problems

1. $I_1 = 20 + j40$ A

$I_2 = -70 - j40$ A

$I_3 = 50 - j50$ A

2. $V_1 = 100 + j20$ V

$V_2 = -60 + j80$ V

$V_3 = -30 - j70$ V

3. $P_1 = 20 + j30$ VA

$P_2 = -20 + j40$ VA

$P_3 = -40 + j20$ VA

Polar Notation

Figure 13-51 shows an alternate method of describing the location of points (or phasors). A point described in the polar coordinate system consists of two parts: the magnitude (length of the phasor) and the angle (relative to the rightmost horizontal axis). Thus, for example, a voltage phasor that is 25 units (volts) in length and is positioned at an angle of 45° is described as 25 V $\angle 45°$. The length of the phasor is always represented with a positive number, regardless of its position. The angle may be expressed in either degrees or radians.

EXAMPLE SOLUTION

Write the polar notation for each of the phasors shown in Figure 13-52.

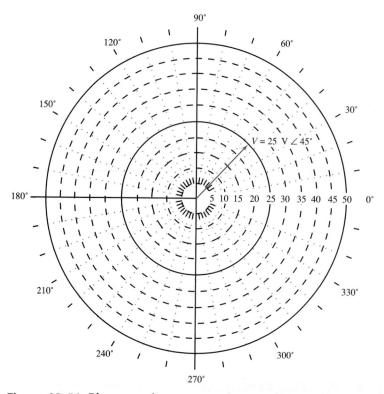

Figure 13-51. Phasor can be represented on a polar coordinate system.

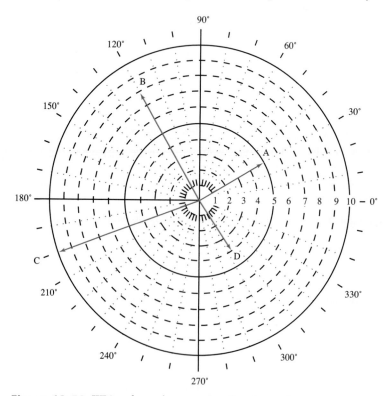

Figure 13-52. Write the polar notation for these phasors.

[EXAMPLE] [SOLUTION]

Phasor A is 5 units long. Its angle is 30°. We can describe the phasor as A = 5 ∠30°. Phasor B is 8 units long and is positioned at 120°. We write it as B = 8 ∠120°. Similarly, phasors C and D can be described as 10 ∠200° and 4 ∠305°.

As with rectangular notation, the units are determined by the quantity being represented. Thus, for example, we may have a voltage that is described as 125 V ∠45° or perhaps a current written as 6.5 mA ∠175°.

Practice Problems

1. Write the polar notation for each of the current phasors shown in Figure 13-53.

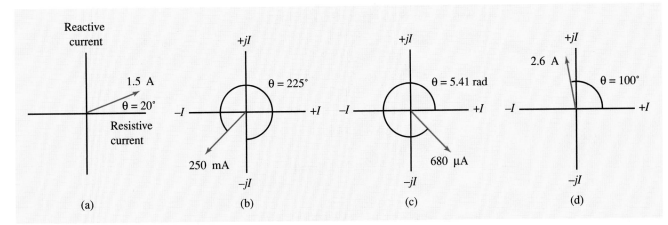

Figure 13-53. Write the polar notation for these current phasors.

2. Write the polar notation for the impedance phasors shown in Figure 13-54.

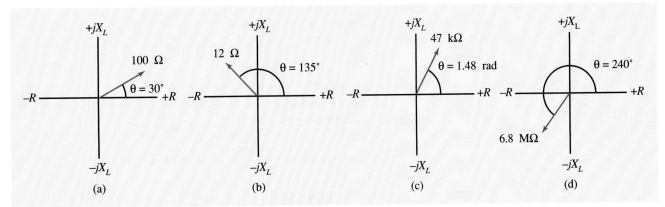

Figure 13-54. Express these impedance phasors in polar form.

3. Write the polar notation for each of the power phasors shown in Figure 13-55.

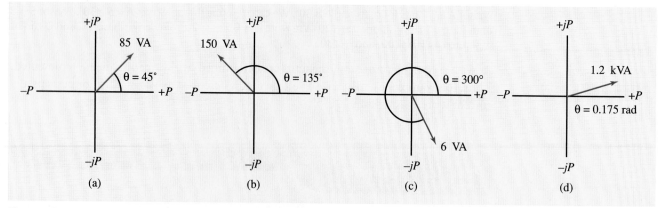

Figure 13-55. Express these power phasors in polar form.

Answers to Practice Problems

1. **a.** 1.5 A ∠20°
    b. 250 mA ∠225°
    c. 680 μA ∠5.41 rad
    d. 2.6 A ∠100°

2. **a.** 100 Ω ∠30°
    b. 12 Ω ∠135°
    c. 47 kΩ ∠1.48 rad
    d. 6.8 MΩ ∠240°

3. **a.** 85 VA ∠45°
    b. 150 VA ∠135°
    c. 6 VA ∠300°
    d. 1.2 kVA ∠0.175 rad

Polar-to-Rectangular Conversions

Certain calculations (e.g., multiplication and division) are more easily accomplished with phasors expressed in polar form. Other calculations (e.g., addition and subtraction) are easier when the phasors are expressed in rectangular form. If you have an engineering calculator, it makes little difference which form you use. But as a technician, you will want to be familiar with both, and you will need to convert between the two notations.

Conversion of polar notation to rectangular notation is just an application of the right-angle trigonometry we discussed in Chapter 11. Figure 13-56 shows how to make the conversion.

The phasor V_A is initially specified in polar form as 100 V ∠55°. This is the hypotenuse of our right triangle. The opposite and adjacent sides of the triangle (relative to angle θ) are V_L and V_R, respectively. We can solve for V_L as follows:

$$\sin\theta = \frac{\text{opposite}}{\text{hypotenuse}} = \frac{V_L}{V_A}$$

Transposing for V_L gives us Equation 13-7.

$$V_L = V_A \sin\theta \qquad (13\text{-}7)$$

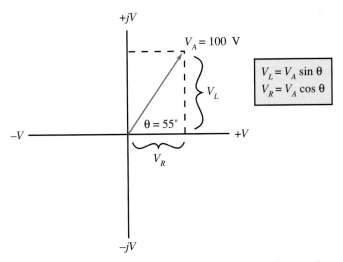

Figure 13-56. Conversion of this voltage phasor from polar to rectangular notation is an application of right-angle trigonometry.

In a similar manner, we can find an expression for V_R.

$$\cos\theta = \frac{\text{adjacent}}{\text{hypotenuse}} = \frac{V_R}{V_A}$$

Transposing for V_R gives us Equation 13-8.

$$V_R = V_A \cos\theta \qquad\qquad \textbf{(13-8)}$$

Substituting our known values into Equation 13-7 gives us the following results:

$$V_L = V_A \sin\theta$$
$$= 100\ \text{V} \times \sin 55°$$
$$= 100\ \text{V} \times 0.8192 = 81.92\ \text{V}$$

Similarly, we find V_R by applying Equation 13-8.

$$V_R = V_A \cos\theta$$
$$= 100\ \text{V} \times \cos 55°$$
$$= 100\ \text{V} \times 0.5736 = 57.36\ \text{V}$$

We can now express our phasor in rectangular form.

$$V_A = 100\ \text{V} \angle 55° = 57.36 + j81.92\ \text{V}$$

Conversion of impedance, power, or current phasors from polar form to rectangular form is approached in the same way. These conversions are summarized in Table 13-1 in the next section.

EXAMPLE SOLUTION

Convert the series impedance phasor 250 Ω ∠30° to an equivalent rectangular form.

EXAMPLE SOLUTION

Figure 13-57 shows a sketch of the given phasor. The known value of impedance is the hypotenuse of our right triangle. The opposite side is X_L and the adjacent side is the value of resistance.

The real or resistive part of our rectangular form will be computed as

$$\cos\theta = \frac{\text{adjacent}}{\text{hypotenuse}}$$

$$\cos\theta = \frac{R}{Z}$$

$$R = Z\cos\theta$$

The imaginary or reactive part of the rectangular form can be found as

$$\sin\theta = \frac{\text{opposite}}{\text{hypotenuse}}$$

$$\sin\theta = \frac{X_L}{Z}$$

$$X_L = Z\sin\theta$$

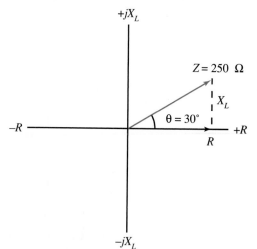

Figure 13-57. Express this phasor in rectangular notation.

Of course, we will preface this with the letter j to identify it as the reactive portion of the impedance phasor. We can combine these two parts into a single expression and obtain Equation 13-9.

$$Z\angle\theta = Z\cos\theta + jZ\sin\theta \qquad (13\text{-}9)$$

Substituting values into Equation 13-9 yields our complete rectangular notation for the given phasor.

$$
\begin{aligned}
Z\angle\theta &= Z\cos\theta + jZ\sin\theta \\
&= 250\ \Omega\cos 30° + j250\ \Omega\sin 30° \\
&= 250\ \Omega \times 0.866 + j250\ \Omega \times 0.5 \\
&= 216.5\ \Omega + j125\ \Omega
\end{aligned}
$$

Practice Problems

1. Convert the phasor shown in Figure 13-58 to rectangular notation.
2. Express the phasor shown in Figure 13-59 in rectangular notation.
3. The impedance phasor for a series circuit is $1{,}800\ \Omega\ \angle 50°$. Express the circuit impedance using rectangular notation.
4. If the total current phasor for a parallel circuit is described as $2.75\ \text{A}\ \angle 125°$, how will the current be expressed in rectangular notation?

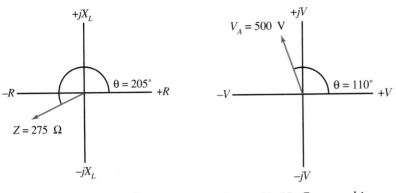

Figure 13-58. Express this phasor in rectangular form.

Figure 13-59. Convert this phasor to rectangular form.

Answers to Practice Problems

1. $Z = -249.2 - j116.2\ \Omega$ 2. $V_A = -171 + j469.8\ V$

3. $Z = 1.16\ k\Omega + j1.38\ k\Omega$ 4. $I_T = -1.58 + j2.25\ A$

Rectangular-to-Polar Conversions

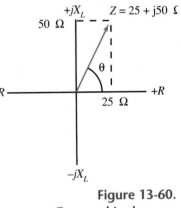

Figure 13-60. Convert this phasor to polar form.

Conversion of a phasor expressed in rectangular notation to an equivalent phasor expressed in polar notation is another application of basic right-triangle mathematics. Consider the phasor shown in Figure 13-60 and expressed as $Z = 25 + j50\ \Omega$.

We have already learned to compute the length of the phasor with Equation 13-4, or simply the Pythagorean theorem. In this case, we can compute the magnitude of Z as follows:

$$Z = \sqrt{R^2 + X_L{}^2}$$
$$= \sqrt{25^2 + 50^2} = 55.9\ \Omega$$

The opposite and adjacent sides of our right triangle are known. The opposite side is X_L (50 Ω), and the adjacent side is R (25 Ω). If we know any two sides of a right triangle, we can find the angle θ by applying one of the basic trigonometric equations presented in Chapter 11. In the present case, we will use the tangent function, since we know the opposite and adjacent sides of the triangle.

$$\tan\theta = \frac{\text{opposite}}{\text{adjacent}}$$
$$= \frac{X_L}{R} = \frac{50\ \Omega}{25\ \Omega} = 2;\text{ therefore}$$
$$\theta = \arctan 2 = 63.4°$$

So, we write $Z = 55.9\ \Omega\ \angle 63.4°$.

EXAMPLE SOLUTION

If the total voltage in a series *RL* circuit is expressed as $V_A = 10 + j7$ V, write this voltage using polar notation.

EXAMPLE **SOLUTION**

It is always a good idea to sketch the problem on a phasor diagram. Figure 13-61 shows a sketch of the given phasor.

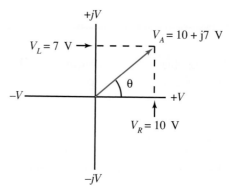

Figure 13-61. Express this voltage in polar notation.

We can use phasor addition (i.e., Equation 13-3) to determine the length of the polar phasor.

$$V_A = \sqrt{V_R^2 + V_L^2}$$
$$= \sqrt{10^2 + 7^2}$$
$$= \sqrt{149} = 12.21 \text{ V}$$

Again, we know the opposite and adjacent sides of a right triangle, so we will want to use the tangent function to find the angle θ.

$$\tan\theta = \frac{\text{opposite}}{\text{adjacent}}$$
$$= \frac{V_L}{V_R} = \frac{7 \text{ V}}{10 \text{ V}} = 0.7; \text{ therefore}$$
$$\theta = \arctan 0.7 \approx 35°$$

So, we write $V_A = 12.21$ V $\angle 35°$.

Practice Problems

1. If the total current in a parallel *RL* circuit is expressed as $I_T = 40 + j10$ mA, write this current using polar notation.

2. Express the impedance of a series circuit in polar notation, if the rectangular form is $Z = 2$ k $+ j3$ kΩ.

3. What is the polar form of the total voltage in a series circuit, if it is expressed in rectangular notation as $V_A = 5 + j2$ V.

Answers to Practice Problems

1. $I_T = 41.23$ mA $\angle 14.04°$ **2.** $Z = 3.6$ kΩ $\angle 56.3°$

3. $V_A = 5.39$ V $\angle 21.8°$

Although conversion from polar to rectangular notation and conversion from rectangular to polar notation is based on previously learned methods, Table 13-1 is provided as a way of summarizing the various conversions.

CIRCUIT TYPE	QUANTITY	POLAR TO RECTANGULAR	RECTANGULAR TO POLAR
Series	Voltage	$V_A \angle \theta = V_A \cos\theta + j\, V_A \sin\theta$	$V_A = \sqrt{V_R^{\,2} + V_L^{\,2}}$ $\theta = \arctan \dfrac{V_L}{V_R}$
Series	Impedance	$Z \angle \theta = Z\cos\theta + j\, Z\sin\theta$	$Z = \sqrt{R^2 + X_L^{\,2}}$ $\theta = \arctan \dfrac{X_L}{R}$
Series	Power	$P_A \angle \theta = P_A \cos\theta + j\, P_A \sin\theta$	$P_A = \sqrt{P_T^{\,2} + P_R^{\,2}}$ $\theta = \arctan \dfrac{P_R}{P_T}$
Parallel	Current	$I_T \angle \theta = I_T \cos\theta + j\, I_T \sin\theta$	$I_T = \sqrt{I_R^{\,2} + I_L^{\,2}}$ $\theta = \arctan \dfrac{I_L}{I_R}$
Parallel	Power	$P_A \angle \theta = P_A \cos\theta + j\, P_A \sin\theta$	$P_A = \sqrt{P_T^{\,2} + P_R^{\,2}}$ $\theta = \arctan \dfrac{P_R}{P_T}$

Table 13-1. Phasor Notation Conversion Chart

Calculator Sequences

Many engineering calculators provide direct conversions between polar and rectangular notation. Typical operation involves keying in the polar form and pressing a key labeled P→R to get the rectangular form. Similarly, the R→P key will convert a rectangular phasor into its polar equivalent. Other calculators use a key labeled POLAR to toggle between the polar and rectangular modes. The phasors may be entered using either type of notation, but they will be displayed in the selected mode.

If your calculator does not have the capability of direct phasor conversion, then you can use one of the pairs of sequences shown in Figures 13-62 and 13-63.

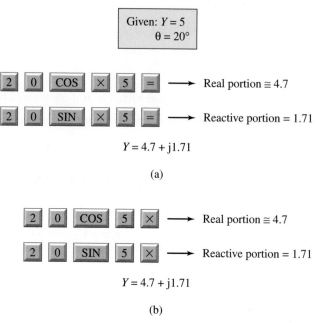

Figure 13-62. Calculator sequences for polar-to-rectangular conversion. Sequences are shown for (a) a standard engineering calculator and (b) an RPN engineering calculator.

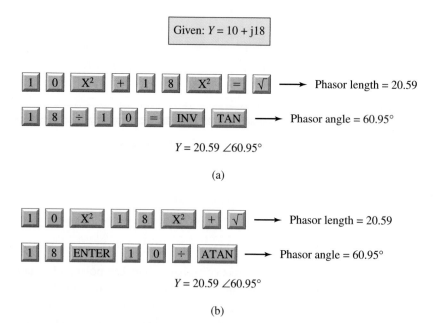

Figure 13-63. Calculator sequences for rectangular-to-polar conversion. Sequences are shown for (a) a standard engineering calculator and (b) an RPN engineering calculator.

13.4 *RL* Circuit Calculations

We are now in a position to completely analyze *RL* circuits. We shall consider series, parallel, series-parallel, and complex circuit configurations. In all cases, it will be assumed that there is no magnetic linkage between the various inductors. Most of our discussion will be simple application of previously learned rules, principles, and procedures. We should be able to compute any of the following circuit quantities in an *RL* circuit: voltage, current, power, phase relationships, impedance, or admittance. Additionally, we should be able to work with sinusoidal quantities expressed in any of the following ways: peak, peak to peak, or rms.

It is not practical to illustrate every possible combination of knowns and unknowns even for a simple *RL* circuit. Therefore, we will concentrate on developing a method of analysis that relies heavily on previously learned techniques. Thus, analysis of *RL* circuits should be viewed as a simple extension of prior knowledge rather than as a totally new subject.

Series *RL* Circuit Computations

We now have all the tools necessary to analyze a series *RL* circuit. We will formally identify some additional equations as we work through the examples, but it is important to remember that the equations are not really new. They are simply applications of previously studied principles. If you view them in this way, then you will be reinforcing previously learned material instead of trying to learn new material.

As with other circuit analysis problems we have done, there are many paths that lead to the correct solution of all quantities. The more experience you gain, the easier it will be to identify an optimum path. In all cases involving single equations, we must know all but one of the parameters in order to solve the equation. You will also remember that it is generally helpful to find currents early in the solution of series circuit problems and voltages early in the solution of parallel circuit problems, since these quantities are common to all components. Finally, if you are unable to compute a particular quantity, then calculate some other value. The more circuit values that become known, the easier it will be to find an equation that can be solved for a particular quantity.

> **● KEY POINTS**
>
> When analyzing series circuits, we try to find current early on. For parallel circuits, we generally strive to find the common voltage early in the problem.

EXAMPLE SOLUTION

Analyze the *RL* circuit shown in Figure 13-64, and complete the matrix shown in Table 13-2.

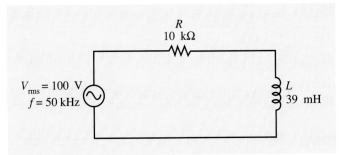

Figure 13-64. Analyze this *RL* circuit.

CIRCUIT QUANTITY		RESISTOR	INDUCTOR	TOTAL
Current (rms)				
Voltage	V_P			
	V_{PP}			
	V_{rms}			100 V
Resistance/Reactance/Impedance		10 kΩ		
Conductance/Susceptance/Admittance				
Power				
Phase Angle (overall)				
Power Factor (overall)				

Table 13-2. Solution Matrix for the Circuit in Figure 13-64

EXAMPLE SOLUTION

Let's compute the peak and the peak-to-peak values for the applied voltage as a first step.

$$V_P = 1.414V_{rms}$$
$$= 1.414 \times 100 \text{ V} = 141.4 \text{ V}$$

We can double this to get the peak-to-peak value.

$$V_{PP} = 2V_P$$
$$= 2 \times 141.4 \text{ V} = 282.8 \text{ V}$$

Since we know the value of inductance and the applied frequency, we can determine the value of inductive reactance.

$$X_L = 2\pi fL$$
$$= 6.28 \times 50 \text{ kHz} \times 39 \text{ mH} = 12.25 \text{ k}\Omega$$

We can now add (phasor addition) the resistance and reactance values to determine total impedance.

$$Z = \sqrt{R^2 + X_L^2}$$
$$= \sqrt{(10 \text{ k}\Omega)^2 + (12.25 \text{ k}\Omega)^2}$$
$$= \sqrt{250.1 \times 10^6} = 15.81 \text{ k}\Omega$$

We can find the conductance, susceptance, and admittance of the circuit by finding the reciprocals of resistance, reactance, and impedance, respectively. Let's begin with conductance.

$$G = \frac{1}{R} = \frac{1}{10 \text{ k}\Omega} = 100 \text{ μS}$$

We find susceptance in a similar manner.

$$B = \frac{1}{X_L} = \frac{1}{12.25 \text{ k}\Omega} = 81.63 \text{ } \mu\text{S}$$

The reciprocal of impedance will give us the value of admittance.

$$Y = \frac{1}{Z} = \frac{1}{15.81 \text{ k}\Omega} = 63.25 \text{ } \mu\text{S}$$

Now that we know total voltage and total impedance in a series circuit, we can apply Ohm's Law to determine the total current. We can express this formally as Equation 13-10.

$$I_T = \frac{V_T}{Z} \qquad\qquad (13\text{-}10)$$

As with any Ohm's Law problem, we may use voltage expressed in any form (i.e., peak, peak-to-peak, or rms), but the computed value of current will be in the same form. In this case, let us compute the rms value of current by using the rms value of applied voltage.

$$I_T = \frac{V_T}{Z} = \frac{100 \text{ V}}{15.81 \text{ k}\Omega} = 6.325 \text{ mA}$$

We can use Ohm's Law to determine the individual voltage drops across the resistance and reactance in the circuit. Let's use rms current, which will produce rms voltage as an answer.

$$V_R = I_R R = 6.325 \text{ mA} \times 10 \text{ k}\Omega = 63.25 \text{ V}$$

Equation 13-11 expresses a similar application of Ohm's Law to determine the voltage across the inductor.

$$V_L = I_T X_L \qquad\qquad (13\text{-}11)$$

For the circuit shown in Figure 13-64, we compute the rms value for V_L as follows:

$$V_L = I_T X_L = 6.325 \text{ mA} \times 12.25 \text{ k}\Omega = 77.48 \text{ V}$$

Determination of peak and peak-to-peak values for the resistive and inductive voltages requires straightforward application of the basic sine wave relationships.

$$V_{R_{(P)}} = 1.414 V_{R_{(rms)}} = 1.414 \times 63.25 \text{ V} = 89.44 \text{ V}$$
$$V_{R_{(PP)}} = 2 V_{R_{(P)}} = 2 \times 89.44 \text{ V} = 178.9 \text{ V}$$

Similarly,

$$V_{L_{(P)}} = 1.414 V_{L_{(rms)}} = 1.414 \times 77.48 \text{ V} = 109.6 \text{ V}$$
$$V_{L_{(PP)}} = 2 V_{L_{(P)}} = 2 \times 109.6 \text{ V} = 219.2 \text{ V}$$

Now let us calculate the power in the circuit. Although some applications (e.g., heat calculations in transistors and radiated power from antennas) require computation of peak and average power, we will concentrate on the more common expression of power that utilizes rms values. Recall that rms values of current and voltage produce the same power (heating effect) as an equivalent amount of dc. Let's first compute the power dissipated in the resistance (i.e., real or true power).

$$P_T = I_{R_{(rms)}} \times V_{R_{(rms)}} = 6.325 \text{ mA} \times 63.25 \text{ V} = 400.1 \text{ mW}$$

We can use a similar calculation to determine the reactive power for the circuit inductance.

$$P_R = I_{L_{(rms)}} V_{R_{(rms)}} = 6.325 \text{ mA} \times 77.48 \text{ V} = 490.1 \text{ mVAR}$$

Finally, we can find apparent power by applying the same procedure using total current and voltage values, or by summing (phasor addition) the values of true power and reactive power. Let's choose the addition method.

$$P_A = \sqrt{P_T{}^2 + P_R{}^2}$$

$$= \sqrt{(400.1 \text{ mW})^2 + (490.1 \text{ mVAR})^2}$$

$$= \sqrt{400.3 \times 10^{-3}} \approx 632.7 \text{ mVA}$$

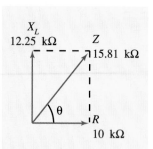

We can obtain the phase angle by using any one of the voltage, impedance, or power phasor diagrams. Figure 13-65 shows the impedance phasor diagram. We shall use it to compute the phase angle (θ).

$$\tan\theta = \frac{\text{opposite}}{\text{adjacent}} = \frac{X_L}{R}$$

$$= \frac{12.25 \text{ k}\Omega}{10 \text{ k}\Omega} = 1.225$$

$$\theta = \arctan 1.225 = 50.77°$$

Figure 13-65.
An impedance phasor diagram for the circuit shown in Figure 13-64.

The power factor of a circuit is another way to describe the phase relation between current and voltage in a circuit. It is simply the cosine of the phase angle as expressed in Equation 13-12.

$$\text{Power factor} = pf = \cos\theta \qquad \textbf{(13-12)}$$

We additionally describe the power factor to be leading or lagging. Current is always assumed to be the reference. In the case of *RL* circuits, the current will always lag the voltage, so we will always have a lagging power factor. In a later chapter, we will study capacitive circuits that have a leading power factor. For the present example, we find the power factor as follows:

$$pf = \cos\theta = \cos 50.77° = 0.632 \text{ (lagging)}$$

This completes our analysis of the circuit shown in Figure 13-64. The completed solution matrix is shown in Table 13-3.

CIRCUIT QUANTITY		RESISTOR	INDUCTOR	TOTAL
Current (rms)		6.325 mA	6.325 mA	6.325 mA
Voltage	V_P	89.44 V	109.6 V	141.4 V
	V_{PP}	178.9 V	219.2 V	282.8 V
	V_{rms}	63.25 V	77.48 V	100 V
Resistance/Reactance/Impedance		10 kΩ	12.25 kΩ	15.81 kΩ
Conductance/Susceptance/Admittance		100 µS	81.63 µS	63.25 µS
Power		400.1 mW	490.1 mVAR	632.7 mVA
Phase Angle (overall)		50.77°		
Power Factor (overall)		0.632 (lagging)		

Table 13-3. Completed Solution Matrix for the Circuit in Figure 13-64

It is possible to write and subsequently memorize literally hundreds of equations related to the solution of series *RL* circuit problems. This approach is not recommended. First, it is a difficult task. Second, it is very unlikely that you will be able to remember hundreds of equations for each type of circuit.

A more practical approach requires you to apply previously learned principles. In the case of *RL* circuit analysis, you can still rely on Ohm's Law, Kirchhoff's Laws, the general power equations, basic sine wave formulas, and the right-triangle relationships previously studied. The only "new" material involves recognition that summation of resistive and reactive quantities requires phasor addition. So in general, it is recommended that you utilize your prior knowledge as much as possible. Not only is this an easier approach to problem solving, but it strengthens your understanding of the fundamental principles that represent the heart of electronics.

Practice Problems

1. An *RL* circuit consists of an 18-kΩ resistor, a 4.0-mH inductor, and an ac voltage source that maintains 500 mV rms at a frequency of 1.2 MHz. Analyze the circuit and complete a solution matrix similar to Table 13-2.

2. A 25-V peak voltage source produces 150-MHz sine waves. It is connected in a series *RL* circuit consisting of a 100-μH coil and a 91-kΩ resistor. Analyze the circuit and complete a solution matrix similar to Table 13-2.

3. What is the value of peak current that flows in the circuit shown in Figure 13-66?

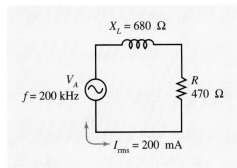

Figure 13-66. A series *RL* circuit.

4. What is the peak-to-peak voltage across the inductor in Figure 13-66?
5. What is the value of impedance for the circuit in Figure 13-66?
6. What is the value of inductance for the coil shown in Figure 13-66?
7. What is the reactive power in Figure 13-66?
8. How much true power is dissipated by the circuit in Figure 13-66?
9. What is the phase angle for the circuit shown in Figure 13-66?
10. What is the rms value of applied voltage (V_A) in Figure 13-66?

Answers to Practice Problems

1.

CIRCUIT QUANTITY		RESISTOR	INDUCTOR	TOTAL
Current (rms)		14.24 µA	14.24 µA	14.24 µA
Voltage	V_P	362.4 mV	606.9 mV	707 mV
	V_{PP}	724.8 mV	1.214 V	1.414 V
	V_{rms}	256.3 mV	429.2 mV	500 mV
Resistance/Reactance/Impedance		18 kΩ	30.14 kΩ	35.11 kΩ
Conductance/Susceptance/Admittance		55.56 µS	33.18 µS	28.48 µS
Power		3.65 µW	6.11 µVAR	7.12 µVA
Phase Angle (overall)		59.16°		
Power Factor (overall)		0.513 (lagging)		

2.

CIRCUIT QUANTITY		RESISTOR	INDUCTOR	TOTAL
Current (rms)		134.96 µA	134.96 µA	134.96 µA
Voltage	V_P	17.37 V	17.98 V	25 V
	V_{PP}	34.74 V	35.95 V	50 V
	V_{rms}	12.28 V	12.71 V	17.68 V
Resistance/Reactance/Impedance		91 kΩ	94.2 kΩ	131 kΩ
Conductance/Susceptance/Admittance		10.99 µS	10.62 µS	7.63 µS
Power		1.66 mW	1.72 mVAR	2.39 mVA
Phase Angle (overall)		45.99°		
Power Factor (overall)		0.695 (lagging)		

3. 282.8 mA   **4.** 384.6 V   **5.** 826.6 Ω

6. 541.4 µH   **7.** 27.2 VAR   **8.** 18.8 W

9. 55.35°   **10.** 165.3 V

Parallel *RL* Circuit Computations

We shall approach the analysis of parallel *RL* circuits as an application of previously learned techniques and concepts. We will highlight some "new" equations and state them formally for completeness. It is important, however, for you to understand that these added equations are simple extensions of basic circuit analysis methods that you already know. Concentrate on understanding how the various methods tie in with previously mastered material, rather than trying to memorize the equations.

EXAMPLE SOLUTION

Analyze the parallel *RL* circuit shown in Figure 13-67, and complete the solution matrix in Table 13-4.

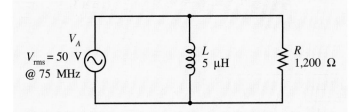

Figure 13-67. Analyze this parallel *RL* circuit.

CIRCUIT QUANTITY		RESISTOR	INDUCTOR	TOTAL
Current (rms)				
Voltage	V_P			
	V_{PP}			
	V_{rms}			50 V
Resistance/Reactance/Impedance		1200 Ω		
Conductance/Susceptance/Admittance				
Power				
Phase Angle (overall)				
Power Factor (overall)				

Table 13-4. Solution Matrix for the Circuit in Figure 13-67

EXAMPLE **SOLUTION**

The applied voltage (50 V rms) is common to all components. We can use the sine wave equations to determine the peak and peak-to-peak values.

$$V_P = 1.414V_{rms} = 1.414 \times 50 \text{ V} = 70.7 \text{ V}$$

$$V_{PP} = 2V_P = 2 \times 70.7 \text{ V} = 141.4 \text{ V}$$

Now let's compute the inductive reactance.

$$X_L = 2\pi fL = 6.28 \times 75 \text{ MHz} \times 5 \text{ μH} = 2.36 \text{ k}\Omega$$

We can apply Ohm's Law to determine the current flow through the two parallel branches.

$$I_R = \frac{V_R}{R} = \frac{50 \text{ V}}{1,200 \text{ }\Omega} = 41.67 \text{ mA, and}$$

$$I_L = \frac{V_L}{X_L} = \frac{50 \text{ V}}{2.36 \text{ k}\Omega} = 21.19 \text{ mA}$$

As with previously studied parallel circuits, we can add the branch currents to determine the total current (Kirchhoff's Current Law). Since our currents are 90° out of phase, we will sum the currents with phasor addition. This can be expressed formally as Equation 13-13.

$$I_T = \sqrt{I_R^2 + I_L^2} \qquad\qquad (13\text{-}13)$$

In the present case, we have

$$\begin{aligned} I_T &= \sqrt{I_R^2 + I_L^2} \\ &= \sqrt{(41.67 \text{ mA})^2 + (21.19 \text{ mA})^2} \\ &= \sqrt{2.185 \times 10^{-3}} = 46.75 \text{ mA} \end{aligned}$$

As with other parallel circuits, we can apply Ohm's Law to find the total opposition to current flow (impedance).

$$Z = \frac{V_A}{I_T} = \frac{50 \text{ V}}{46.75 \text{ mA}} = 1.07 \text{ k}\Omega$$

We can compute conductance, susceptance, and admittance by finding the reciprocals of resistance, reactance, and impedance. We compute conductance as

$$G = \frac{1}{R} = \frac{1}{1,200 \ \Omega} = 833.33 \ \mu\text{S}$$

Susceptance is the reciprocal of reactance.

$$B = \frac{1}{X_L} = \frac{1}{2.36 \text{ k}\Omega} = 423.7 \ \mu\text{S}$$

In a similar manner, admittance is the reciprocal of impedance.

$$Y = \frac{1}{Z} = \frac{1}{1.07 \text{ k}\Omega} = 934.58 \ \mu\text{S}$$

The true power dissipated in the resistor can be computed with any one of the basic power formulas.

$$P_T = \frac{V_R^2}{R} = \frac{(50 \text{ V})^2}{1,200 \ \Omega} = 2.08 \text{ W}$$

The reactive power is found in a similar manner.

$$P_R = I_L V_L = 21.19 \text{ mA} \times 50 \text{ V} = 1.06 \text{ VAR}$$

Finally, apparent power can be found as the phasor sum of true power and reactive power, or we can simply apply one of the power equations to the circuit using total values. Let's choose the latter method using total voltage and total current.

$$P_A = I_T V_A = 46.75 \text{ mA} \times 50 \text{ V} = 2.34 \text{ VA}$$

Figure 13-68 shows a phasor diagram for the circuit shown in Figure 13-67. With the help of this diagram, we can readily determine the phase angle and power factor.

Since we know all three sides of the right triangle shown in Figure 13-68, we can use any one of the sine, cosine, or tangent functions. Let's choose the cosine function, since the cosine will also provide the value of the power factor.

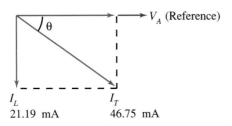

Figure 13-68. A phasor diagram for the circuit shown in Figure 13-67.

$$\cos\theta = \frac{\text{adjacent}}{\text{hypotenuse}} = \frac{I_R}{I_T}$$

$$= \frac{41.67 \text{ mA}}{46.75 \text{ mA}} = 0.891$$

$$\theta = \arccos 0.891 \approx 27°$$

This completes the analysis of the circuit shown in Figure 13-67. The completed solution matrix is shown in Table 13-5.

CIRCUIT QUANTITY		RESISTOR	INDUCTOR	TOTAL
Current (rms)		41.67 mA	21.19 mA	46.75 mA
Voltage	V_P	70.7 V	70.7 V	70.7 V
	V_{PP}	141.4 V	141.4 V	141.4 V
	V_{rms}	50 V	50 V	50 V
Resistance/Reactance/Impedance		1,200 Ω	2.36 kΩ	1.07 kΩ
Conductance/Susceptance/Admittance		833.33 µS	423.7 µS	934.58 µS
Power		2.08 W	1.06 VAR	2.34 VA
Phase Angle (overall)		27°		
Power Factor (overall)		0.891 (lagging)		

Table 13-5. Completed Solution Matrix for the Circuit in Figure 13-67

Practice Problems

1. What is the inductive reactance of the coil shown in Figure 13-69?
2. What is the rms voltage across the inductor in Figure 13-69?
3. How much peak voltage is across the inductor in Figure 13-69?

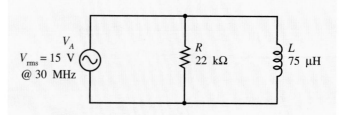

Figure 13-69. A parallel *RL* circuit.

4. The value of resistor voltage in Figure 13-69 is greater than the value of coil voltage. (True or False)
5. The resistor voltage in Figure 13-69 is in phase with the coil voltage. (True or False)
6. How much peak current flows through the resistor in Figure 13-69?
7. What is the rms current through the coil in Figure 13-69?
8. What is the total rms current for the circuit in Figure 13-69?
9. What is the impedance of the circuit shown in Figure 13-69?
10. What is the power factor of the circuit shown in Figure 13-69?
11. Calculate the apparent power for Figure 13-69.
12. Calculate the true power for Figure 13-69.
13. What is the value of reactive power in Figure 13-69?
14. What is the phase angle between voltage and current in Figure 13-69?
15. Calculate the peak value of total current for the circuit in Figure 13-69.
16. Compute the susceptance of the coil in Figure 13-69.
17. What is the admittance of the circuit shown in Figure 13-69?

Answers to Practice Problems

1. 14.13 kΩ	**2.** 15 V	**3.** 21.21 V
4. False	**5.** True	**6.** 964.1 μA
7. 1.06 mA	**8.** 1.26 mA	**9.** 11.89 kΩ
10. 0.541	**11.** 18.9 mVA	**12.** 10.23 mW
13. 15.92 mVAR	**14.** 57.29°	**15.** 1.78 mA
16. 70.77 μS	**17.** 84.1 μS	

Series-Parallel *RL* Circuits with Sinusoidal Currents

For the most part, analysis of series-parallel *RL* circuits consists of applying techniques and equations previously learned. Try to consider this section as an extension of what you already know. Do not think of it as an entirely new subject.

CIRCUIT SIMPLIFICATION

The first step toward analyzing a series-parallel *RL* circuit is to reduce the circuit complexity by combining all sets of series or parallel resistances and inductances. Sets of series resistances or inductances are combined into an equivalent resistance or inductance by adding the individual component values. Sets of parallel resistances or inductances are combined into an equivalent resistance or inductance by using your choice of a parallel resistor/inductor equation.

EXAMPLE SOLUTION

Simplify the *RL* circuit shown in Figure 13-70 by combining sets of series and parallel resistances and inductances.

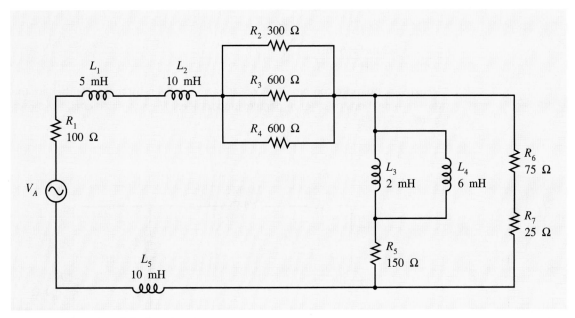

Figure 13-70. Simplify this circuit.

EXAMPLE **SOLUTION**

We can start by noting that resistors R_2, R_3, and R_4 are in parallel. We can combine them with the reciprocal formula for parallel resistors.

$$R_{2,3,4} = \cfrac{1}{\cfrac{1}{R_2} + \cfrac{1}{R_3} + \cfrac{1}{R_4}}$$

$$= \cfrac{1}{\cfrac{1}{300} + \cfrac{1}{600} + \cfrac{1}{600}} = 150 \ \Omega$$

This result is in series with R_1. We compute this equivalent as follows:

$$R_{1,2,3,4} = R_1 + R_{2,3,4}$$

$$= 100 \ \Omega + 150 \ \Omega = 250 \ \Omega$$

KEY POINTS

For series-parallel circuits, we combine sets of series and parallel components through a series of progressively simpler sketches, until we reach a fully simplified circuit that reflects the total impedance. We then work our way back through the intermediate sketches computing voltage and current values for each component.

In a similar manner, we can combine series resistors R_6 and R_7.

$$R_{6,7} = R_6 + R_7$$
$$= 75\ \Omega + 25\ \Omega = 100\ \Omega$$

There are no more series or parallel combinations of resistors, so let's combine the inductances. First, we note that L_1, L_2, and L_5 are in series. We combine them as follows:

$$L_{1,2,5} = L_1 + L_2 + L_5$$
$$= 5\ \text{mH} + 10\ \text{mH} + 10\ \text{mH} = 25\ \text{mH}$$

Inductors L_3 and L_4 are in parallel. We can use the reciprocal or the product-over-the-sum equation. Let's choose the latter.

$$L_{3,4} = \frac{L_3 L_4}{L_3 + L_4}$$
$$= \frac{2\ \text{mH} \times 6\ \text{mH}}{2\ \text{mH} + 6\ \text{mH}} = 1.5\ \text{mH}$$

There are no more combinations of series or parallel resistances. Neither are there any more combinations of series or parallel inductances. The simplified circuit is shown in Figure 13-71.

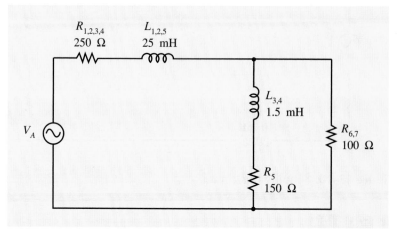

Figure 13-71. The simplified circuit for Figure 13-70.

Practice Problems

1. Simplify the series-parallel *RL* circuit shown in Figure 13-72.
2. Combine sets of series and parallel resistances and inductances in Figure 13-73 to produce a simplified circuit.
3. Simplify the *RL* circuit shown in Figure 13-74.

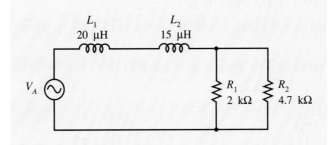

Figure 13-72. Simplify this series-parallel *RL* circuit.

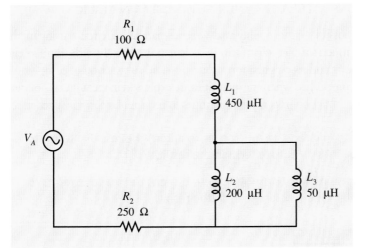

Figure 13-73. Simplify this *RL* circuit.

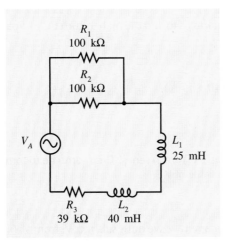

Figure 13-74. Simplify this series-parallel *RL* circuit.

Answers to Practice Problems

1. **2.** **3.**

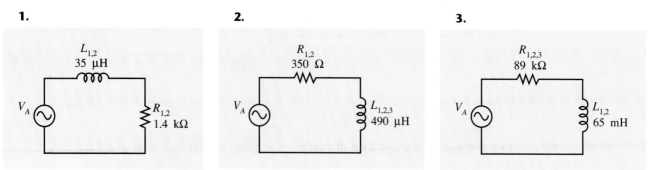

CALCULATIONS WITH POLAR AND RECTANGULAR NOTATION

Although it is possible to thoroughly analyze series-parallel *RL* circuits using methods previously discussed, it is much simpler to perform the calculations directly with complex circuit quantities expressed in polar and rectangular form. Addition and subtraction of complex quantities are most easily accomplished when the quantities are expressed in rectangular notation. The rule for addition and subtraction of complex quantities in rectangular form is stated as follows:

> Combine (add or subtract as required) the resistive terms to obtain the resistive term in the result.
>
> Combine (add or subtract as required) the reactive terms to obtain the reactive term in the result.

EXAMPLE SOLUTION

A parallel *RL* circuit has branch currents of $25 + j15$ A (I_1) and $10 + j5$ A (I_2). What is the total current?

EXAMPLE **SOLUTION**

Kirchhoff's Current Law requires us to add the branch currents in a parallel circuit to find the total current.

$$I_T = I_1 + I_2$$
$$= (25 + j15 \text{ A}) + (10 + j5 \text{ A})$$
$$= 35 + j20 \text{ A}$$

EXAMPLE SOLUTION

Two complex voltages (V_1 and V_2) are in series. They combine to form V_A. If V_A is $100 + j50$ V and V_1 is $20 + j10$ V, what is the value of V_2?

EXAMPLE **SOLUTION**

According to Kirchhoff's Voltage Law, we must subtract V_1 from V_A (i.e., $V_2 = V_A - V_1$).

$$V_2 = V_A - V_1$$
$$= (100 + j50 \text{ V}) - (20 + j10 \text{ V})$$
$$= 80 + j40 \text{ V}$$

Multiplication and division of complex circuit quantities is most easily accomplished if the values are expressed in polar notation. The rule for multiplication and division of quantities expressed in polar notation is as follows:

> Multiply or divide (as required) the two magnitudes to obtain the magnitude portion of the result, and
>
> Add the angles to obtain the angle in the result for multiplication, or
>
> Subtract the divisor (bottom number) angle from the dividend (top number) angle to obtain the angle in the result for division.

EXAMPLE SOLUTION

Use Ohm's Law to compute voltage if the current is 25 mA $\angle 40°$ and the impedance is 35 Ω $\angle 25°$.

EXAMPLE **SOLUTION**

We apply the multiplication rule for polar notation as follows:

$V = IZ$

$\quad = 25 \text{ mA} \angle 40° \times 35 \ \Omega \ \angle 25°$

$\quad = 0.875 \text{ V} \angle 65°$

EXAMPLE SOLUTION

Use Ohm's Law to compute current flow in a circuit, if the voltage is 50 V $\angle 75°$ and the impedance is 10 Ω $\angle 20°$.

EXAMPLE **SOLUTION**

$I = \dfrac{V}{Z}$

$\quad = \dfrac{50 \text{ V} \angle 75°}{10 \ \Omega \ \angle 20°} = 5 \text{ A} \angle 55°$

Practice Problems

1. Use Ohm's Law to find the voltage in a circuit, where the current is 5 mA $\angle 20°$ and the impedance is 2 kΩ $\angle 5°$.

2. Use Ohm's Law to calculate the impedance in a circuit, where the voltage is 75 V $\angle 80°$ and the current is 5 mA $\angle 10°$.

3. How much current flows in a circuit that has a voltage of 50 V $\angle 25°$ and an impedance of 10 Ω $\angle 20°$?

Answers to Practice Problems

1. 10 V $\angle 25°$ 2. 15 kΩ $\angle 70°$ 3. 5 A $\angle 5°$

SERIES-PARALLEL *RL* CIRCUIT COMPUTATIONS

We now have all the tools necessary to fully analyze a series-parallel *RL* circuit. Remember that there are many alternative routes to a solution. Just have confidence in Ohm's and Kirchhoff's Laws, and rely on your knowledge of series-parallel circuits to evolve a solution.

EXAMPLE SOLUTION

Analyze the series-parallel *RL* circuit shown in Figure 13-75, and complete the solution matrix shown in Table 13-6.

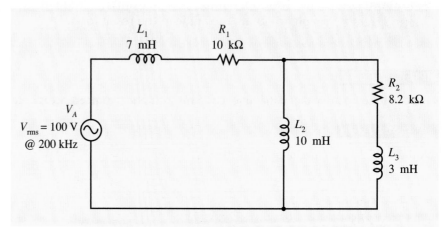

Figure 13-75. A series-parallel *RL* circuit.

CIRCUIT QUANTITY	R_1	R_2	L_1	L_2	L_3	TOTAL
Voltage (rms)						100 V
Current (rms)						
Resistance/Reactance/Impedance	10 kΩ	8.2 kΩ				
Conductance/Susceptance/Admittance						
Power						
Phase Angle (overall)						
Power Factor (overall)						

Table 13-6. A Solution Matrix for the Circuit in Figure 13-75

EXAMPLE **SOLUTION**

The first step is to simplify the circuit by combining sets of series and parallel resistors and inductors. In the case of Figure 13-75, no direct simplifications are possible. For our next step, let's compute the reactance of the three inductors.

$$X_{L_1} = 2\pi fL = 6.28 \times 200 \text{ kHz} \times 7 \text{ mH} = 8.79 \text{ k}\Omega$$

$$X_{L_2} = 2\pi fL = 6.28 \times 200 \text{ kHz} \times 10 \text{ mH} = 12.56 \text{ k}\Omega$$

$$X_{L_3} = 2\pi fL = 6.28 \times 200 \text{ kHz} \times 3 \text{ mH} = 3.77 \text{ k}\Omega$$

Now let's work toward finding the impedance of the circuit. We would take this same general approach if the circuit were a purely resistive circuit. We begin by finding the impedance presented by the parallel branches consisting of L_2 and the series combination of R_2 and L_3. Since there are only two branches, we can use the product-over-the-sum approach. We will use the references shown in Figure 13-76. We shall use polar notation when multiplication and division are required. In cases involving addition and subtraction, we will use rectangular notation. Impedances Z_B and Z_C can be written as

$$Z_B = 0 + j12.56 \text{ k}\Omega$$
$$Z_C = 8.2 \text{ k}\Omega + j3.77 \text{ k}\Omega$$

We can also express each of these in polar form.

$$Z_B = \sqrt{R^2 + X_{L_2}^2}$$
$$= \sqrt{0^2 + (12.56 \text{ k}\Omega)^2} = 12.56 \text{ k}\Omega$$
$$\theta_B = 90° \text{ (purely inductive); therefore}$$
$$Z_B = 12.56 \text{ k}\Omega \angle 90°$$

We find the polar form of Z_C in a similar manner.

$$Z_C = \sqrt{R_2^2 + X_{L_3}^2}$$
$$= \sqrt{(8.2 \text{ k}\Omega)^2 + (3.77 \text{ k}\Omega)^2} = 9.03 \text{ k}\Omega$$
$$\theta_C = \arctan\frac{X_{L_3}}{R_2} = \arctan\frac{3.77 \text{ k}\Omega}{8.2 \text{ k}\Omega}$$
$$= \arctan 0.46 = 24.7°; \text{ therefore}$$
$$Z_C = 9.03 \text{ k}\Omega \angle 24.7°$$

We can now combine Z_B and Z_C using the product-over-the-sum equation.

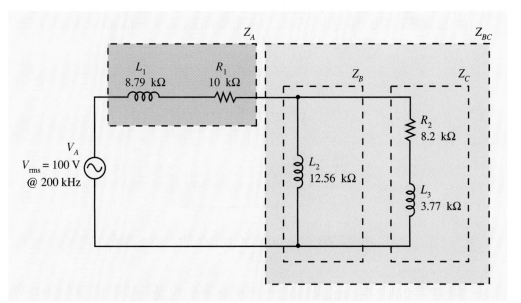

Figure 13-76. Network reference designation for the circuit shown in Figure 13-75.

$$Z_{BC} = \frac{Z_B Z_C}{Z_B + Z_C}$$

$$= \frac{(12.56 \text{ k}\Omega \angle 90°)(9.03 \text{ k}\Omega \angle 24.7°)}{(0 + j12.56 \text{ k}\Omega) + (8.2 \text{ k}\Omega + j3.77 \text{ k}\Omega)}$$

$$= \frac{(113.4 \times 10^6) \angle 114.7°}{8.2 \text{ k}\Omega + j16.33 \text{ k}\Omega}$$

$$= \frac{(113.4 \times 10^6) \angle 114.7°}{18.27 \text{ k}\Omega \angle 63.34°} = 6.21 \text{ k}\Omega \angle 51.36°$$

$$= 3.88 \text{ k}\Omega + j4.85 \text{ k}\Omega$$

Our progress to this point is shown in Figure 13-77.

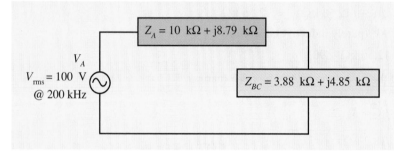

Figure 13-77. Result of combining Z_B and Z_C in Figure 13-76.

We now have a simple series circuit. To find total impedance, we simply add the two series impedances.

$$Z_T = Z_A + Z_{BC}$$

$$= (10 \text{ k}\Omega + j8.79 \text{ k}\Omega) + (3.88 \text{ k}\Omega + j4.85 \text{ k}\Omega)$$

$$= 13.88 \text{ k}\Omega + j13.64 \text{ k}\Omega = 19.46 \text{ k}\Omega \angle 44.5°$$

This calculation yields the total impedance and the phase angle of the circuit. Figure 13-78 shows the fully simplified circuit.

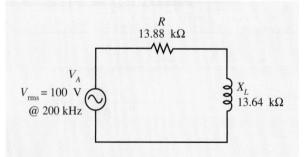

Figure 13-78. An equivalent circuit for the original circuit shown in Figure 13-75.

Just as we would do with a resistive circuit analysis, we now find the total current and work our way back through the partially simplified circuit sketches. We find total current by applying Ohm's Law.

$$I_T = \frac{V_A}{Z_T}$$

$$= \frac{100 \text{ V}}{19.46 \text{ k}\Omega \ \angle 44.5°}$$

$$= 5.14 \text{ mA} \ \angle{-44.5°}$$

By inspection of the original circuit, we can see that this same current flows through L_1 and R_1. We can use Ohm's Law to compute the voltage drop across these two components.

$$V_{L_1} = I_T X_{L_1}$$

$$= (5.14 \text{ mA} \ \angle{-44.5°}) \times (8.79 \text{ k}\Omega \ \angle 90°)$$

$$= 45.18 \text{ V} \ \angle 45.5°, \text{ and}$$

$$V_{R_1} = I_T R_1$$

$$= (5.14 \text{ mA} \ \angle{-44.5°}) \times (10 \text{ k}\Omega \ \angle 0°)$$

$$= 51.4 \text{ V} \ \angle{-44.5°}$$

The total current divides (Figure 13-76) through branch impedances Z_B and Z_C. We can determine the values of current in each branch with the current divider formula, or by applying Ohm's and Kirchhoff's Laws. Let's choose the latter approach. First, we find the voltage dropped across Z_{BC} with Ohm's Law.

$$V_{BC} = I_T Z_{BC}$$

$$= (5.14 \text{ mA} \ \angle{-44.5°}) \times (6.21 \text{ k}\Omega \ \angle 51.36°)$$

$$= 31.92 \text{ V} \ \angle 6.86°$$

This voltage will be felt across the parallel combination of L_2 and the R_2, L_3 network. We can find the current through either branch with Ohm's Law.

$$I_B = \frac{V_B}{Z_B}$$

$$= \frac{31.92 \text{ V} \ \angle 6.86°}{12.56 \text{ k}\Omega \ \angle 90°}$$

$$= 2.54 \text{ mA} \ \angle{-83.14°}$$

Applying Kirchhoff's Current Law will give us the value of current through the Z_C branch.

$$I_C = I_T - I_B$$

$$= (3.67 \text{ mA} - \text{j}3.6 \text{ mA}) - (303.4 \ \mu\text{A} - \text{j}2.52 \text{ mA})$$

$$= 3.36 \text{ mA} - \text{j}1.08 \text{ mA} = 3.53 \text{ mA} \ \angle{-17.82°}$$

We can see from Figure 13-76, that the I_C current flows through both R_2 and L_3. We can use Ohm's Law to find the voltage drops across these two components.

$$V_{R_2} = I_C R_2$$

$$= (3.53 \text{ mA} \ \angle{-17.82°}) \times (8.2 \text{ k}\Omega \ \angle 0°)$$

$$= 28.95 \text{ V} \ \angle{-17.82°}, \text{ and}$$

$$V_{L_3} = I_C X_{L_3}$$

$$= (3.53 \text{ mA} \ \angle{-17.82°}) \times (3.77 \text{ k}\Omega \ \angle 90°)$$

$$= 13.31 \ \angle 72.18°$$

This completes the voltage and current calculations for the circuit. We can complete the conductance/susceptance/admittance row in Table 13-6 by finding the reciprocal of the corresponding resistance, reactance, or impedance.

$$G_1 = \frac{1}{R_1} = \frac{1}{10 \text{ k}\Omega} = 100 \text{ }\mu\text{S}$$

$$G_2 = \frac{1}{R_2} = \frac{1}{8.2 \text{ k}\Omega} = 122 \text{ }\mu\text{S}$$

$$B_1 = \frac{1}{X_{L_1}} = \frac{1}{8.79 \text{ k}\Omega} = 113.8 \text{ }\mu\text{S}$$

$$B_2 = \frac{1}{X_{L_2}} = \frac{1}{12.56 \text{ k}\Omega} = 79.62 \text{ }\mu\text{S}$$

$$B_3 = \frac{1}{X_{L_3}} = \frac{1}{3.77 \text{ k}\Omega} = 265.3 \text{ }\mu\text{S}$$

$$Y_T = \frac{1}{Z_T} = \frac{1}{19.46 \text{ k}\Omega} = 51.39 \text{ }\mu\text{S}$$

We can find the various power values with any of the power formulas. Let's use the $P = VI$ form.

$$P_{R_1} = V_{R_1}I_T = 51.4 \text{ V} \times 5.14 \text{ mA} = 264.2 \text{ mW}$$

$$P_{R_2} = V_{R_2}I_C = 28.95 \text{ V} \times 3.53 \text{ mA} = 102.2 \text{ mW}$$

$$P_{L_1} = V_{L_1}I_T = 45.18 \text{ V} \times 5.14 \text{ mA} = 232.2 \text{ mVAR}$$

$$P_{L_2} = V_{L_2}I_B = 31.92 \text{ V} \times 2.54 \text{ mA} = 81.08 \text{ mVAR}$$

$$P_{L_3} = V_{L_3}I_C = 13.31 \text{ V} \times 3.53 \text{ mA} = 46.98 \text{ mVAR}$$

$$P_T = V_AI_T = 100 \text{ V} \times 5.14 \text{ mA} = 514 \text{ mVA}$$

Finally, we can compute the overall circuit power factor by finding the cosine of the overall phase angle.

$$\text{Power factor} = \cos\theta = \cos 44.5° = 0.713 \text{(lagging)}$$

This completes our analysis of the circuit shown in Figure 13-75. The completed solution matrix is shown in Table 13-7.

Although the calculations may seem rather extensive, it is important to note that they are all based on circuit analysis principles that you have already studied. Confidence will come through practice.

○ **KEY POINTS**

Series-parallel seems more complicated since it requires us to use polar or rectangular notation to keep track of the various phase angles in the circuit. The basic procedure, however, is consistent with the analysis of resistive series-parallel circuits.

CIRCUIT QUANTITY	R_1	R_2	L_1	L_2	L_3	TOTAL
Voltage (rms)	51.4 V	28.95 V	45.18 V	31.92 V	13.31 V	100 V
Current (rms)	5.14 mA	3.53 mA	5.14 mA	2.54 mA	3.53 mA	5.14 mA
Resistance/Reactance/ Impedance	10 kΩ	8.2 kΩ	8.79 kΩ	12.56 kΩ	3.77 kΩ	19.46 kΩ
Conductance/Susceptance/Admittance	100 μS	122 μS	113.8 μS	79.62 μS	265.3 μS	51.39 μS
Power	264.2 mW	102.2 mW	232.2 mVAR	81.08 mVAR	46.98 mVAR	514 mVA
Phase Angle (overall)	44.5°					
Power Factor (overall)	0.713 (lagging)					

Table 13-7. A Completed Solution Matrix for the Circuit in Figure 13-75

Practice Problems

1. Analyze the *RL* circuit shown in Figure 13-79 and complete the solution matrix shown in Table 13-8.

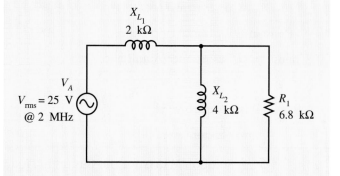

Figure 13-79. Analyze this *RL* circuit.

CIRCUIT QUANTITY	R_1	L_1	L_2	TOTAL
Voltage (rms)				25 V
Current (rms)				
Resistance/Reactance/Impedance	6.8 kΩ	2 kΩ	4 kΩ	
Conductance/Susceptance/Admittance				
Power				
Phase Angle (overall)				
Power Factor (overall)				

Table 13-8. A Solution Matrix for the Circuit in Figure 13-79

2. Analyze the *RL* circuit shown in Figure 13-80 and complete the solution matrix shown in Table 13-9.

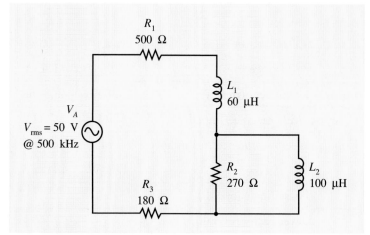

Figure 13-80. Analyze this *RL* circuit.

CIRCUIT QUANTITY	R_1	R_2	R_3	L_1	L_2	TOTAL
Voltage (rms)						50 V
Current (rms)						
Resistance/Reactance/Impedance	500 Ω	270 Ω	180 Ω			
Conductance/Susceptance/Admittance						
Power						
Phase Angle (overall)						
Power Factor (overall)						

Table 13-9. A Solution Matrix for the Circuit in Figure 13-80

Answers to Practice Problems

1.

CIRCUIT QUANTITY	R_1	L_1	L_2	TOTAL
Voltage (rms)	16.36 V	9.49 V	16.36 V	25 V
Current (rms)	2.4 mA	4.74 mA	4.1 mA	4.74 mA
Resistance/Reactance/Impedance	6.8 kΩ	2 kΩ	4 kΩ	5.27 kΩ
Conductance/Susceptance/Admittance	147.1 μS	500 μS	250 μS	189.8 μS
Power	39.3 mW	45 mVAR	67.1 mVAR	118.5 mVA
Phase Angle (overall)	70.63°			
Power Factor (overall)	0.332 (lagging)			

2.

CIRCUIT QUANTITY	R_1	R_2	R_3	L_1	L_2	TOTAL
Voltage (rms)	27.95 V	11.43 V	10.1 V	10.5 V	11.43 V	50 V
Current (rms)	55.9 mA	42.3 mA	55.9 mA	55.9 mA	36.4 mA	55.9 mA
Resistance/Reactance/Impedance	500 Ω	270 Ω	180 Ω	188.4 Ω	314 Ω	895.1 Ω
Conductance/Susceptance/Admittance	2 mS	3.7 mS	5.6 mS	5.3 mS	3.2 mS	1.1 mS
Power	1.56 W	484 mW	565 mW	587 mVAR	416 mVAR	2.79 VA
Phase Angle (overall)	21.1°					
Power Factor (overall)	0.933 (lagging)					

Complex *RL* Circuit Computations

Although it will not be formally presented here, it is important for you to realize that analysis of complex *RL* circuits can be accomplished using the same network theorems presented for analysis of resistive circuits. That is, Thevenin's Theorem, Norton's Theorem, tee-to-pi conversions, mesh analysis, and so on can be applied to the solution of complex *RL* circuits. The only significant difference is that all calculations must account for the presence of a nonzero phase angle. That is, your circuit quantities must be expressed in polar or rectangular notation.

⟶

◯ KEY POINTS

Even complex *RL* networks can be analyzed in a manner similar to complex resistive networks, provided the circuit quantities are expressed in polar or rectangular notation.

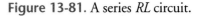

Exercise Problems 13.4

Refer to Figure 13-81 for Problems 1–10.

1. What is the reactance of L_1?
2. What is the impedance of the circuit?
3. What is the admittance of the circuit?
4. How much current flows through R_1?
5. What is the voltage drop across L_1?
6. What is the power dissipated by R_2?
7. What is the phase angle between total voltage and total current in the circuit?
8. What is the power factor of the circuit?
9. How much current flows through L_1?
10. What is the apparent power in the circuit?

Refer to Figure 13-82 for Problems 11–20.

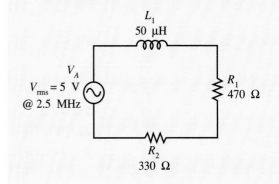

Figure 13-81. A series *RL* circuit.

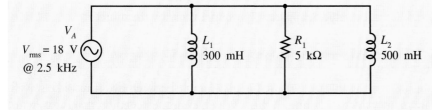

Figure 13-82. A parallel *RL* circuit.

11. What is the voltage across L_1?
12. What is the voltage across L_2?
13. How much current flows through R_1?
14. How much current flows through L_1?
15. What is the total current flow in the circuit?
16. What is the total impedance of the circuit?
17. What is the susceptance of L_2?

18. How much true power is dissipated in the circuit?
19. What is the power factor of the circuit?
20. What is the phase angle between total current and total voltage in the circuit?
Refer to Figure 13-83 for Problems 21–30.

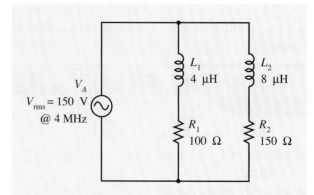

Figure 13-83. A series-parallel *RL* circuit.

21. What is the series branch impedance of L_1 and R_1?
22. What is the series branch impedance of L_2 and R_2?
23. What is the total impedance in the circuit?
24. How much total current flows in the circuit?
25. What is the total admittance in the circuit?
26. What is the voltage drop across R_1?
27. What is the voltage drop across L_2?
28. What is the phase angle between total voltage and total current in the circuit?
29. What is the overall power factor of the circuit?
30. What is the value of apparent power delivered by the source?

13.5 Phase Measurements with a Scope

A technician must be able to measure the phase angle between two sinusoidal waveforms. There are many ways to accomplish this. We will examine a method that is easily understood and produces excellent results.

Most oscilloscopes in use today have at least two independent vertical channels (many have more). Phase measurements with a dual-channel scope consist of the following steps:

1. Connect the two waveforms to be measured to the vertical input jacks of the oscilloscope.
2. Connect the ground jack of the scope—or, preferably, the ground clip on one of the probes—to the circuit common.
3. Adjust the vertical deflection (i.e., vertical gain) of each channel such that the waveforms fill the whole screen. The zero-reference of the sine waves should be in

the center of the screen. Note that the vertical channels do not have to remain calibrated for phase measurements.

4. Adjust the sweep rate and horizontal position controls until one half-cycle of the waveforms spans nine divisions on the scope's graticule.

Figure 13-84(a) shows a simple *RL* circuit. Figure 13-84(b) shows a scope screen after the preceding sequence has been accomplished. Since one half-cycle covers nine divisions, this means that each major division on the scope graticule represents 20°. Further, since each major division consists of five smaller divisions, each smaller graticule mark represents 20°/5 or 4°.

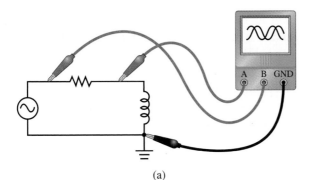

(a)

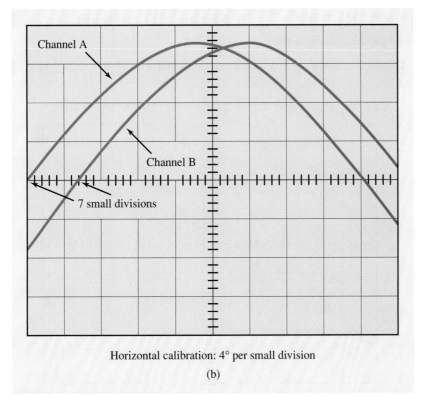

Horizontal calibration: 4° per small division

(b)

Figure 13-84. Phase measurements with a dual-channel oscilloscope.

KEY POINTS

The phase difference may be read directly from the screen by counting the number of divisions between the zero-crossing points of the two waveforms.

The phase difference between the two waveforms is determined by simply counting the number of small divisions between corresponding points on the two waveforms. It is most convenient and accurate to measure between two points on the center graticule line of the scope. For the case shown in Figure 13-84, the two waveforms are seven small divisions apart or

$$\text{Phase angle} = \theta = \text{number of divisions} \times \text{degrees per division}$$

$$= 7 \text{ divisions} \times \frac{4°}{\text{division}} = 28°$$

There are other combinations of vertical and horizontal settings that can be used similarly. For example, the horizontal controls can be adjusted so that one full cycle spans six major divisions. In this case, each major division represents 360°/6 or 60°. Each minor division now represents 60°/5 or 12°. In general, greater reading accuracy can be achieved when the waveform is expanded as much as possible. In the case of the horizontal axis, nine major divisions for one half-cycle works well for most oscilloscopes. The vertical channel may be set for any desired gain as long as the zero reference remains in the center of the screen. For optimum reading accuracy, the vertical gain should be as high as practical. Even if the waveform extends beyond the vertical limits of the screen, accurate measurements in the center of the screen can be made. The large vertical deflection makes it easier to identify the exact point of intersection on the zero-reference line.

Practice Problems

1. Determine the phase angle between the waveforms shown in Figure 13-85.

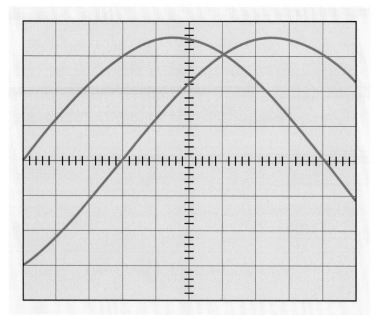

Figure 13-85. Determine the phase angle between the two sine waves.

2. What phase angle is being displayed in Figure 13-86?

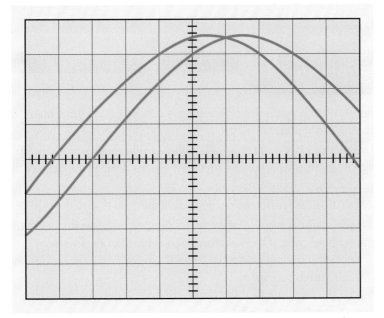

Figure 13-86. Measure the phase angle being displayed.

3. Measure the phase angle between the two waveforms in Figure 13-87.

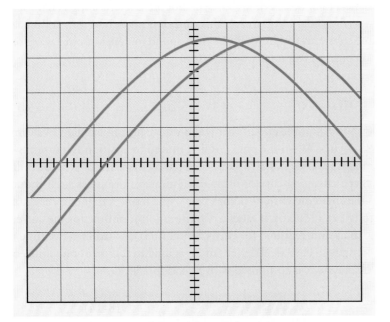

Figure 13-87. Determine the phase angle being displayed.

Answers to Practice Problems

1. 60°   **2.** 24°   **3.** 26°

1. If one half-cycle spans three divisions on a scope screen, how many degrees does each division represent?
2. If each major division of an oscilloscope is calibrated to represent 30° and each major division consists of five smaller divisions, how many degrees does each smaller division represent?
3. What is the phase difference being described?
   a. Each major division of the scope is divided into five smaller divisions.
   b. One half-cycle of the waveforms spans nine major divisions.
   c. The zero-crossing points of the two waveforms are two major plus two smaller divisions apart.
4. Explain why larger vertical deflections make it easier to obtain accurate interpretation of phase relationships.

13.6 Pulse Response of *RL* Circuits

KEY POINTS

Current cannot change abruptly in an inductor. If the voltage across an inductor is changed suddenly, then the current will also change, but more gradually.

We have thoroughly discussed the analysis of *RL* circuits that have sinusoidal inputs. Nonsinusoidal input voltages cause a radically different circuit response and require substantially different analytical methods. Although we will not present a thorough analysis of *RL* circuit response to nonsinusoidal waveforms at this time, it is important for a technician to understand *L/R* time constants and how *RL* circuits respond to nonsinusoidal waveforms. We will concentrate on pulse or rectangular waveforms.

L/R Time Constant

KEY POINTS

It takes five time constants (5τ) for the current to make its full change. During the first time constant, the current will make about 63% of its total change.

Figure 13-88 shows a simple circuit that will produce nonsinusoidal waveforms (pulses) for a series *RL* circuit. When the switch is first moved to position A, current will try to increase from zero to some nonzero value (limited by the value of *R*). You will recall from Chapter 12 that a changing current through an inductor produces a self-induced voltage that opposes the changing current (Lenz's Law). The result is that current cannot build up instantly through an inductor. It takes a definite amount of time for the current to increase. The total time required for current buildup is divided into five time periods called time constants. The Greek letter tau (τ) is used to represent one time constant. In the case of *RL* circuits, τ is computed with Equation 13-14.

$$\tau = \frac{L}{R} \tag{13-14}$$

where τ is measured in seconds, *L* in henrys, and *R* in ohms.

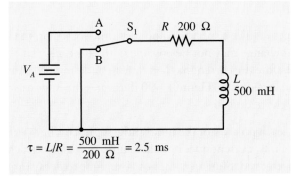

$$\tau = L/R = \frac{500 \text{ mH}}{200 \text{ }\Omega} = 2.5 \text{ ms}$$

Figure 13-88. An *RL* circuit with a pulse input.

Figure 13-89(a) shows how the current builds up through the series circuit. At *t* = 0 (the first instant), the self-induced voltage in the coil prevents any current flow. At time *t* = τ, the inductor current has risen to 63.2% of its final value. During each additional time period of τ seconds, the current builds to 63.2% of the remaining distance. For example, at the end of the first time interval (τ) the current has another 36.8% to go. During the time between τ and 2τ, it will increase 63.2% of this 36.8% or 23.3% for a total of 86.5% at time *t* = 2τ.

Once 5τ seconds have elapsed, the current will have climbed to more than 99% of its final value. In theory, it will continue increasing forever, but in practice, we consider it as having reached its final value in time period 5τ. The final value of current can be computed with Ohm's Law. It is determined by the value of dc input voltage and the value of the series resistance.

When the switch is returned to position B in Figure 13-88, the current will decay toward zero. But, again, the inductor will oppose the changing current. In this case, the voltage induced by the collapsing magnetic field of the inductor acts as an energy source to keep current flowing. As the field decays, so does the inductor current. Figure 13-89(b) shows that the decaying current also takes five time constants (τ) to reach its final value (zero).

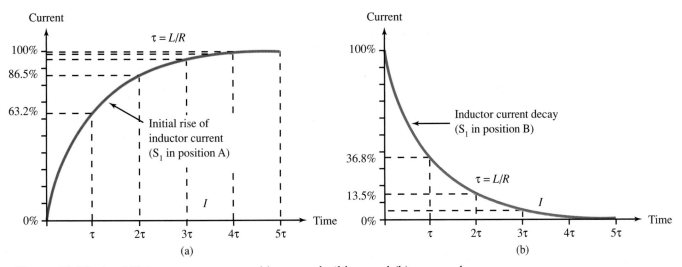

Figure 13-89. An *L/R* time constant curve: (a) current buildup, and (b) current decay.

Circuit Waveforms

Since current changes require a specific amount of time (based on the values of L and R), then a given current change may not be possible in the time allowed. That is, if the input voltage is removed before the current has had time to build to maximum, then it will begin decaying from some lower value. Figure 13-90 illustrates the response of an RL circuit to a pulse of three different frequencies.

In Figure 13-90(b), each polarity of the input pulse is present for a period of time equal to one time constant. Thus, current does not have sufficient time to reach maximum before the input voltage is removed. Similarly, it is not given time to decay to zero between pulses.

Figure 13-90(c) illustrates a short time constant. Here, the input pulse duration is present for an amount of time equal to ten time constants. Clearly, the current (and therefore resistor voltage) is allowed to reach maximum and to decay to zero. The inductor voltage appears as short-duration voltage spikes. Notice that the inductor waveform has a dual

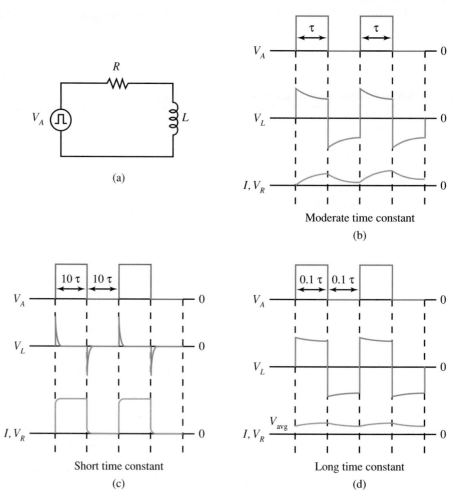

Figure 13-90. (a) An RL circuit and the effect of (b) moderate, (c) short, and (d) long time constants on RL circuit response.

polarity. The expanding and collapsing magnetic field causes opposite polarities of induced voltage in the inductor. The waveform across the inductor is called a differentiated waveform. The entire circuit is often called a **differentiator** circuit. To qualify as a differentiator, the circuit must have a short time constant and the output must be taken across the inductor.

Finally, Figure 13-90(d) illustrates the effects of a long time constant, where the input pulse duration is one-tenth of one time constant. Here, the current is barely allowed to increase or decrease. That is, the long time constant produces a nearly steady current flow. This effect is useful for filtering circuits in electronic power supplies. If the output is taken across the resistor, we call the circuit an **integrator** circuit. An integrator circuit requires a long time constant.

Magnitude of Self-Induced Voltage

We know from Chapter 12 that the magnitude of induced voltage in an inductor is determined by the rate of change of current. This can be expressed formally as Equation 13-15.

$$V_L = L\frac{di}{dt} = L\frac{\Delta i}{\Delta t} \qquad \text{(13-15)}$$

The di or Δi stands for change in current and dt or Δt stands for change in time. Inductance (L) is measured in henrys.

EXAMPLE SOLUTION

If the current through a 10-mH inductor changes steadily by 2 A over a period of 500 ms, what is the value of self-induced voltage?

EXAMPLE **SOLUTION**

We apply Equation 13-15 as follows:

$$V_L = L\frac{di}{dt}$$

$$= 10 \text{ mH}\left(\frac{2 \text{ A}}{500 \text{ ms}}\right) = 40 \text{ mV}$$

EXAMPLE SOLUTION

At a particular instant, the current through a 100-μH inductor is changing at the rate of 5 A/ms. What is the value of induced voltage?

EXAMPLE **SOLUTION**

$$V_L = L\frac{di}{dt}$$

$$= 100 \text{ μH}\left(\frac{5 \text{ A}}{1.0 \text{ ms}}\right) = 500 \text{ mV}$$

KEY POINTS

If the output is taken across the inductor in an RL circuit with a short time constant, the circuit is called a differentiator circuit.

KEY POINTS

If the RL circuit has a long time constant and the output is taken across the resistor, then the circuit is called an integrator circuit.

KEY POINTS

The value of induced voltage in an inductor is directly proportional to the inductance. It is also directly proportional to the rate of change of current.

1. What is the L/R time constant for a series circuit consisting of a 250-mH coil and a 1.5-kΩ resistor?

2. If the current through an inductor tries to change from 0 to 5 A, what will be the value of current after 1 time constant?

3. If the current through an inductor tries to decrease from 400 mA to 0, what will be the value of current after 2 time constants?

4. When current tries to change in a series RL circuit consisting of a 10-mH coil and a 10-kΩ resistor, how long does it take for the current to reach its final value?

5. If the current through a 175-μH inductor changes at the rate of 10 mA/ns, what is the value of induced voltage?

13.7 Applied Technology: *RL* Circuits

There are numerous applications for RL circuits. Most applications are an integral part of a more extensive circuit (e.g., a palm-top computer). Let's examine the basic operation of two common RL circuit applications: power supply filters and frequency selective circuits.

Power Supply Filter Circuits

KEY POINTS

Electronic power supplies can use *RL* circuits to smooth the pulsating output current so that it more closely approximates the steady dc from a battery.

Figure 13-91 illustrates the basic operation of a filter circuit for an electronic power supply. Most electronic circuits require dc voltage for operation, but it is often desirable to operate the system from the standard 120 Vac power line. An electronic power supply circuit is used to convert the 120-Vac, 60-Hz power distributed by the power company to a pulsating dc voltage. This pulsating or surging voltage can then be applied to an RL circuit as shown in Figure 13-91. Since the inductor opposes any changes in current, the current is held fairly constant. If the current through the inductor remains constant, then

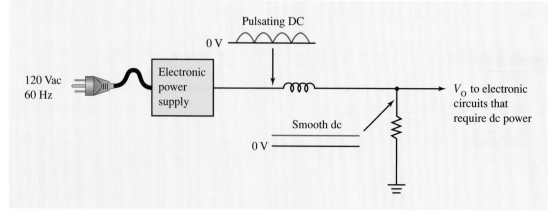

Figure 13-91. An RL circuit can smooth the output of an electronic power supply.

the voltage across the resistor and the voltage to the electronic circuitry will be held constant. The result is a smooth dc voltage similar to that which would be produced by a battery.

Frequency Selective Circuits

Electronic circuits often need to distinguish between waveforms that differ in frequency. Figure 13-92 shows how an *RL* circuit can accept a mixture of 1-kHz and 100-kHz sine waves at its input but produce separate outputs for the two differing frequencies.

Let's consider what happens to a 100-kHz waveform as it passes through the circuit. First, we see that the series combination of R_1, L_1 is in parallel with the series combination of R_2, L_2. Both *RL* circuits will receive the 100-kHz waveform. In the case of the R_1, L_1 branch, nearly all of the voltage will be dropped across L_1, since its reactance is ten times greater than the resistance of R_1. So, if we measure the voltage across L_1, we will get nearly 100% of the full amplitude of the 100-kHz voltage.

When the 100-kHz waveform is applied to the R_2, L_2 network, nearly all of the voltage is dropped across L_2 for reasons previously listed. However, in this case, the output signal is taken across R_2. Therefore, R_2 will have only a very small percentage of the original 100-kHz input voltage.

If we consider the circuit effects on the 1-kHz voltage input, we get an opposite result. The reactance of L_1 and L_2 is only one-tenth the value of R_1 and R_2 at a frequency of 1 kHz. This means that R_1 will drop nearly all of the voltage at 1 kHz, leaving very little to be measured across L_1. Similarly, L_2 drops only a very small percentage of the 1-kHz voltage, which means that most of it is developed across R_2. Thus, the 1-kHz input voltage appears at the lower output, but it is prevented from passing through to the upper output. This general principle is used for tone controls and crossover networks in audio equipment.

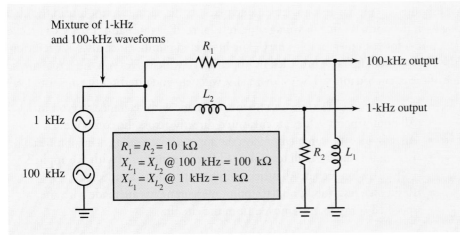

Figure 13-92. A frequency selective *RL* filter circuit.

Exercise Problems 13.7

1. In your own words, explain how a pulsating current can be smoothed with an *RL* circuit.

2. Refer to Figure 13-92. If a 100-Hz sine wave were applied to the circuit, describe the circuit behavior.

3. Describe the response of the circuit in Figure 13-92, if a 2-MHz sine wave were connected to the input.

13.8 Troubleshooting *RL* Circuits

It is generally not difficult to troubleshoot *RL* circuits. They are essentially combinations of the purely resistive and purely inductive circuits previously studied. The following represent the most probable defects in an *RL* circuit:

- open coil
- open resistor
- coil winding-to-core short
- shorted turns on the coil
- shorted resistor (usually solder bridge on a printed circuit board)
- resistor value out of tolerance

All of these defects for series, parallel, or more complex *RL* networks can be located using the same troubleshooting logic presented for purely resistive circuits coupled with the coil verification checks presented in Chapter 12.

Exercise Problems 13.8

Following are several troubleshooting problems using the Pshooter method. Recall that each Pshooter circuit has an associated table that lists the various testpoints in the circuit along with the normal value of voltage and resistance. The table also provides a bracketed ([ ]) number for each measurable entry. The bracketed number identifies a specific entry in the Pshooter lookup table provided in Appendix A, which gives you the actual measured value of the circuit quantity. The following list will help you interpret the measured values:

- All testpoint (TPxx) measurements are made with reference to ground.
- All nontestpoint values are measured directly across the component.
- All resistance measurements reflect the approximate reading of an ohmmeter.
- Resistance values for all testpoints (TPxx) are measured with the applied voltage disconnected. All other components remain connected.
- Resistance tests for all non-testpoint measurements are made with the specified component removed from the circuit.

1. Refer to Figure 13-93 and the Pshooter chart shown in Table 13-10. Locate the defective component in as few measurements as possible by applying a logical, systematic troubleshooting method.

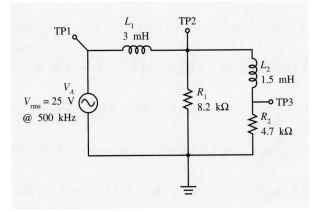

Figure 13-93. Troubleshoot this circuit

TEST-POINT	VOLTAGE (rms)		RESISTANCE	
	NORMAL	ACTUAL	NORMAL	ACTUAL
V_A	25 V	[78]	—	—
R_1	8.51 V	[200]	8.2 kΩ	[164]
R_2	6.02 V	[72]	4.7 kΩ	[12]
TP1	25 V	[163]	2.99 kΩ	[196]
TP2	8.51 V	[41]	2.99 kΩ	[185]
TP3	6.02 V	[137]	2.99 kΩ	[42]
L_1	20.19 V	[70]	1.2 Ω	[36]
L_2	6.02 V	[105]	0.7 Ω	[94]

Table 13-10. PShooter Data for Figure 13-93

2. Use the PShooter data in Table 13-11 to troubleshoot the circuit shown in Figure 13-93.

TEST-POINT	VOLTAGE (rms)		RESISTANCE	
	NORMAL	ACTUAL	NORMAL	ACTUAL
V_A	25 V	[154]	—	—
R_1	8.51 V	[152]	8.2 kΩ	[143]
R_2	6.02 V	[209]	4.7 kΩ	[36]
TP1	25 V	[190]	2.99 kΩ	[159]
TP2	8.51 V	[69]	2.99 kΩ	[96]
TP3	6.02 V	[85]	2.99 kΩ	[101]
L_1	20.19 V	[216]	1.2 Ω	[213]
L_2	6.02 V	[144]	0.7 Ω	[203]

Table 13-11. PShooter Data for Figure 13-93

3. Use the PShooter data in Table 13-12 to troubleshoot the circuit shown in Figure 13-93.

TEST-POINT	VOLTAGE (rms)		RESISTANCE	
	NORMAL	ACTUAL	NORMAL	ACTUAL
V_A	25 V	[21]	—	—
R_1	8.51 V	[178]	8.2 kΩ	[17]
R_2	6.02 V	[20]	4.7 kΩ	[100]
TP1	25 V	[180]	2.99 kΩ	[171]
TP2	8.51 V	[37]	2.99 kΩ	[23]
TP3	6.02 V	[168]	2.99 kΩ	[108]
L_1	20.19 V	[129]	1.2 Ω	[10]
L_2	6.02 V	[27]	0.7 Ω	[61]

Table 13-12. PShooter Data for Figure 13-93

Chapter Summary

- Series, parallel, series-parallel, and complex *RL* circuits share many basic characteristics with purely resistive circuits. The current is the same for all components in a series circuit. The voltage is the same for all components in a parallel circuit. Ohm's and Kirchhoff's Laws may be applied to *RL* circuits as long as we account for the effects of out-of-phase quantities.

- Total opposition to current flow in an *RL* circuit is called impedance (Z) and is measured in ohms. The reciprocal of impedance is called admittance (Y) and is measured in siemens.

- Sets of series or parallel inductors may be combined to simplify the circuit. Simplification equations are similar to those used for resistive circuits, as long as there is no magnetic linkage between the coils.

- Summing of quantities that are 90° out of phase requires a process called phasor addition. The result of phasor addition is larger than either of the two original numbers but smaller than their arithmetic sum.

- There are three power measurements that are important in an *RL* circuit. True power is dissipated by the resistance in the circuit and measured in watts. Reactive power is acquired by the inductance in the circuit and measured in volt-amperes-reactive (VAR). The product of total voltage and total current (also the phasor sum of true and reactive power) is called apparent power and is measured in volt-amperes (VA). The relative magnitudes of reactive and true power determine the power factor of the circuit. Power factor is equal to the cosine of the phase angle between true power and apparent power.

- Out-of-phase circuit quantities (e.g., current, voltage, impedance, and power) can be represented in either of two ways: polar or rectangular notation. Polar notation specifies the magnitude of the phasor and its angle (e.g., $V_3 = 150$ V $\angle 35°$). Rectangular notation describes a phasor in terms of its real (horizontal axis) and reactive (vertical axis) components (e.g., $Z_T = 25 + j75$ Ω). Conversion from one form to the other can be done with basic right-triangle relationships. Engineering calculators make the conversion process very easy.

- Series and parallel *RL* circuit analysis can be accomplished using the same basic techniques applicable to resistive circuits provided phase relationships are included. When circuit quantities that are 90° out of phase are summed (e.g., the voltage drops around a series circuit or the branch currents in a parallel circuit), then they must be summed with phasor addition.

- Analysis techniques used with resistive circuits are also applicable to series-parallel (or even complex) *RL* circuits, but the out-of-phase circuit quantities must be represented with polar or rectangular notation. Addition and subtraction is generally easier when the numbers are expressed in rectangular form. Polar form makes multiplication and division simpler.

- When a pulse waveform is applied to an *RL* circuit, it takes a definite amount of time for the current to increase through the coil. One time constant (τ) is equal to the inductance divided by the resistance ($\tau = L/R$). The current can increase (or decrease) 63.2% of the total change in one time constant. For practical purposes, it takes five time constants for the current to stabilize after a pulse input.

Review Questions

Section 13.1: Series *RL* Circuits with Sinusoidal Currents

1. The current is the same through all components in a series *RL* circuit. (True or False)

2. In a series *RL* circuit, the highest component voltage drop will be across the component with the (*highest, lowest*) resistance or reactance.

3. If a 10-kΩ resistor is in series with a coil having an inductive reactance of 27 kΩ, which will drop the most voltage?

4. What is the phase relationship between voltage and current through the resistance of a series *RL* circuit?

5. What is the phase relationship between voltage and current through the inductance of a series *RL* circuit?

6. The current waveform through the resistance and the current waveform through the inductance in a series *RL* circuit are in phase. (True or False)

7. The voltage waveform across the resistance and the voltage waveform across the inductance in a series *RL* circuit are in phase. (True or False)

8. Total opposition to current flow in a series *RL* circuit is called _____ .

9. Susceptance is measured in _____ .

10. What is the unit of measurement for admittance?

11. Impedance of a series RL circuit is measured in _____ .

12. Draw an equivalent circuit for the circuit shown in Figure 13-94.

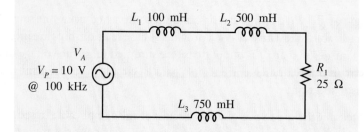

Figure 13-94. Draw an equivalent circuit.

13. A series RL circuit consists of the following: a 10-kΩ resistor, 2.5-kΩ resistor, 5-mH coil, 2-mH coil, and an ac source. Draw the simplified circuit.

14. What circuit quantity is used as the reference phasor in a series RL circuit?

15. Draw an impedance phasor diagram to represent the circuit shown in Figure 13-95. Include the value of impedance.

16. Draw a voltage phasor diagram to represent the circuit shown in Figure 13-95. Include the value of applied voltage.

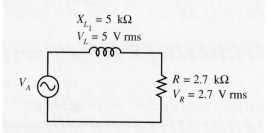

Figure 13-95. A series RL circuit.

17. True power is a measure of the power dissipated in the (*resistance, inductance*) of an RL circuit.

18. Reactive power is measured in _____ .

19. In any given RL circuit, which of the following—true power, reactive power, or apparent power—is always the largest? Why?

20. What is the susceptance of a coil that has an inductive reactance of 2.9 kΩ?

Section 13.2: Parallel RL Circuits with Sinusoidal Currents

21. In a parallel RL circuit, larger resistances or reactances have larger voltage drops. (True or False)

22. In a parallel *RL* circuit, smaller resistances or reactances have larger currents. (True or False)

23. The voltage and current through the resistance in a parallel *RL* circuit are in phase. (True or False)

24. The voltage and current through the inductance in a parallel *RL* circuit are in phase. (True or False)

25. If a two-branch parallel *RL* circuit has currents of $I_R = 1.5$ A and $I_L = 2.5$ A, what is the total current in the circuit?

26. If the total current in a two-branch parallel circuit is 500 mA and the resistive current is 250 mA, what is the value of inductive current?

27. How much resistive current must flow in a parallel *RL* circuit to produce 500 µA when combined with 350 µA of inductive current?

28. Draw the simplified circuit for the *RL* circuit shown in Figure 13-96.

29. What is the peak-to-peak voltage across L_2 in Figure 13-96?

30. How much peak current flows through R_1 in Figure 13-96?

31. What is the rms current through R_1 in Figure 13-96?

32. Calculate the total rms current in Figure 13-96.

33. What is the total impedance of the circuit shown in Figure 13-96?

34. Draw a current phasor diagram to represent the circuit shown in Figure 13-96.

35. Draw a power phasor diagram to represent the circuit shown in Figure 13-96.

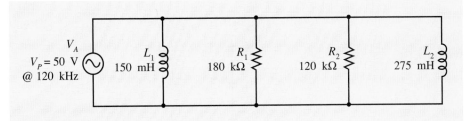

Figure 13-96. A parallel *RL* circuit.

Section 13.3: Representing Circuit Quantities

36. Write the rectangular notation to describe each of the points shown in Figure 13-97.

37. Write the rectangular notation for each of the current phasors shown in Figure 13-98.

38. Write the rectangular notation for each of the voltage phasors shown in Figure 13-99.

39. Convert the series impedance phasor 100 Ω ∠20° to rectangular notation.

40. Convert the series impedance phasor 2,700 Ω ∠45° to rectangular notation.

41. If the total current phasor for a parallel circuit were described as 150 mA ∠75°, how would the current be expressed in rectangular notation?

42. If the total voltage in a series *RL* circuit is expressed as 125 + j55 V, write this voltage using polar notation.

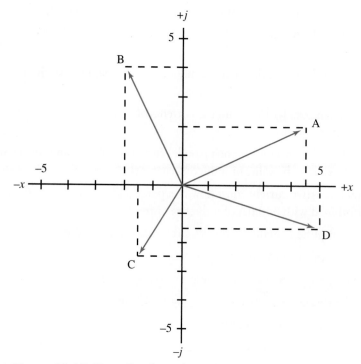

Figure 13-97. Describe the indicated points.

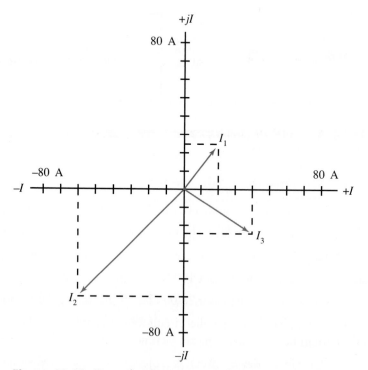

Figure 13-98. Describe these current phasors.

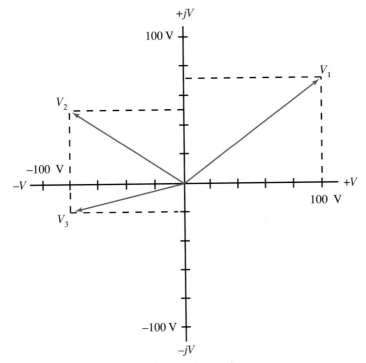

Figure 13-99. Describe these voltage phasors.

43. The total current in a parallel circuit is described as 27 + j25 mA. Express this current in polar notation.

44. What is the polar form of a voltage that is described as 250 + j100 V?

Section 13.4: *RL* Circuit Calculations

Refer to Figure 13-100 for Questions 45–55.

45. What is the value of inductive reactance?

46. Compute the total circuit impedance.

47. How much current flows through the coil?

48. How much current flows through the resistor?

49. What is the voltage drop across the coil?

50. How much voltage is dropped across the resistor?

51. How much power is dissipated by the resistor?

52. What is the reactive power in the circuit?

53. Calculate the apparent power in the circuit.

54. What is the phase angle between total voltage and total current in the circuit?

55. What is the power factor of the circuit?

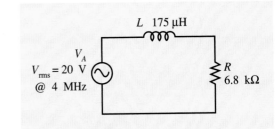

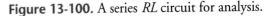

Figure 13-100. A series *RL* circuit for analysis.

Refer to Figure 13-101 for Questions 56–65.

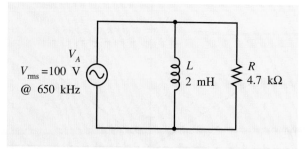

Figure 13-101. A parallel circuit for analysis.

56. What is the value of inductive reactance?

57. What is the voltage across the coil?

58. What is the voltage drop across the resistor?

59. How much current flows through the coil?

60. What is the total current in the circuit?

61. What is the total impedance of the circuit?

62. Compute the total admittance for the circuit.

63. What is the value of true power in the circuit?

64. What is the phase angle between total voltage and total current in the circuit?

65. What is the power factor for the circuit?

Refer to Figure 13-102 for Questions 66–75.

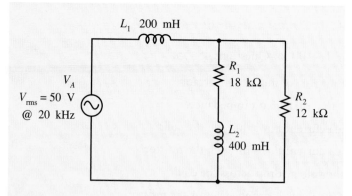

Figure 13-102. A series-parallel circuit for analysis.

66. What is the impedance of the series combination of R_1 and L_2?

67. What is the combined impedance of R_1, R_2, and L_2?

68. What is the total impedance of the circuit?

69. How much current flows through L_1?

70. What is the voltage drop across L_1?
71. What is the voltage drop across R_2?
72. How much current flows through R_2?
73. What is the true power in the circuit?
74. What is the phase angle between total voltage and total current in the circuit?
75. Calculate the circuit's power factor.

Section 13.5: Phase Measurements with a Scope

76. When measuring the phase angle between two sine waves with a dual-trace oscilloscope, why is it helpful to adjust the controls until the waveforms fill the major part of the screen?
77. What phase relationship is being displayed in Figure 13-103?

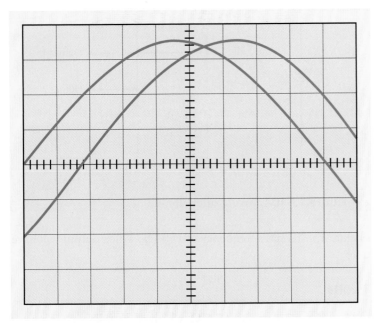

Figure 13-103. Measure the phase angle.

Section 13.6: Pulse Response of *RL* Circuits

78. A time constant is measured in _____ .
79. The Greek letter _____ is used to represent a time constant.
80. What is the time constant of a series *RL* circuit consisting of a 470-Ω resistor and a 375-mH coil?
81. Current in a series *RL* circuit can rise to _____ percent of its final value in one time constant when it is driven by a pulse voltage.
82. It takes _____ time constants for current in a series *RL* circuit to reach its approximate final value when driven by a voltage pulse.

83. If a pulse is applied to a series *RL* circuit consisting of a 200-Ω resistor and a 750-μH inductance, how long does it take for the current to reach its maximum value?

84. If the current through a 250-mH inductor changes at the rate 2.75 A/s, how much voltage is developed across the coil?

85. How much voltage is developed across a 120-mH coil if the current through it changes at the rate of 600 mA/μs?

Section 13.7: Applied Technology: *RL* Circuits

86. If V_A in Figure 13-104 has a frequency of 100 kHz, which output will have the greatest amplitude?

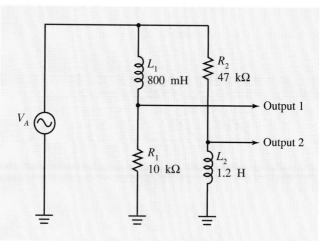

Figure 13-104. An *RL* filter circuit.

87. If V_A in Figure 13-104 has a frequency of 150 Hz, which output will have the greatest amplitude?

Section 13.8: Troubleshooting *RL* Circuits

88. If a 10-mH coil has a resistance of 2.5 Ω, which of the following is most likely correct?
    a. open coil   b. shorted coil   c. normal coil

89. If the coil in a series *RL* circuit develops an open, describe the voltage that will be measured across the coil.

90. If the resistor in a series *RL* circuit develops an open, describe the voltage that will be measured across the coil.

91. If the coil in a series *RL* circuit is found to be open, which of the following may have caused the problem originally?
    a. series resistor open   b. series resistor shorted   c. power supply voltage too low

It is important for a technician to be able to apply previously learned knowledge and skills to the solution of unfamiliar problems. Figure 13-105 gives you an opportunity to apply your circuit analysis skills to a complex *RL* circuit.

We have not formally discussed the solution of complex *RL* networks, but we have discussed all of the individual tools needed to analyze the problem. Apply what you have learned in this and previous chapters and meet the technician challenge!

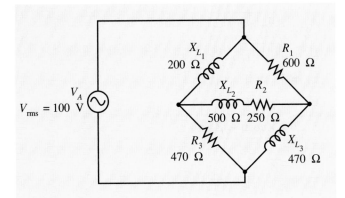

Figure 13-105. Analyze this complex *RL* circuit.

Here's the challenge. Analyze the circuit shown in Figure 13-105 to determine the following values:

- total current
- phase angle between total current and total voltage
- voltage across X_{L_2}
- current through R_1
- total impedance of the circuit

Equation List

(13-1) $\quad B = \dfrac{1}{X_L}$

(13-2) $\quad Y = \dfrac{1}{Z}$

(13-3) $\quad V_T = V_A = \sqrt{V_R{}^2 + V_L{}^2}$

(13-4) $\quad Z = \sqrt{R^2 + X_L{}^2}$

(13-5) $\quad P_A = \sqrt{P_T{}^2 + P_R{}^2}$

(13-6) $\quad I_T = \sqrt{I_R{}^2 + I_L{}^2}$

(13-7) $\quad V_L = V_A \sin\theta$

(13-8) $\quad V_R = V_A \cos\theta$

(13-9) $\quad Z \angle \theta = Z\cos\theta + jZ\sin\theta$

(13-10) $\quad I_T = \dfrac{V_T}{Z}$

(13-11) $\quad V_L = I_T X_L$

(13-12) $\quad$ Power factor $= pf = \cos\theta$

(13-13) $\quad I_T = \sqrt{I_R{}^2 + I_L{}^2}$

(13-14) $\quad \tau = \dfrac{L}{R}$

(13-15) $\quad V_L = L\dfrac{di}{dt} = L\dfrac{\Delta i}{\Delta t}$

key terms

capacitive reactance   leakage current
dielectric   permittivity
dielectric constant   power factor
dissipation factor   quality factor
ESL   temperature coefficient
ESR

objectives

After completing this chapter, you should be able to:

1. List the basic requirements of a capacitor.

2. List the factors that affect capacitance.

3. Describe the current flow in an ac or dc capacitive circuit.

4. Name at least five types of capacitors and describe their unique features.

5. Interpret the value of a capacitor from the manufacturer's markings.

6. Calculate the total capacitance of multiple capacitors connected in a series, parallel, series-parallel, or complex network.

7. Test a capacitor to verify its condition or identify a defect.

8. Identify the following capacitor lead styles: axial, radial, SMT, integrated package.

Capacitance and Capacitive Reactance

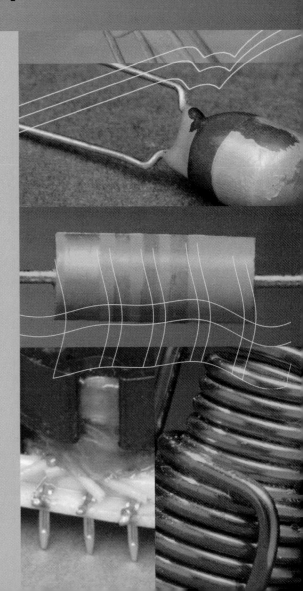

A capacitor is another fundamental electronic component like resistors and inductors. Certain characteristics of the capacitor are similar to characteristics of resistors or inductors. Other characteristics are unique to capacitors. Since capacitors are used in nearly every nontrivial electronic system, you will want to learn all you can about how they work.

14.1 Capacitance Fundamentals

Capacitance can be defined as the ability to store electrical energy in an electrostatic field. This is somewhat comparable to inductance, which is the ability to store electrical energy in an electromagnetic field. A capacitor is simply a physical device designed to have a certain amount of capacitance.

Figure 14-1(a) shows the essential parts of a simple parallel-plate capacitor. It consists of two conductors—generally called the plates of the capacitor—separated by an insulator. The insulator material is called the **dielectric**. Figure 14-1(b) shows the generic schematic symbol for a capacitor. We will look at other, more specific, symbols in a later section.

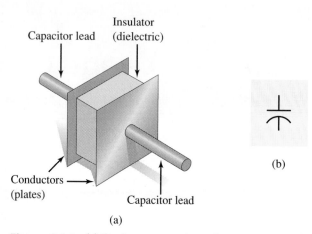

Figure 14-1. (a) Basic construction of a capacitor and (b) the generic symbol for a capacitor.

Charges and Electric Fields

Figure 14-2 shows a capacitor connected through a switch to a battery and a series resistor. In Figure 14-2(a), the switch is open and no current is flowing in the circuit. The capacitor has 0 V across it, as you might anticipate.

In Figure 14-2(b), the switch has been closed. The potential on the negative battery terminal causes electrons to leave the battery and move to the lower plate of the capacitor. Since the dielectric of the capacitor is an insulator, the electrons cannot continue through the capacitor. However, a similar process is occurring on the upper capacitor plate. Here, the positive potential of the battery terminal attracts electrons from the upper capacitor plate. As electrons leave the upper plate and travel to the battery terminal, the upper plate of the capacitor is left with a deficiency of electrons (i.e., a positive charge).

You will recall from Chapter 2, that an electric field exists between charged bodies. In the case of the capacitor in Figure 14-2(b), there is an electrostatic field set up within the dielectric that extends between the positive and negative plates of the capacitor. We refer to the accumulation of charges on the capacitor plates as "charging the capacitor." A voltmeter connected across the capacitor (as shown in Figure 14-2) will increase as the capacitor is charged.

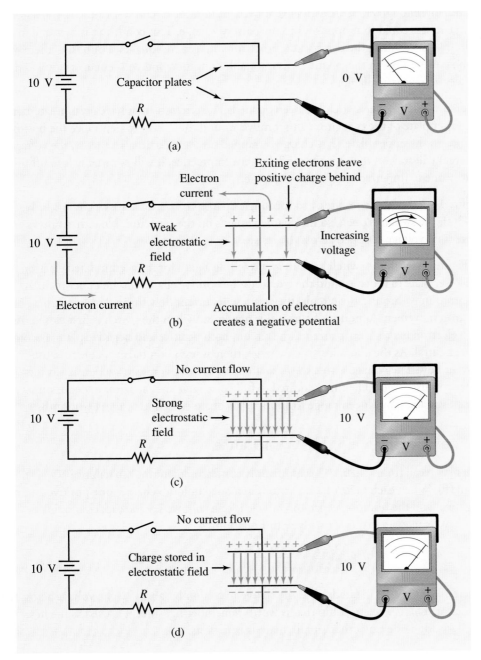

Figure 14-2. Charging a capacitor.

If you closely examine the polarity of the charge that is accumulating on the capacitor plates in Figure 14-2(b), you will see that the increasing capacitor voltage is opposing the battery voltage. Each time an electron moves to the lower capacitor plate and/or leaves the upper plate, the charge on the capacitor and the opposition to the battery voltage increases. The increased opposition results in reduced current flow.

KEY POINTS

When a capacitor is first connected to a dc source, a charging current flows through the external circuit. The charging current decays as the capacitor accumulates a charge. The charging current stops when the capacitor voltage reaches the value of supply voltage.

Eventually, enough electrons will have moved around the circuit to produce a capacitor charge that is equal (but opposite) to the battery voltage. This condition is pictured in Figure 14-2(c). Since the battery and capacitor voltages are equal and opposite, there will be no current flow in the circuit. This is a stable condition and will remain as long as the battery voltage is available.

In Figure 14-2(d), the switch has been opened. The electrons that have accumulated on the lower plate of the capacitor cannot move around the circuit to neutralize the positive charge on the upper plate. The charge is trapped on the capacitor. In theory, the voltage (charge) will stay on the capacitor indefinitely. In practice, it will eventually leak off primarily due to imperfections in the dielectric.

Figure 14-3 shows the results of connecting a charged capacitor across a circuit. In Figure 14-3(a), the switch is open, so the charge remains on the capacitor. No current flows and there is no voltage dropped across the resistor.

In Figure 14-3(b), the switch has closed, providing a path for the accumulated electrons on the lower plate to move around the circuit to the positive charge on the upper plate. As the electrons move around the circuit, they represent current flow through the resistor. The electron movement (amount of current) is maximum when the switch is first closed. As each electron makes its trip around the circuit, both positive and negative plates become more neutral. As the plates lose their charge, there is less potential available to cause current flow. The voltage across the capacitor and across the resistor will decay as the capacitor discharges. The time required to fully discharge the capacitor depends on several circuit variables, but it can range from fractions of a picosecond to literally months.

Unit of Measurement for Capacitance

You may recall from Chapter 1 that the unit of measurement for capacitance (C) is the farad (F). When each plate of a capacitor has a one-coulomb charge (one positive and one negative) and the resulting capacitor voltage is one volt, we say the capacitance is one farad. We can express this formally with Equation 14-1.

$$C = \frac{Q}{V} \tag{14-1}$$

where C is expressed in farads, Q is the charge in coulombs, and V is the voltage across the capacitor. This is a relationship that is worth remembering, since it is used as the heart of the derivation of many other circuit analysis equations.

EXAMPLE SOLUTION

If 250 μC of charge produce a 6-V potential across a capacitor, what is the value of the capacitor?

EXAMPLE **SOLUTION**

We apply Equation 14-1 as follows:

$$C = \frac{Q}{V}$$

$$= \frac{250 \ \mu C}{6 \ V} = 41.67 \ \mu F$$

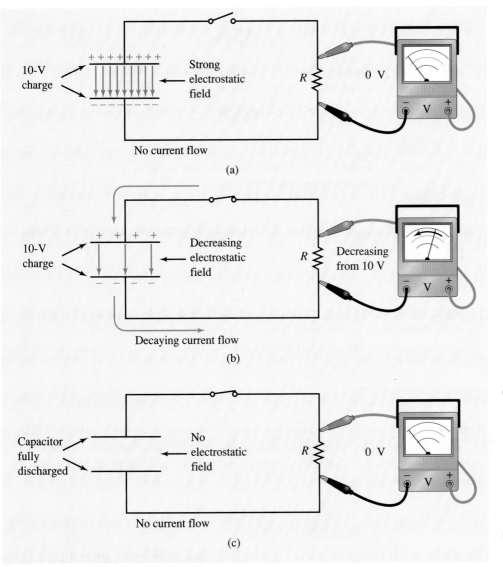

Figure 14-3. Discharging a capacitor.

Values for practical capacitors are generally in the subfarad range. Values of 10 pF, 0.01 μF, and 10,000 μF are representative values for typical capacitors.

Factors Affecting Capacitance

It is the physical characteristics of a capacitor that determine its capacitance. There are three primary factors to consider: area of the plates, distance between the plates, and the type of material used for the dielectric. Figure 14-4 illustrates these factors.

PLATE AREA

The greater the plate area, the more charge the capacitor can hold. If all other factors remain constant and we double the area of the plates, then we can store twice as much

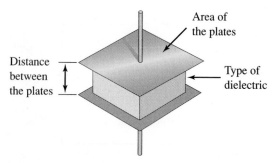

Figure 14-4. The physical characteristics of a capacitor determine its value.

charge for a given voltage. The value of capacitance is directly proportional to the area of the plates.

PLATE SEPARATION

By contrast, if all other factors remain the same and we double the distance between the plates of a capacitor, then we will only have half as much electric field intensity for a given voltage. The value of capacitance is inversely proportional to the distance between the plates.

DIELECTRIC MATERIAL

Permittivity is a measure of a material's ability to concentrate an electrostatic field. This is similar to permeability with reference to magnetic fields. Relative permittivity (ϵ_r) of a material is the ratio of its absolute permittivity (ϵ_m) to the absolute permittivity of a vacuum (ϵ_0). That is,

$$\epsilon_r = \frac{\epsilon_m}{\epsilon_0} \qquad (14\text{-}2)$$

The relative permittivity of a dielectric is generally called its **dielectric constant** (k). The value of capacitance is directly proportional to the permittivity of the dielectric material. Table 14-1 lists the dielectric constants for several materials used as insulators for capacitors.

Since capacitance is directly proportional to the area of the plates (A) and the permittivity of the dielectric (ϵ_m), but is inversely proportional to the distance between the plates (d), we may write the following equation:

$$C = \frac{\epsilon_m A}{d}$$

But from Equation 14-2, we can write

$$\epsilon_r = \frac{\epsilon_m}{\epsilon_0} = \text{dielectric constant} = k, \text{ or}$$

$$\epsilon_m = k\epsilon_0$$

TYPE OF MATERIAL	APPROXIMATE DIELECTRIC CONSTANT
Air	1.0
Aluminum oxide	8
Ceramic	>1,000
Glass	7.0
Mica	6.0
Mylar	3.0
Polystyrene	2.5
Tantalum oxide	24
Teflon®	2.0
Waxed paper	3.0

Table 14-1. Dielectric Materials Used in Capacitors and Their Approximate Dielectric Constants

Substituting this result into the prior equation gives us

$$C = \frac{k\epsilon_0 A}{d}$$

The absolute permittivity of a vacuum (ϵ_0) is equal to 8.85×10^{-12}. Replacing ϵ_0 in the prior equation with this constant gives us an equation for capacitance in terms of its physical characteristics.

$$C = \frac{8.85 \times 10^{-12} kA}{d}$$

Rearranging this equation gives us Equation 14-3, which is a form that technicians generally prefer.

$$C = \frac{8.85 kA}{10^{12} d} \qquad (14\text{-}3)$$

where C is in farads, d is in meters, and A is in square meters. Table 14-2 summarizes these same relationships.

FACTOR	PROPORTIONALITY	EXAMPLE
Plate area	Direct	Area ↑ Capacitance ↑
Distance between plates	Inverse	Distance ↑ Capacitance ↓
Dielectric constant (k)	Direct	k ↑ Capacitance ↑

Table 14-2. Relationship of Physical Factors Affecting Capacitance

EXAMPLE SOLUTION

Calculate the capacitance of a parallel-plate capacitor with a plate area of 0.05 m², a plate separation of 0.01 m, and a mylar dielectric.

EXAMPLE **SOLUTION**

From Table 14-1, we know the dielectric constant of mylar is 3.0. Substituting this into Equation 14-3 gives us the following results.

$$C = \frac{8.85kA}{10^{12}d}$$

$$= \frac{8.85 \times 3 \times 0.05}{10^{12} \times 0.01} = 132.8 \text{ pF}$$

Multiplate Capacitors

Manufacturers often use multiple sets of capacitor plates to obtain higher values of capacitance. Figure 14-5 illustrates multiplate construction.

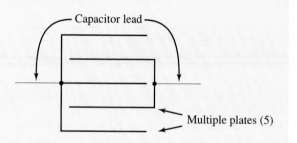

Figure 14-5. Multiple sets of plates produce higher values of capacitance.

KEY POINTS

Although the capacitor is a two-lead component, multiple plates can be connected to each lead to form a multiplate capacitor. This provides greater capacity (i.e., more plate area).

The total capacitance for a multiplate capacitor is computed in basically the same way as for a two-plate capacitor, but we need to include the effects of the added plates. Equation 14-4 includes this added factor.

$$C = \frac{8.85kA}{10^{12}d}(n-1) \qquad (14\text{-}4)$$

where n is the total number of conductive plates in the capacitor.

EXAMPLE SOLUTION

Compute the value of the capacitor illustrated in Figure 14-6.

EXAMPLE **SOLUTION**

We apply Equation 14-4 as follows:

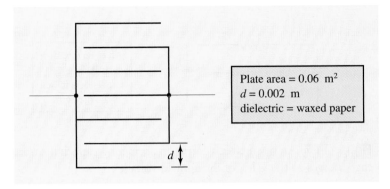

Plate area = 0.06 m²
$d = 0.002$ m
dielectric = waxed paper

Figure 14-6. Compute the value of this capacitor.

$$C = \frac{8.85kA}{10^{12}d}(n-1)$$

$$= \frac{8.85 \times 3 \times 0.06}{10^{12} \times 0.002}(7-1)$$

$$= 0.0048 \ \mu F$$

Note that technically, the answer could be expressed as 4.8 nF, but it is industry practice to express capacitance in terms of picofarad (pF) or microfarad (μF) units.

Current Flow in a Capacitive Circuit

It is interesting that a capacitor has an internal insulator (open circuit), and yet current can flow through the external circuit. It is important for you to be able to visualize this action. The discussion relevant to Figure 14-2 illustrated current flow in a dc capacitive circuit. In the circuit external to the capacitor, there will be current flow (i.e., movement of electrons) as long as the capacitor is either charging or discharging. Once the capacitor has fully charged or fully discharged, there is no current in the circuit. The length of time that the current flows is directly proportional to the size of the capacitor. The greater the capacitance, the longer it takes to charge or discharge it through a given circuit.

One interesting application of capacitance—although not intentional—is illustrated in Figure 14-7. You already know that an open in a series circuit will drop the entire applied voltage. An open circuit is essentially a capacitor, since it is two conductors (the wires on either side of the open) separated by an insulator (the air between the two conductors). As you might expect, the value of capacitance is very small, so it charges almost instantly to the applied voltage. Nevertheless, it is a capacitor, and now you have yet another way to view the effects of an open circuit.

Figure 14-8 illustrates current flow in an ac circuit. In this case the source voltage is changing continuously—in both polarity and amplitude—so the capacitor is charging or discharging continuously. This means there will always be current in the external circuit. It appears as if the current were actually flowing through the capacitor, but it is important to remember that the dielectric is an insulator, so no current can literally flow through the capacitor. The value of current in a capacitive circuit with an alternating source is directly proportional to the value of the capacitor. Greater capacitance corresponds to increased current flow.

KEY POINTS

When a capacitor is connected to an ac source, the applied voltage is continuously changing polarities and amplitudes. This causes the capacitor to be in a continuous state of charge or discharge. This means there will be current through the external circuit as long as the ac source is connected.

KEY POINTS

No current flows through the capacitor with either dc or ac supplies because the dielectric is an insulator.

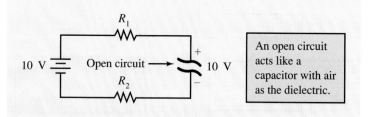

Figure 14-7. An open circuit forms an accidental capacitance that charges to the value of the applied voltage.

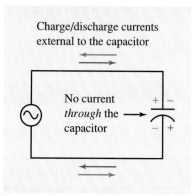

Figure 14-8. Current flow in an ac circuit.

Exercise Problems 14.1

1. Capacitors store energy in a(n) _____ field.
2. A capacitor is basically two _____ separated by a(n) _____.
3. The dielectric in a capacitor is a good conductor. (True or False)
4. In a dc circuit, electrons flow through the capacitor. (True or False)
5. In an ac circuit, electrons flow through the capacitor. (True or False)
6. In a capacitive circuit with a dc source voltage, electrons flow continuously through the external circuit. (True or False)
7. Capacitance is measured in _____.
8. What is the value of a capacitor that has 25 V across it, when it has a charge of 6.5 mC?
9. Name the three primary factors that affect the value of a capacitor.
10. If the dielectric of a capacitor were changed from air to glass with no other physical changes, what would happen to the value of capacitance?
11. Calculate the capacitance of a parallel-plate capacitor with a plate area of 0.04 m^2, a plate separation of 0.003 m, and a mylar dielectric.
12. Calculate the capacitance of a parallel-plate capacitor with a total of nine plates, a plate area of 0.035 m^2, a plate separation of 0.0015 m, and a mica dielectric.

14.2 Capacitor Construction

There are many different kinds of capacitors. They vary dramatically in size, shape, value, reliability, stability, and so on. Nevertheless, they all share the same fundamental characteristic: two conductors separated by an insulator.

Capacitor Types

It is important for a technician to be able to identify the major capacitor types by their physical appearance. Additionally, you should know any outstanding advantages or disadvantages of a particular technology. This latter subject will be discussed in a later section.

There are many characteristics that can be used to classify capacitors. Some are physical and some are electrical. Electrical factors include such things as capacitance, operating voltage, temperature performance, frequency of operation, and either fixed or variable capacitance. Physical factors include size, weight, and lead arrangement.

Lead Styles

Although there are many subtle variations, there are four major arrangements for lead placement. Figure 14-9 shows capacitors with the leads protruding from opposite ends of a cylindrical body. This type of lead pattern is called axial leads.

Figure 14-10 shows radial-lead capacitors. A capacitor with radial leads can be identified by both leads protruding from the same end of the body. The body may be cylindrical, square, flat, or another shape.

Surface-mount technology (SMT) is rapidly becoming the standard for many products (e.g., computers, consumer electronics, and satellite communications). Figure 14-11 shows some typical surface-mount capacitors. These are very small and delicate. Products that utilize surface-mount components are generally assembled and soldered by automatic machines or robots. However, component-level repair and replacement is generally the responsibility of an electronics technician.

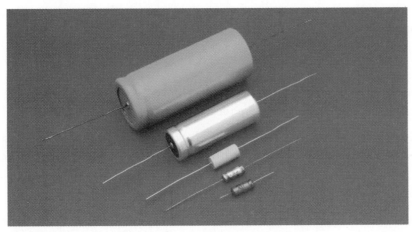

Figure 14-9. Capacitors with axial leads.

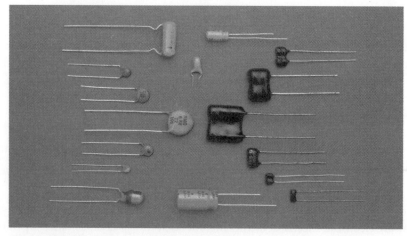

Figure 14-10. Capacitors with radial leads.

Figure 14-11. Surface-mount capacitors. The head of a common straight pin is shown for a size comparison.

Figure 14-12 shows some integrated capacitors. This type of device provides several capacitors (and sometimes other components) within a single package. The individual components may be isolated from each other or they may be connected as a network. There are many package styles and interconnect options.

FIXED AND VARIABLE CAPACITORS

All of the capacitors pictured in Figures 14-9 through 14-12 are fixed-value capacitors. Their capacitance value is determined at the time of manufacture and cannot be altered.

Figure 14-13 shows some variable capacitors. The basic range of adjustment is established during manufacture of the capacitor, but the exact value can be adjusted in the field by a technician.

POLARIZED AND NONPOLARIZED CAPACITORS

Most capacitors are nonpolarized, which means that they can be inserted into the circuit in either direction. Some types of capacitors, however, are polarized. Polarized capacitors

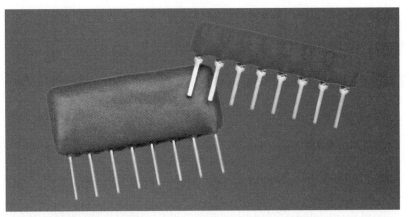

Figure 14-12. Integrated capacitors have multiple capacitors inside a single, multipin package.

Figure 14-13. The capacitance value of variable capacitors can be adjusted.

always have markings to indicate the polarity of the capacitor. One common marking method is to put a plus (+) sign near the positive terminal. Alternatively, some manufacturers place a series of minus signs (–) along one side of the capacitor with an arrow pointing to the negative terminal. When the technician inserts a polarized capacitor into a circuit, it is very important that the positive side of the capacitor be connected to the more positive terminal in the circuit. If a polarized capacitor is inserted backward, then it is very likely to explode violently. At a minimum, you will be startled when the capacitor explodes with the loudness of a firecracker. Worse, you may receive eye damage or skin cuts from flying debris or have chemicals splattered on your face. You should not be afraid of polarized capacitors, but it certainly makes sense to be very certain that they are connected properly before applying power. Since a polarized capacitor must always have the correct voltage polarity across it, you should never connect a polarized capacitor to an ac source.

ACCIDENTAL CAPACITORS

Not all capacitance in a practical circuit is put there in the form of a physical capacitor. Recall the basic description of a capacitor is two conductors separated by an insulator. This definition extends to include all sets of conductors that are separated with a nonconductive material. Figure 14-14 illustrates an accidental or stray (also called parasitic) capacitance formed between two insulated wires connected between two circuits. The wires (two conductors) are separated by an insulator (air and wire insulation), which satisfies the

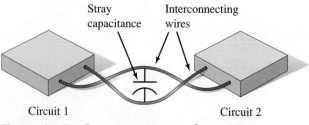

Figure 14-14. Stray capacitance is formed between any two conductors that are separated by a nonconducting material.

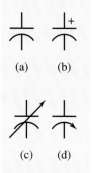

Figure 14-15.
Schematic symbols for (a) a generic capacitor, (b) a polarized capacitor, and (c) and (d) variable capacitors.

requirement for capacitance. Stray capacitance is also formed between nearby copper traces on a printed circuit board.

For many applications, stray capacitance can be safely ignored because it is usually quite small (a few picofarads). However, in high-frequency circuits, stray capacitance can interfere with the desired operation of the circuit. In these cases, technicians use very short wires, coaxial cable, and well-planned cable routing to minimize the effects of stray capacitance.

SCHEMATIC SYMBOLS

There are several schematic symbols for capacitors that a technician must be able to interpret. Figure 14-15(a) shows the general symbol for capacitance. This symbol is used unless a more specific symbol is needed. Figure 14-15(b) shows the schematic representation for a polarized capacitor. The plus (+) sign, of course, indicates the side of the capacitor that is connected to the more positive potential. Figure 14-15(c) shows the schematic symbol for a variable capacitor. The symbol shown in Figure 14-15(d) also represents a variable capacitor, but generally implies a very limited range of adjustment.

All of the schematic symbols shown in Figure 14-15 have one straight and one curved line to represent the capacitor. These are the most widely used symbols. A capacitor symbol is sometimes drawn with two straight lines. This is less common, but it is accepted practice in some industries.

Capacitor Ratings and Marking

Capacitors have numerous ratings, but the five that are most important to a technician are capacitance value, voltage rating, temperature coefficient, tolerance, and leakage.

CAPACITANCE VALUE

This rating needs minimal explanation, since the very purpose of the capacitor is to provide a certain amount of capacitance. Capacitance values are nearly always specified in either picofarads or microfarads.

In older style capacitors, the values were often indicated by colored dots or bands similar to a resistor color code. Several different color codes were used on capacitors, but most are now obsolete. Values for today's capacitors are generally indicated by printing directly on the capacitor. The value is expressed is picofarads or microfarads. Figure 14-16 shows how the popular picofarad code is interpreted.

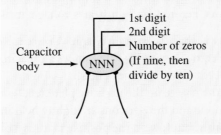

Figure 14-16. Interpretation of the picofarad code for capacitors.

EXAMPLE SOLUTION

A ceramic capacitor has a value code of 102. What is its value?

EXAMPLE SOLUTION

The code is interpreted as shown in Figure 14-16 as 10 plus 2 more zeros, or 1,000 pF.

Practice Problems

1. Determine the value of capacitance for each of the following capacitor markings:
   a. 103   **b.** 225   **c.** 105

Answers to Practice Problems

1. **a.** 0.01 µF   **2.** **b.** 2.2 µF   **3.** **c.** 1.0 µF

An alternative to the picofarad code is to simply print the value directly on the capacitor. For example, a 100-pF capacitor might be marked with 100. Similarly, a 0.05-µF capacitor might be marked as .05. Since both of these are simply numbers with no indication of the units (picofarad or microfarad), interpretation can be confusing at first. With practice, however, a technician can readily determine the correct value. Correct interpretation relies on the technician's knowledge of physical capacitor sizes. A 0.05-µF capacitor, for example, might be roughly the same diameter as your index finger. A 0.05-pF capacitor, by contrast, would be so small you could hardly see it. Similarly, a 1,000-pF capacitor might be about 1/8 inch across, whereas a 1,000-µF capacitor might be 1 to 3 inches long. Thus, with a little experience, there is rarely any confusion. Additionally, by the time the capacitance value is 10 µF or so, the capacitors are usually physically large enough to include a µ, µF, mfd, or even MFD to indicate microfarads.

Surface-mount capacitors generally have no printed markings to indicate value. Here, a technician must measure the capacitance, or, in most cases, simply replace a suspected component.

VOLTAGE RATING

Every capacitor has a voltage rating. This specifies the peak ac voltage or the maximum dc voltage that can be applied to the capacitor. If this voltage is exceeded, the dielectric can break down and allow current to flow through the capacitor. This is a destructive process for most types of capacitors. Figure 14-17 illustrates voltage breakdown in a capacitor.

Figure 14-17(a) illustrates a capacitor with no charge. Notice the undistorted orbits of the atoms making up the dielectric. Figure 14-17(b) shows a capacitor that has been charged to a voltage less than the breakdown voltage. The charge on the positive plate attracts the orbiting electrons, while the charge on the negative plate repels the electrons. Since the atoms are relatively immobile and the electrons are tightly held in their orbits, the orbits are distorted. The electrons strain toward the positive plate as a direct result of the electrostatic field that passes through the dielectric.

Figure 14-17(c) shows what happens if the voltage across the capacitor exceeds the breakdown voltage rating. Here, the electrostatic field has become so intense that it has actually ripped some of the electrons out of their orbits. Once an electron is free, it moves quickly toward the positive plate. On the way to the plate, the electron may collide with other particles and free even more electrons. Electrons moving toward the positive plate constitute current flow. Because the dielectric has a relatively high voltage across it, a substantial amount of power (heat) is produced (i.e., $P = VI$). This releases even more electrons and contributes to the breakdown of the dielectric. In an instant, a current path has been established between the plates of the capacitor. The applied voltage must be interrupted to stop the current flow.

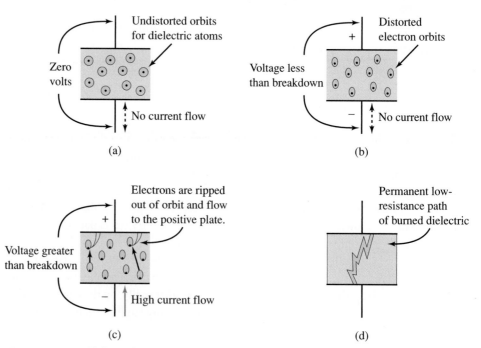

Figure 14-17. If the voltage across a capacitor exceeds its voltage rating, then the dielectric will puncture or break down.

Once the applied voltage has been removed, the dielectric may or may not "heal" itself. In most cases, the high current flow and intense, localized heat causes a conductive path of burned material to form between the plates. The capacitor is shorted or, at least, resistive. This is illustrated in Figure 14-17(d). Certain types of capacitors (e.g., oil dielectric) are self-healing. Once the excessive voltage has been removed, the dielectric regains its high resistance properties.

The value of voltage breakdown is determined by the dielectric strength of the dielectric and the spacing between the plates of the capacitor. Dielectric strength is specified as volts per meter. Do not confuse dielectric strength with dielectric constant (previously discussed). Table 14-3 lists the approximate dielectric strengths of some materials commonly used as capacitor dielectrics.

TYPE OF MATERIAL	APPROXIMATE DIELECTRIC STRENGTH (VOLTS/METER)
Air	3×10^6
Ceramic	39×10^6
Glass	50×10^6
Mica	200×10^6
Polystyrene	24×10^6
Tantalum oxide	4×10^6
Teflon®	60×10^6
Waxed paper	47×10^6

Table 14-3. Dielectric Materials Used in Capacitors and Their Approximate Dielectric Strengths

TEMPERATURE COEFFICIENT

The **temperature coefficient** of a capacitor describes how the value of capacitance varies with changes in temperature. The temperature coefficient specification consists of two parts: polarity and magnitude.

The polarity of the temperature coefficient tells whether the capacitance increases or decreases with increasing temperature. The capacitance of a capacitor with a positive temperature coefficient increases as temperature increases. The capacitance of a capacitor with a negative temperature coefficient decreases as the temperature increases. Some capacitors are designed to have a zero temperature coefficient, which means their capacitance value is relatively unaffected by changes in temperature.

The magnitude portion of the temperature coefficient specification tells how much the capacitance value changes for a given change in temperature. It is specified in parts per million per degree Centigrade (ppm/°C).

KEY POINTS

The temperature coefficient of a capacitor describes how the capacitance tracks with temperature. It can be positive, negative, or zero and is specified as parts per million per degree Centigrade (ppm/°C).

The complete temperature coefficient is always specified in the manufacturer's specification sheets, but it is not always printed on the physical capacitor. When it is printed on the capacitor, the polarity is listed first as N, P, or NP for negative, positive, and zero temperature coefficients, respectively. The magnitude is listed next.

EXAMPLE SOLUTION

Three capacitors have the markings N750, P350, and NPO. What do these marks mean?

EXAMPLE **SOLUTION**

These are the temperature coefficients for the capacitors. The N750 mark indicates a capacitor with a negative temperature coefficient of 750 ppm/°C. The P350 mark identifies a positive temperature coefficient of 350 ppm/°C. The NPO marking specifies a capacitor with a zero temperature coefficient. Practical capacitors with NPO ratings still vary slightly with temperature, but their coefficients are generally less than 30 ppm/°C.

The value of a particular capacitor for a given temperature change and a given temperature coefficient can be found with Equation 14-5.

$$C_{actual} = C_{rated} + \left((T_{actual} - T_{rated}) \frac{T_C}{10^6} \right) C_{rated} \quad (14\text{-}5)$$

where C_{rated} is the nominal capacitance at the rated temperature (T_{rated}), and T_C is the capacitor's temperature coefficient. The sign of T_C is positive (+) or negative (–) for positive or negative temperature coefficients, respectively.

EXAMPLE SOLUTION

If a capacitor is rated for 1,000 pF at 25°C, and is marked as N250, how much capacitance will it have at 60°C?

EXAMPLE **SOLUTION**

First, we compute the magnitude of the change as follows:

$$C_{actual} = C_{rated} + \left((T_{actual} - T_{rated}) \frac{T_C}{10^6} \right) C_{rated}$$

$$= 1{,}000 \text{ pF} + \left((60°C - 25°C) \frac{-250}{10^6} \right) 1{,}000 \text{ pF}$$

$$= 1{,}000 \text{ pF} - 8.75 \text{ pF} = 991.25 \text{ pF}$$

Practice Problems

1. Compute the value of a capacitor rated for 25 µF at 25°C and a P350 temperature coefficient if the capacitor is operated at 75°C.

2. Find the value of a capacitor rated for 800 pF at 25°C and a temperature coefficient of N650 if the capacitor is operated at 5°C.

3. What is the value of a 470-pF capacitor (rated at 25°C) if it is marked as NPO and is operated at 45°C?

Answers to Practice Problems

1. 25.44 µF   **2.** 810.4 pF   **3.** 470 pF

TOLERANCE

The tolerance of a capacitor is interpreted the same way as the tolerance rating on a resistor. That is, although a particular capacitor is intended to have a specific value of capacitance, manufacturing tolerances may introduce some error. Thus, a 680-pF capacitor with a ±10% tolerance may have actual capacitance values in the following range.

$$\text{maximum deviation} = \text{tolerance} \times \text{marked value}$$
$$= 0.1 \times 680 \text{ pF} = 68 \text{ pF, and}$$
$$\text{capacitance range} = \text{marked value} \pm \text{maximum deviation}$$
$$= 680 \text{ pF} \pm 68 \text{ pF, so}$$
$$C_{minimum} = 612 \text{ pF, and}$$
$$C_{maximum} = 748 \text{ pF}$$

Capacitor tolerances may be high relative to many resistors. Additionally, they are often asymmetrical. Typical symmetrical tolerances for capacitors include ±5%, ±10%, and ±20%, although tighter tolerances are available. Typical asymmetrical tolerances include –10%/+150%, –20%/+80%, and –0%/+50%.

LEAKAGE CURRENT

Ideally, the dielectric of a capacitor is a perfect insulator and allows no current flow. A practical dielectric, however, does permit a small current to flow. The current that flows through the dielectric is called **leakage current.** Do not confuse leakage current with the current that flows through the dielectric after breakdown occurs. Breakdown current can be quite large and destructive. Leakage current, by contrast, flows at normal operating voltages and is very small.

Some manufacturers specify the leakage of a capacitor in terms of insulation resistance rather than leakage current. This is the value of dc resistance measured between the terminals of the capacitor. As you would expect, this is a very high value (often beyond the range of ordinary ohmmeters).

In general, we want the leakage current to be as small as possible. This is equivalent to saying we want the dielectric resistance to be as high as possible. In either case, the leakage rating must be specified at a particular voltage, temperature, and humidity, since each of these factors affects the absolute value of leakage.

Capacitor Technologies

Many different types of materials are used to manufacture capacitors. A technician should know the major characteristics of a given capacitor technology. We will take a brief look at several of the more common types.

ALUMINUM ELECTROLYTIC

Probably the two most outstanding characteristics of aluminum electrolytic capacitors are their high capacities and the fact that they are polarized. The basic construction of an aluminum electrolytic capacitor is illustrated in Figure 14-18. The plates of the capacitor are made from aluminum sheets or ribbons that have been etched to create a rough surface. A rough surface provides much greater surface area (i.e., higher capacitance) than a smooth polished surface. The plates are separated with a thin paper or gauze that is saturated with a conductive material called the electrolyte. The sandwich shown in Figure 14-18(a) is rolled tightly and inserted into an aluminum can. The negative plate is generally connected to the metal can. A lead is welded to the positive plate and brought out through an insulative seal on the top of the aluminum can as shown in Figure 14-18(b).

At this point in the manufacture of the aluminum capacitor, its positive and negative plates are shorted by the conductive electrolyte. The dielectric is formed chemically by connecting a voltage to the capacitor. As current flows through the newly constructed capacitor, a thin coating (about 1×10^{-8} inch thick) of aluminum oxide is formed on the surface of the positive plate. This oxide is an insulator and forms the dielectric for the capacitor. As the dielectric forms, the effective dc resistance of the capacitor increases until

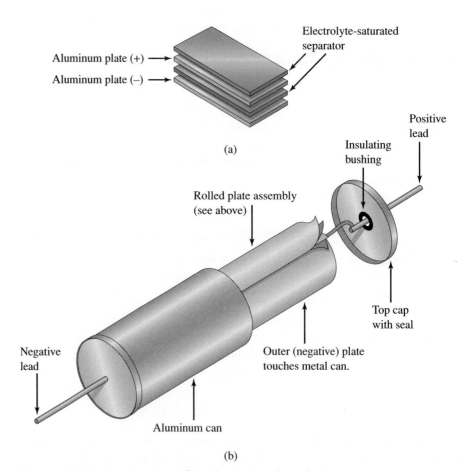

Figure 14-18. Construction of an aluminum electrolytic capacitor.

it reaches the prescribed levels. It should be noted, however, that leakage currents for electrolytic capacitors are much higher than for other types of capacitors. The paper separator material in the capacitor roll prevents direct electrical contact between the two plates.

Figure 14-19 shows some representative aluminum electrolytic capacitors. Typical values range from a few microfarads to tens of thousands of microfarads. Breakdown voltages range from a few volts to several hundred volts. Reverse voltages of as little as 1 or 2 V can destroy the dielectric. Aluminum electrolytics are only useful at low frequencies. Higher frequencies (as low as hundreds of kilohertz) cause the capacitor to exhibit high impedances due to the inadvertent series inductance (called equivalent series inductance, or **ESL**) associated with the construction of the capacitor.

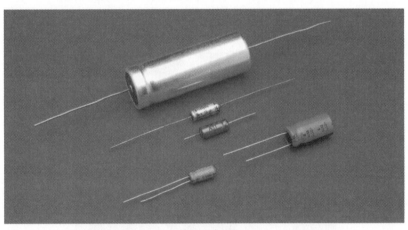

Figure 14-19. Some representative aluminum electrolytic capacitors.

Aluminum electrolytics have a somewhat limited shelf life. The dielectric can deteriorate through lack of use. This condition can sometimes be detected with an ohmmeter before inserting the capacitor into a circuit. Although most aluminum electrolytics are polarized, a few are made nonpolar by creating an oxide coating on both of the aluminum plates.

CERAMIC

Figure 14-20 illustrates the basic construction of a ceramic capacitor. It consists of two metal disks or plates separated by a thin ceramic sheet (dielectric). The entire assembly is covered with an insulative coating. Practical values of capacitance can be obtained in relatively small packages due to the high dielectric constant (>1,000) exhibited by ceramic materials.

A multilayer ceramic capacitor has a similar construction, but it uses several alternating layers of metal and dielectric to obtain a greater total surface area, and, therefore, increased capacitance. Multilayer ceramic capacitors are also called monolithic ceramic capacitors.

Ceramic capacitor values range from as small as 1 pF (disk) to at least 10 μF (multilayer). Common voltage ratings extend from as low as 3 V to as high as several thousand volts. Ceramic capacitors are well-suited for high-frequency applications due to their low series inductance (ESL). Figure 14-21 shows some representative ceramic capacitors.

Figure 14-22 shows an array of multilayer ceramic chip capacitors.

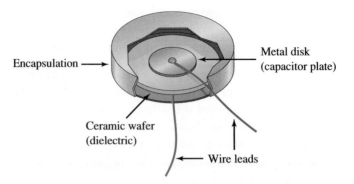

Encapsulation

Metal disk
(capacitor plate)

Ceramic wafer
(dielectric)

Wire leads

Figure 14-20. Construction of a ceramic disk capacitor.

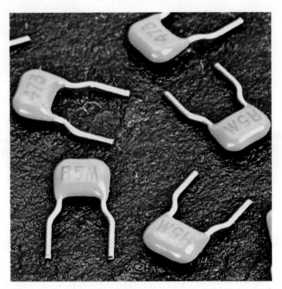

Figure 14-21. Ceramic capacitors. (Courtesy of
AVX Corporation)

Figure 14-22. Multilayer ceramic chip capacitors. (Courtesy of AVX
Corporation)

PLASTIC FILM

Figure 14-23 shows the basic construction of a film capacitor. A four-layer sandwich made of alternating layers of metal foil and insulative film (dielectric) is rolled into a compact cylinder. There is a wide array of materials used for the dielectric film, including polystyrene, mylar, polypropylene, and polycarbonate.

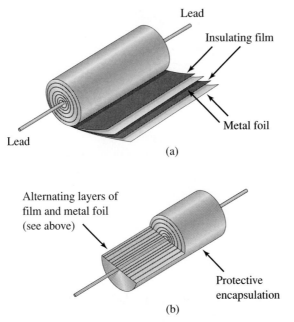

Lead

Insulating film

Metal foil

Lead

(a)

Alternating layers of film and metal foil (see above)

Protective encapsulation

(b)

Figure 14-23. Construction of plastic film capacitors.

Film capacitor values range from as low as 47 pF to as high as 25 μF. Voltage ratings are available from 50 to over 1,000 V. The electrical performance of the capacitor varies with the specific type of plastic used for the dielectric film. Figure 14-24 shows some representative plastic film capacitors.

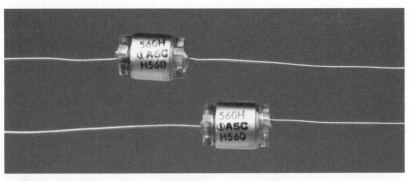

Figure 14-24. Plastic film capacitors.

METALLIZED FILM

Figure 14-25 illustrates the construction of a metallized film (also called metal-film) capacitor. It is made by depositing a thin metal coating on the surface of two plastic (e.g., polycarbonate,

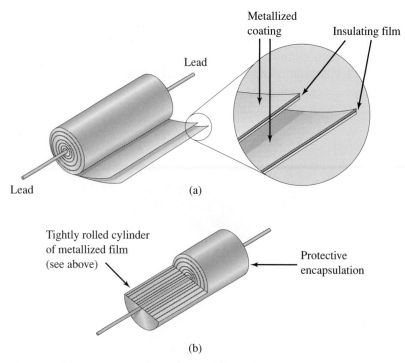

Figure 14-25. Construction of a metallized film capacitor.

polypropylene) sheets or films. The two films are then stacked and rolled into a compact cylinder. Leads are attached, and the entire assembly is sealed with a protective coating.

Values for metallized film capacitors begin as low as 0.0033 μF and range as high as 75 μF. Breakdown voltages of 50 to several hundred volts are typical. One interesting characteristic of a metallized film capacitor is that it tends to be self-healing after it has experienced dielectric breakdown. This is because the metal coatings (capacitor plates) are so thin that they vaporize around the point where the breakdown occurred. Even though a portion of the plate is essentially gone after a breakdown, the two plates are prevented from shorting together by the absence of conductive material in the vicinity of the pinhole that was punched through the dielectric by the high voltage. As long as the breakdown was confined to a small pinhole in the dielectric, the capacitor can continue to perform satisfactorily after a breakdown. Figure 14-26 shows some representative metallized film capacitors.

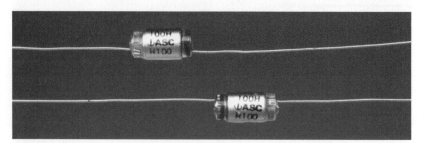

Figure 14-26. Some metallized film capacitors.

MICA

Figure 14-27 shows some mica capacitors. Their construction is similar to a multilayer ceramic capacitor, except that the dielectric material is a thin sheet of mica. The plates of the capacitor can be actual ribbons of metal foil, or they may take the form of a deposited coating like that used in metallized film capacitors. Silver is the metal that is deposited on the mica sheets. This type of capacitor is also called a silver mica capacitor. The completed assembly is generally dipped to provide a durable, insulative seal around the capacitor.

Mica capacitors are available with values as low as 2 pF and as high as several tens of thousands of picofarads. Breakdown voltages range from 100 V to several thousand volts.

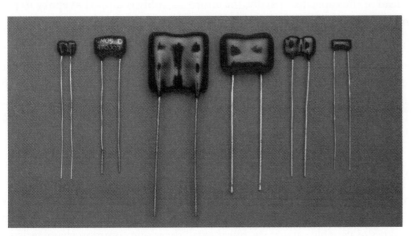

Figure 14-27. Representative mica capacitors.

PAPER

Paper capacitors are constructed essentially the same way as plastic film capacitors illustrated in Figure 14-23. The dielectric material, however, is a thin ribbon of paper instead of the plastic sheets used in plastic film capacitors. The paper is generally impregnated with oil, which increases the overall dielectric strength of the insulating material.

Paper capacitor technology is one of the oldest. It has been replaced in many applications by other newer technologies. Paper capacitor values range from as low as 0.01 μF to as high as 10 μF. Very high breakdown voltages are available, including values as high as several tens of thousands of volts.

TANTALUM

Tantalum capacitors are polarized electrolytics, similar in many ways to the aluminum electrolytics. They are characterized by high values of capacitance for a given physical size. This space savings is caused by two factors. First, the dielectric is a very thin layer of tantalum oxide (comparable to the aluminum oxide dielectric in aluminum electrolytics). Second, the dielectric constant of tantalum oxide is relatively high (24).

There are three types of tantalum capacitor technologies: wet foil, wet slug, and solid slug. The wet foil construction is comparable to the construction of the aluminum electrolytic, but a thin tantalum foil is used instead of aluminum foil. The wet slug uses a sintered slug of tantalum as the positive electrode. The electrolyte is a gel, which surrounds the tantalum slug. A layer of tantalum oxide is formed between the electrolyte and the tantalum, which serves as the dielectric.

Figure 14-28 illustrates the construction of a solid slug tantalum capacitor. The positive electrode is a porous pellet of tantalum. As with other electrolytic capacitors, a thin insulative film (tantalum pentoxide) is formed through electrochemical action. This is the dielectric of the capacitor. The electrolyte is dry and is pressed between the tantalum core and an outer electrode made of silver and coated with graphite. The silver electrode is the negative lead of the capacitor. Finally, the entire assembly is dipped in epoxy to provide a protective seal for the capacitor.

Tantalum capacitors have a much longer (indefinite) shelf life than aluminum electrolytics, and they exhibit substantially lower leakage currents. Most tantalum capacitors are designed for low voltage (i.e., <100 V) operation. Under certain conditions (e.g., high-impedance circuits), the tantalum oxide dielectric is self-healing after a voltage breakdown. Typical values for tantalum electrolytics range from 0.1 μF to as high as 2,200 μF. Figure 14-29 shows some representative tantalum capacitors.

VARIABLE CAPACITORS

A variable capacitor is manufactured to have a nominal range of capacitance. The exact value of the capacitor is then set by the technician or operator in the field. There are many different types of variable capacitors, but they all share one common characteristic—their specific capacitance can be adjusted.

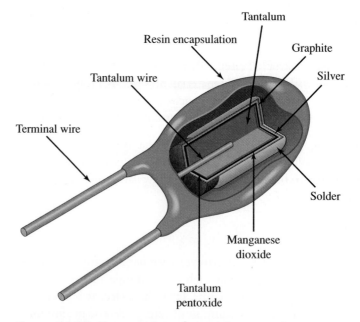

Figure 14-28. Construction of a tantalum capacitor.

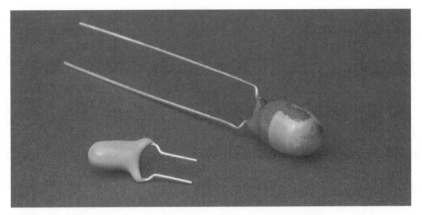

Figure 14-29. Tantalum capacitors offer a very high capacitance-to-volume ratio.

Exercise Problems 14.2

1. When a capacitor's leads protrude from opposite ends of its body, the leads are called _____ leads.
2. When both leads protrude from the same end of the capacitor's body, they are called _____ leads.
3. Describe the lead arrangement on a surface-mount capacitor.
4. Describe why it is important for a technician to distinguish between polarized and nonpolarized capacitors.
5. Explain how stray capacitance is formed in a circuit.
6. Draw the schematic symbol for a variable capacitor.
7. What is the ideal value of current that flows through the dielectric of a capacitor?
8. What is the name of the current that flows through the dielectric of a capacitor that is being operated below its rated voltage value?
9. What happens to the value of current through a capacitor's dielectric if the voltage rating on the capacitor is exceeded?
10. Explain the meaning of the marking N750 on a capacitor.
11. If a capacitor is rated for 2,500 µF at 25°C and is marked as P500, how much capacitance will it have at 75°C?
12. What is the range of allowable values that a 25-µF capacitor can have if its tolerance is listed as −20%/+80%?
13. Capacitors are either fixed or _____.

14.3 Multiple Circuit Capacitances

Two or more capacitors may be connected in series, parallel, or other configuration to produce an equivalent value of capacitance. The equations for combining capacitors are different than the equations for resistors, but they are very easy to remember if you learn them in a logical way (i.e., avoid casual memorization).

Series-Connected Capacitors

Figure 14-30(a) shows two series-connected capacitors. Figure 14-30(b) illustrates a way to help you remember the relative (i.e., larger or smaller) value of the equivalent capacitance. As shown in Figure 14-30(b), when the capacitors are connected in series, we are essentially increasing the thickness of the dielectric. That is, we are increasing the distance between the plates. You already know that increased plate separation results in decreased capacitance. So, we can make the following conclusion:

> When capacitors are connected in series, the total capacitance is less than the value of any of the individual capacitances.

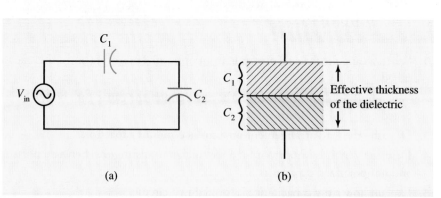

Figure 14-30. (a) Series-connected capacitors. (b) The distance between the plates is effectively increased when capacitors are connected in series.

TOTAL CAPACITANCE

Equation 14-6 can be used to compute the equivalent capacitance for series-connected capacitors. Note that it is the same basic form as the reciprocal equation used to compute the equivalent resistance of parallel-connected resistors.

$$C_T = \cfrac{1}{\cfrac{1}{C_1} + \cfrac{1}{C_2} + ... + \cfrac{1}{C_N}} \qquad \text{(14-6)}$$

EXAMPLE SOLUTION

A 4.7-µF and a 6.8-µF capacitor are connected in series. What is the total capacitance?

EXAMPLE **SOLUTION**

We apply Equation 14-6 as follows:

$$C_T = \cfrac{1}{\cfrac{1}{C_1} + \cfrac{1}{C_2}}$$

$$= \cfrac{1}{\cfrac{1}{4.7 \ \mu F} + \cfrac{1}{6.8 \ \mu F}}$$

$$= \cfrac{1}{359.82 \times 10^3} = 2.78 \ \mu F$$

Practice Problems

1. Calculate the value of a 4.7-μF and a 10-μF capacitor in series.
2. What is the total capacitance when a 200-pF capacitor is connected in series with a 680-pF capacitor?
3. What is the total capacitance of four series-connected capacitors that have the following values: 330 μF, 470 μF, 680 μF, and 1,000 μF?

Answers to Practice Problems

1. 3.2 μF 2. 154.6 pF   3. 131.1 μF

The shortcut equations that were used for computing the resistance of parallel resistors can also be applied to the solution of series-connected capacitors. For example, if several equal-value capacitors are connected in series, their combined capacitance can be computed with Equation 14-7.

$$C_T = \frac{C_X}{N} \qquad \text{(14-7)}$$

where C_X is the common capacitor value and N is the number of equal-valued capacitors.

Similarly, the product-over-the-sum formula used to find the combined resistance of two parallel-connected resistors can be used to compute the total capacitance of two series-connected capacitors as represented by Equation 14-8.

$$C_T = \frac{C_1 C_2}{C_1 + C_2} \qquad \text{(14-8)}$$

Practice Problems

1. What is the combined value of four series-connected 100-μF capacitors?
2. What is the value of five 20-μF capacitors connected in series?
3. What is the value of a 20-μF and a 5-μF capacitor connected in series?

Answers to Practice Problems

1. 25 μF   **2.** 4 μF   **3.** 4 μF

SERIES CAPACITORS WITH A dc SOURCE

If two capacitors are connected in series across a dc source, a charging current will flow until the total charge on the capacitors is equal to the value of the applied voltage. Since the capacitors are in series, the current—and therefore the accumulated coulombs of charge—will be the same. However, rearrangement of Equation 14-1 shows us that the voltage on a given capacitor is inversely proportional to the value of capacitance. That is,

$$C = \frac{Q}{V}, \text{ or}$$

$$V = \frac{Q}{C}$$

This means that when two capacitors are connected in series across a dc source, the one with the smallest capacitance will have the most voltage. Of course, the sum of the two voltage drops must still be equal to the applied voltage according to Kirchhoff's Voltage Law.

Parallel-Connected Capacitors

> **KEY POINTS**
>
> Parallel-connected capacitances combine like resistors in series. The total capacitance of parallel-connected capacitors is equal to the sum of the individual capacitances.

Figure 14-31(a) shows two capacitors connected in parallel. Figure 14-31(b) illustrates a way to help you remember the relative (i.e., larger or smaller) value of the equivalent capacitance. As capacitors are added in parallel, the effective plate area, and therefore the total capacitance, increases.

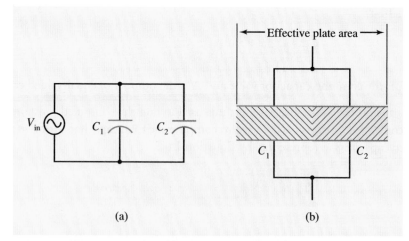

(a)   (b)

Figure 14-31. (a) Parallel-connected capacitors. (b) The effective area of the plates is increased when capacitors are connected in parallel.

We can make the following conclusion:

> When capacitors are connected in parallel, the total capacitance is equal to the sum of the individual capacitances.

Although the reasons are totally different, you should recognize this general statement as being similar to the rule for series-connected resistors. Equation 14-9 can be used to compute the equivalent capacitance for parallel-connected capacitors.

$$C_T = C_1 + C_2 + \ldots + C_N \qquad \text{(14-9)}$$

EXAMPLE SOLUTION

A 33-μF and a 10-μF capacitor are connected in parallel. What is the total capacitance?

EXAMPLE **SOLUTION**

We apply Equation 14-9 as follows:

$$C_T = C_1 + C_2$$
$$= 33 \ \mu F + 10 \ \mu F = 43 \ \mu F$$

Practice Problems

1. Calculate the value of a 27-μF and a 47-μF capacitor in parallel.
2. What is the total capacitance when a 270-pF capacitor is connected in parallel with a 470-pF capacitor?
3. What is the total capacitance of four parallel-connected capacitors that have the following values: 200 μF, 390 μF, 430 μF, and 1,000 μF?

Answers to Practice Problems

1. 74 μF   2.   740 pF   3.   2,020 μF

Series-Parallel Capacitor Networks

The total capacitance of several capacitors connected in a series-parallel circuit is found in a way similar to that used for series-parallel resistive circuits. That is, we replace sets of series-connected capacitors and sets of parallel-connected capacitors with a single equivalent capacitor. When replacing a set of series capacitors, we use the series capacitor equation (Equation 14-6). When a set of parallel capacitors is replaced, we use the parallel capacitor equation (Equation 14-9). The replacement process continues until we have a single equivalent capacitor whose value is equal to the total capacitance of the original circuit.

EXAMPLE SOLUTION

What is the total capacitance of the circuit shown in Figure 14-32?

EXAMPLE **SOLUTION**

First, we combine parallel-connected capacitors C_2 and C_3 by applying Equation 14-9 as follows:

$$C_{2,3} = C_2 + C_3$$
$$= 20 \ \mu F + 80 \ \mu F = 100 \ \mu F$$

> **KEY POINTS**
>
> The basic analysis method for a series-parallel capacitive circuit is similar to that used to analyze series-parallel resistive circuits:
>
> • Sets of pure series or pure parallel capacitances are replaced with an equivalent capacitance.
> • The equivalent capacitance is found by applying the appropriate series or parallel capacitor equation.
> • Substitution continues until only a single capacitance (total capacitance) remains.

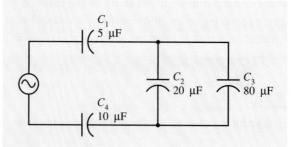

Figure 14-32. What is the total capacitance of this series-parallel circuit?

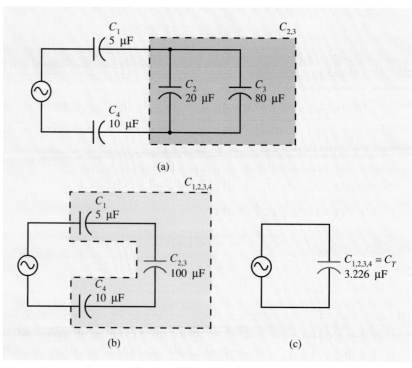

Figure 14-33. Steps in the simplification of the circuit shown in Figure 14-33.

Figures 14-33(a) and (b) show our progress so far.

Next, we can replace series-connected capacitors C_1, $C_{2,3}$, and C_4 with an equivalent capacitance by applying Equation 14-6.

$$C_T = \frac{1}{\dfrac{1}{C_1} + \dfrac{1}{C_{2,3}} + \dfrac{1}{C_4}}$$

$$= \frac{1}{\dfrac{1}{5\ \mu F} + \dfrac{1}{100\ \mu F} + \dfrac{1}{10\ \mu F}} = 3.226\ \mu F$$

This completes the simplification of our circuit. The result is shown in Figure 14-33(c).

Practice Problems

1. Compute the total capacitance for the circuit shown in Figure 14-34.

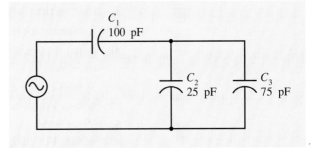

Figure 14-34.
Determine the total capacitance in this circuit.

2. What is the total capacitance of the circuit shown in Figure 14-35?

$$C_{1,2} = \cfrac{1}{\cfrac{1}{2\mu F} + \cfrac{1}{5\mu F}} = 1.43 \mu F$$

$$C_{2,3,} = 15\mu F + 5\mu F = 20\mu F + 6\mu F$$
$$= 26\mu F$$

$$C_T = \cfrac{1}{\cfrac{1}{1.43\mu F} + \cfrac{1}{26\mu F}} =$$

$$C_T = 1.515\mu F$$

$$C_{2,3,4,5} = 7.09 \mu F$$

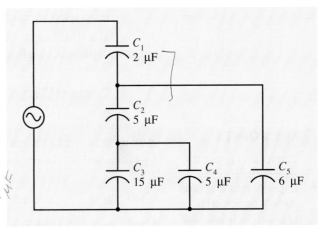

Figure 14-35.
Find the total capacitance.

3. What is the value of capacitor C_1 in Figure 14-36?

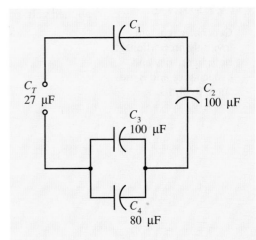

Figure 14-36.
Find the value of C_1.

Answers to Practice Problems

1. 50 pF   **2.** 1.67 µF   **3.** 46.55 µF

Exercise Problems 14.3

1. Connecting capacitors in series (*decreases, increases*) the total capacitance.
2. Connecting capacitors in parallel (*decreases, increases*) the total capacitance.
3. What is the combined capacitance of a 15-μF and a 10-μF capacitor connected in series?
4. What value of capacitance must be connected in series with a 680-pF capacitor to obtain a total capacitance of 300 pF?
5. What is the total capacitance when a 470-pF capacitor is connected in parallel with a 330-pF capacitor?
6. What is the total capacitance if five 100-pF capacitors are connected in parallel?
7. What is the total capacitance if five 100-pF capacitors are connected in series?
8. If a technician has three capacitors and wants to combine them to produce the highest possible capacitance, they should be connected in (*series, parallel, series-parallel*).
9. If a 10-μF capacitor is connected in series with a parallel network consisting of 5-μF and 20-μF capacitors, what is the total capacitance?

14.4 Capacitive Reactance

Capacitors offer opposition to current flow in a manner similar to resistors and inductors, although the mechanism is different. The opposition to sinusoidal current flow presented by a capacitor is called **capacitive reactance.** As you might expect, it is measured in ohms.

CAPACITIVE REACTANCE VARIES WITH FREQUENCY

Capacitive reactance, like inductive reactance, is affected by frequency. Capacitive reactance is inversely proportional to frequency. Thus, the higher the frequency of operation for a given capacitor size, the lower the value of capacitive reactance. Figure 14-37 illustrates this important relationship. In each of the three sketches in Figure 14-37, the applied voltage is held constant at 10 V. Only the frequency is changed.

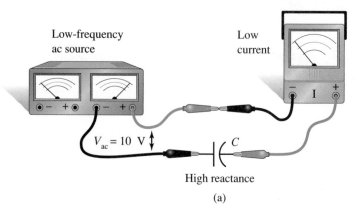

Figure 14-37. Higher frequencies produce lower capacitive reactances.

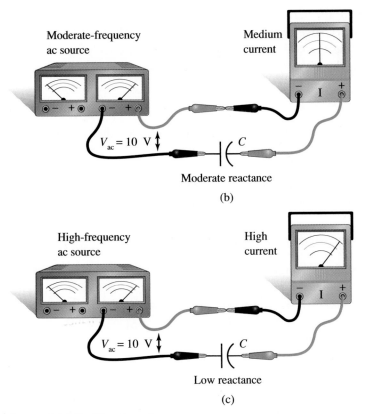

Figure 14-37. *(Continued)*

Let's examine this relationship yet another way. To charge a given capacitor to a given voltage requires a definite amount of charge (Equation 14-1). As the frequency is increased, the same amount of charge (i.e., same number of coulombs) must move past a given point in the circuit in less time. With more coulombs of charge flowing past a point every second, we must have a higher current. Recall that current is a measure of coulombs per second flowing past a given point (Equation 2-3). Now, if the voltage is constant and the current has increased, then Ohm's Law will tell us that resistance (in this case reactance) must have decreased.

EXAMPLE SOLUTION

If the frequency in a capacitive circuit is reduced to one-half of its original value, what happens to the capacitive reactance in the circuit?

EXAMPLE **SOLUTION**

The capacitive reactance will increase, since capacitive reactance is inversely proportional to frequency. In the present example, the capacitive reactance would double.

CAPACITIVE REACTANCE VARIES WITH CAPACITANCE

Capacitive reactance is inversely proportional to capacitance. If the capacitance in a circuit is increased, then the capacitive reactance will decrease (for a fixed frequency). This is shown numerically in the next section. However, we know intuitively that it takes less current flow to charge a smaller capacitor to a given voltage than it does to charge a larger capacitor to the same voltage. Having less current in a circuit for a given voltage is equivalent to saying there is more opposition—capacitive reactance in this case—to current flow.

CAPACITORS IN DC CIRCUITS

If a dc source (i.e., $f = 0$ Hz) is connected to a capacitor, then current will only flow long enough to charge the capacitor. Once the capacitor is charged to the applied voltage, no more current flows, and the dc circuit is essentially open-circuited by the capacitor. The term capacitive reactance has no meaning in the case of dc circuits. Capacitive reactance applies only to sinusoidal circuits.

Calculating Capacitive Reactance

We can determine the value of capacitive reactance for a given capacitor at a given frequency by applying Equation 14-10.

$$X_C = \frac{1}{2\pi f C} \tag{14-10}$$

Many technicians prefer to divide the 2π to obtain an alternate form of the equation. We express it here as Equation 14-11.

$$X_C = \frac{0.159}{f C} \tag{14-11}$$

In either case, we can see that capacitive reactance is inversely proportional to both frequency and capacitance.

Compute the reactance of a 560-pF capacitor when operated at 150 kHz. Also determine the amount of current that will flow if the 150-kHz source supplies 120 V rms.

EXAMPLE SOLUTION

We apply Equation 14-10 (or Equation 14-11) to compute the value of capacitive reactance.

$$X_C = \frac{1}{2\pi f C}$$

$$= \frac{1}{6.28 \times 150 \times 10^3 \times 560 \times 10^{-12}}$$

$$= 1.896 \text{ k}\Omega$$

Now we can apply Ohm's Law to determine the current flow.

$$I_C = \frac{V_C}{X_C}$$

$$= \frac{120 \text{ V}}{1.896 \text{ k}\Omega} = 63.29 \text{ mA rms}$$

Practice Problems

1. What is the reactance of a 100-pF capacitor operated at 10 MHz?
2. How much reactance is provided by a 25-µF capacitor when powered by a 350-Hz source?
3. At what frequency does a 0.01-µF capacitor have a reactance of 5 kΩ?
4. If a 470-pF capacitor must provide 12 kΩ of capacitive reactance, what must be the frequency of operation?
5. What value of capacitor will provide 100 kΩ of reactance at a frequency of 500 Hz?

Answers to Practice Problems

1. 159.2 Ω   2. 18.2 Ω   3. 3.18 kHz

4. 28.2 kHz   5. 0.0032 µF

Capacitive Reactance in Series

When several values of capacitive reactance are connected in series, they can be combined just like series resistances. That is, the total capacitive reactance is simply the sum of the individual reactances. We express this formally with Equation 14-12.

$$X_{C_T} = X_{C_1} + X_{C_2} + \ldots + X_{C_N} \qquad (14\text{-}12)$$

Do not confuse capacitive reactance with total capacitance, which requires use of the reciprocal equation (Equation 14-6).

> **KEY POINTS**
>
> Capacitive reactances in series combine like series resistances; total reactance is equal to the sum of the individual reactances.

EXAMPLE SOLUTION

Determine the total capacitive reactance for the circuit shown in Figure 14-38.

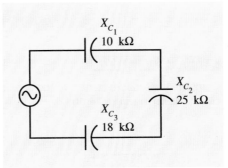

Figure 14-38. What is the total capacitive reactance of this circuit?

EXAMPLE **SOLUTION**

We apply Equation 14-12 as follows:

$X_{C_T} = X_{C_1} + X_{C_2} + X_{C_3}$

$\quad = 10\ \text{k}\Omega + 25\ \text{k}\Omega + 18\ \text{k}\Omega = 53\ \text{k}\Omega$

Practice Problems

1. Find the total reactance of the series circuit shown in Figure 14-39.

2. What is the total reactance if three identical capacitors are connected in series and each has a reactance of 40 kΩ?

3. How much capacitive reactance must be connected in series with a capacitive reactance of 600 Ω to produce a total capacitive reactance of 2 kΩ?

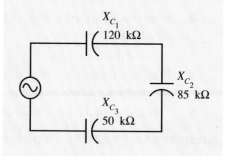

Figure 14-39. Find the total reactance in this circuit.

Answers to Practice Problems

1. 255 kΩ   2. 120 kΩ   3. 1.4 kΩ

Capacitive Reactance in Parallel

When capacitive reactances are connected in parallel, they combine like resistances in parallel. We can express this formally with Equation 14-13.

$$X_{C_T} = \frac{1}{\dfrac{1}{X_{C_1}} + \dfrac{1}{X_{C_2}} + \dots + \dfrac{1}{X_{C_N}}} \qquad (14\text{-}13)$$

EXAMPLE SOLUTION

Compute the total reactance for the parallel circuit shown in Figure 14-40.

EXAMPLE SOLUTION

We apply Equation 14-13 as follows:

$$X_{C_T} = \frac{1}{\dfrac{1}{X_{C_1}} + \dfrac{1}{X_{C_2}}}$$

$$= \frac{1}{\dfrac{1}{100\ \Omega} + \dfrac{1}{400\ \Omega}} = 80\ \Omega$$

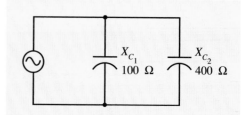

Figure 14-40. What is the total capacitive reactance in this circuit?

Practice Problems

1. What is the total capacitive reactance if three capacitors with reactances of 680 Ω, 820 Ω, and 1,000 Ω are connected in parallel?
2. What is the total capacitive reactance if three identical capacitors having individual reactances of 100 Ω are connected in parallel?
3. How much capacitive reactance must be connected in parallel with a 12-kΩ capacitive reactance to produce a total capacitive reactance of 4,000 Ω?

Answers to Practice Problems

1. 271 Ω   **2.** 33.33 Ω   **3.** 6 kΩ

Series-Parallel Capacitive Reactance

Series-parallel connections of capacitive reactances are simplified in exactly the same way as their resistive counterparts. That is, sets of series or parallel reactances are replaced with an equivalent reactance. The value of the equivalent reactance is found by applying the relevant series (Equation 14-12) or parallel (Equation 14-13) reactance equation.

Analysis of Complex Capacitive Circuits

It is unlikely that you will have a real-world need to analyze purely capacitive circuits connected in a complex circuit configuration. You may, however, encounter such a scheme as part of a theoretical study. In any case, capacitive reactance provides you with a convenient tool for determining the total capacitance of a complex capacitive circuit. The sequential procedure follows:

1. Assume an applied frequency unless one is given.
2. Compute the values of capacitive reactance for each capacitor in the network.
3. Apply your favorite network theorem to the reactance values using the exact procedures presented for use with resistive circuits.
4. Compute total capacitance from the resulting value of total reactance.

KEY POINTS

Series-parallel connections of capacitive reactance can be simplified in the same way series-parallel resistive circuits are simplified—sets of series or parallel reactances are replaced with an equivalent reactance.

KEY POINTS

The total capacitance of a complex capacitive network can be found by determining the reactances of the individual capacitors, simplifying the reactances with a network theorem, and then computing total capacitance from the value of total reactance provided by the network simplification.

Exercise Problems 14.4

1. _____ _____ is the opposition to current flow offered by a capacitor.
2. If the frequency applied to a capacitive circuit decreases, what happens to the value of capacitance?
3. If the frequency applied to a capacitive circuit decreases, what happens to the value of capacitive reactance?
4. Capacitive reactance is (*directly, inversely*) proportional to frequency.

5. Capacitive reactance is (*directly, inversely*) proportional to capacitance.

6. What is the reactance of a 15-μF capacitor operating at 200 Hz?

7. What value of capacitor provides 1,000 Ω of reactance at a frequency of 2.5 MHz?

8. If the following capacitive reactances—100 Ω, 250 Ω, 680 Ω—are connected in series, what is the total capacitive reactance of the circuit?

9. If the following capacitive reactances— 270 Ω, 390 Ω, 820 Ω—are connected in parallel, what is the total capacitive reactance of the circuit?

10. If a capacitor having a reactance of 1,000 Ω is connected in series with the parallel reactance combination of 2,500 Ω and 1,500 Ω, what is the total reactance of the circuit?

14.5 Power Dissipation

An ideal capacitor, like an ideal inductor, dissipates no power. It takes energy from the circuit while being charged, but subsequently returns that power to the circuit when it is discharged. The net consumption of power by the capacitor is, therefore, zero.

Power Losses in a Practical Capacitor

There are losses in a practical capacitor that convert some of the stored energy to heat. Basically there are three causes of power loss or power dissipation in a capacitor:

1. nonzero resistance of the capacitor plates and the connecting wires,

2. leakage resistance of the dielectric, and

3. dielectric dissipation (also called dielectric hysteresis).

These losses are represented in Figure 14-41.

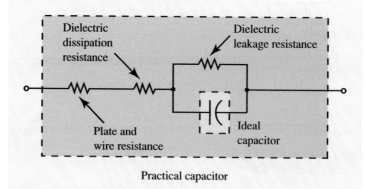

Figure 14-41. Losses in a practical capacitor can be viewed as resistances.

PLATE AND LEAD WIRE RESISTANCE

Although the capacitor plates and connecting lead wires are conductors, they are not ideal conductors. They have some resistance. The amount of resistance added by the plates and lead wires is quite small and varies with temperature and frequency. As shown in Figure 14-41, this resistive loss appears as a series resistance. For many noncritical applications, the effects of plate and lead wire resistance are negligible.

DIELECTRIC LEAKAGE RESISTANCE

The capacitor's dielectric material is an insulator, but it is not a perfect insulator. Its resistance is less than infinity. As shown in Figure 14-41, the dielectric leakage acts like a high-value resistance in parallel with an ideal capacitor. The effects of dielectric leakage loss can be disregarded for many noncritical applications.

DIELECTRIC DISSIPATION RESISTANCE

In a previous discussion on capacitor voltage ratings (refer to Figure 14-17), we noted that the orbits of the atoms in the dielectric material were distorted by the charge on the capacitor. When the charge decreases to zero, the distorted orbits return to their normal shape. When the orbits change from normal to distorted, energy is taken from the circuit. As the orbits return to their normal shape, some energy is converted to heat in the dielectric. Although it is not technically accurate, many technicians like to think of dielectric dissipation as heat produced by friction as the immobile dielectric atoms are pulled one way and then the other each half-cycle.

The two series resistances shown in Figure 14-41 are generally grouped into a single series resistance called the **equivalent series resistance** or ESR. This value is provided by the capacitor manufacturer. In most cases, we want the ESR of the capacitor to be as low as possible.

Quality of a Capacitor

The ratio of energy stored to energy converted to heat is called the **quality factor** or Q of the capacitor. The quality factor is a simple ratio (i.e., no units of measure). It is interpreted much the same way as Q for inductors. It is defined as a ratio of reactance to resistance as we did with inductors. In the case of capacitors, Q can be expressed with Equation 14-14.

$$Q = \frac{X_C}{\text{ESR}} \qquad \textbf{(14-14)}$$

where ESR is the equivalent series resistance of the capacitor. Since X_C varies with frequency, we know that Q will also vary with frequency.

The **dissipation factor** is the inverse of the quality factor. Thus, the higher the Q of a capacitor, the lower the dissipation factor (i.e., less energy converted to heat). The dissipation factor can be computed with Equation 14-15.

$$\text{DF} = \frac{1}{Q} \qquad \textbf{(14-15)}$$

The energy loss in a capacitor can also be described by the capacitor's **power factor.** The power factor of a capacitor can be computed with Equation 14-16.

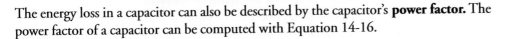

> ⬤ **KEY POINTS**
>
> The ESR is composed of two losses:
>
> • resistance of capacitor plates and lead wires and
> • dielectric dissipation.

> ⬤ **KEY POINTS**
>
> The ratio of stored energy to energy lost in the ESR is called the quality factor of the capacitor. It is more often described as the ratio of reactance to resistance, where the resistance is the ESR of the capacitance.

$$pf = \frac{ESR}{\sqrt{ESR^2 + X_C^2}} \qquad (14\text{-}16)$$

Chapter 15 presents additional material regarding calculation of power factors in an *RC* circuit. A nonideal capacitor is itself an *RC* circuit (refer to Figure 14-41).

Exercise Problems 14.5

1. How much power is dissipated as heat in an ideal capacitor?
2. List and describe the three causes of heat loss in a practical capacitor.
3. Plate and lead wire resistance in a capacitor is generally very (*low, high*).
4. Dielectric leakage resistance in a capacitor is generally very (*low, high*).
5. Dielectric dissipation resistance in a capacitor is generally very (*low, high*).
6. If the reactance of a particular capacitor is 1,000 Ω, and its ESR is 10, what is the *Q* of the capacitor?
7. If the reactance of a particular capacitor is 1,000 Ω, and its ESR is 10, what is the dissipation factor of the capacitor?
8. If the dissipation factor of a particular capacitor is 0.009 (0.9%), what is its *Q* ?
9. What is the dissipation factor of a capacitor that has a *Q* of 200?
10. If the reactance of a capacitor is 250 Ω and the ESR is 5 Ω, what is the power factor of the capacitor?

14.6 Troubleshooting Capacitors

Capacitor malfunctions may be divided into three general classes of failures: open, short, and increased leakage. A technician must be able to test capacitors and determine their condition. Three methods that can be used to diagnose capacitor malfunctions are substitution, use of a capacitance tester, and ohmmeter tests.

Substitution

The condition of a suspected capacitor can easily be determined by replacing it in the circuit with another capacitor known to be good. At first this appears to be a poor technique, but it is actually wise in many cases. First, most capacitors are very inexpensive and readily available. You can remove and replace a capacitor faster than you can remove, test, and replace it. Generally, the labor savings far outweighs the cost of the capacitor. Second, the act of removing the capacitor for testing and the subsequent resoldering can stress an otherwise good capacitor, which may introduce even more trouble. In the case of surface-mount capacitors (quickly becoming the most popular type), substitution is the recommended method. You should always keep a supply of common capacitor values on hand for this purpose.

Substitution for purposes of troubleshooting is of no value unless the substituted component is *known to be good*. Many technicians and repair shops eventually accumulate a wide assortment of new and used parts mixed together in a box or drawer. Beware! If you accidentally substitute a defective capacitor, then your results will be misleading.

Capacitance Testers

Second only to substitution, the use of a capacitor tester is the preferred way to determine the condition of a capacitor. Although some capacitor testers are restricted to the testing of capacitors only, many technicians use an LCR tester, which can be used to test inductors, capacitors, and resistors. A representative LCR tester is shown in Figure 14-42.

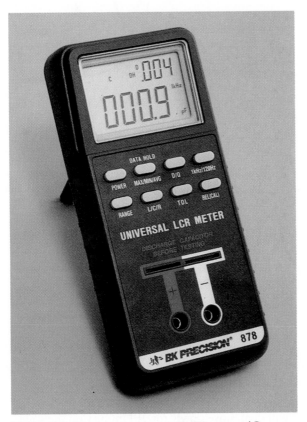

Figure 14-42. A representative LCR tester. (Courtesy B&K Precision)

The use of the capacitor (or LCR) tester is very straightforward. The technician connects the capacitor to be tested, and the display indicates the capacitance value. The leakage resistance can also be measured in some cases. Finally, if the capacitor is open or shorted, it is indicated by the tester.

Ohmmeter Tests

In some cases, a technician can get an estimate of the condition of a capacitor by using an analog ohmmeter. The method is illustrated in Figure 14-43. First, the capacitor to be tested is fully discharged by shorting its leads as shown in Figure 14-43(a). Next, the ohmmeter is switched to one of the higher ranges (e.g., R × 10k, R × 100k, or R × 1M) and connected across the capacitor (observe the polarity of electrolytics). As soon as the leads make contact, the meter pointer will swing to near 0 Ω on the scale as indicated in

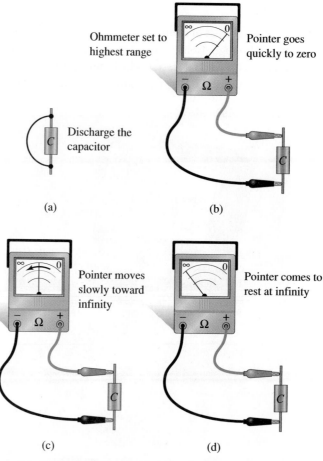

Figure 14-43. Testing the condition of a capacitor with an ohmmeter.

Figure 14-43(b). It will then move slowly toward infinity on the scale, as shown in Figure 14-43(c), as the capacitor charges to the internal battery voltage of the ohmmeter. Finally, the pointer will come to rest near infinite ohms as shown in Figure 14-43(d). Now that we have discussed the general method, let us be more specific.

First, the time required for the meter to move between zero and infinite ohms (Figure 14-43[b] through Figure 14-43[d]) varies dramatically from several minutes to a few microseconds. The exact time depends on the meter (and range) used as well as the size of the capacitor. If the time span is too short, the pointer movement may be barely perceptible or even undetectable. In this case, use the highest range on the ohmmeter. For larger capacitor sizes (e.g., 0.1 μF and up), the pointer movement is easily detected. Generally, the larger the value of capacitance, the lower the range on the ohmmeter that gives a usable indication.

Regardless of the capacitor size, a shorted capacitor will cause the ohmmeter to deflect to zero ohms and remain there. This means the dielectric has been damaged and the capacitor plates are electrically connected. The capacitor must be replaced.

If the capacitor is open, there will be no ohmmeter indication. This is a useful test for large capacitors, but provides no detectable information for smaller capacitors.

Finally, a capacitor that has a low dielectric leakage resistance (called a leaky capacitor) will cause the pointer to come to rest at some resistance lower than infinity. The classification of the measured value as good or bad must be made by the technician based on a comparison with a good capacitor of the same type. Ceramic capacitors, for example, have normal leakage resistances so high that most ohmmeters indicate infinite ohms. Aluminum electrolytics, by contrast, may have normal leakage resistances as low as 1 mΩ.

In general, the ohmmeter test for capacitors should be interpreted as follows. If the ohmmeter test indicates a defective capacitor (i.e., open, shorted, or leaky), then it is definitely defective. If, however, no defective indication can be observed on the meter, the capacitor might be good. You cannot be certain with an ohmmeter test.

Increased ESR

The ESR of a capacitor—particularly electrolytic capacitors—can increase as the capacitor ages. This causes circuit symptoms that may be the same as if a capacitor with too small of a value were used. This effect is often seen when troubleshooting power supply circuits. Detection of this type of defect is strongly dependent on the technician's knowledge of the circuit and the normal behavior of the capacitor in the given circuit.

● **KEY POINTS**

Leaky capacitors can sometimes be located with an ohmmeter, particularly when measuring high values of capacitance.

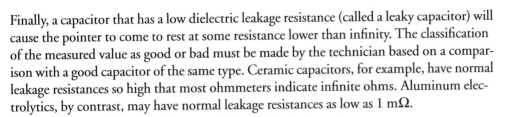

Exercise Problems 14.6

1. Explain why capacitor substitution is used by many technicians as a cost-effective test method.
2. An LCR tester can be used to detect shorted or open capacitors. (True or False)
3. An ohmmeter has the following indications while testing a capacitor: When the meter is first connected, the pointer moves to zero and remains there. What is the condition of the capacitor?

Chapter Summary

- A capacitor is formed when two conductors are separated by an insulator. Capacitance is measured in farads. The value of a capacitor is determined by its physical characteristics: plate area, plate separation, and type of dielectric. Capacitance is directly proportional to the total area of the plates and the dielectric constant of the material separating the plates. It is inversely proportional to the distance between the plates.

- No current (except a tiny leakage current) flows through a capacitor. However, any change in circuit voltage causes a charging or discharging current through the circuit external to the capacitor. The dc circuits have only momentary current in the external circuit. Sinusoidal circuits have sinusoidal current flowing in the external circuits.

- Capacitors are available in several lead styles (e.g., axial, radial, SMT). They can be fixed or variable, polarized or nonpolarized, and they may be intentional (as a physical capacitor) or accidental (stray capacitance). All capacitors have capacitance, breakdown voltage, tolerance, leakage current, and temperature coefficient ratings. There

are numerous technologies used to manufacture capacitors. Each technology has relative advantages and disadvantages.

• Series-connected capacitors combine like parallel-connected resistors (i.e., reciprocal equation). Parallel-connected capacitors combine like series-connected resistors (i.e., they add directly). Series-parallel combinations of capacitance can be simplified by replacing sets of series or parallel capacitors with an equivalent capacitance.

• Capacitive reactance is the opposition to sinusoidal current flow provided by a capacitor. It is measured in ohms and is inversely proportional to both frequency and capacitance. Connections of multiple capacitive reactances can be simplified using the same procedures used for resistive circuits.

• Ideal capacitors do not dissipate power. Practical capacitors have internal losses that appear as resistances and dissipate power in the form of heat. The resistance of the plates and leads and the dielectric dissipation are collectively called the equivalent series resistance (ESR). The ESR causes power dissipation in a capacitor. The quality (Q) of a capacitor is specified by the ratio of reactance to ESR at a particular frequency.

• Technicians must be able to test and classify capacitors as good or defective. A defective capacitor may be shorted, open, or leaky. Identification of a defective capacitor can be achieved by substitution or by using an LCR tester, a capacitance tester, or an ohmmeter. Substitution provides the most reliable indication, while ohmmeter tests are generally the most unreliable.

Review Questions

Section 14.1: Capacitance Fundamentals

1. A capacitor stores energy in an electromagnetic field. (True or False)

2. A capacitor consists of two _____ separated by a(n) _____.

3. The insulator material used in a capacitor is called the _____.

4. When a capacitor is connected to a dc source, substantial dc current flows through the dielectric. (True or False)

5. Capacitance is measured in _____.

6. If a charge of 100 µC produces a 10-V potential across a capacitor, what is the value of the capacitor?

7. A 680-pF capacitor has a voltage of 25 V across it. What is its charge in coulombs?

8. The ability of a material to concentrate an electrostatic field is called its

   _____.

9. Relative permittivity of a material is more commonly called its _____ _____.

10. Rank the following materials based on their approximate dielectric constant: air, ceramic, tantalum oxide.

11. Capacitance is (*directly, inversely*) proportional to the area of the plates.

12. Capacitance is (*directly, inversely*) proportional to the separation of the plates.

13. Capacitance is (*directly, inversely*) proportional to the dielectric constant.

14. Manufacturers often use multiple plates in a capacitor to increase the value of capacitance. (True or False)

Section 14.2: Capacitor Construction

15. In which style of capacitor do the leads extend from opposite ends of a cylindrical body?

16. In which style of capacitor do the leads extend from the same end of the capacitor?

17. What style of capacitor has no wire leads?

18. What type of capacitor package provides several capacitors within a single physical package?

19. Why is it important to connect a polarized capacitor correctly?

20. Explain the term stray capacitance.

21. What happens if the voltage rating of a capacitor is exceeded?

22. What is a self-healing capacitor?

23. A ceramic capacitor is marked as N750. What does this indicate?

24. What do the letters NPO on a capacitor indicate?

25. If a capacitor is rated for 560 pF at 25°C and is marked as P750, how much capacitance will it have at 50°C?

26. What is the value of a 1,000-pF capacitor (rated at 25°C) if it is marked as NPO and is operated at 35°C?

27. Compute the value of a capacitor that is rated for 680 pF at 25°C, has an N750 temperature coefficient, and is operated at 80°C.

28. A practical capacitor permits a small current to flow through the dielectric. This current is called _____ _____.

29. Capacitors with the largest values are electrolytics. (True or False)

30. Name the two types of electrolytic capacitors.

31. How can a technician identify an electrolytic capacitor from its physical markings?

32. What type of capacitor technology provides the highest capacitance for a given physical size?

Section 14.3: Multiple Circuit Capacitances

33. When capacitors are connected in series, total capacitance is (*increased, decreased*).

34. Paralleling capacitors (*increases, decreases*) total capacitance.

35. Multiple capacitances in series combine like resistances connected in _____.

36. Multiple capacitances in parallel combine like resistances in _____.

37. What is the total capacitance of a 2,700-pF and a 1,800-pF capacitor in series?

38. If four 1,000-pF capacitors are connected in series, what is the total capacitance?

39. What size capacitor must be connected in series with a 0.01-μF capacitor to produce a total capacitance of 0.002 μF?

40. What is the combined capacitance of the following capacitors—680 pF, 1,000 pF and 1,500 pF—if they are connected in series?

41. The total capacitance of a parallel capacitive circuit is less than the smallest branch capacitance. (True or False)

42. What is the total capacitance if 100 μF and 250 μF are in parallel?

43. Calculate the total capacitance when the following capacitors—270 pF, 330 pF, and 470 pF—are connected in parallel.

44. What value capacitor must be connected in parallel with 2.2 μF to produce a total capacitance of 5.5 μF?

45. What is the total capacitance of the circuit shown in Figure 14-44?

46. Find the total capacitance for the circuit shown in Figure 14-45.

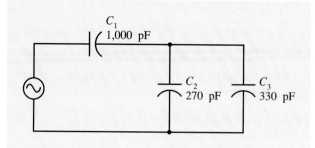

Figure 14-44. Calculate total capacitance.

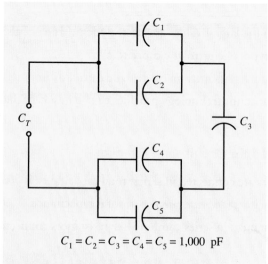

$C_1 = C_2 = C_3 = C_4 = C_5 = 1,000$ pF

Figure 14-45. Find total capacitance.

Section 14.4: Capacitive Reactance

47. Capacitive reactance opposes sinusoidal current flow. (True or False)
48. Capacitive reactance opposes dc current flow. (True or False)
49. As frequency increases for a given capacitance, what happens to the value of capacitive reactance?
50. Capacitive reactance is directly proportional to frequency. (True or False)
51. What is the value of capacitive reactance for a 2,700-pF capacitor when operated at 250 MHz?
52. How much capacitive reactance is presented by a 0.005-μF capacitor at a frequency of 750 Hz?
53. At what frequency does a 0.05-μF capacitor have a reactance of 53 kΩ?
54. What value of capacitor is required to produce 10 kΩ of reactance at a frequency of 50 MHz?
55. What is the total reactance if reactances of 10 kΩ and 25 kΩ are connected in series?
56. Compute the total reactance of the following series-connected capacitive reactances: 150 kΩ, 220 kΩ, 270 kΩ, and 330 kΩ.
57. Capacitive reactances in series combine like resistors in _____.
58. Capacitive reactances in parallel combine like resistances in _____.
59. What is the total capacitive reactance if capacitive reactances of 500 Ω and 1,000 Ω are connected in parallel?
60. If three capacitive reactances of 100 Ω each are connected in parallel, what is the total reactance?
61. Calculate the total capacitive reactance for the circuit shown in Figure 14-46.

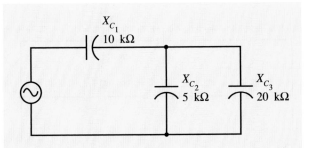

Figure 14-46. Find total capacitive reactance.

62. What is the total capacitive reactance for the circuit shown in Figure 14-47?
63. Find the total capacitance for the bridge circuit shown in Figure 14-48.
64. Compute the total capacitance for the circuit shown in Figure 14-49.

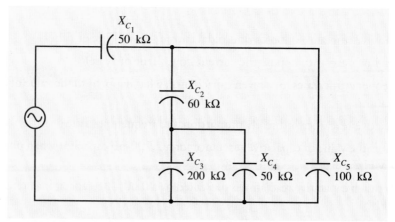

Figure 14-47. Compute total capacitive reactance.

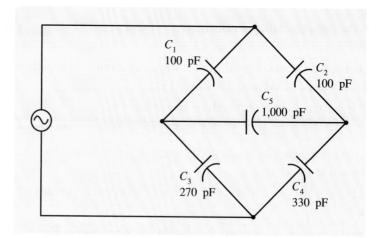

Figure 14-48. Compute total capacitance.

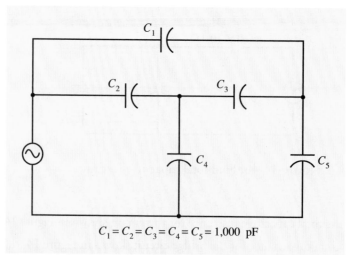

$C_1 = C_2 = C_3 = C_4 = C_5 = 1,000$ pF

Figure 14-49. Find total capacitance.

Section 14.5: Power Dissipation

65. An ideal capacitor dissipates no power. (True or False)

66. A practical capacitor converts some energy to heat. (True or False)

67. What is the ideal value of resistance for the capacitor's plates and lead wires?

68. What is the ideal value of resistance for the capacitor's dielectric?

69. Name two factors comprising the ESR of a capacitor.

70. If the reactance of a capacitor remained constant but the ESR could be reduced, what would happen to the Q of the capacitor?

71. If the Q of a capacitor is increased, what happens to the dissipation factor?

72. If the reactance of a capacitor is 2,500 Ω and its ESR is 5 Ω, what is the Q of the capacitor?

73. What is the dissipation factor of a 1,000-pF capacitor with an ESR of 5 Ω, if it is operated at 320 kHz?

74. What is the power factor of a capacitor with a reactance of 1,000 Ω and an ESR of 12 Ω?

Section 14.6: Troubleshooting Capacitors

75. Explain what is meant by the substitution method of capacitor checking.

76. Explain why an LCR tester or a capacitor tester is a better diagnostic tool for checking capacitors than a simple ohmmeter.

77. When testing a 10-pF capacitor with an ohmmeter, it measures 0 Ω at all times. Is the capacitor definitely defective?

78. When testing a 10-pF capacitor with an ohmmeter, it measures infinite ohms at all times. Is the capacitor definitely defective?

79. When testing a 1,000-μF capacitor with an ohmmeter, it first measures 0 Ω, but then slowly increases to 6.5 MΩ. Is the capacitor probably good or probably defective?

TECHNICIAN CHALLENGE

Let us assume that you are the senior technician on a remote radar site in northern Alaska. You have diagnosed a malfunction in the system's transmitter and have identified three defective capacitors. The capacitors are nonstandard values installed at the factory during final alignment of the transmitter. The values are 1,270 pF, 1,930 pF, and 1,333 pF.

The only capacitors that you have in your supply room are 270 pF, 390 pF, and 1,000 pF. Your challenge is to develop circuit configurations using any number of the available capacitors to produce the three values of needed capacitance.

Equation List

$$(14\text{-}1) \quad C = \frac{Q}{V}$$

$$(14\text{-}2) \quad \epsilon_r = \frac{\epsilon_m}{\epsilon_0}$$

$$(14\text{-}3) \quad C = \frac{8.85kA}{10^{12}d}$$

$$(14\text{-}4) \quad C = \frac{8.85kA}{10^{12}d}(n-1)$$

$$(14\text{-}5) \quad C_{actual} = C_{rated} + \left(\left(T_{actual} - T_{rated}\right)\frac{T_C}{10^6}\right)C_{rated}$$

$$(14\text{-}6) \quad C_T = \frac{1}{\dfrac{1}{C_1} + \dfrac{1}{C_2} + \dots + \dfrac{1}{C_N}}$$

$$(14\text{-}7) \quad C_T = \frac{C_X}{N}$$

$$(14\text{-}8) \quad C_T = \frac{C_1 C_2}{C_1 + C_2}$$

$$(14\text{-}9) \quad C_T = C_1 + C_2 + \dots + C_N$$

$$(14\text{-}10) \quad X_C = \frac{1}{2\pi f C}$$

$$(14\text{-}11) \quad X_C = \frac{0.159}{fC}$$

$$(14\text{-}12) \quad X_{C_T} = X_{C_1} + X_{C_2} + \dots + X_{C_N}$$

$$(14\text{-}13) \quad X_{C_T} = \frac{1}{\dfrac{1}{X_{C_1}} + \dfrac{1}{X_{C_2}} + \dots + \dfrac{1}{X_{C_N}}}$$

$$(14\text{-}14) \quad Q = \frac{X_C}{ESR}$$

$$(14\text{-}15) \quad DF = \frac{1}{Q}$$

$$(14\text{-}16) \quad pf = \frac{ESR}{\sqrt{ESR^2 + X_C^2}}$$

objectives

After completing this chapter, you should be able to:

1. Use both polar and rectangular notation to calculate the following quantities in a series, parallel, or series-parallel *RC* circuit:

admittance	power factor
apparent power	reactive power
component currents	total current
component voltages	total impedance
phase angle between total voltage and total current	true power

2. Draw a phasor diagram to represent a given series or parallel *RC* circuit.

3. Express circuit quantities in either polar or rectangular form.

4. Name at least two applications that utilize *RC* circuits.

5. Calculate the *RC* time constant of an *RC* circuit.

6. State the general requirements for differentiator, integrator, and *RC* coupling circuits.

7. Determine the approximate pulse response of an *RC* circuit.

8. Troubleshoot an *RC* circuit.

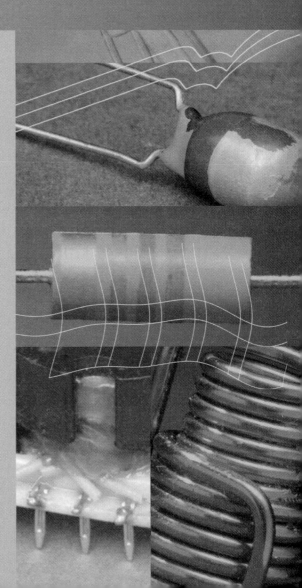

Resistive-Capacitive Circuit Analysis

When resistance (R) and capacitance (C) are combined in the same circuit, we refer to it as an RC circuit. The characteristics of an RC circuit lie somewhere between those of a purely resistive circuit and a purely capacitive circuit. RC circuits may be configured as series, parallel, series-parallel, or complex circuits. The basic circuit analysis methods presented in previous chapters are applicable to RC circuits, but we need to consider phase relationships much in the same way as we did with RL circuits.

15.1 Series *RC* Circuits with Sinusoidal Current

As we work through the basic characteristics of series *RC* circuits, you should try to relate the information to previously studied material. There is a high degree of similarity between series *RC* circuits and other series circuits, in particular series *RL* circuits.

Series *RC* Circuit Characteristics

Figure 15-1 shows a series *RC* circuit consisting of one resistor and one capacitor. Let's examine the characteristics of this circuit configuration.

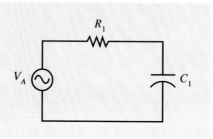

Figure 15-1. A series *RC* circuit.

CURRENT

Because the circuit in Figure 15-1 can be identified as a series circuit, we immediately know that the current must be the same in all parts of the circuit. If, for example, we knew that the current through C_1 was 575 μA, then we would also know that 575 μA was flowing through R_1 and the source. This is an important circuit characteristic. It is illustrated in Figure 15-2.

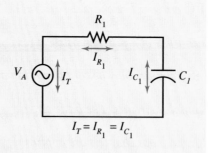

Figure 15-2. The current is the same through all components in a series *RC* circuit.

VOLTAGE DROPS

Ohm's Law tells us that the voltage across a component is proportional to its resistance (or reactance) and the value of current flowing through it. In the case of a series *RC* circuit, the current is the same through all components. Therefore, the various components will have voltage drops that are proportional to the resistance or reactance values. Those with higher resistances or reactances will have correspondingly higher voltage drops than components with less resistance or reactance. This circuit principle is illustrated in Figure 15-3.

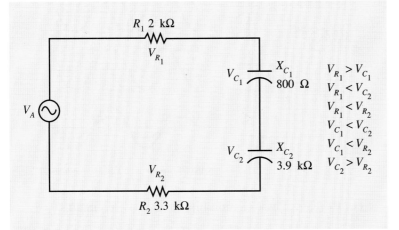

Figure 15-3. Component voltage drops in a series RC circuit are proportional to the resistance or reactance values.

Additionally, the voltage drops in a series circuit can be summed to find total voltage (Kirchhoff's Voltage Law). In the case of series RC circuits, the voltages must be summed using phasor addition, but the basic law is still valid.

PHASE RELATIONSHIPS

Our understanding of resistors and capacitors as isolated components will allow us to determine the phase relationships in a series RC circuit. We already know these things:

- Current is the same in all parts of the circuit at all times.
- Current and voltage are in phase in a resistance.
- Current leads voltage by 90° in a capacitor.

Figure 15-4 illustrates the phase relationships in the various components of a series RC circuit. Note that the current waveform is the same for all components. Also note that the current and voltage are in phase in the resistances. In the case of the capacitors, the current leads the voltage by 90°. Since the two capacitors have identical currents and the respective voltages both lag by 90°, it follows that the voltage waveforms for C_1 and C_2 are in phase with each other.

POWER FACTOR

The power factor in an RC circuit has the same meaning as the power factor in an RL circuit. That is, the power factor indicates the relative phase relationship between total current and total voltage. Since current is always used as a reference when speaking of power factors, we know that an RC circuit must have a leading power factor, since current leads voltage.

KEY POINTS

Total voltage is found, according to Kirchhoff's Voltage Law, by summing (phasor addition) the individual component voltage drops.

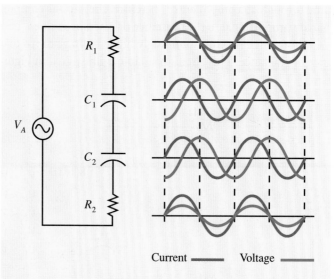

Figure 15-4. Phase relationships in a series *RC* circuit.

The power factor for an *RC* circuit is computed the same way as for an *RL* circuit (power factor = cos θ).

IMPEDANCE

As with *RL* circuits, impedance is the total opposition to current flow. It includes the combined effects of the resistance and capacitive reactance in the circuit. You will recall from your knowledge of series circuits that total opposition to current flow is found by adding the individual component resistances or reactances. In the case of *RC* circuits, we must use phasor addition, since the resistive and reactive components are 90° out of phase. Impedance in a series *RC* circuit can be found with Equation 15-1:

$$Z = \sqrt{R^2 + X_C^2} \qquad (15\text{-}1)$$

You will recognize this as a phasor addition problem similar to the impedance calculation for series *RL* circuits.

EXAMPLE SOLUTION

Calculate the impedance for the circuit shown in Figure 15-5.

EXAMPLE SOLUTION

We apply Equation 15-1 as follows:

$$Z = \sqrt{R^2 + X_C^2}$$
$$= \sqrt{(10 \text{ k}\Omega)^2 + (20 \text{ k}\Omega)^2} = 22.36 \text{ k}\Omega$$

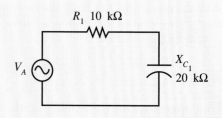

Figure 15-5. What is the impedance of this circuit?

Practice Problems

1. What is the impedance of a series circuit consisting of a 4.7-kΩ resistor and a 2.2-kΩ capacitive reactance?

2. Calculate the impedance of a series circuit consisting of a 680-Ω resistor and a 1.5-kΩ capacitive reactance.

3. What is the impedance of a series circuit consisting of a 2.7-kΩ resistor and a 1,000-pF capacitor? The circuit is operating at 40 kHz.

Answers to Practice Problems

1. 5.19 kΩ   2. 1.65 kΩ   3. 4.81 kΩ

SUSCEPTANCE AND ADMITTANCE

Susceptance and admittance have essentially the same meaning for RC circuits as they do for RL circuits. In the case of RC circuits, susceptance (B) is the reciprocal of capacitive reactance, as reflected in Equation 15-2.

$$B = \frac{1}{X_C} \qquad (15\text{-}2)$$

Admittance is defined as the reciprocal of impedance, just as it is in RL circuits. Recall that both susceptance and admittance are measured in siemens (S).

EXAMPLE SOLUTION

Find the susceptance and the admittance for the circuit shown in Figure 15-6.

EXAMPLE SOLUTION

We find the susceptance by direct application of Equation 15-2.

$$B = \frac{1}{X_C}$$

$$= \frac{1}{600 \ \Omega} = 1.67 \text{ mS}$$

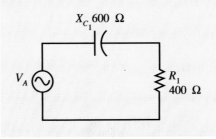

Figure 15-6. What is the susceptance and admittance of this circuit?

Next, we find the impedance of the circuit by applying Equation 15-1.

$$Z = \sqrt{R^2 + X_C^2}$$

$$= \sqrt{(400 \ \Omega)^2 + (600 \ \Omega)^2} = 721.11 \ \Omega$$

The reciprocal of impedance gives us the value of admittance:

$$Y = \frac{1}{Z} = \frac{1}{721.11 \ \Omega} = 1.39 \text{ mS}$$

Practice Problems

1. What is the susceptance of a 0.01-µF capacitor when it is operating at a frequency of 2.5 MHz?
2. If the capacitive reactance of a capacitor is 2.9 kΩ, what is its susceptance?
3. What is the admittance of a series *RC* circuit whose impedance is 18 kΩ?

Answers to Practice Problems

1. 157 mS   2. 344.8 µS   3. 55.56 µS

Circuit Simplification

Simplification of a series *RC* circuit is a straightforward process that combines the various resistive elements into a single resistance and all capacitive elements into a single capacitance. Recall that series resistances are combined by simple addition, but series capacitances require use of the reciprocal equation.

EXAMPLE SOLUTION

Simplify the circuit shown in Figure 15-7.

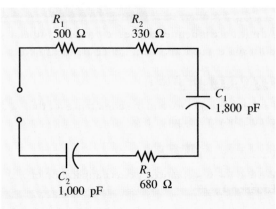

Figure 15-7. Simplify this circuit.

EXAMPLE **SOLUTION**

We combine the resistors as we would in a simple resistive circuit.

$$R_T = R_1 + R_2 + R_3$$

$$= 500 \ \Omega + 330 \ \Omega + 680 \ \Omega = 1.51 \ \text{k}\Omega$$

Next, we combine C_1 and C_2 using the reciprocal equation presented in Chapter 13.

$$C_T = \frac{1}{\dfrac{1}{C_1} + \dfrac{1}{C_2}}$$

$$= \frac{1}{\dfrac{1}{1,800 \ \text{pF}} + \dfrac{1}{1,000 \ \text{pF}}} = 642.86 \ \text{pF}$$

The simplified circuit is shown in Figure 15-8. It could be further simplified by combining the total resistance and total capacitance into an equivalent impedance.

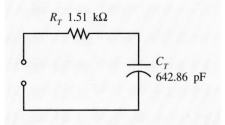

Figure 15-8. A simplified version of the circuit shown in Figure 15-7.

Practice Problems

1. Simplify the RC circuit shown in Figure 15-9.

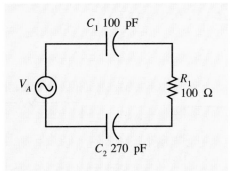

Figure 15-9. Simplify this circuit.

2. Reduce the circuit shown in Figure 15-10 to a circuit consisting of one resistance and one capacitance.

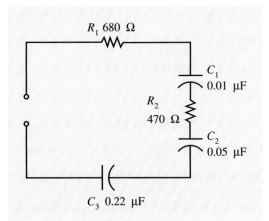

Figure 15-10. Reduce this circuit.

3. Simplify the *RC* circuit shown in Figure 15-11.

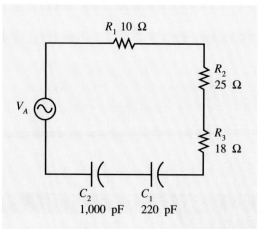

Figure 15-11. Simplify this circuit.

Answers to Practice Problems

1.

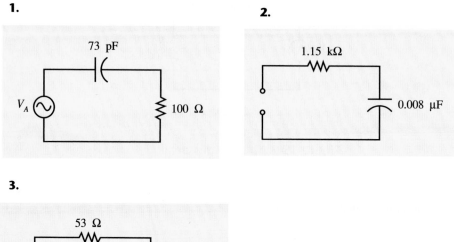

2.

3.

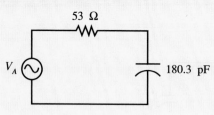

Phasor Representation

Technicians often use phasor diagrams to represent the phase relationships in a series *RC* circuit. In principle, phasor diagrams for *RC* circuits are identical to the ones used to explain *RL* circuits. They differ somewhat, however, since current leads voltage in a capacitive circuit, but lags in an inductive circuit.

VOLTAGE PHASORS

Current is the same for all components in a series *RC* circuit. For this reason, we will use current as the reference phasor. The various voltage phasors can then be properly drawn with reference to the common current phasor. Also recall that the total voltage in a series circuit is found by adding the individual component voltage drops. In the case of an *RC* circuit, we must use phasor addition as reflected in Equation 15-3:

$$V_A = \sqrt{V_R^2 + V_C^2} \qquad \text{(15-3)}$$

Recall that the resistive and capacitive voltage drops are 90° out of phase with each other.

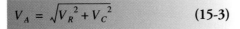

EXAMPLE SOLUTION

Draw a voltage phasor diagram to represent the circuit shown in Figure 15-12.

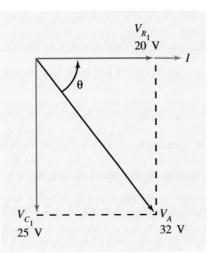

Figure 15-12. Draw a voltage phasor diagram for this circuit.

EXAMPLE **SOLUTION**

First, we draw a horizontal phasor extending to the right as our reference phasor. This represents the current in our series circuit. This phasor is shown in Figure 15-13.

Next, we add our resistive voltage phasor. Since voltage and current are in phase in a resistance, our resistive voltage phasor has the same position as the current phasor. This is shown in Figure 15-13. Recall that the length of a voltage phasor with respect to a current phasor is arbitrary.

We can now sketch the phasor to represent the capacitive voltage. Since voltage in a capacitor lags the current by 90°, we will draw our V_{C_1} phasor downward (i.e., 90° behind the current phasor). Recall that the phasors are assumed to rotate in a counterclockwise direction. Figure 15-13 shows the position of the capacitive voltage phasor. Also note the relative lengths of the two voltage phasors.

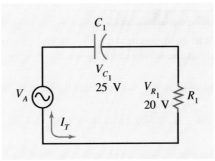

Figure 15-13. A voltage phasor diagram for the circuit shown in Figure 15-12.

We can add (phasor addition) the values of V_{R_1} and V_{C_1} to find total voltage. You will recall that we can perform this addition graphically, by simply completing a parallelogram between the two phasors being added. In Figure 15-13, we complete a parallelogram between V_{R_1} and V_{C_1}. Their phasor sum corresponds to total voltage. It is represented by the diagonal of the parallelogram. The value of the applied voltage can be found by performing the numerical phasor addition process with Equation 15-3.

$$V_A = \sqrt{V_{R_1}^2 + V_{C_1}^2}$$
$$= \sqrt{(20 \text{ V})^2 + (25 \text{ V})^2} = 32.02 \text{ V}$$

Finally, we label the angle between total current and total voltage as θ. Figure 15-13 illustrates the completed phasor diagram.

IMPEDANCE PHASORS

Impedance phasors show how the resistance and capacitive reactance in a series RC circuit combine to form circuit impedance. Because the component voltage drops in a series circuit are directly proportional to the relative resistances and reactances, the impedance phasor diagram has the same basic relationships as the voltage phasor diagram.

EXAMPLE SOLUTION

Draw an impedance phasor diagram to represent the circuit shown in Figure 15-14.

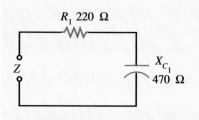

Figure 15-14. Draw an impedance phasor diagram for this circuit.

EXAMPLE SOLUTION

It is customary to draw the resistance phasor in the reference position (i.e., extending horizontally to the right). This is shown in Figure 15-15.

Next, we add the phasor to represent capacitive reactance. We draw this phasor 90° behind the resistive phasor as shown in Figure 15-15. By completing the parallelogram between the R_1 and X_{C_1} phasors, we can sketch the position of circuit impedance. Recall that impedance in a series circuit is equal to the sum (phasor sum in this case) of the individual component resistances or reactances.

Finally, as shown in Figure 15-15, we label the circuit phase angle as θ. This is always the angle formed by the resistance and impedance phasors.

POWER PHASORS

The power phasor diagram for a series RC circuit is similar to the power phasor diagram for a series RL circuit, except the reactive power lags true power in a series RC circuit. Figure 15-16 shows a basic power phasor diagram for a series RC circuit.

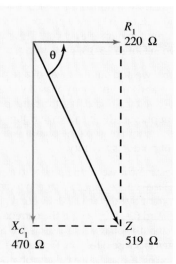

Figure 15-15. An impedance phasor diagram to represent the circuit shown in Figure 15-14.

The phase angle (θ) is formed between the true power and the apparent power phasors. The basic relationships between true power, reactive power, and apparent power were discussed in Chapter 13 and are not repeated here.

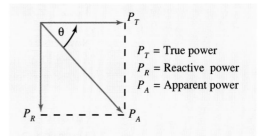

P_T = True power
P_R = Reactive power
P_A = Apparent power

Figure 15-16. A power phasor diagram for a series *RC* circuit.

Exercise Problems 15.1

1. If the current through the resistance in a series *RC* circuit is 225 mA, what is the current through the series capacitance?

2. If the current through the resistance in a series *RC* circuit increases, what must happen to the current through the series capacitance?

3. What is the relationship between the voltage drops in a series *RC* circuit and the applied voltage?

4. The current through a series *RC* circuit leads the resistive voltage drop by 90°. (True or False)

5. The current through a series *RC* circuit leads the capacitive voltage drop by 90°. (True or False)

6. The voltage drop across the resistance in a series *RC* circuit leads the capacitive voltage drop by 90°. (True or False)

7. Total opposition to current flow in a series *RC* circuit is called _____.

8. What is the admittance of a series *RC* circuit whose impedance is 150 kΩ?

9. What is the impedance of a 120-kΩ resistor in series with a capacitive reactance of 85 kΩ?

10. What is the susceptance of a capacitor that has a reactance of 250 Ω?

11. Draw a voltage phasor diagram to represent the circuit shown in Figure 15-17. Be sure to include the value of V_A.

12. Draw an impedance phasor diagram for the circuit shown in Figure 15-17. Be sure to include the value of impedance.

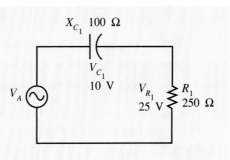

Figure 15-17. A series *RC* circuit.

13. In a series *RC* circuit, apparent power is the phasor sum of true power and reactive power. (True or False)

15.2 Parallel *RC* Circuits with Sinusoidal Current

Now let's examine parallel *RC* circuits and identify some of their important characteristics. You will find much similarity between parallel *RC* circuits and other parallel circuits studied previously (i.e., resistive and inductive circuits).

Parallel *RC* Circuit Characteristics

VOLTAGE DROPS

The voltage drop is the same across all components in a parallel *RC* circuit, just as it is the same for every parallel circuit. Figure 15-18 illustrates this point. If we know the voltage across any one component in a parallel circuit, we immediately know the voltage across all components.

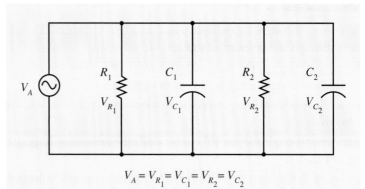

$$V_A = V_{R_1} = V_{C_1} = V_{R_2} = V_{C_2}$$

Figure 15-18. Every component in a parallel *RC* circuit has the same voltage drop.

PHASE RELATIONSHIPS

It is easy to predict the phase relationships in a parallel *RC* circuit if you simply apply what you have already learned. Consider the following:

- Voltage is the same across all components in the circuit.
- Current and voltage are in phase in a resistance.
- Current leads voltage by 90° in a capacitance.

Applying these three known relationships allows us to sketch the current and voltage waveforms shown in Figure 15-19. First, note that the voltage waveforms across all components are identical. Next, see that the current and voltage waveforms for the resistances are in phase. The current waveform through the capacitors, by contrast, leads the capacitive voltage waveforms by 90°. Finally, we see that the total current waveform leads the total voltage waveform by some angle less than 90°. We would expect the total current and voltage to have a relationship somewhere between a purely resistive circuit ($\theta = 0°$) and a purely capacitive circuit ($\theta = 90°$).

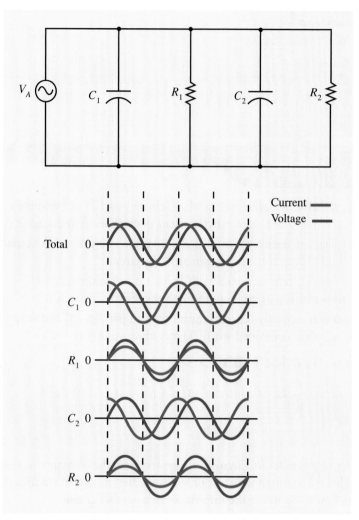

Figure 15-19. Phase relationships in a parallel RC circuit.

CURRENT

As with all parallel circuits, the current through each branch of a parallel RC circuit is determined by the applied voltage and the resistance or reactance of the particular branch. The current in a given branch is unaffected by the currents in other branches.

We know that the individual branch currents in a parallel circuit combine to form total current. This is also true for a parallel RC circuit, but the resistive and capacitive currents must be combined with phasor addition as indicated by Equation 15-4.

$$I_T = \sqrt{I_R^2 + I_C^2} \qquad (15\text{-}4)$$

KEY POINTS

The branch currents combine (phasor addition) to form total current.

EXAMPLE SOLUTION

Compute the total current in a parallel RC circuit if the resistive branch has 2.6 A of current and the capacitive branch has 1.8 A.

EXAMPLE SOLUTION

We apply Equation 15-4 as follows:

$$I_T = \sqrt{I_R^2 + I_C^2}$$

$$= \sqrt{(2.6 \text{ A})^2 + (1.8 \text{ A})^2} = 3.16 \text{ A}$$

Practice Problems

1. If the resistive branch of a parallel RC circuit has 125 mA and the capacitive branch has 250 mA, how much current flows through the source?

2. The resistive current in a parallel RC circuit is 500 μA and the capacitive current is 375 μA. What is the total current in the circuit?

3. If the total current in a parallel RC circuit is 5 A and the capacitive branch has 3 A, how much current flows through the resistive branch?

4. How much capacitive current must flow in a parallel RC circuit to produce 180 mA when combined with 100 mA of resistive current?

Answers to Practice Problems

1. 279.5 mA   2. 625 μA   3. 4 A   4. 149.7 mA

IMPEDANCE

The impedance of a parallel RC circuit is always less than the resistance or reactance of any one branch. This is consistent with our previous studies of parallel circuits. As before, we can use Ohm's Law to compute the impedance of a parallel circuit.

EXAMPLE SOLUTION

If the resistive current in a parallel RC circuit is 100 mA and the capacitive current is 50 mA when 100 V are applied to the circuit, what is the impedance of the circuit?

EXAMPLE SOLUTION

In order to apply Ohm's Law to find total impedance, we need to find total voltage and total current. We use Equation 15-4 to compute total current.

$$I_T = \sqrt{I_R^2 + I_C^2}$$

$$= \sqrt{(100 \text{ mA})^2 + (50 \text{ mA})^2} = 111.8 \text{ mA}$$

Since total voltage is given, we may now use Ohm's Law to compute impedance.

$$Z = \frac{V_A}{I_T}$$

$$= \frac{100 \text{ V}}{111.8 \text{ mA}} = 894.45 \text{ }\Omega$$

SUSCEPTANCE AND ADMITTANCE

Definitions and relationships for susceptance and admittance in parallel RC circuits are similar to those discussed with reference to series RC circuits. They are not repeated here.

Circuit Simplification

A parallel RC circuit consisting of multiple resistances and/or multiple capacitances can be simplified to a circuit consisting of a single resistance and a single capacitance. Resistive branches are combined according to the rules for parallel resistive circuits. Capacitive branches are combined according to the rules for capacitive circuits.

KEY POINTS

Susceptance and admittance have definitions and relationships similar to those in series RC circuits.

EXAMPLE SOLUTION

Simplify the parallel RC circuit shown in Figure 15-20.

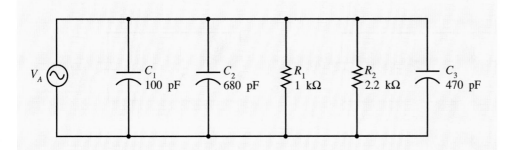

Figure 15-20. Simplify this circuit.

KEY POINTS

A parallel RC circuit consisting of multiple resistive branches and/or multiple capacitive branches can be simplified by combining similar branches.

EXAMPLE **SOLUTION**

First, we combine the resistive branches.

$$R_T = \frac{R_1 R_2}{R_1 + R_2}$$

$$= \frac{1.0 \text{ k}\Omega \times 2.2 \text{ k}\Omega}{1.0 \text{ k}\Omega + 2.2 \text{ k}\Omega} = 687.5 \ \Omega$$

KEY POINTS

Resistive branches are combined with the reciprocal equation, whereas capacitive branches are additive.

Next, we combine the capacitive branches.

$$C_T = C_1 + C_2 + C_3$$

$$= 100 \text{ pF} + 680 \text{ pF} + 470 \text{ pF} = 1{,}250 \text{ pF}$$

The simplified circuit is shown in Figure 15-21.

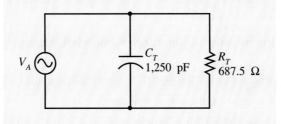

Figure 15-21. The simplified form of the circuit shown in Figure 15-20.

Practice Problems

1. Draw the equivalent circuit if three resistors having values of 330 Ω, 470 Ω, and 680 Ω are connected in parallel with two capacitors having values of 25 μF and 80 μF.

2. Draw the equivalent circuit if three capacitors having values of 2,200 pF, 1,000 pF, and 1,800 pF are connected in parallel with three resistors having values of 10 kΩ, 22 kΩ, and 18 kΩ.

3. Draw the simplified circuit if a 120-kΩ resistor is connected in parallel with two capacitors having values of 5 μF and 25 μF.

Answers to Practice Problems

1.   **2.**

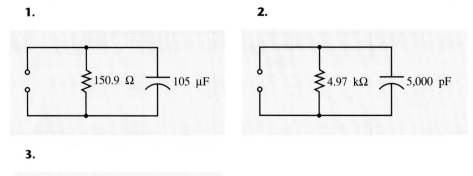

3.

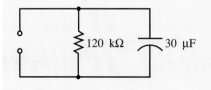

Phasor Representation

The two types of phasor diagrams that are most useful to a technician when analyzing parallel *RC* circuits are current phasors and power phasors.

CURRENT PHASORS

If we apply what we already know about resistors, capacitors, and basic circuit theory, we should be able to determine the phase relationships between current and voltage in a parallel *RC* circuit. Consider the following:

- The branch currents must be summed to find total current (Kirchhoff's Current Law).
- Voltage is the same across all components in a parallel circuit.
- Current and voltage are in phase in a resistance.
- Current leads voltage by 90° in a capacitance.

EXAMPLE SOLUTION

Draw a current phasor diagram for the circuit shown in Figure 15-22.

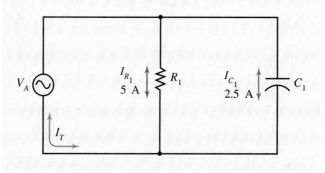

Figure 15-22. Draw a current phasor diagram for this circuit.

EXAMPLE SOLUTION

Since voltage is common to all components in a parallel circuit, we will use voltage as the reference phasor. Figure 15-23 shows the voltage phasor V_A drawn in the reference position.

Next, we draw the resistive current phasor at the same angle as our reference phasor, since current and voltage are in phase in a resistance. The phasor representing capacitive current must be shown leading the voltage by 90°. Since the phasors rotate counterclockwise, we will have to sketch the capacitive current phasor in the upward direction. This phasor is labeled as I_{C_1} in Figure 15-23.

We can determine the location of the total current phasor by completing the parallelogram between the capacitive and resistive current phasors. We can determine the numerical value of this phasor by applying Equation 15-4.

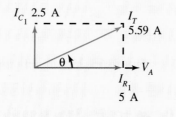

Figure 15-23. A current phasor diagram for the circuit shown in Figure 15-22.

$$I_T = \sqrt{I_R^2 + I_C^2}$$
$$= \sqrt{(5 \text{ A})^2 + (2.5 \text{ A})^2} = 5.59 \text{ A}$$

Finally, as shown in Figure 15-23, we label the phase angle (θ) between total current and total voltage.

Practice Problems

1. Draw a current phasor diagram for the circuit shown in Figure 15-24. Be sure to compute the value of total current.
2. Simplify the circuit shown in Figure 15-25 by combining similar currents, then draw the current phasor diagram and compute total current.

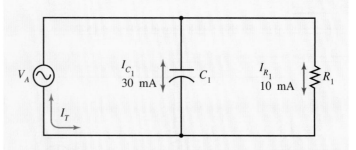

Figure 15-24. Draw the current phasor diagram for this circuit.

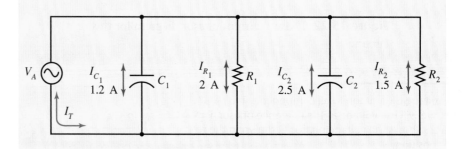

Figure 15-25. Simplify this circuit and draw a current phasor diagram.

Answers to Practice Problems

1.

2.

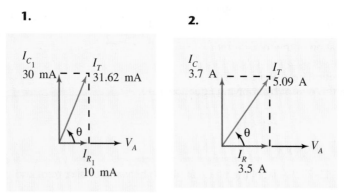

POWER PHASORS

The relationships between true power, reactive power, and apparent power are similar for both series and parallel RC circuits. The power phasor diagram for a parallel RC circuit is drawn in the same relative position as the current phasors, where true power, reactive power, and apparent power correspond to the phasor positions of resistive current, capacitive current, and total current, respectively. Figure 15-26 shows the relationships in a power phasor diagram for a parallel RC circuit.

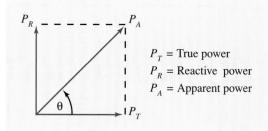

P_T = True power
P_R = Reactive power
P_A = Apparent power

Figure 15-26. A generic power phasor diagram for a parallel RC circuit.

Exercise Problems 15.2

1. The total voltage in a parallel RC circuit is equal to the phasor sum of the individual branch voltages. (True or False)
2. What is the phase relationship between current and voltage in a resistive branch of a parallel RC circuit?
3. What is the phase relationship between current and voltage in a capacitive branch of a parallel RC circuit?
4. What is the phase relationship between total current and total voltage in a parallel RC circuit?
5. The total current in a parallel RC circuit can be found by summing (phasor addition) the individual branch currents. (True or False)
6. If the resistive branch current of a parallel RC circuit is 125 mA and the capacitive current is 75 mA, how much current flows through the source?
7. If the total current in a parallel RC circuit is 200 µA and the resistive current is 100 µA, what is the value of capacitive current?
8. What is the impedance of a parallel RC circuit if the applied voltage is 12 V rms and the total current is 1.6 A rms?
9. Simplify the parallel RC circuit shown in Figure 15-27.

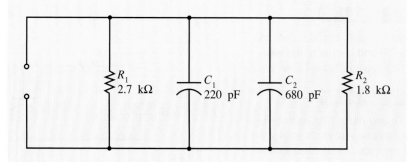

Figure 15-27. Simplify this circuit.

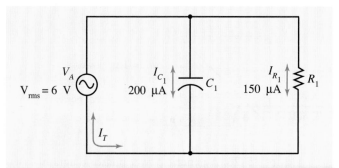

Figure 15-28. A parallel *RC* circuit.

10. Draw the current phasor diagram to represent the circuit shown in Figure 15-28. Be sure to compute the value of I_T.

11. Refer to Figure 15-28. What is the impedance of the circuit?

12. What is the susceptance of the capacitive branch of the circuit in Figure 15-28?

13. Compute the admittance of the circuit shown in Figure 15-28.

15.3 *RC* Circuit Calculations

KEY POINTS

The numerical analysis of an *RC* circuit is based on the same principles as the analysis of resistive circuits.

We are now ready to thoroughly analyze all types of circuit configurations for *RC* circuits. We shall explore series, parallel, series-parallel, and complex circuits. In all cases, we will rely heavily on previously learned equations, relationships, and techniques. As much as practical, we will apply our prior knowledge to the logical solution of unfamiliar problems. This method is much better than rote memorization of lists of equations suited to a specific kind of problem. Once you gain confidence in applying the basic circuit analysis techniques to new circuit types, you will have some very powerful skills that will serve you the rest of your career.

Series *RC* Circuit Computations

KEY POINTS

Since current is the same for all components in a series circuit, it should be found as soon as practical in an analysis problem.

When analyzing series *RC* circuits, as with any series circuit, it is generally helpful to compute current as soon as practical. Once you know current, then you have one factor that is common to all components. Remember, if you know any two factors (e.g., current, voltage, power, resistance, reactance, and so on), then you can calculate most of the remaining factors. There are a few exceptions involving frequency.

EXAMPLE SOLUTION

Analyze the series *RC* circuit shown in Figure 15-29, and complete the solution matrix shown in Table 15-1.

EXAMPLE SOLUTION

There are many paths that lead to the solution of this type of problem. Experience will help you find the most direct one, but for now, compute any unknown you can. The more values you compute, the more options you will

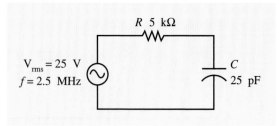

Figure 15-29. Analyze this series *RC* circuit.

CIRCUIT QUANTITY		RESISTOR	CAPACITOR	TOTAL
Current (rms)				
Voltage	V_P			
	V_{PP}			
	V_{rms}			25 V
Resistance/Reactance/Impedance		5 kΩ		
Conductance/Susceptance/Admittance				
Power				
Phase Angle (overall)				
Power Factor (overall)				

Table 15-1. Solution Matrix for the Circuit in Figure 15-29

have for subsequent calculations. Let's begin by computing the peak and peak-to-peak values of applied voltage.

$$V_P = 1.414V_{\text{rms}}$$
$$= 1.414 \times 25 \text{ V} = 35.35 \text{ V}$$

Doubling the peak voltage will give us the peak-to-peak value.

$$V_{PP} = 2V_P$$
$$= 2 \times 35.35 \text{ V} = 70.7 \text{ V}$$

We can now find the value of capacitive reactance, since we know the capacitance and the frequency.

$$X_C = \frac{1}{2\pi fC}$$
$$= \frac{1}{6.28 \times 2.5 \text{ MHz} \times 25 \text{ pF}} = 2.55 \text{ k}\Omega$$

We now have enough information to find the circuit impedance by applying Equation 15-1.

$$Z = \sqrt{R^2 + X_C^2}$$
$$= \sqrt{(5 \text{ k}\Omega)^2 + (2.55 \text{ k}\Omega)^2} = 5.61 \text{ k}\Omega$$

Since we know the applied voltage and the circuit impedance, we can compute current flow in the circuit. We normally use rms values unless we have a specific reason to do otherwise.

$$I_T = \frac{V_A}{Z}$$
$$= \frac{25 \text{ V}}{5.61 \text{ k}\Omega} = 4.46 \text{ mA}$$

Of course, if we want to know the peak or peak-to-peak current, we can repeat this calculation, or simply convert the rms current value directly. In any case, the value of current that we have computed will flow through the entire circuit.

We can now find the individual component voltage drops by applying Ohm's Law.

$$V_R = I_R R$$
$$= 4.46 \text{ mA} \times 5 \text{ k}\Omega = 22.3 \text{ V}$$

A similar calculation gives us the capacitor voltage drop.

$$V_C = I_C X_C$$
$$= 4.46 \text{ mA} \times 2.55 \text{ k}\Omega = 11.37 \text{ V}$$

We should always be alert for opportunities to catch any errors. We know that Kirchhoff's Voltage Law says the sum of the component voltage drops in a series circuit must equal the supply voltage. Do they in this case? Well, probably so, if we remember that the resistor and capacitor voltages are out of phase, so they must be added with phasor addition. Let's check our work at this point with Kirchhoff's Law.

$$V_A = \sqrt{V_R^2 + V_C^2}$$
$$= \sqrt{(22.3 \text{ V})^2 + (11.37 \text{ V})^2} = 25 \text{ V}$$

We now have the confidence to proceed. Let's use our knowledge of basic sine wave relationships and convert the rms component voltage drops to peak and peak-to-peak values.

$$V_{R_P} = 1.414 V_{R_{rms}} = 1.414 \times 22.3 \text{ V} = 31.53 \text{ V}$$
$$V_{R_{PP}} = 2 V_{R_P} = 2 \times 31.53 \text{ V} = 63.06 \text{ V}$$

Similarly,

$$V_{C_P} = 1.414 V_{C_{rms}} = 1.414 \times 11.37 \text{ V} = 16.08 \text{ V}$$
$$V_{C_{PP}} = 2 V_{C_P} = 2 \times 16.08 \text{ V} = 32.16 \text{ V}$$

We can find the values of conductance, susceptance, and admittance by simply taking the reciprocal of resistance, reactance, and impedance, respectively.

$$G = \frac{1}{R} = \frac{1}{5 \text{ k}\Omega} = 200 \text{ }\mu\text{S}$$

We find susceptance in a similar manner.

$$B = \frac{1}{X_C} = \frac{1}{2.55 \text{ k}\Omega} = 392.2 \text{ }\mu\text{S}$$

The reciprocal of impedance will give us the value of admittance.

$$Y = \frac{1}{Z} = \frac{1}{5.61 \text{ k}\Omega} = 178.25 \text{ }\mu\text{S}$$

We can use any of the basic power relationships to compute power in the circuit. We normally use rms values, unless we have some specific reason to compute another quantity (e.g., peak power). Let's begin by finding true power (i.e., that which is dissipated by the resistance as heat).

$$P_T = I_{R_{rms}} \times V_{R_{rms}} = 4.46 \text{ mA} \times 22.3 \text{ V} = 99.5 \text{ mW}$$

A similar calculation will give us the value of reactive power due to the capacitance.

$$P_R = I_{C_{rms}} \times V_{C_{rms}} = 4.46 \text{ mA} \times 11.37 \text{ V} = 50.7 \text{ mVAR}$$

Finally, we can sum (phasor addition) the true and reactive powers to find total or apparent power.

$$P_A = \sqrt{P_T^2 + P_R^2}$$

$$= \sqrt{(99.5 \text{ mW})^2 + (50.7 \text{ mVAR})^2} = 111.7 \text{ mVA}$$

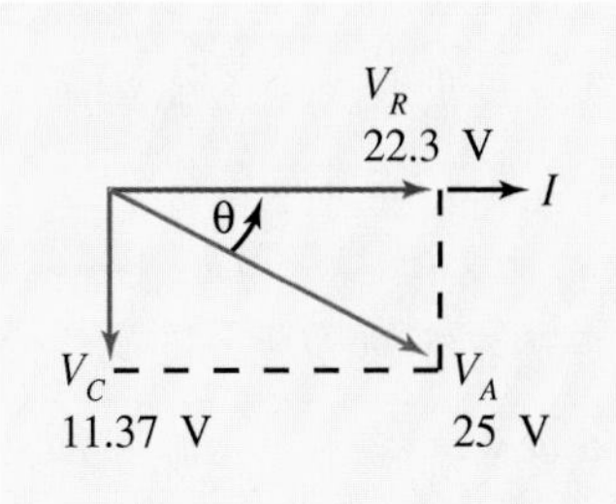

Let's use the voltage phasor diagram to help us identify the phase angle. Figure 15-30 shows the voltage phasor diagram for the circuit in Figure 15-29. The phase angle (θ) is always the angle between total voltage and total current. Since we know all three sides of the right triangle, we can use any of the basic trigonometric functions to find the phase angle. Let's choose the cosine function, so that we will also be finding the power factor of the circuit (i.e., power factor = cos θ).

$$\cos\theta = \frac{\text{adjacent}}{\text{hypotenuse}} = \frac{V_R}{V_A} = \frac{22.3 \text{ V}}{25 \text{ V}} = 0.892$$

$$\theta = \arccos 0.892 = 26.9°$$

The power factor can be further described as leading, since current is always assumed to be the reference when describing power factors as leading or lagging.

This completes our analysis of the circuit shown in Figure 15-29. The completed solution matrix is shown in Table 15-2.

Figure 15-30.
Voltage phasor diagram for the circuit in Figure 15-29.

CIRCUIT QUANTITY		RESISTOR	CAPACITOR	TOTAL
Current (rms)		4.46 mA	4.46 mA	4.46 mA
Voltage	V_P	31.53 V	16.08 V	35.35 V
	V_{PP}	63.06 V	32.16 V	70.7 V
	V_{rms}	22.3 V	11.37 V	25 V
Resistance/Reactance/Impedance		5 kΩ	2.55 kΩ	5.61 kΩ
Conductance/Susceptance/Admittance		200 μS	392.2 μS	178.25 μS
Power		99.5 mW	50.7 mVAR	111.7 mVA
Phase Angle (overall)		26.9°		
Power Factor (overall)		0.892 (leading)		

Table 15-2. Solution Matrix for the Circuit in Figure 15-29

We could also have solved this problem using rectangular and polar notation to describe the various circuit quantities. When representing capacitive reactance with rectangular notation we use the $-j$ prefix. Use of polar and rectangular notation can reduce your calculations, depending on the type of engineering calculator you are using. For example, let us recompute current using complex notation.

$$I_T = \frac{V_A}{Z}$$

$$= \frac{25 \text{ V}}{5 \text{ k}\Omega - j2.55 \text{ k}\Omega}$$

$$= 4.46 \text{ mA} \angle 26.9°$$

We get the value of current and the phase angle in a single calculation.

Practice Problems

1. Analyze the series RC circuit shown in Figure 15-31, and complete a solution matrix similar to Table 15-1.

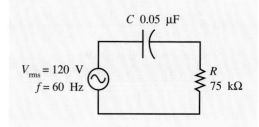

Figure 15-31. Analyze this circuit.

2. Analyze the circuit shown in Figure 15-32 and complete a solution matrix like Table 15-1.

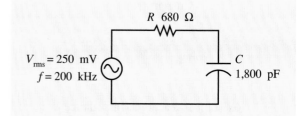

Figure 15-32. Analyze this circuit.

3. Analyze the circuit shown in Figure 15-33, and complete a solution matrix similar to Table 15-1. Be sure to include an entry in the matrix for frequency.

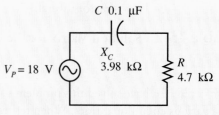

Figure 15-33. Analyze this circuit.

Answers to Practice Problems

1.

CIRCUIT QUANTITY		RESISTOR	CAPACITOR	TOTAL
Current (rms)		1.31 mA	1.31 mA	1.31 mA
Voltage	V_P	139 V	98.4 V	169.7 V
	V_{PP}	278 V	196.8 V	339.4 V
	V_{rms}	98.3 V	69.6 V	120 V
Resistance/Reactance/Impedance		75 kΩ	53.1 kΩ	91.9 kΩ
Conductance/Susceptance/Admittance		13.3 μS	18.8 μS	10.9 μS
Power		128.8 mW	91.2 mVAR	157.2 mVA
Phase Angle (overall)		35.3°		
Power Factor (overall)		0.816 (leading)		

2.

CIRCUIT QUANTITY		RESISTOR	CAPACITOR	TOTAL
Current (rms)		308.2 μA	308.2 μA	308.2 μA
Voltage	V_P	0.296 V	0.193 V	0.35 V
	V_{PP}	0.593 V	0.386 V	0.7 V
	V_{rms}	0.210 V	0.136 V	0.25 V
Resistance/Reactance/Impedance		680 Ω	442.3 Ω	811.2 Ω
Conductance/Susceptance/Admittance		1.47 mS	2.26 mS	1.23 mS
Power		64.7 μW	41.9 μVAR	77.1 μVA
Phase Angle (overall)		33°		
Power Factor (overall)		0.839 (leading)		

3.

CIRCUIT QUANTITY		RESISTOR	CAPACITOR	TOTAL
Current (rms)		2.07 mA	2.07 mA	2.07 mA
Voltage	V_P	13.8 V	11.7 V	18 V
	V_{PP}	27.5 V	22.3 V	36 V
	V_{rms}	9.7 V	8.2 V	12.7 V
Resistance/Reactance/Impedance		4.7 kΩ	3.98 kΩ	6.16 kΩ
Conductance/Susceptance/Admittance		212.8 μS	251.3 μS	162.3 μS
Power		20.1 mW	17 mVAR	26.3 mVA
Phase Angle (overall)		40.3°		
Power Factor (overall)		0.763 (leading)		
Frequency (overall)		400.1 Hz		

Parallel *RC* Circuit Computations

KEY POINTS

When analyzing a parallel circuit, voltage should be found early in the problem, since it is common to all components.

Analysis of parallel *RC* circuits should seem like a logical progression that represents more of an application of previously learned material than a series of new concepts. There is no need to memorize a set of new, specialized equations. Ohm's and Kirchhoff's Laws and basic circuit theory are all you need.

EXAMPLE SOLUTION

Complete the solution matrix given in Table 15-3 for the parallel *RC* circuit shown in Figure 15-34.

CIRCUIT QUANTITY		RESISTOR	CAPACITOR	TOTAL
Current (rms)				
Voltage	V_P			
	V_{PP}			
	V_{rms}			75 V
Resistance/Reactance/Impedance		2.2 kΩ		
Conductance/Susceptance/Admittance				
Power				
Phase Angle (overall)				
Power Factor (overall)				

Table 15-3. Solution Matrix for the Circuit in Figure 15-34

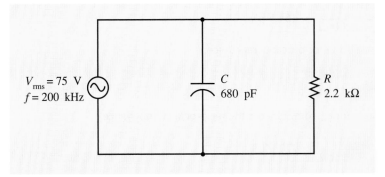

$V_{rms} = 75$ V
$f = 200$ kHz

C
680 pF

R
2.2 kΩ

Figure 15-34. Analyze this parallel *RC* circuit.

In a parallel circuit, the voltage is common to all components. Let's begin by applying the basic sine wave equations to convert the rms voltage to peak and peak-to-peak values.

$$V_{A_P} = 1.414 V_{A_{rms}} = 1.414 \times 75 \text{ V} = 106.05 \text{ V}$$

$$V_{A_{PP}} = 2V_{A_P} = 2 \times 106.05 \text{ V} = 212.1 \text{ V}$$

Of course, these values are the same for the applied voltage, the resistor voltage, and the capacitor voltage, since they are all in parallel.

Now, let's compute the capacitive reactance of the circuit.

$$X_C = \frac{1}{2\pi f C} = \frac{1}{6.28 \times 200 \text{ kHz} \times 680 \text{ pF}} = 1.17 \text{ k}\Omega$$

Since we know the voltage and the resistance or reactance for each branch, we can now compute the current flow in each branch with Ohm's Law. First, let's compute the resistive current.

$$I_R = \frac{V_R}{R} = \frac{75 \text{ V}}{2.2 \text{ k}\Omega} = 34.1 \text{ mA}$$

We have computed rms current, but we could easily convert it to peak or peak-to-peak with the basic sine wave equations. We find current through the capacitive branch in a similar way.

$$I_C = \frac{V_C}{X_C} = \frac{75 \text{ V}}{1.17 \text{ k}\Omega} = 64.1 \text{ mA}$$

Total current in a parallel circuit is equal to the sum (phasor sum in the case of *RC* circuits) of the individual branch currents. We use Equation 15-4 to compute the phasor sum.

$$I_T = \sqrt{I_R^2 + I_C^2}$$

$$= \sqrt{(34.1 \text{ mA})^2 + (64.1 \text{ mA})^2} = 72.61 \text{ mA}$$

With known values for total current and total voltage, we can apply Ohm's Law to find circuit impedance.

$$Z = \frac{V_A}{I_T} = \frac{75 \text{ V}}{72.61 \text{ mA}} = 1.03 \text{ k}\Omega$$

We can compute conductance, susceptance, and admittance by finding the reciprocals of resistance, reactance, and impedance, respectively. We compute conductance as

$$G = \frac{1}{R} = \frac{1}{2,200 \ \Omega} = 454.5 \ \mu S$$

Susceptance is the reciprocal of reactance.

$$B = \frac{1}{X_C} = \frac{1}{1.17 \ k\Omega} = 854.7 \ \mu S$$

In a similar manner, admittance is the reciprocal of impedance.

$$Y = \frac{1}{Z} = \frac{1}{1.03 \ k\Omega} = 970.9 \ \mu S$$

We can use the basic power equations to compute the various powers in the circuit. Let's begin with the true power dissipated in the resistance.

$$P_T = V_R I_R = 75 \ V \times 34.1 \ mA = 2.56 \ W$$

The reactive power is found in a similar manner.

$$P_R = V_C I_C = 75 \ V \times 64.1 \ mA = 4.81 \ VAR$$

Total power in any circuit is the sum of the individual powers. In this case, we have true power and reactive power, which are 90° out of phase, so we must sum them with phasor addition to get total, or apparent power.

$$P_A = \sqrt{P_T{}^2 + P_R{}^2}$$
$$= \sqrt{(2.56 \ W)^2 + (4.81 \ VAR)^2} = 5.45 \ VA$$

Of course, we could also have used one of the basic power equations to compute total (apparent) power.

Figure 15-35 shows a phasor diagram for the circuit shown in Figure 15-34. With the aid of this diagram, we can easily find the phase angle and power factor.

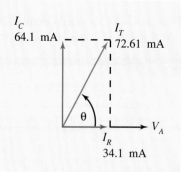

Figure 15-35. A phasor diagram for the circuit shown in Figure 15-34.

Since we now know all three sides of the right triangle shown in Figure 15-35, we can use any one of the sine, cosine, or tangent functions to find the phase angle (θ). If we choose the cosine function, it will also provide us with the power factor of the circuit (power factor = cos θ).

$$\cos\theta = \frac{\text{adjacent}}{\text{hypotenuse}} = \frac{I_R}{I_T}$$

$$= \frac{34.1 \text{ mA}}{72.61 \text{ mA}} = 0.47$$

$$\theta = \arccos 0.47 = 61.97°$$

Since current is always the reference when describing power factors, we will list the power factor as leading.

This completes our analysis of the circuit shown in Figure 15-34. The completed solution matrix is given in Table 15-4.

CIRCUIT QUANTITY		RESISTOR	CAPACITOR	TOTAL
Current (rms)		34.1 mA	64.1 mA	72.61 mA
Voltage	V_P	106.05 V	106.05 V	106.05 V
	V_{PP}	212.1 V	212.1 V	212.1 V
	V_{rms}	75 V	75 V	75 V
Resistance/Reactance/Impedance		2.2 kΩ	1.17 kΩ	1.03 kΩ
Conductance/Susceptance/Admittance		454.5 µS	854.7 µS	970.9 µS
Power		2.56 W	4.81 VAR	5.45 VA
Phase Angle (overall)		61.97°		
Power Factor (overall)		0.47 (leading)		

Table 15-4. Completed Solution Matrix for the Circuit in Figure 15-34.

Practice Problems

1. Complete a solution matrix similar to Table 15-3 for the circuit shown in Figure 15-36.

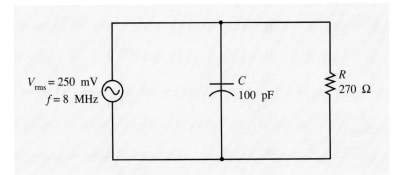

$V_{rms} = 250$ mV
$f = 8$ MHz
C 100 pF
R 270 Ω

Figure 15-36. Analyze this circuit.

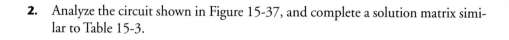

2. Analyze the circuit shown in Figure 15-37, and complete a solution matrix similar to Table 15-3.

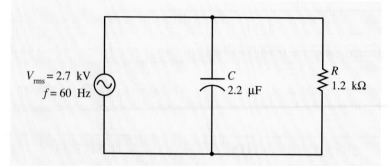

Figure 15-37. Analyze this circuit.

3. Complete a solution matrix similar to Table 15-3 for the circuit shown in Figure 15-38.

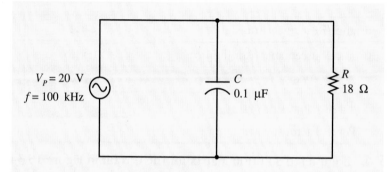

Figure 15-38. Analyze this circuit.

Answers to Practice Problems

1.

CIRCUIT QUANTITY		RESISTOR	CAPACITOR	TOTAL
Current (rms)		925.9 μA	1.26 mA	1.56 mA
Voltage	V_P	0.354 V	0.354 V	0.354 V
	V_{PP}	0.707 V	0.707 V	0.707 V
	V_{rms}	0.25 V	0.25 V	0.25 V
Resistance/Reactance/Impedance		270 Ω	199 Ω	159.9 Ω
Conductance/Susceptance/Admittance		3.7 mS	5.03 mS	6.25 mS
Power		231.5 μW	315 μVAR	390 μVA
Phase Angle (overall)		53.6°		
Power Factor (overall)		0.594 (leading)		

2.

CIRCUIT QUANTITY		RESISTOR	CAPACITOR	TOTAL
Current (rms)		2.25 A	2.23 A	3.17 A
Voltage	V_P	3.82 kV	3.82 kV	3.82 kV
	V_{PP}	7.64 kV	7.64 kV	7.64 kV
	V_{rms}	2.7 kV	2.7 kV	2.7 kV
Resistance/Reactance/Impedance		1.2 kΩ	1.21 kΩ	852.3 Ω
Conductance/Susceptance/Admittance		833 μS	826 μS	1.17 mS
Power		6.08 kW	6.02 kVAR	8.56 kVA
Phase Angle (overall)		44.8°		
Power Factor (overall)		0.71 (leading)		

3.

CIRCUIT QUANTITY		RESISTOR	CAPACITOR	TOTAL
Current (rms)		785.7 mA	888 mA	1.19 A
Voltage	V_P	20 V	20 V	20 V
	V_{PP}	40 V	40 V	40 V
	V_{rms}	14.14 V	14.14 V	14.14 V
Resistance/Reactance/Impedance		18 Ω	15.92 Ω	11.88 Ω
Conductance/Susceptance/Admittance		55.56 mS	62.81 mS	84.16 mS
Power		11.11 W	12.56 VAR	16.83 VA
Phase Angle (overall)		48.7°		
Power Factor (overall)		0.66 (leading)		

Series-Parallel *RC* Circuits with Sinusoidal Current

The solution of series-parallel *RC* problems is very similar to the simplification of resistive or *RL* series-parallel circuit problems. First we simplify the circuit, then we perform computations to determine total current, impedance, and so on. Finally, we work to expand the circuit to compute the individual component voltages, currents, and so forth.

Circuit Simplification

To simplify a series-parallel *RC* circuit, we replace sets of series or parallel resistances with an equivalent resistance. Similarly, we replace sets of series or parallel capacitances with an equivalent capacitance. In each case, we use the basic equations for combining series or parallel resistances or capacitances.

EXAMPLE SOLUTION

Simplify the circuit shown in Figure 15-39 by combining sets of series and parallel resistances and capacitances.

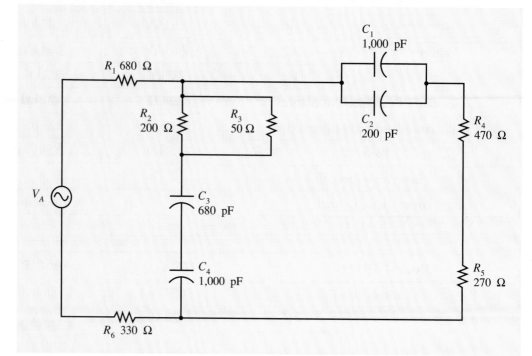

Figure 15-39. Simplify this circuit.

EXAMPLE **SOLUTION**

Let's start by noting that capacitors C_1 and C_2 are in parallel. We combine them as follows:

$$C_{1,2} = C_1 + C_2 = 1,000 \text{ pF} + 200 \text{ pF} = 1,200 \text{ pF}$$

Resistors R_4 and R_5 are in series and can be combined.

$$R_{4,5} = R_4 + R_5 = 470 \ \Omega + 270 \ \Omega = 740 \ \Omega$$

Resistors R_1 and R_6 are in series and combine as follows.

$$R_{1,6} = R_1 + R_6 = 680 \ \Omega + 330 \ \Omega = 1,010 \ \Omega$$

Resistors R_2 and R_3 are directly in parallel and can be replaced with an equivalent value.

$$R_{2,3} = \frac{R_2 R_3}{R_2 + R_3} = \frac{200 \ \Omega \times 50 \ \Omega}{200 \ \Omega + 50 \ \Omega} = 40 \ \Omega$$

Capacitors C_3 and C_4 are in series and can be combined with the reciprocal equation.

$$C_{3,4} = \cfrac{1}{\cfrac{1}{C_3} + \cfrac{1}{C_4}}$$

$$= \cfrac{1}{\cfrac{1}{680 \text{ pF}} + \cfrac{1}{1,000 \text{ pF}}} = 404.8 \text{ pF}$$

There are no more straightforward series or parallel combinations. Our circuit simplification at this point is shown in Figure 15-40. We can further simplify the circuit, but we will need to use rectangular or polar notation to represent the various branch impedances. We will perform this type of calculation in the next section.

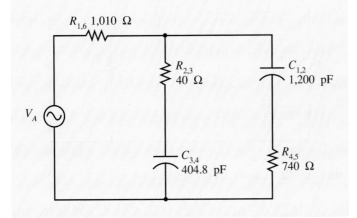

Figure 15-40. A partially simplified version of the circuit shown in Figure 15-39.

Practice Problems

1. Simplify the circuit shown in Figure 15-41 by replacing sets of series or parallel components.

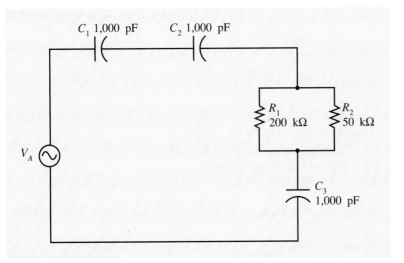

Figure 15-41. Simplify this circuit.

2. Simplify the circuit shown in Figure 15-42 by replacing sets of series or parallel components.

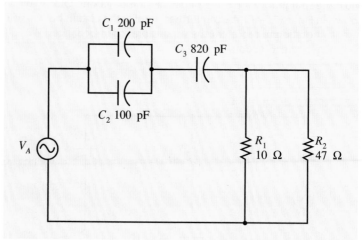

Figure 15-42. Simplify this circuit.

3. Simplify the circuit shown in Figure 15-43 by replacing sets of series or parallel components.

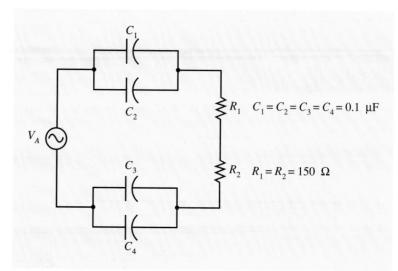

Figure 15-43. Simplify this circuit.

Answers to Practice Problems

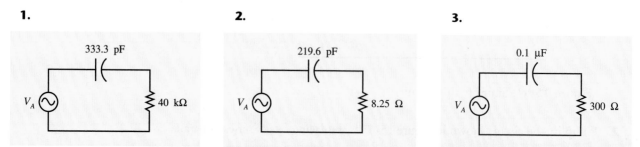

1.

2.

3.

CIRCUIT COMPUTATIONS

We now have all the tools necessary to fully analyze a series-parallel *RC* circuit. You must remember that there are many paths that lead to a valid solution. At this point, calculate any circuit value you can find. The more values you have, the more options you will have for subsequent calculations. As always, use Ohm's and Kirchhoff's Laws and your basic knowledge of circuit configurations as the foundation of your analysis.

EXAMPLE SOLUTION

Analyze the series-parallel *RC* circuit shown in Figure 15-44, and complete the solution matrix given in Table 15-5.

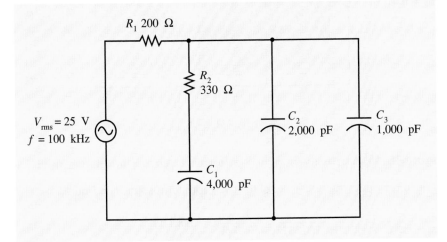

Figure 15-44. A series-parallel *RC* circuit.

CIRCUIT QUANTITY	R_1	R_2	C_1	C_2	C_3	TOTAL
Voltage (rms)						25 V
Current (rms)						
Resistance/Reactance/Impedance	200 Ω	330 Ω				
Conductance/Susceptance/Admittance						
Power						
Phase Angle (overall)						
Power Factor (overall)						

Table 15-5. A Solution Matrix for the Circuit in Figure 15-44

EXAMPLE SOLUTION

Our first step will be to combine any sets of series or parallel resistances or capacitances. By inspection, we see that capacitors C_2 and C_3 are in parallel and can be combined.

$$C_{2,3} = C_2 + C_3 = 2{,}000 \text{ pF} + 1{,}000 \text{ pF} = 3{,}000 \text{ pF}$$

There are no more resistances or capacitances that are directly in series or parallel. Our partially simplified circuit is shown in Figure 15-45.

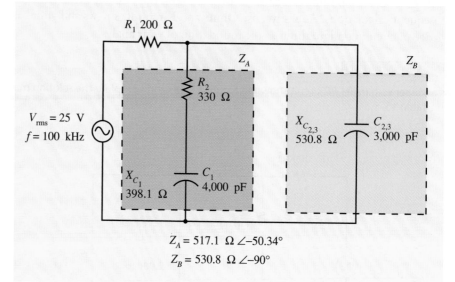

$$Z_A = 517.1 \ \Omega \ \angle{-50.34°}$$
$$Z_B = 530.8 \ \Omega \ \angle{-90°}$$

Figure 15-45. A partially simplified version of the circuit shown in Figure 15-44.

Now let us compute the reactances of the two capacitances shown in Figure 15-45.

$$X_{C_1} = \frac{1}{2\pi f C_1} = \frac{1}{6.28 \times 100 \text{ kHz} \times 4{,}000 \text{ pF}} = 398.1 \ \Omega$$

Similarly, we find the reactance of equivalent capacitor $C_{2,3}$.

$$X_{C_{2,3}} = \frac{1}{2\pi f C_{2,3}} = \frac{1}{6.28 \times 100 \text{ kHz} \times 3{,}000 \text{ pF}} = 530.8 \ \Omega$$

The reactances for C_1 and $C_{2,3}$ are labeled on Figure 15-45. The two parallel branches are also labeled as Z_A and Z_B to simplify their reference in equations.

The next step toward fully simplifying this circuit is to combine parallel branches Z_A and Z_B. These impedances can be expressed individually as follows:

$$Z_A = 330 \ \Omega - j398.1 \ \Omega$$
$$Z_B = 0 - j530.8 \ \Omega$$

It might be beneficial (depending on your specific calculator) to also determine the polar form of these impedances. Note the minus sign associated with the capacitive reactance, since it is drawn downward on the impedance phasor diagram.

$$Z_A = \sqrt{R_2{}^2 + X_{C_1}{}^2}$$

$$= \sqrt{(330 \ \Omega)^2 + (398.1 \ \Omega)^2} = 517.1 \ \Omega$$

$$\theta_A = \arctan \frac{X_{C_1}}{R_2} = \arctan \frac{-398.1 \ \Omega}{330 \ \Omega}$$

$$= \arctan -1.206 = -50.34°; \text{ therefore}$$

$Z_A = 517.1 \ \Omega \ \angle{-50.34°}$

Conversion of Z_B to polar form is rather straightforward.

$Z_B = 530.8 \ \Omega \ \angle{-90°}$

Since impedances Z_A and Z_B are in parallel, we can combine them with the reciprocal equation, or simply the product-over-the-sum approach.

$$Z_{A,B} = \frac{Z_A Z_B}{Z_A + Z_B}$$

$$= \frac{(517.1 \ \Omega \ \angle{-50.34°}) \ (530.8 \ \Omega \ \angle{-90°})}{(330 \ \Omega - j398.1 \ \Omega) + (0 - j530.8 \ \Omega)}$$

$$= \frac{(274.48 \times 10^3) \ \angle{-140.34°}}{330 \ \Omega - j928.9 \ \Omega}$$

$$= 278.44 \ \Omega \ \angle{-69.9°} \ = 95.7 \ \Omega - j261.5 \ \Omega$$

Figure 15-46 shows the results of our simplification to this point.

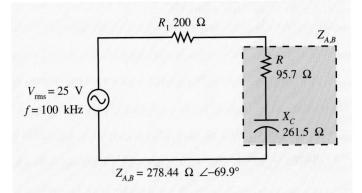

Figure 15-46. A partially simplified version of the circuit shown in Figure 15-44.

In the equivalent series circuit shown in Figure 15-46, we can see that total impedance can be found by summing R_1 and $Z_{A,B}$. We perform this calculation as follows:

$$Z_T = R_1 + Z_{A,B}$$

$$= 200 \ \Omega + (95.7 \ \Omega - j261.5 \ \Omega)$$

$$= 295.7 \ \Omega - j261.5 \ \Omega \ = 394.7 \ \Omega \ \angle{-41.5°}$$

By converting our final impedance value to polar form, we also find the phase angle of the circuit. The fully simplified circuit is shown in Figure 15-47. Of course, we could determine the value of equivalent capacitance, if desired. That is,

$$X_C = \frac{1}{2\pi f C}, \ \text{or}$$

$$C = \frac{1}{2\pi f X_C}$$

$$= \frac{1}{6.28 \times 100 \ \text{kHz} \times 261.5 \ \Omega} = 6,089 \ \text{pF}$$

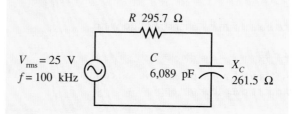

Figure 15-47. A fully simplified equivalent circuit for the circuit originally shown in Figure 15-44.

Now, just as we would do in a resistive circuit analysis problem, we want to find total current and then work our way back through the partially simplified sketches as we compute individual component voltages and currents. If desired, we could use rectangular or polar notation for the current, voltages, and impedances in the following calculations. While this complicates the calculations, it does give us the phase angle at every point in the circuit. For purposes of this example, we will use the magnitude portion of the circuit quantities only. This will give us the correct values of current, voltage, and so on, but we will not have the phase angles at the intermediate circuit points. Let's compute total current with Ohm's Law.

$$I_T = \frac{V_A}{Z_T} = \frac{25 \text{ V}}{394.7 \ \Omega} = 63.34 \text{ mA}$$

Let's transfer this total current value to the partially simplified sketch shown in Figure 15-46. Clearly, total current flows through R_1. We can apply Ohm's Law to compute the voltage drop across R_1.

$$V_{R_1} = I_{R_1}R_1 = 63.34 \text{ mA} \times 200 \ \Omega = 12.67 \text{ V}$$

The remaining voltage is dropped across $Z_{A,B}$ in Figure 15-46. We compute its voltage drop as follows:

$$V_{Z_{A,B}} = I_{Z_{A,B}}Z_{A,B} = 63.34 \text{ mA} \times 278.44 \ \Omega = 17.64 \text{ V}$$

By inspection of Figures 15-45 and 15-46, we can see that this same voltage will be felt across both branches Z_A and Z_B.

Now, let's apply Ohm's Law to branches Z_A and Z_B to find the current flow.

$$I_{Z_A} = \frac{V_{Z_A}}{Z_A} = \frac{17.64 \text{ V}}{517.1 \ \Omega} = 34.11 \text{ mA}$$

$$I_{Z_B} = \frac{V_{Z_B}}{Z_B} = \frac{17.64 \text{ V}}{530.8 \ \Omega} = 33.23 \text{ mA}$$

We can see from the circuit diagram in Figure 15-45, that the I_{Z_A} current flows through R_2 and C_1. Similarly, the I_{Z_B} current flows through $C_{2,3}$. To determine the amount of current through C_2 and C_3 individually, we can use the current divider method or simply apply Ohm's Law. Let's choose the latter approach. First, we need to compute the individual reactances of C_2 and C_3.

$$X_{C_2} = \frac{1}{2\pi f C_2} = \frac{1}{6.28 \times 100 \text{ kHz} \times 2,000 \text{ pF}} = 796.18 \ \Omega$$

$$X_{C_3} = \frac{1}{2\pi f C_3} = \frac{1}{6.28 \times 100 \text{ kHz} \times 1,000 \text{ pF}} = 1.59 \text{ k}\Omega$$

Now applying Ohm's Law, we get

$$I_{C_2} = \frac{V_{C_2}}{X_{C_2}} = \frac{17.64 \text{ V}}{796.18 \text{ } \Omega} = 22.16 \text{ mA}$$

$$I_{C_3} = \frac{V_{C_3}}{X_{C_3}} = \frac{17.64 \text{ V}}{1.59 \text{ k}\Omega} = 11.09 \text{ mA}$$

The individual voltage drops across R_2 and C_1 can be found by applying Ohm's Law.

$$V_{R_2} = I_{R_2}R_2 = 34.11 \text{ mA} \times 330 \text{ } \Omega = 11.26 \text{ V}$$

$$V_{C_1} = I_{C_1}X_{C_1} = 34.11 \text{ mA} \times 398.1 \text{ } \Omega = 13.58 \text{ V}$$

This completes the voltage and current calculations for the circuit. We can complete the Conductance/Susceptance/Admittance row in Table 15-5 by finding the reciprocal of the corresponding resistance, reactance, or impedance.

$$G_1 = \frac{1}{R_1} = \frac{1}{200 \text{ } \Omega} = 5 \text{ mS}$$

$$G_2 = \frac{1}{R_2} = \frac{1}{330 \text{ } \Omega} = 3.03 \text{ mS}$$

$$B_1 = \frac{1}{X_{C_1}} = \frac{1}{398.1 \text{ } \Omega} = 2.51 \text{ mS}$$

$$B_2 = \frac{1}{X_{C_2}} = \frac{1}{796.18 \text{ } \Omega} = 1.26 \text{ mS}$$

$$B_3 = \frac{1}{X_{C_3}} = \frac{1}{1.59 \text{ k}\Omega} = 628.9 \text{ } \mu\text{S}$$

$$Y_T = \frac{1}{Z_T} = \frac{1}{394.7 \text{ } \Omega} = 2.53 \text{ mS}$$

We can compute the various powers with any of the power equations. Let's choose to use the $P = VI$ form in all cases.

$$P_{R_1} = V_{R_1}I_{R_1} = 12.67 \text{ V} \times 63.34 \text{ mA} = 802.5 \text{ mW}$$

$$P_{R_2} = V_{R_2}I_{R_2} = 11.26 \text{ V} \times 34.11 \text{ mA} = 384.1 \text{ mW}$$

$$P_{C_1} = V_{C_1}I_{C_1} = 13.58 \text{ V} \times 34.11 \text{ mA} = 463.2 \text{ mVAR}$$

$$P_{C_2} = V_{C_2}I_{C_2} = 17.64 \text{ V} \times 22.16 \text{ mA} = 390.9 \text{ mVAR}$$

$$P_{C_3} = V_{C_3}I_{C_3} = 17.64 \text{ V} \times 11.09 \text{ mA} = 195.6 \text{ mVAR}$$

$$P_T = V_TI_T = 25 \text{ V} \times 63.34 \text{ mA} = 1.58 \text{ VA}$$

Of course, we could have computed total power as a sum (phasor addition) of the individual powers.

The last entry in our solution matrix is power factor. Power factor, you will recall, is simply the cosine of the phase angle (θ). In the present case, we have

$$\text{power factor} = \cos\theta = \cos -41.5° = 0.749$$

It is a leading power factor, since we have a capacitive circuit.

This completes our analysis of the circuit shown in Figure 15-44. The completed solution matrix is shown in Table 15-6.

CIRCUIT QUANTITY	R_1	R_2	C_1	C_2	C_3	TOTAL
Voltage (rms)	12.67 V	11.26 V	13.58 V	17.64 V	17.64 V	25 V
Current (rms)	63.34 mA	34.11 mA	34.11 mA	22.16 mA	11.09 mA	63.34 mA
Resistance/Reactance/Impedance	200 Ω	330 Ω	398.1 Ω	796.18 Ω	1.59 kΩ	394.7 Ω
Conductance/Susceptance/Admittance	5 mS	3.03 mS	2.51 mS	1.26 mS	628.9 µS	2.53 mS
Power	802.5 mW	384.1 mW	463.2 mVAR	390.9 mVAR	195.6 mVAR	1.58 VA
Phase Angle (overall)	$-41.5°$					
Power Factor (overall)	0.749 (leading)					

Table 15-6. A Completed Solution Matrix for the Circuit in Figure 15-44

Practice Problems

1. Analyze the circuit shown in Figure 15-48, and complete a solution matrix similar to the one in Table 15-5.
2. Analyze the circuit shown in Figure 15-49, and complete a solution matrix similar to the one in Table 15-5.

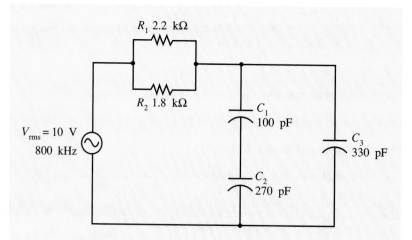

Figure 15-48. Analyze this *RC* circuit.

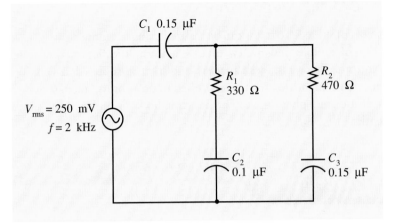

Figure 15-49. Analyze this *RC* circuit.

Answers to Practice Problems

1.

CIRCUIT QUANTITY	R_1	R_2	C_1	C_2	C_3	TOTAL
Voltage (rms)	8.95 V	8.95 V	3.26 V	1.21 V	4.47 V	10 V
Current (rms)	4.07 mA	4.97 mA	1.64 mA	1.64 mA	7.4 mA	9.04 mA
Resistance/Reactance/Impedance	2.2 kΩ	1.8 kΩ	1.99 kΩ	737.2 Ω	603.2 Ω	1.11 kΩ
Conductance/Susceptance/Admittance	455 µS	556 µS	503 µS	1.36 mS	1.66 mS	901 µS
Power	36.4 mW	44.5 mW	5.35 mVAR	1.98 mVAR	33.1 mVAR	90.4 mVA
Phase Angle (overall)	–26.5°					
Power Factor (overall)	0.895 (leading)					

2.

CIRCUIT QUANTITY	R_1	R_2	C_1	C_2	C_3	TOTAL
Voltage (rms)	42.5 mV	73.6 mV	149.4 mV	102.6 mV	83.1 mV	0.25 V
Current (rms)	128.8 µA	156.6 µA	281.5 µA	128.8 µA	156.6 µA	281.5 µA
Resistance/Reactance/Impedance	330 Ω	470 Ω	530.8 Ω	796.2 Ω	530.8 Ω	888 Ω
Conductance/Susceptance/Admittance	3.03 mS	2.13 mS	1.88 mS	1.26 mS	1.88 mS	1.13 mS
Power	5.47 µW	11.53 µW	42.1 µVAR	13.2 µVAR	13 µVAR	70.4 µVA
Phase Angle (overall)	–76°					
Power Factor (overall)	0.242 (leading)					

Complex *RC* Circuit Computations

The solution of complex *RC* circuits can be realized using the same network theorems used for the solution of complex resistive circuits. When simplification methods such as Thevenin's and Norton's Theorems, mesh analysis, and so on are applied to a complex *RC* network, the circuit quantities must be expressed in polar or rectangular notation to account for the nonzero phase angle. The basic method of simplification, however, remains identical.

Exercise Problems 15.3

Refer to Figure 15-50 for Problems 1–10.

1. What is the reactance of C?
2. What is the impedance of the circuit?
3. What is the admittance of the circuit?
4. How much current flows through R?
5. What is the total current in the circuit?
6. What is the voltage drop across R?
7. What is the voltage drop across C?
8. What is the phase angle (θ) between total voltage and total current in the circuit?
9. What is the power factor of the circuit?
10. What is the apparent power in the circuit?

Refer to Figure 15-51 for Problems 11–20.

11. What is the peak voltage across C_1?
12. What is the rms voltage across C_2?

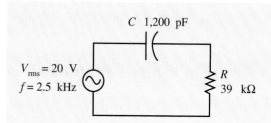

Figure 15-50. A series *RC* circuit.

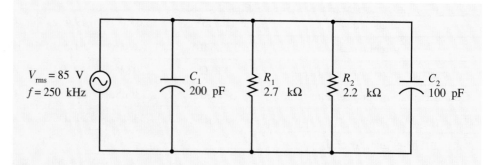

Figure 15-51. A parallel *RC* circuit.

13. How much current flows through R_1?
14. How much current flows through C_2?
15. What is the total current in the circuit?
16. What is the total impedance of the circuit?
17. What is the susceptance of C_1?
18. How much true power is dissipated by the circuit?
19. What is the phase angle between total voltage and total current in the circuit?
20. What is the apparent power in the circuit?

Refer to Figure 15-52 for Problems 21–30.

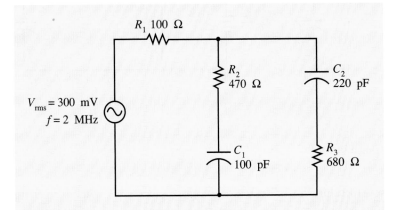

Figure 15-52. A series-parallel RC circuit.

21. What is the branch impedance of R_2 and C_1?
22. What is the branch impedance of R_3 and C_2?
23. What is the total impedance of the circuit?
24. How much current flows in the circuit?
25. What is the total admittance of the circuit?
26. What is the voltage drop across R_1?
27. What is the voltage drop across the entire R_2C_1 branch?
28. How much voltage is dropped across R_3?
29. What is the overall power factor of the circuit?
30. How much apparent power is delivered by the source?

15.4 Pulse Response of RC Circuits

We have thoroughly discussed the analysis of RC circuits with sinusoidal inputs. Nonsinusoidal input waveforms cause a radically different circuit response and require different analytical methods. It is not necessary for you to be able to thoroughly analyze the nonsinusoidal response of an RC circuit at this time, but it is important for you to understand RC time constants and how an RC circuit responds to a pulse or rectangular waveform.

RC Time Constant

Figure 15-53 shows a simple circuit that will manually produce pulse waveforms to an *RC* circuit as the switch is moved between positions A and B. When the switch is first moved to position A (Figure 15-53a), current will flow through the *RC* circuit and begin to charge the capacitor. The initial value of current is limited only by the resistor. Charging current continues until the capacitor voltage is equal to the battery voltage.

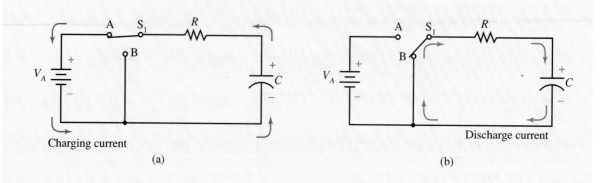

Charging current

(a)

Discharge current

(b)

Figure 15-53. An *RC* circuit with a pulse input.

Now we know from previous discussions that for a given size capacitor to charge to a particular voltage requires a definite amount of charge (i.e., a definite number of electrons). You will recall the expression for charge is $Q = CV$. It takes time for the electrons to move around the circuit and accumulate on the capacitor. How long does it take for enough electrons to move around the circuit to charge the capacitor to a value equal to the supply voltage? Well, that depends on the value of charging current. Remember, current is a measure of how many electrons move past a given point in one second. As stated previously, the resistor limits the value of current in the circuit. The more resistance we have in the resistor, the lower the current and the longer it takes the capacitor to reach full charge.

It is also important to note that the value of charging current decays as the capacitor becomes charged. In essence, the accumulating charge on the capacitor provides more and more opposition to the applied voltage (like series-opposing voltage sources). When the capacitor is fully charged, the opposing voltages are equal and no more current can flow.

The total time required for the capacitor to fully charge is divided into five time periods called time constants. The Greek letter tau (τ) is used to represent one time constant. In the case of *RC* circuits, τ is computed with Equation 15-5.

$$\tau = RC \qquad\qquad (15\text{-}5)$$

where τ is measured in seconds, R is measured in ohms, and C is measured in farads.

Figure 15-54(a) illustrates the timing of the capacitor voltage and the charging current. The graph indicates that after a time interval of $t = \tau$, the capacitor voltage has increased to 63.2% of its full-charge value. At that same time, charging current has decreased to 36.8% of its initial value. During each additional time period of τ seconds, the capacitor voltage increases by 63.2% of the remaining voltage. For example, at the end of the first time interval (τ), the capacitor voltage has another 36.8% to go. During the time between τ and 2τ it will increase 63.2% of this 36.8% or 23.3% for a total of 86.5% at time $t = 2\tau$.

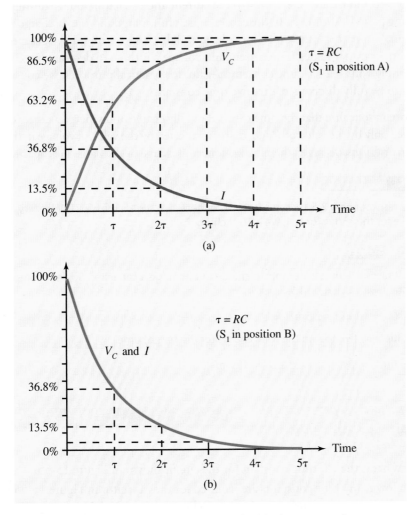

Figure 15-54. An *RC* time constant graph: (a) charging and (b) discharging.

Once 5τ seconds have elapsed, the capacitor voltage will have increased to more than 99% of its full-charge value. Likewise, the charging current will have decreased to less than 1% of its initial value. For practical purposes, we consider the capacitor to have reached full charge in five time constants (5τ).

If the capacitor in Figure 15-53(a) has reached full charge with the switch in position A, there will be no additional current flow. The charge on the capacitor is equal, but opposite, to the battery potential. Now, if we move the switch to position B, the charge on the capacitor acts like a voltage source and causes a discharge current to flow. This action is illustrated in Figure 15-53(b). Again, the amount of initial current is limited by the resistor. The higher the discharge current (i.e., the lower the value of the resistor), the quicker the capacitor can discharge its accumulated voltage. The discharge current will continue until the charge on the capacitor has decreased to zero.

Figure 15-54(b) illustrates the timing of the current and capacitor voltage during the discharging period. At time $t = 0$, the capacitor is at full charge and the discharge current is maximum. At time $t = \tau$, the capacitor voltage and discharge current have decayed to 36.8% of their initial values. The current and voltage continue to decrease by 63.2% of the remaining voltage each time constant. Again, for practical purposes, we consider the capacitor to be fully discharged after five time constants (5τ).

It is important to realize that the time required to fully charge or discharge a capacitor (5τ) is determined only by the value of R and C. It is unaffected by the value of voltage in the circuit. If either R or C is made larger, then it takes longer to charge or discharge the capacitor.

EXAMPLE SOLUTION

If a 10-kΩ resistor and a 2.5-μF capacitor are connected in series across a 10-V battery, how long does it take for the capacitor to have a 10-V charge?

EXAMPLE **SOLUTION**

We know it takes five time constants to charge or discharge a capacitor. So, let's compute the time constant with Equation 15-5.

$\tau = RC = 10\ \text{k}\Omega \times 2.5\ \mu\text{F} = 25\ \text{ms}$

We multiply by five to find the total charge (or discharge) time.

charge time $= 5\tau = 5 \times 25\ \text{ms} = 125\ \text{ms}$

Practice Problems

1. What is the RC time constant for the circuit shown in Figure 15-55?
2. How many time constants are required for the capacitor in Figure 15-55 to reach full charge, once the switch has been closed?

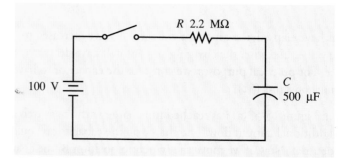

Figure 15-55. An RC circuit.

3. What will be the approximate value of current in the circuit shown in Figure 15-55, after five time constants?

4. Refer to Figure 15-56. Capacitor C_1 is charged to 1.5 V. Capacitor C_2 is charged to 2.0 kV. The two switches are mechanically linked and move together. When the switches are closed, which capacitor will discharge to 0 V first? Explain.

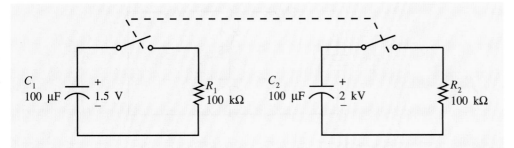

Figure 15-56. An *RC* time constant problem.

Answers to Practice Problems

1. 1,100 s or 18.33 min   **2.** 5   **3.** zero

4. Both capacitors will discharge in five time constants. Since the time constants are the same, the discharge time will be the same.

Precise *RC* Calculations

If we need to know the voltage or current in an *RC* circuit at some specific instant in time while it is charging or discharging to some given dc level, then the preceding calculations are insufficient. A more accurate method requires application of Equation 15-6 (for voltage) and Equation 15-7 (for current):

$$v_C = V - (V - V_0)\epsilon^{-t/\tau} \qquad (15\text{-}6)$$

$$i_C = I - (I - I_0)\epsilon^{-t/\tau} \qquad (15\text{-}7)$$

where

v_C and i_C are the capacitor voltage and current at a specific time t;

V and I are the circuit values that will exist after five time constants;

V_0 and I_0 are the initial values of voltage and current;

ϵ is a constant equal to 2.718 (natural logarithm base);

t is the specific time when voltage or current is to be computed;

τ is the *RC* time constant.

EXAMPLE SOLUTION

Assume that the switch in Figure 15-57 was left in position B until the capacitor had fully discharged. What is the voltage on the capacitor 0.5 s after moving the switch to position A?

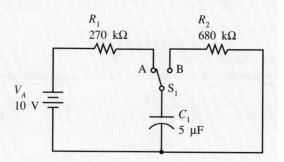

Figure 15-57. An *RC* charge/discharge circuit.

EXAMPLE SOLUTION

Equation 15-6 provides the tool for this type of problem. Here, the initial capacitor voltage (V_0) is zero. The final voltage after five time constants (V) will be 10 V. Since the switch will be in position A, the time constant is computed with Equation 15-5.

$$\tau = R_1C_1$$
$$= 270 \text{ k}\Omega \times 5 \text{ μF} = 1.35 \text{ s}$$

We can now apply Equation 15-6 to determine the capacitor voltage after 0.5 s.

$$v_C = V - (V - V_0)\epsilon^{-t/\tau}$$
$$= 10 - (10 - 0)\epsilon^{-0.5/1.35}$$
$$= 10 - 10 \times 0.6905 = 3.095 \text{ V}$$

Practice Problems

Refer to Figure 15-57 for the following practice problems.

1. If the capacitor has been fully discharged in position B, calculate the capacitor voltage 1.9 s after the switch is moved to position A.

2. If the capacitor has been fully charged in position A, calculate the capacitor voltage 200 ms after moving the switch to position B.

3. The capacitor is fully discharged in position B. It is moved to position A for 1.5 s, then switched back to position B. What is the capacitor voltage 750 ms after returning to position B?

Answers to Practice Problems

1. 7.55 V   2. 9.43 V   3. 5.38 V

Sometimes we are interested in how long it takes a capacitor to charge or discharge to a particular voltage.

$$t = \tau ln\left(\frac{V - V_0}{V - v_C}\right) \qquad (15\text{-}8)$$

EXAMPLE SOLUTION

If the capacitor in Figure 15-57 has been fully charged in position A, how long does it take to reach 4 V after the switch is moved to position B?

EXAMPLE SOLUTION

We apply Equation 15-8 directly.

$$t = \tau ln\left(\frac{V - V_0}{V - v_c}\right)$$

$$= 680 \text{ k}\Omega \times 5 \text{ }\mu\text{F} \times ln\left(\frac{0 - 10}{0 - 4}\right)$$

$$= 3.4 \times ln\,2.5 = 3.4 \times 0.9163 = 3.115 \text{ s}$$

Practice Problems

Refer to Figure 15-57 for the following problems.

1. If the capacitor has been fully discharged in position B, how long does it take to reach 2 V after the switch is moved to position A?
2. If the capacitor has been fully charged in position A, how long does it take to reach 8 V after the switch is moved to position B?
3. The capacitor is fully charged in position A. The switch is moved to position B for 4 s and then returned to position A. How long does it take for the capacitor to reach 8 V after the switch has been returned to position A?

Answers to Practice Problems

1. 301.2 ms   2. 758.7 ms   3. 1.68 s

Circuit Waveforms

Charging and discharging of a capacitor in an *RC* circuit requires a definite amount of time (determined by the values of resistance and capacitance). If the input voltage level changes too quickly, the capacitor may not have enough time to fully charge or discharge. Figure 15-58 illustrates the response of an *RC* circuit to a pulse of three different frequencies.

In Figure 15-58(b), each polarity of the input pulse is present for a period of time equal to one time constant. Thus, the capacitor does not have sufficient time to reach full charge before the input voltage is removed. Similarly, it is not given time to decay to zero between pulses.

KEY POINTS

When an *RC* circuit is supplied by a pulsed voltage waveform, its response is dependent on the length of the *RC* time constant relative to the duration of the pulse voltages.

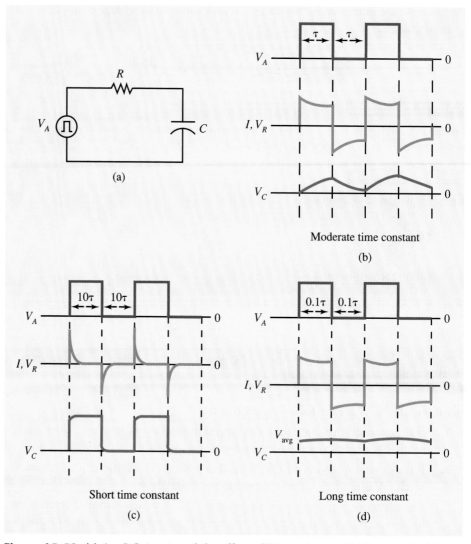

Figure 15-58. (a) An *RC* circuit and the effect of (b) moderate, (c) short, and (d) long time constant on *RC* circuit response.

Figure 15-58(c) illustrates a short time constant. Here, the input pulse duration is present for an amount of time equal to ten time constants. Clearly, the capacitor voltage is allowed time to reach maximum and to decay to zero. The resistor voltage appears as short duration voltage spikes. Notice that the resistor waveform has a dual polarity caused by the opposite direction of current flow during the charge and discharge periods. The waveform across the resistor is called a differentiated waveform. The entire circuit is often called a **differentiator** circuit. To qualify as a differentiator, the circuit must have a short time constant and the output must be taken across the resistor.

Finally, Figure 15-58(d) illustrates the effects of a long time constant, where the input pulse duration is one-tenth of one time constant. Here, the capacitor voltage is barely allowed time to increase or decrease. The resistor voltage has a waveform that is nearly identical to the input waveform. This effect is useful for coupling signals between subsequent stages in an amplifier circuit. When the output is taken across the resistor, the circuit is called an *RC* **coupling** circuit. If the output is taken across the capacitor, we call the circuit an **integrator** circuit. Both coupling and integrator circuits require long time constants.

Magnitude of Capacitor Current

The value of charging (or discharging) current in a capacitor is directly related to the rate of change of voltage across the capacitor. The higher the current, the faster the voltage can increase or decrease. In the same way, if the voltage across a capacitor changes, then a charging or discharging current must flow. The value of that current is proportional to the rate of change of capacitor voltage. This is an important concept and is expressed more formally by Equation 15-9.

$$i_c = C\frac{dv}{dt} = C\frac{\Delta v}{\Delta t} \qquad (15\text{-}9)$$

where i_c is the instantaneous capacitor current, C is the value of the capacitor in farads, dv or Δv stands for change in voltage, and dt or Δt stands for change in time.

EXAMPLE SOLUTION

If the voltage across a 1,000-pF capacitor increases steadily by 5 V over a period of 250 μs, what is the value of capacitor current?

EXAMPLE **SOLUTION**

First, it is interesting to note that you may encounter this type of problem when working on analog-to-digital converter circuits used in computers. We apply Equation 15-9 as follows:

$$i_c = C\frac{dv}{dt}$$

$$= 1{,}000 \text{ pF} \times \frac{5 \text{ V}}{250 \text{ μs}} = 20 \text{ μA}$$

EXAMPLE SOLUTION

At a particular instant, the voltage across a 25-μF capacitor is changing at the rate of 10 V/ms. What is the value of capacitor current at that time?

EXAMPLE **SOLUTION**

We apply Equation 15-9 as follows.

$$i_c = C\frac{dv}{dt}$$

$$= 25 \text{ μF} \times \frac{10 \text{ V}}{1 \text{ ms}} = 250 \text{ mA}$$

Practice Problems

1. What is the current through a 150-µF capacitor if its voltage is changing by 4 V every 2 µs?

2. What value of current must be provided to a 1,500-pF capacitor in order to cause its voltage to increase by 5 V in 100 ms?

3. The voltage across a capacitor increases by 25 V in 1.5 µs when it is supplied from a 2.75-A current source. What is the value of the capacitor?

Answers to Practice Problems

1.   300 A   **2.**   75 nA   **3.**   0.165 µF

Exercise Problems 15.4

1. What is the RC time constant of an 1,800-pF capacitor in series with a 1.5-MΩ resistor?

2. What is the RC time constant of a 25-µF capacitor and a 200-kΩ resistor?

3. What size capacitor must be connected in series with a 75-kΩ resistor to produce a circuit with a 165-ms time constant?

4. If the voltage waveform across the resistor in a series RC circuit with a pulse input is nearly identical to the input pulse shape, the circuit must have a (*short, long*) time constant.

5. If the pulse duration of an input waveform is 100 times longer than the RC time constant of a series RC circuit, the circuit has a (*short, long*) time constant.

6. If the voltage across a 2.2-µF capacitor increases by 15 V in 3 ms, what is the value of current flow?

15.5 Applied Technology: *RC* Circuits

RC circuits are used in nearly every practical electronic device. This includes such things as computers, microwave ovens, telephone systems, satellite communications equipment, industrial control equipment, automotive electronics, and so on. We will briefly examine three common *RC* circuit applications: power supply filters, frequency selective circuits, and time delay circuits.

Power Supply Filter Circuits

Figure 15-59 illustrates the basic operation of a filter circuit for an electronic power supply. Most electronic circuits require dc voltage for operation, but it is often desirable to operate the system from the standard 120-Vac power line. A power supply circuit is used to convert the 120-Vac, 60-Hz power distributed by the power company to a pulsating dc voltage. This pulsating or surging voltage can then be applied to an *RC* circuit as shown in

Figure 15-59. The *RC* network is designed to have a long time constant. This means the voltage across the capacitor cannot follow the quick increases and decreases in the pulsating voltage from the electronic power supply. Rather, the capacitor voltage is a relatively smooth dc. The voltage across the capacitor is used to supply power to the subsequent electronic circuitry. The overall result is a smooth dc voltage similar to that produced by a battery.

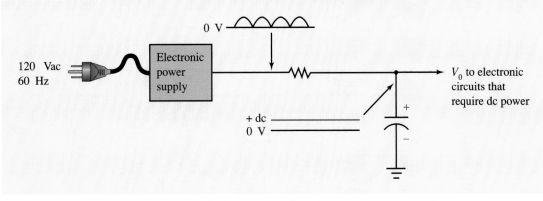

Figure 15-59. An *RC* circuit can smooth the output of an electronic power supply.

Frequency Selective Circuits

RC circuits can be used for frequency selective circuits in the same way as described in Chapter 13 for *RL* circuits. This is a very common application. Figure 15-60 shows a closely related application involving a public address system.

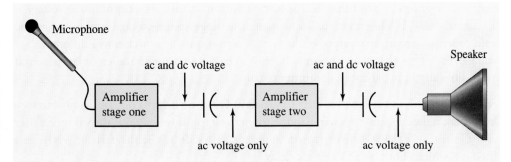

Figure 15-60. A public address (PA) system.

KEY POINTS

RC networks can be configured to distinguish between two or more signals on the basis of their frequency.

KEY POINTS

Capacitors can be used to block or stop the passage of dc through a circuit, while at the same time providing a low-reactance path for the desired ac waveforms.

Here, a weak microphone signal is amplified by two sequential amplifier stages and used to drive a speaker. The electronic amplifier stages require dc voltages in order to operate, but the ac signals representing the sound into the microphone are the only voltages that should be allowed to pass through the system. By connecting the stages together with a capacitor, we can isolate the dc voltages of the two stages and yet couple the desired ac signal. Remember that capacitors act like open circuits to dc voltages, but can have low reactances to ac if they are sized correctly. Another capacitor is used to couple the signal from the last amplifier stage to the speaker. Here again, we only want the ac signals to reach the speaker. If dc is allowed to pass through the speaker, the sound may be distorted and/or damage may result.

Time Delay Circuits

RC circuits are widely used to provide time delay action in electronic circuits. Figure 15-61 illustrates one particular method.

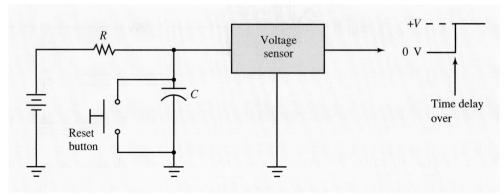

Figure 15-61. *RC* circuits can be used to provide electronic time delays.

When the reset button in Figure 15-61 is pressed, the capacitor voltage is quickly discharged via the low resistance of the switch contacts. When the button is released, the capacitor begins to charge via resistor *R*. As the capacitor charges, its voltage is monitored by an electronic circuit called a voltage sensor. As long as the capacitor voltage is below a certain voltage level (established by the voltage sensor circuit), the output of the voltage sensor will be 0 V. When the capacitor reaches the trigger-point voltage established by the voltage sensor circuit, the output of the voltage sensor quickly switches to a different voltage level. This change in output voltage can be used to drive an indicator lamp, sound an audible alarm, or activate a computer circuit.

So what determines the length of the time delay? The time delay is determined by how long it takes the capacitor to charge to the trigger voltage. If we increase the value of either *R* or *C*, the time delay will be increased. In practical time delay circuits, resistor *R* is often a rheostat, which allows a variable time delay.

Exercise Problems 15.5

1. In your own words, explain how a pulsating waveform can be smoothed with an *RC* circuit that has a long time constant.
2. In your own words, explain why a capacitor appears to block dc in an application like that shown in Figure 15-60.
3. Refer to Figure 15-61. During the time delay, the capacitor is (*charging, discharging*).

15.6 Troubleshooting *RC* Circuits

RC circuits are relatively easy to troubleshoot. The possible malfunctions are essentially combinations of the troubles found in the purely resistive and purely capacitive circuits previously studied. The following represent the most probable defects in an *RC* circuit:

- open capacitor
- open resistor
- shorted capacitor
- shorted resistor (usually solder bridge on a printed circuit board)
- leaky capacitor
- resistor value out of tolerance

All of these defects for series, parallel, or more complex *RC* networks can be located using the same troubleshooting logic presented for purely resistive circuits coupled with the capacitor verification checks presented in Chapter 14.

KEY POINTS

RC circuits can exhibit any combination of the defects found in purely resistive circuits and in purely capacitive circuits.

KEY POINTS

Locating a defect in an *RC* circuit requires the same basic strategies as presented with reference to resistive circuits.

Exercise Problems 15.6

Following are several troubleshooting problems using the PShooter method. Recall that each PShooter circuit has an associated table that lists the various testpoints in the circuit along with the normal values of voltage and resistance. The table also provides a bracketed ([ ]) number for each measurable entry. The bracketed number identifies a specific entry in the PShooter lookup table provided in Appendix A, which gives you the actual measured value of the circuit quantity. The following list will help you interpret the measured values:

- All testpoint (TPxx) measurements are made with reference to ground.
- All non-testpoint values are measured directly across the component.
- All resistance measurements reflect the approximate reading of an ohmmeter.
- Resistance values for all testpoints (TPxx) are measured with the applied voltage disconnected. All other components remain connected.
- Resistance tests for all non-testpoint measurements are made with the specified component removed from the circuit.
- Capacitance measurements are made with the component removed from the circuit.
- The entry 0→∞ is used to indicate the normal movement of an ohmmeter pointer when testing a capacitor (i.e., it starts at zero and moves toward infinity).

1. Refer to Figure 15-62 and the PShooter chart shown in Table 15-7. Locate the defective component in as few measurements as possible by applying a logical, systematic troubleshooting method.

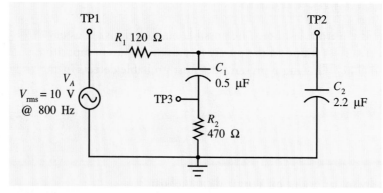

Figure 15-62. Troubleshoot this circuit.

TESTPOINT	rms VOLTAGE		CAPACITANCE		RESISTANCE	
	NORMAL	ACTUAL	NORMAL	ACTUAL	NORMAL	ACTUAL
V_A	10 V	[35]	—	—	—	—
C_1	3.49 V	[29]	0.5 μF	[118]	0→∞	[191]
C_2	5.4 V	[6]	2.2 μF	[115]	0→∞	[5]
R_1	7.88 V	[44]	—	—	120 Ω	[66]
R_2	4.12 V	[126]	—	—	470 Ω	[187]
TP1	10 V	[104]	—	—	∞	[196]
TP2	5.4 V	[148]	—	—	∞	[113]
TP3	4.12 V	[54]	—	—	470 Ω	[80]

Table 15-7. PShooter Data for Figure 15-62

TESTPOINT	rms VOLTAGE		CAPACITANCE		RESISTANCE	
	NORMAL	ACTUAL	NORMAL	ACTUAL	NORMAL	ACTUAL
V_A	10 V	[49]	—	—	—	—
C_1	3.49 V	[105]	0.5 μF	[88]	0→∞	[22]
C_2	5.4 V	[179]	2.2 μF	[30]	0→∞	[32]
R_1	7.88 V	[71]	—	—	120 Ω	[150]
R_2	4.12 V	[25]	—	—	470 Ω	[62]
TP1	10 V	[208]	—	—	∞	[64]
TP2	5.4 V	[40]	—	—	∞	[4]
TP3	4.12 V	[155]	—	—	470 Ω	[112]

Table 15-8. PShooter Data for Figure 15-62

2. Use the PShooter data in Table 15-8 to troubleshoot the circuit shown in Figure 15-62.

3. Use the PShooter data in Table 15-9 to troubleshoot the circuit shown in Figure 15-62.

TESTPOINT	rms VOLTAGE		CAPACITANCE		RESISTANCE	
	NORMAL	ACTUAL	NORMAL	ACTUAL	NORMAL	ACTUAL
V_A	10 V	[146]	—	—	—	—
C_1	3.49 V	[200]	0.5 μF	[68]	0→∞	[82]
C_2	5.4 V	[41]	2.2 μF	[194]	0→∞	[140]
R_1	7.88 V	[104]	—	—	120 Ω	[113]
R_2	4.12 V	[188]	—	—	470 Ω	[134]
TP1	10 V	[184]	—	—	∞	[36]
TP2	5.4 V	[67]	—	—	∞	[196]
TP3	4.12 V	[176]	—	—	470 Ω	[121]

Table 15-9. PShooter Data for Figure 15-62

Chapter Summary

- Series, parallel, series-parallel, and complex RC circuits are similar to simple resistive circuits in many ways. The current is the same in all parts of a series circuit, whereas the voltage is the same across all components in a parallel circuit. Simplification of series-parallel and complex RC circuits is accomplished using the same methods as used with resistive circuits. The difference is that circuit quantities for RC circuits must be represented in polar or rectangular notation to account for the effects of phase differences. Basic circuit theory, Ohm's Law, and Kirchhoff's Laws still apply and still form the basis of all RC circuit analyses with sinusoidal input voltages.

- Total opposition to current flow in an RC circuit is called impedance (Z) and is measured in ohms. Its reciprocal is called admittance (Y) and is measured in siemens. True power is dissipated in the resistance of an RC circuit. Reactive power is caused by the capacitance in the circuit. As with RL circuits, total power is called apparent power and is the phasor sum of the true and reactive power components.

- When a pulse waveform is applied to an RC circuit, it takes a definite amount of time for the capacitor to charge or discharge. One time constant (τ) is equal to the resistance in ohms times the capacitance in farads ($\tau = RC$). The capacitor voltage can increase (or decrease) 63.2% of its total charge in one time constant. For practical purposes, it takes five time constants for a capacitor to fully charge or discharge after an abrupt voltage change at the input of the RC circuit.

- The relative lengths of the RC time constant and the duration of an input pulse voltage determine how an RC circuit will respond to a pulse. If the time constant is ten or more times as long as the input pulse duration, we say it is a long time constant. If the time constant is one-tenth of the pulse duration or less, then it is classed as a short time constant.

- Troubleshooting of *RC* circuits requires application of the troubleshooting methods used for comparable resistive circuit and capacitive circuit configurations. As with any troubleshooting problem, a technician should make smart measurements, but make as few as practical to locate the defect.

Review Questions

Section 15.1: Series *RC* Circuits with Sinusoidal Current

1. The current is the same magnitude through all components in a series *RC* circuit. (True or False)

2. The current through every component in a series *RC* circuit is in phase with the current through every other component. (True or False)

3. A series *RC* circuit consists of a 10-kΩ resistance and a 5-kΩ capacitive reactance. If total current is 10 mA, how much current flows through the resistance? How much through the capacitance?

4. The total voltage in a series *RC* circuit is equal to the phasor sum of the individual component voltage drops. (True or False)

5. Each resistance or reactance in a series *RC* circuit drops a voltage that is inversely proportional to the value of resistance or reactance. (True or False)

6. What is the phase relationship between voltage and current in a capacitor that is part of a series *RC* circuit?

7. What is the phase relationship between voltage and current in a resistor that is part of a series *RC* circuit?

8. What can be said about the range of possible values for the overall phase angle in a series *RC* circuit?

9. The impedance in a series *RC* circuit is equal to the phasor sum of the individual resistances and reactances. (True or False)

10. Calculate the impedance of a series *RC* circuit consisting of a 1,500-pF capacitor and a 5-Ω resistor if they are operated at 30 MHz.

11. What is the impedance of a series circuit consisting of a 3.9-kΩ resistor and a 680-pF capacitor if the operating frequency is 50 kHz?

12. The total impedance of a series *RC* circuit decreases as frequency increases. (True or False)

13. What size capacitor must be connected in series with a 22-kΩ resistor to produce an impedance of 27 kΩ if the operating frequency is 4.6 MHz?

14. If a series *RC* circuit has a resistance of 300 Ω, a capacitive reactance of 400 Ω, and an impedance of 500 Ω, what is the susceptance of the circuit? What is the admittance of the circuit?

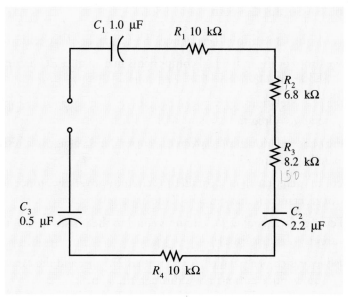

Figure 15-63. Simplify this circuit.

15. Draw an equivalent simplified circuit for the circuit shown in Figure 15-63.

16. Draw the voltage phasor diagram for the circuit shown in Figure 15-64. Include the value of V_A.

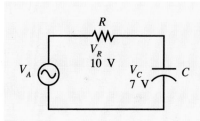

Figure 15-64. A series RC circuit.

17. Draw the impedance phasor diagram for the circuit shown in Figure 15-65. Include the value of Z.

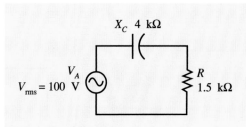

Figure 15-65. A series RC circuit.

18. Draw the power phasor diagram for the circuit shown in Figure 15-65.

19. In a series RC circuit, reactive power and true power are always the same value. (True or False)

20. In a series RC circuit, apparent power is the phasor sum of the capacitive (reactive) and resistive (true) powers. (True or False)

Section 15.2: Parallel *RC* Circuits with Sinusoidal Current

21. The current is the same through every branch of a parallel *RC* circuit. (True or False)

22. The voltage drops of the individual components in a parallel *RC* circuit may be summed with phasor addition to find total voltage. (True or False)

23. What is the phase relationship between the current and voltage in a capacitor that is part of a parallel *RC* circuit?

24. What is the phase relationship between the current and voltage in a resistor that is part of a parallel *RC* circuit?

25. The current in each branch of a parallel *RC* circuit is inversely proportional to the resistance or reactance in that branch. (True or False)

26. The total current in a parallel *RC* circuit is equal to the phasor sum of the individual branch currents. (True or False)

27. If the resistive branch of a parallel *RC* circuit has 275 mA and the capacitive branch has 325 mA, how much current flows through the source?

28. If the total current in a parallel *RC* circuit is 1.5 A and the resistive branch has 0.75 A, how much current flows through the capacitive branch?

29. The impedance of a parallel *RC* circuit is always less than the resistance or reactance of a given branch. (True or False)

30. If the resistive current in a parallel *RC* circuit is 22 mA and the capacitive current is 35 mA when the input voltage is 75 V, what is the impedance of the circuit?

31. Simplify the circuit shown in Figure 15-66.

32. Draw the equivalent, simplified circuit if three capacitors having values of 100 pF, 200 pF, and 300 pF are connected in parallel with three resistors having values of 100 Ω, 200 Ω, and 300 Ω.

33. Draw the current phasor diagram for the circuit shown in Figure 15-67. Include the value of total current.

34. Draw the power phasor diagram for the circuit shown in Figure 15-67.

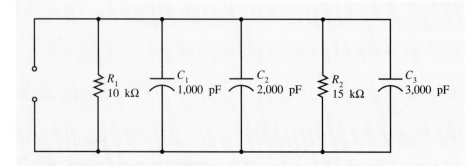

Figure 15-66. Simplify this circuit.

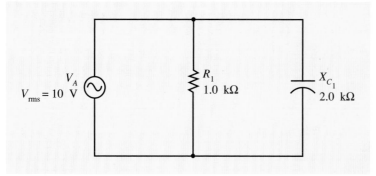

Figure 15-67. A parallel *RC* circuit.

Section 15.3: *RC* Circuit Calculations

Refer to Figure 15-68 for Questions 35–44.

35. What is the reactance of *C*?

36. What is the impedance of the circuit?

37. How much current flows through the resistor?

38. What is the voltage drop across *C*?

39. What is the voltage drop across *R*?

40. What is the power factor of the circuit?

41. What is the phase angle (θ) of the circuit?

42. What is the apparent power in the circuit?

43. How much true power is dissipated by the circuit?

44. What is the susceptance in the circuit?

45. Complete the solution matrix in Table 15-10 for the circuit shown in Figure 15-69.

46. Complete a solution matrix like the one in Table 15-10 for the circuit shown in Figure 15-70.

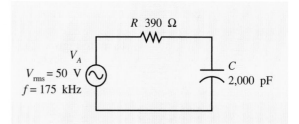

Figure 15-68. Analyze this *RC* circuit.

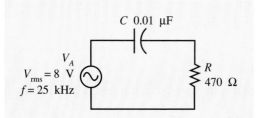
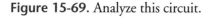

Figure 15-69. Analyze this circuit.

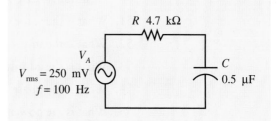
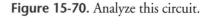

Figure 15-70. Analyze this circuit.

CIRCUIT QUANTITY		RESISTOR	CAPACITOR	TOTAL
Current (rms)				
Voltage	V_P			
	V_{PP}			
	V_{rms}			
Resistance/Reactance/Impedance				
Conductance/Susceptance/Admittance				
Power				
Phase Angle (overall)				
Power Factor (overall)				

Table 15-10. A Solution Matrix

Refer to Figure 15-71 for Questions 47–58.

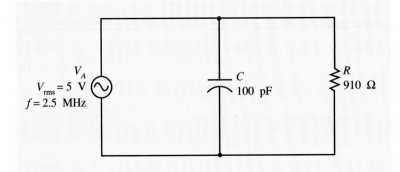

Figure 15-71. A parallel *RC* circuit.

47. What is the value of capacitive reactance?
48. What is the value of susceptance in the circuit?
49. How much current flows through *C*?
50. How much current flows through *R*?
51. What is the value of total current in the circuit?
52. What is the impedance of the circuit?
53. What is the admittance of the circuit?
54. What is the phase angle between total voltage and total current in the circuit?
55. What is the power factor of the circuit?
56. How much reactive power is in the circuit?
57. How much true power is dissipated in the resistance?

58. What is the value of apparent power?

59. Complete a solution matrix like Table 15-10 for the circuit shown in Figure 15-72.

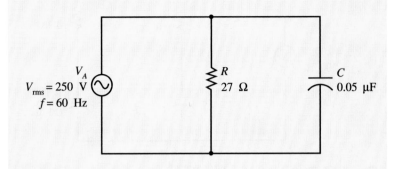

Figure 15-72. Analyze this circuit.

60. Complete a solution matrix like Table 15-10 for the circuit shown in Figure 15-73.

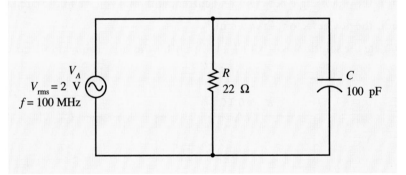

Figure 15-73. Analyze this circuit.

Refer to Figure 15-74 for Questions 61–75.

61. What is the reactance of C_1?

62. What is the reactance of C_2?

63. What is the impedance of the R_1, C_2 branch?

64. What is the impedance of the R_2, C_3 branch?

65. What is the total impedance of the circuit?

66. How much total current flows in the circuit?

67. What is the voltage drop across C_1?

68. What is the voltage drop across R_1?

69. What is the current through C_3?

70. What is the voltage drop across R_2?

71. What is the value of apparent power in the circuit?

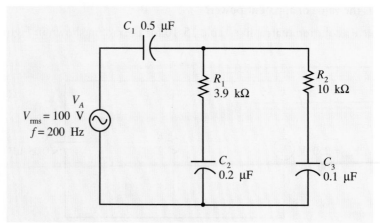

Figure 15-74. A series-parallel *RC* circuit.

72. What is the phase angle between current and voltage in C_3?
73. What is the phase angle between current and voltage in R_1?
74. What is the phase angle between total current and total voltage in the circuit?
75. What is the power factor of the circuit?
76. Complete the solution matrix in Table 15-11 for the circuit shown in Figure 15-75.

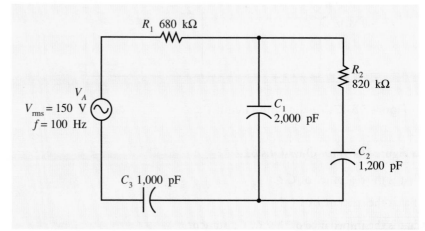

Figure 15-75. Analyze this circuit.

CIRCUIT QUANTITY	R_1	R_2	C_1	C_2	C_3	TOTAL
Voltage (rms)						
Current (rms)						
Resistance/Reactance/Impedance						
Conductance/Susceptance/Admittance						
Power						
Phase Angle (overall)						
Power Factor (overall)						

Table 15-11. A Solution Matrix

Section 15.4: Pulse Response of *RC* Circuits

77. A capacitor will charge to 63.2% of the applied voltage in one time constant. (True or False)

78. If a capacitor that is charged to 100 V is connected across a resistor, how many time constants does it take for the capacitor voltage to decrease to about 36.8 V?

79. If the *RC* time constant of a circuit is 2.5 S, how long does it take to fully charge the capacitor?

80. What is the *RC* time constant of a series circuit consisting of a 100-μF capacitor and a 2.7-kΩ resistor?

81. What value of resistance must be used with a 2,200-pF capacitor to produce a time constant of 220 μs?

82. It takes more total time to discharge a capacitor with 100 V than it does if the capacitor only had 10 V. (True or False)

83. If the pulse duration applied to an *RC* circuit is much longer than the *RC* time constant, we can classify the time constant as a _____ time constant.

84. If the time constant of an *RC* circuit is much longer than the input pulse duration, we can classify the time constant as a _____ time constant.

85. At a particular instant, the voltage across a 0.005-μF capacitor is changing at the rate of 100 V/μs. What is the value of capacitor current at that time?

86. If the rate of change of voltage across a capacitor is increased, what happens to the charging or discharging current?

87. When the voltage across a capacitor changes from 5 V to 10 V in 1 ms, the current is 10 μA. How much current would flow if the voltage changed from 1,000 V to 1,005 V in 1 ms?

88. A 100-kΩ resistor and a 1,000-pF capacitor are connected in series. What is the voltage across the capacitor 50 μs after a 25-V source is connected to the *RC* circuit?

89. A 10-μF capacitor is charged to 25 V. If it is then connected across a 150-kΩ resistor, how long does it take to discharge to 2.5 V?

Section 15.5: Applied Technology: *RC* Circuits

90. List two applications that use *RC* circuits.

91. If an *RC* circuit were providing the delay for a time delay circuit, what would happen to the delay time if the capacitor was increased? What if the resistor was increased?

92. Explain how an *RC* circuit can be used to distinguish between ac and dc voltages.

Section 15.6: Troubleshooting *RC* Circuits

93. Name three possible defects in a capacitor.

94. Name three possible defects in a resistor.

95. Use the PShooter data provided in Table 15-12 to troubleshoot the circuit shown in Figure 15-76.

TESTPOINT	rms VOLTAGE		CAPACITANCE		RESISTANCE	
	NORMAL	ACTUAL	NORMAL	ACTUAL	NORMAL	ACTUAL
V_A	75 V	[28]	—	—	—	—
C_1	18.1 V	[117]	0.5 μF	[34]	0→∞	[82]
C_2	33.6 V	[72]	0.33 μF	[141]	0→∞	[105]
R_1	18.1 V	[189]	—	—	1.8 kΩ	[59]
R_2	47 V	[125]	—	—	2.7 kΩ	[91]
TP1	75 V	[136]	—	—	∞	[123]
TP2	57.7 V	[75]	—	—	∞	[91]
TP3	33.6 V	[22]	—	—	∞	[67]

Table 15-12. PShooter Data for Figure 15-76

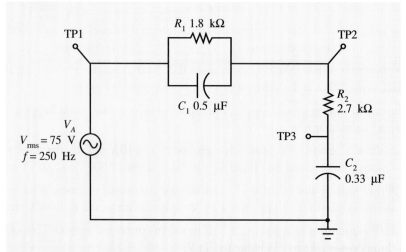

Figure 15-76. Troubleshoot this circuit.

TECHNICIAN CHALLENGE

A technician must be able to apply previously learned knowledge and skills to the solution of unfamiliar problems. Figure 15-77 gives you an opportunity to apply your circuit analysis skills to a complex *RC* circuit.

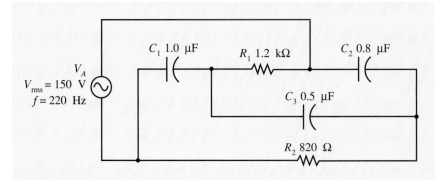

Figure 15-77. Analyze this complex *RC* circuit.

We have not formally discussed the solution of complex *RC* circuits, but we have discussed all of the individual tools needed to analyze the problem. Apply what you have learned in this and preceding chapters and meet the technician challenge!

Here's the challenge. Analyze the circuit shown in Figure 15-77 to determine the following values:

- total current
- phase angle between total current and total voltage
- voltage across C_1
- current through R_2
- total impedance of the circuit (express in polar form)

Equation List

(15-1) $\quad Z = \sqrt{R^2 + X_C^2}$

(15-2) $\quad B = \dfrac{1}{X_C}$

(15-3) $\quad V_A = \sqrt{V_R^2 + V_C^2}$

(15-4) $\quad I_T = \sqrt{I_R^2 + I_C^2}$

(15-5) $\quad \tau = RC$

(15-6) $\quad v_C = V - (V - V_0)\epsilon^{-t/\tau}$

(15-7) $\quad i_C = I - (I - I_0)\epsilon^{-t/\tau}$

(15-8) $\quad t = \tau \ln\!\left(\dfrac{V - V_0}{V - v_C}\right)$

(15-9) $\quad i_c = C\dfrac{dv}{dt} = C\dfrac{\Delta v}{\Delta t}$

objectives

After completing this chapter, you should be able to:

1. Draw an equivalent RC or RL circuit for a given RLC circuit.

2. Calculate the following quantities in a series, parallel, or series-parallel RLC circuit:

   admittance
   apparent power
   component currents
   component voltages
   phase angle between total
      voltage and total current

   power factor
   reactive power
   total current
   total impedance
   true power
   susceptance

3. State the following characteristics of series and parallel RLC circuits at resonance, above resonance, and below resonance: a. phase relationships; b. relative component voltages and currents; c. equivalent circuit.

4. Explain the causes and effects of self-resonance for inductors and capacitors.

5. Explain how to tune an RLC circuit to a given resonant frequency.

6. Troubleshoot an RLC circuit.

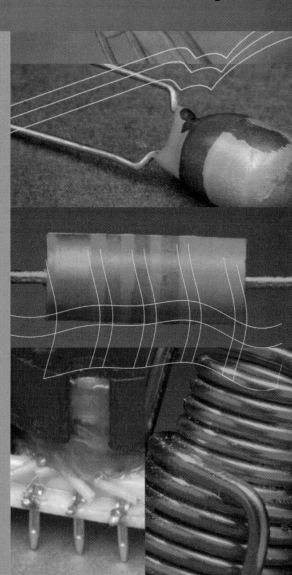

RLC Circuit Analysis

Because we have emphasized the application of Ohm's and Kirch-hoff's Laws for all types of circuit analysis problems presented in previous chapters, the analysis of RLC circuits should seem very logical to you. We will continue to apply our previously mastered skills and knowledge to the solution of unfamiliar circuit problems. This approach drastically reduces your effort (e.g., very few new equations and concepts), and it gives you ongoing practice in the basic techniques, which will increase your skills and your long-term memory of the important circuit analysis methods.

16.1 Introduction to *RLC* Circuits

When inductance, capacitance, and resistance are all part of the same circuit, we call it an *RLC* circuit. As you might expect, the characteristics of an *RLC* circuit can appear capacitive, resistive, or inductive, depending on the relative component values. Before we begin a rigorous numerical analysis of *RLC* circuits, let's examine the basic characteristics of series and parallel *RLC* networks.

Series *RLC* Circuits

Figure 16-1 shows a series *RLC* circuit. Most of the characteristics of series *RLC* circuits are similar to previously studied series circuits.

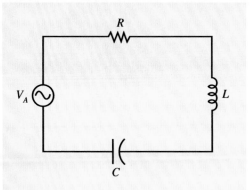

Figure 16-1. A series *RLC* circuit.

CURRENT

The current in a series *RLC* circuit is the same through every component. The current has exactly the same value at the same time in all parts of the circuit. This is equivalent to saying that the current through any given component is in phase with the current through every other component. This important relationship is illustrated in Figure 16-2.

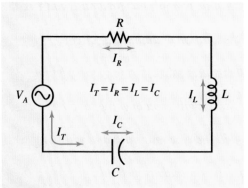

Figure 16-2. The current is the same in all parts of a series *RLC* circuit.

VOLTAGE DROPS

Since the current is the same through all components in a series *RLC* circuit, it follows that the voltage drops across the various components will be determined by the relative resistance or reactance of the component. Higher resistances or reactances will drop more voltage (Ohm's Law). This is illustrated in Figure 16-3.

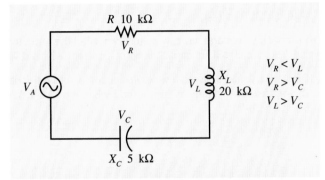

Figure 16-3. Components in an *RLC* circuit drop voltage in proportion to the resistance or reactance.

As with every other series circuit, the sum of the voltage drops must equal the applied voltage (Kirchhoff's Voltage Law). As you might expect, however, the voltages in a series *RLC* circuit must be summed with phasor addition to include the effects of the relative phases. Since inductive voltages lead the common current by 90° and capacitive voltages lag the common current by 90°, it follows that inductive and capacitive voltages are 180° out of phase in a series *RLC* circuit. This means that they tend to cancel each other. We can express this more formally with Equation 16-1.

$$V_{REACTIVE} = V_L + V_C \qquad (16\text{-}1)$$

where V_L is always positive and V_C is always negative. This assignment of polarities follows from the orientation of the capacitive and inductive voltage phasors. If the result is positive, then the net reactive voltage is inductive (i.e., voltage will be leading current). If the result is negative, then the net reactive voltage is capacitive (i.e., current will be leading voltage).

EXAMPLE SOLUTION

If the inductive voltage in a series *RLC* circuit is 10 V and the capacitive voltage is 8 V, what is the net effect of these two voltages?

EXAMPLE **SOLUTION**

Since they are 180° out of phase, they act like two opposing voltage sources. The result is found with Equation 16-1.

$$V_{REACTIVE} = V_L + V_C = 10 \text{ V} + (-8 \text{ V}) = 2 \text{ V}$$

This means that the inductive voltage has cancelled the capacitive voltage and still has a 2-V net potential. The circuit will act inductively (i.e., voltage will lead current).

EXAMPLE SOLUTION

What is the net reactive voltage in a series *RLC* circuit that has 25 V across the inductor and 45 V across the capacitor?

EXAMPLE **SOLUTION**

We apply Equation 16-1 as follows:

$$V_{REACTIVE} = V_L + V_C = 25\ V + (-45\ V) = -20\ V$$

This means that the capacitive voltage has completely cancelled the inductive voltage and still has a 20-V potential. The circuit will act capacitively (i.e., current will lead voltage).

In order to apply Kirchhoff's Voltage Law to a series *RLC* circuit, we find the phasor sum of the resistive voltage and the net reactive voltage as computed by Equation 16-1. We can combine these two steps into Equation 16-2.

> **KEY POINTS**
>
> Phasor addition is used to combine the net reactive voltage with the resistive voltage since they are 90° out of phase.

$$V_A = \sqrt{(V_L - V_C)^2 + V_R^2}\ ,\ \text{or}$$

$$V_A = \sqrt{V_R^2 + (V_L - V_C)^2} \tag{16-2}$$

Clearly, these two alternatives are equivalent, but some technicians have a strong preference for one form or the other. In either case, the calculations have been combined into one equation. Additionally, both reactive voltages can be entered as positive numbers, so there is less opportunity for error.

EXAMPLE SOLUTION

What is the value of input voltage for the circuit shown in Figure 16-4?

EXAMPLE **SOLUTION**

We apply Equation 16-2 as follows:

$$V_A = \sqrt{(V_L - V_C)^2 + V_R^2}$$

$$= \sqrt{(20\ V - 15\ V)^2 + (10\ V)^2} = 11.18\ V$$

> **KEY POINTS**
>
> It is possible for the applied voltage to be less than one or more of the component voltages.

This value should seem peculiar to you at first, since you are not accustomed to seeing individual component voltage drops in a series circuit that are numerically larger than the input voltage. This is a very interesting characteristic of the *RLC* circuit and one that will be explained in more detail in a later section. For now, trust Kirchhoff's Voltage Law.

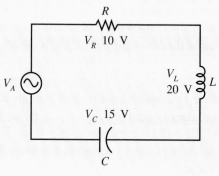

Figure 16-4. Find the value of V_A.

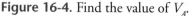

Practice Problems

1. If a series *RLC* circuit has an inductive voltage drop of 18 V, a capacitive voltage drop of 15 V, and a resistive voltage drop of 6 V, what is the value of applied voltage?

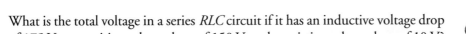

2. What is the total voltage in a series *RLC* circuit if it has an inductive voltage drop of 175 V, a capacitive voltage drop of 150 V, and a resistive voltage drop of 10 V?

3. If a series *RLC* circuit has an inductive voltage drop of 200 mV, a capacitive voltage drop of 100 mV, and a resistive voltage drop of 100 mV, what is the value of applied voltage?

Answers to Practice Problems

1. 6.7 V   **2.** 26.9 V   **3.** 141.4 mV

IMPEDANCE

The impedance of any series circuit is equal to the sum of the individual resistances and reactances. In the case of a series *RLC* circuit, the summing operation must include the effects of differing phase relationships. You will recall from the phasor diagrams for series *RL* and series *RC* circuits, that X_L is shown at 90° and X_C is drawn at –90°. Since the two reactances are 180° out of phase they tend to cancel. Their net result and the resistance are then summed with phasor addition to yield the value of total impedance. We can express this process with Equation 16-3.

$$Z = \sqrt{(X_L - X_C)^2 + R^2}, \text{ or}$$

$$Z = \sqrt{R^2 + (X_L - X_C)^2}$$

(16-3)

EXAMPLE SOLUTION

What is the total impedance of the circuit shown in Figure 16-5?

EXAMPLE **SOLUTION**

We apply Equation 16-3 as follows:

$$Z = \sqrt{(X_L - X_C)^2 + R^2}$$

$$= \sqrt{(4 \text{ k}\Omega - 7 \text{ k}\Omega)^2 + (5 \text{ k}\Omega)^2} = 5.83 \text{ k}\Omega$$

Here again, your prior experience may alert you that this is a peculiar value. You have never seen a series circuit whose total impedance was less than the resistance or reactance of some of its series components. This interesting characteristic of a series *RLC* circuit is very important and will be addressed further in a later section. For now, accept that the total impedance is sometimes less than the reactance of the inductor or the capacitor.

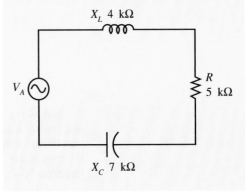

Figure 16-5. Find the impedance of this circuit.

PHASOR RELATIONSHIPS

The phase relationships and the related phasor diagram for a series *RLC* circuit is a logical extension of *RL* and *RC* circuits. It is essentially a combination of the two. The only new aspect is that the two reactive components (voltage, reactance, or reactive power) must be combined algebraically, since they are 180° out of phase, before you complete the parallelogram to locate total voltage, impedance, or apparent power.

EXAMPLE SOLUTION

Draw the voltage phasor diagram for the circuit shown in Figure 16-6.

EXAMPLE **SOLUTION**

Because it is a series circuit, we will use current as the reference phasor. The resistive voltage will be in phase with the current (as in all resistors). The inductive voltage will be leading the current by 90° (as in all inductors), and the capacitive voltage will be lagging the current by 90° (as in all capacitors). These relationships are shown in Figure 16-7.

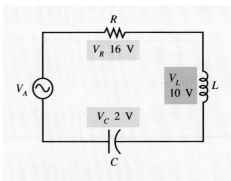

Figure 16-6. Draw the voltage phasor diagram for this circuit.

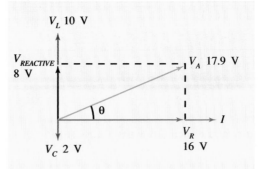

Figure 16-7. A voltage phasor diagram for the circuit shown in Figure 16-6.

Next, we combine the inductive voltage (V_L) and the capacitive voltage (V_C) algebraically to find the net reactive voltage ($V_{REACTIVE}$). By inspection, we can see that the difference is 8 V and that the inductive voltage is larger. So, we can plot the $V_{REACTIVE}$ phasor as shown in Figure 16-7. If the magnitude and direction of the $V_{REACTIVE}$ phasor is not obvious, then we can always apply Equation 16-1 as follows:

$$V_{REACTIVE} = V_L + V_C = 10 \text{ V} + (-2 \text{ V}) = +8 \text{ V}$$

We can now complete the parallelogram to locate the position of the total voltage phasor (V_A). We can compute its value by finding the phasor sum of $V_{REACTIVE}$ and V_R by applying Equation 16-2.

$$V_A = \sqrt{(V_L - V_C)^2 + V_R^2}$$
$$= \sqrt{(10 \text{ V} - 2 \text{ V})^2 + (16 \text{ V})^2} = 17.9 \text{ V}$$

This value is shown on the completed phasor diagram in Figure 16-7. Also shown is the phase angle (θ) between total voltage and total current.

Draw an impedance phasor diagram for the circuit shown in Figure 16-8.

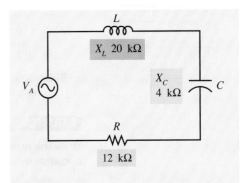

Figure 16-8. Draw the impedance phasor diagram for this circuit.

EXAMPLE SOLUTION

First, we draw the resistance phasor in the reference position. As with *RL* circuits, the inductive reactance phasor is drawn 90° ahead of the resistance phasor. The capacitive reactance phasor, as with *RC* circuits, is drawn 90° behind the resistive phasor. These are all shown in Figure 16-9.

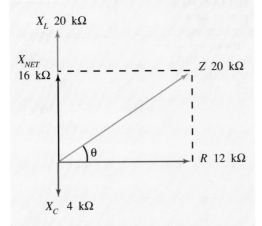

Figure 16-9. An impedance phasor diagram for the circuit shown in Figure 16-8.

Since the phasors representing inductive and capacitive reactance are 180° out of phase, we combine them algebraically to find the net reactance (X_{NET}). In most cases, the magnitude and polarity of X_{NET} is apparent from the phasor diagram. If necessary, we can consider X_L to be positive and X_C to be negative and then apply Equation 16-4.

$$X_{NET} = X_L + X_C \qquad (16\text{-}4)$$

In our present example, we have

$$X_{NET} = X_L + X_C = 20 \text{ k}\Omega + (-4 \text{ k}\Omega) = 16 \text{ k}\Omega$$

Finally, we combine the net reactance (X_{NET}) with the resistance (*R*) with phasor addition to find the circuit impedance. We can locate the phasor graphically by completing the parallelogram as shown in Figure 16-9. The numerical value is found with Equation 16-3.

$$Z = \sqrt{(X_L - X_C)^2 + R^2}$$
$$= \sqrt{(20 \text{ k}\Omega - 4 \text{ k}\Omega)^2 + (12 \text{ k}\Omega)^2} = 20 \text{ k}\Omega$$

This is shown on the completed phasor diagram in Figure 16-9. Also shown is the phase angle (θ) between the resistance and impedance phasors.

EXAMPLE SOLUTION

Draw the power phasor diagram for the circuit shown in Figure 16-10.

EXAMPLE SOLUTION

First, we draw true power in the reference position. Reactive power due to the inductive reactance (P_{R_L}) is drawn 90° ahead of the true power phasor. Reactive power due to the capacitive reactance (P_{R_C}) is drawn 90° behind the true power phasor. These are shown in Figure 16-11. They are consistent with the phasor diagrams for *RC* and *RL* circuits.

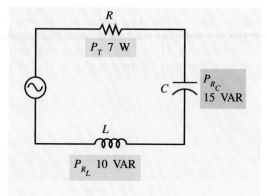

Figure 16-10. Draw the power phasor diagram for this circuit.

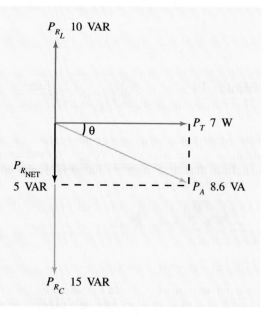

Figure 16-11. A power phasor diagram for the circuit shown in Figure 16-10.

Next, we find the net reactive power ($P_{R_{NET}}$) by algebraically combining the two reactive power phasors (P_{R_L} and P_{R_C}). In most cases, the magnitude and direction can be determined by inspection, but Equation 16-5 provides a more formal approach.

$$P_{R_{NET}} = P_{R_L} + P_{R_C} \qquad (16\text{-}5)$$

where P_{R_L} is assumed to be positive and P_{R_C} is assumed to be negative. For our present example, we have

$$P_{R_{NET}} = P_{R_L} + P_{R_C} = 10\ \text{VAR} + (-15\ \text{VAR}) = -5\ \text{VAR}$$

where the minus sign tells us that the net reactive power is capacitive.

Finally, we sum (phasor addition) the net reactive power with the true power to find the total or apparent power. Graphically, we can complete the parallelogram as shown in Figure 16-11. Numerically, we can apply Equation 16-6.

$$P_A = \sqrt{(P_{R_L} - P_{R_C})^2 + P_T^2},\ \text{or} \qquad (16\text{-}6)$$
$$P_A = \sqrt{P_T^2 + (P_{R_L} - P_{R_C})^2}$$

In the case of Figure 16-11, we compute apparent power as

$$P_A = \sqrt{(P_{R_L} - P_{R_C})^2 + P_T^2}$$
$$= \sqrt{(10\ \text{VAR} - 15\ \text{VAR})^2 + (7\ \text{W})^2} = 8.6\ \text{VA}$$

This is shown on the completed phasor diagram in Figure 16-11. Also shown is the phase angle (θ), which is always drawn between the true power and apparent power phasors.

Parallel RLC Circuits

Figure 16-12 shows a basic parallel RLC circuit. These circuits possess many of the characteristics of other parallel circuits.

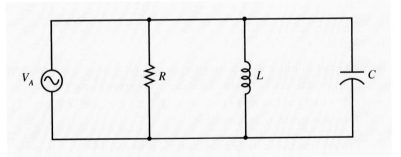

Figure 16-12. A parallel RLC circuit.

CURRENT

As with other parallel circuits, the total current in a parallel RLC circuit is equal to the sum of the individual branch currents. Since the branch currents are out of phase, however, they must be summed with phasor addition. More specifically, capacitive branch current and inductive branch current are 180° out of phase and must be combined algebraically to find the net reactive current (I_X). This is expressed more formally by Equation 16-7.

KEY POINTS

The voltage drop is the same across every component in a parallel RLC circuit.

$$I_X = I_L + I_C \qquad (16\text{-}7)$$

where I_L is assumed to be negative and I_C is assumed to be positive. These polarity assignments are based on the phasor diagrams for parallel RL, RC, and RLC circuits. Total current is then the phasor sum of resistive current and the net reactive current. All of this can be expressed simply as Equation 16-8.

$$I_T = \sqrt{(I_L - I_C)^2 + I_R^2}, \text{ or} \qquad (16\text{-}8)$$
$$I_T = \sqrt{I_R^2 + (I_L - I_C)^2}$$

EXAMPLE SOLUTION

What is the total current flow for the circuit shown in Figure 16-13?

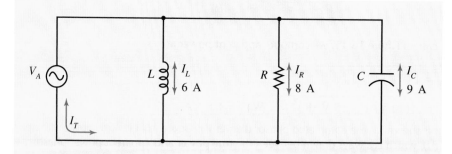

Figure 16-13. Find the total current flow in this circuit.

EXAMPLE SOLUTION

We apply Equation 16-8 directly.

$$I_T = \sqrt{(I_L - I_C)^2 + I_R^2}$$
$$= \sqrt{(6 \text{ A} - 9 \text{ A})^2 + (8 \text{ A})^2} = 8.54 \text{ A}$$

This illustrates an interesting characteristic of a parallel RLC circuit; one or more branch currents may be larger than total current. This seems contrary to common sense at first, but if you remember that the inductive and capacitive currents are 180° out of phase and tend to cancel, then it is more understandable.

Yet another way to explain this strange characteristic is to consider that because the two reactive currents are 180° out of phase, when current is flowing upward in the inductive branch, it will be flowing downward in the capacitive branch. For purposes of illustration, let's assume that the value of inductive current is larger than the value of capacitive current. If we examine the electron flow in the circuit at a specific instant in time and apply Kirchhoff's Current Law, it will appear as shown in Figure 16-14. Not all of I_C and I_L flow back to the source. Part of the current circulates between L and C. Only the difference between I_L and I_C flows to the source. This difference is, of course, the net reactive current (I_X).

Another characteristic of a parallel RLC circuit is that the individual branch currents are inversely proportional to the branch resistance (Ohm's Law). The higher the resistance or

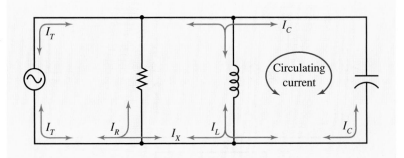

Figure 16-14. Some current circulates between the inductive and capacitive branches.

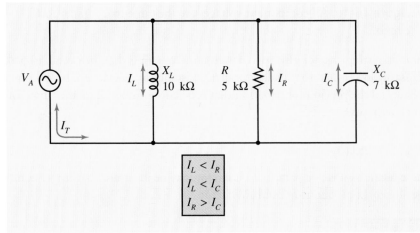

Figure 16-15. Branch current in a parallel *RLC* circuit is inversely proportional to the branch resistance or reactance.

reactance in a particular branch, the lower the current through that particular branch. Figure 16-15 illustrates this relationship.

VOLTAGE DROPS

The voltage is the same across every component in a parallel *RLC* circuit, just as with every other parallel circuit you have studied. Regardless of the relative values of resistance or reactance in the branches, the voltages across every component will be identical at all times. This also implies that the voltage waveform across a given component is in phase with the voltage waveform of every other component. Figure 16-16 illustrates the voltage relationships in a parallel *RLC* circuit.

IMPEDANCE

The impedance of a parallel circuit can be found with Ohm's Law ($Z = V_A/I_T$), just as we have done with previous parallel circuits. We can also compute impedance with the reciprocal equation provided we represent the circuit quantities in polar and/or rectangular form to account for the effects of differing phase angles.

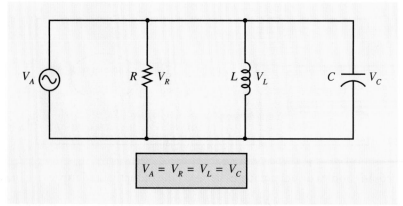

$$V_A = V_R = V_L = V_C$$

Figure 16-16. All component voltages are the same in a parallel *RLC* circuit.

One very interesting characteristic of a parallel *RLC* circuit is that the overall impedance is not necessarily lower than the smallest branch resistance or reactance. This follows from Ohm's Law and the previous observation that total current may be smaller than some of the branch currents.

PHASE RELATIONSHIPS

The phase relationships in a parallel *RLC* circuit may be illustrated by simply combining what we already know about *RC* and *RL* circuits.

EXAMPLE SOLUTION

Draw the current phasor diagram for the circuit shown in Figure 16-17.

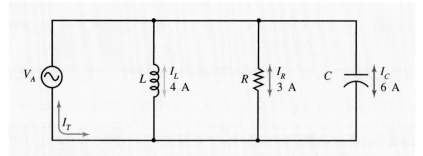

Figure 16-17. Draw a current phasor diagram for this circuit.

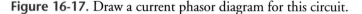

EXAMPLE SOLUTION

First, we draw the voltage phasor as a reference, since it is common to all components. The resistive current phasor (I_R) is drawn in phase with the voltage phasor. The inductive current phasor (I_L) lags the circuit voltage by 90°, and the capacitive current phasor (I_C) leads the circuit voltage by 90°. These phasor positions are all shown in Figure 16-18.

Next, we algebraically combine the inductive and capacitive currents to find the net reactive current (I_X). If its magnitude and direction are not obvious, we can use Equation 16-7 to determine its value.

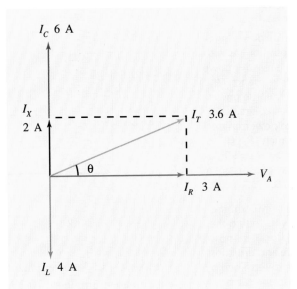

Figure 16-18. A current phasor diagram for the circuit shown in Figure 16-17.

$$I_X = I_L + I_C = -4 \text{ A} + 6 \text{ A} = 2 \text{ A}$$

Once we have located the net reactive current phasor (I_X), we can combine it with the resistive current phasor (I_R) to find total current (I_T). We do this graphically by completing the parallelogram as shown in Figure 16-18. We find its numerical value through phasor addition by applying Equation 16-8.

$$I_T = \sqrt{(I_L - I_C)^2 + I_R^2}$$
$$= \sqrt{(4 \text{ A} - 6 \text{ A})^2 + (3 \text{ A})^2} = 3.6 \text{ A}$$

This is shown on the completed phasor diagram in Figure 16-18. Also shown is the phase angle (θ), which is always located between the total voltage and total current phasors.

EXAMPLE SOLUTION

Draw the power phasor diagram for the circuit shown in Figure 16-19.

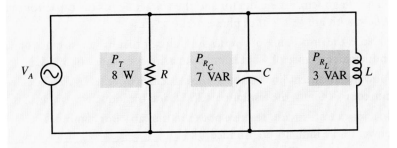

Figure 16-19. Draw the power phasor diagram for this circuit.

KEY POINTS

The power relationships in a series or parallel *RLC* circuit are essentially a combination of the relationships found in *RL* and *RC* circuits.

EXAMPLE SOLUTION

First, we sketch the true power phasor in the reference position, as with *RC* and *RL* circuits. The reactive power phasor for the inductive branch (P_{R_L}) is drawn 90° behind the true power phasor, as we did with *RL* circuits. Similarly, the reactive power phasor for the capacitive branch (P_{R_C}) is drawn leading true power by 90°, as with *RC* circuits. These phasors are all shown in Figure 16-20.

Next, we algebraically combine the two reactive powers to find the net reactive power ($P_{R_{NET}}$). In most cases, the magnitude and direction of the phasor can be determined by inspection. Otherwise, we can apply Equation 16-5.

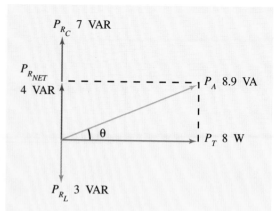

Figure 16-20. A power phasor diagram for the circuit shown in Figure 16-19.

$$P_{R_{NET}} = P_{R_L} + P_{R_C} = -3 \text{ VAR} + 7 \text{ VAR} = 4 \text{ VAR}$$

We can now combine the net reactive power phasor ($P_{R_{NET}}$) with the true power phasor (P_T) to find total or apparent power (P_A). We can locate the phasor position graphically by completing the parallelogram as shown in Figure 16-20. The numerical value of the phasor is found with Equation 16-6.

$$P_A = \sqrt{(P_{R_L} - P_{R_C})^2 + P_T^2}$$
$$= \sqrt{(3 \text{ VAR} - 7 \text{ VAR})^2 + (8 \text{ W})^2} = 8.9 \text{ VA}$$

This is shown on the completed phasor diagram in Figure 16-20. The phase angle (θ) is also labeled. It is always the angle between true power (P_T) and apparent power (P_A).

Exercise Problems 16.1

1. The voltage is the same across all components in a series *RLC* circuit. (True or False)

2. The voltage across the inductor and the voltage across the capacitor in a series *RLC* circuit are 180° out of phase. (True or False)

3. What is the impedance of a series *RLC* circuit that has a resistance of 22 kΩ, inductive reactance of 47 kΩ, and a capacitive reactance of 35 kΩ?

4. How much current flows through the capacitance of a series *RLC* circuit if the total current is 100 mA, the resistance is 25 Ω, and the inductive reactance is 50 Ω?

5. In a series *RLC* circuit, reactive power in the capacitor combines with reactive power in the inductor to produce _____ _____ _____.

6. Is it possible for the total voltage in a series *RLC* circuit to be less than the voltage across a single component?

7. The voltage across every component in a parallel circuit is in phase with the voltage across every other component. (True or False)

8. The current through every component in a parallel circuit is in phase with the current through every other component. (True or False)

9. It is possible for the total voltage in a parallel *RLC* circuit to be less than one of the branch voltage drops. (True or False)

10. How much total current flows through a parallel *RLC* circuit that has 10-mA resistive current, 25-mA capacitive current, and 30-mA inductive current?

16.2 *RLC* Circuit Calculations

We now have all the analytical tools needed to thoroughly analyze an *RLC* circuit with a sinusoidal input voltage. The analysis procedure should appear as a logical extension of *RC* and *RL* circuits. Rely on Ohm's and Kirchhoff's Laws and your basic understanding of circuit configurations to guide you through the analysis.

Series *RLC* Circuits

Analysis of series *RLC* circuits is similar to the analysis of *RC* or *RL* circuits. The specific steps, of course, vary with the problem, but the general sequence follows:

1. Compute all reactances.
2. Calculate impedance.
3. Find total current.
4. Compute component voltage drops.
5. Calculate other circuit parameters (e.g., power, phase angle, power factor).

> **KEY POINTS**
>
> Series, parallel, series-parallel, and complex *RLC* circuits are analyzed in basically the same way as their resistive counterparts.

> **KEY POINTS**
>
> The rules for combining series and parallel components are applied to the series and parallel portions of the circuit being analyzed.

EXAMPLE SOLUTION

Analyze the circuit shown in Figure 16-21, and complete the solution matrix in Table 16-1.

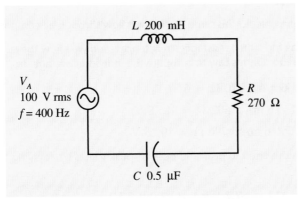

Figure 16-21. Analyze this series *RLC* circuit.

CIRCUIT QUANTITY		RESISTOR	INDUCTOR	CAPACITOR	TOTAL
Current (rms)					
Voltage	V_P				
	V_{PP}				
	V_{rms}				100 V
Resistance/Reactance/Impedance		270 Ω			
Conductance/Susceptance/Admittance					
Power					
Phase Angle (overall)					
Power Factor (overall)					

Table 16-1. Solution Matrix for the Circuit in Figure 16-21

EXAMPLE SOLUTION

Let's first find the reactances in the circuit.

$$X_L = 2\pi fL = 6.28 \times 400 \text{ Hz} \times 200 \text{ mH} = 502 \text{ Ω}$$

$$X_C = \frac{1}{2\pi fC} = \frac{1}{6.28 \times 400 \text{ Hz} \times 0.5 \text{ μF}} = 796 \text{ Ω}$$

We can now apply Equation 16-3 to find the impedance of the circuit.

$$Z = \sqrt{(X_L - X_C)^2 + R^2}$$
$$= \sqrt{(502 \text{ Ω} - 796 \text{ Ω})^2 + (270 \text{ Ω})^2} = 399 \text{ Ω}$$

Now we use Ohm's Law to find total current in the circuit.

$$I_T = \frac{V_A}{Z} = \frac{100 \text{ V}}{399 \text{ Ω}} = 250.6 \text{ mA}$$

Because it is a series circuit, this same current will flow through all components.

We now know the individual resistances/reactances, and we know the current through each component. We can use Ohm's Law to compute the individual voltage drops.

$$V_R = I_R R = 250.6 \text{ mA} \times 270 \text{ Ω} = 67.7 \text{ V}$$
$$V_L = I_L X_L = 250.6 \text{ mA} \times 502 \text{ Ω} = 125.8 \text{ V}$$
$$V_C = I_C X_C = 250.6 \text{ mA} \times 796 \text{ Ω} = 199.5 \text{ V}$$

These can all be converted to peak and peak-to-peak values by applying the basic sine wave equations.

$$V_{R_p} = V_{R_{rms}} \times 1.414 = 67.7 \text{ V} \times 1.414 = 95.7 \text{ V}$$
$$V_{R_{PP}} = V_{R_p} \times 2 = 95.7 \text{ V} \times 2 = 191.4 \text{ V}$$

$$V_{L_p} = V_{L_{rms}} \times 1.414 = 125.8 \text{ V} \times 1.414 = 177.9 \text{ V}$$

$$V_{L_{PP}} = V_{L_p} \times 2 = 177.9 \text{ V} \times 2 = 355.8 \text{ V}$$

$$V_{C_p} = V_{C_{rms}} \times 1.414 = 199.5 \text{ V} \times 1.414 = 282.1 \text{ V}$$

$$V_{C_{PP}} = V_{C_L} \times 2 = 282.1 \text{ V} \times 2 = 564.2 \text{ V}$$

The rms value of input voltage can also be converted to peak and peak-to-peak values in the same way.

$$V_{A_P} = V_{A_{rms}} \times 1.414 = 100 \text{ V} \times 1.414 = 141.4 \text{ V}$$

$$V_{A_{PP}} = V_{A_P} \times 2 = 141.4 \text{ V} \times 2 = 282.8 \text{ V}$$

We can find conductance, susceptance, and admittance by simply taking the reciprocal of the resistance, reactance, and impedance values, respectively.

$$G = \frac{1}{R} = \frac{1}{270 \; \Omega} = 3.7 \text{ mS}$$

$$B_L = \frac{1}{X_L} = \frac{1}{502 \; \Omega} = 1.99 \text{ mS}$$

$$B_C = \frac{1}{X_C} = \frac{1}{796 \; \Omega} = 1.26 \text{ mS}$$

$$Y = \frac{1}{Z} = \frac{1}{399 \; \Omega} = 2.51 \text{ mS}$$

True power dissipated by the resistance can be found with any one of the basic power equations. Let's use the $P = VI$ relationship.

$$P_T = V_R I_R = 67.7 \text{ V} \times 250.6 \text{ mA} = 16.97 \text{ W}$$

Reactive power in each of the reactances is found in a similar way.

$$P_{R_L} = V_L I_L = 125.8 \text{ V} \times 250.6 \text{ mA} = 31.53 \text{ VAR}$$

$$P_{R_C} = V_C I_C = 199.5 \text{ V} \times 250.6 \text{ mA} = 49.99 \text{ VAR}$$

Total power can also be found with our choice of basic power equations, or we can use Equation 16-6 as a way to sum the individual component powers. Let's continue with the $P = VI$ method.

$$P_A = V_A I_T = 100 \text{ V} \times 250.6 \text{ mA} = 25.1 \text{ VA}$$

Let's take time out to draw the phasor diagram for the circuit. It will help ensure that we use the correct values to compute phase angle and power factor. We can use our choice of voltage, impedance, or power phasor diagrams. Let's choose to sketch a diagram for the voltage phasors. Because it is a series circuit, we will use current as the reference phasor. The resistive voltage phasor (V_R) is always in phase with current. Inductive voltage always leads current by 90°, and capacitive voltage always lags current by 90°. These phasors are all shown in Figure 16-22.

Next, we find the net reactive voltage ($V_{REACTIVE}$) by applying Equation 16-1.

$$V_{REACTIVE} = V_L + V_C = 125.8 \text{ V} + (-199.5 \text{ V}) = -73.7 \text{ V}$$

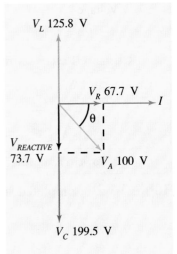

Figure 16-22.
Voltage phasor diagram for the circuit shown in Figure 16-21.

This allows us to locate and sketch the phasor representing total voltage (V_A) as shown in Figure 16-22.

The phase angle (θ) always appears between total current and total voltage. We can find its value by applying any of the basic right-triangle equations. Let's use the cosine equation so that we will find the power factor at the same time.

$$\text{power factor} = \cos\theta = \frac{\text{adjacent}}{\text{hypotenuse}} = \frac{V_R}{V_A}$$

$$= \frac{67.7\text{ V}}{100\text{ V}} = 0.677$$

$$\text{phase angle} = \theta = \arccos 0.677 = 47.39°$$

Since current leads the voltage in this circuit, we will label the power factor as leading. The completed solution matrix is given in Table 16-2.

The completed phasor diagram in Figure 16-22 clearly shows that total current is leading total voltage in the circuit. You will recall that this is a characteristic of a capacitive (RC) circuit. In effect, the high value of capacitive reactance (796 Ω) has cancelled the smaller value of inductive reactance (502 Ω). The remaining capacitive reactance (294 Ω) combines with the resistance (270 Ω) to produce the characteristics of a simple RC circuit (i.e., current leads voltage).

CIRCUIT QUANTITY		RESISTOR	INDUCTOR	CAPACITOR	TOTAL
Current (rms)		250.6 mA	250.6 mA	250.6 mA	250.6 mA
Voltage	V_P	95.7 V	177.9 V	282.1 V	141.4 V
	V_{PP}	191.4 V	355.8 V	564.2 V	282.8 V
	V_{rms}	67.7 V	125.8 V	199.5 V	100 V
Resistance/Reactance/Impedance		270 Ω	502 Ω	796 Ω	399 Ω
Conductance/Susceptance/Admittance		3.7 mS	1.99 mS	1.26 mS	2.51 mS
Power		16.97 W	31.53 VAR	49.99 VAR	25.1 VA
Phase Angle (overall)		47.39°			
Power Factor (overall)		0.677 (leading)			

Table 16-2. Completed Solution Matrix for the Circuit in Figure 16-21

Practice Problems

1. Analyze the circuit shown in Figure 16-23, and complete a solution matrix similar to Table 16-1.

2. Analyze the circuit shown in Figure 16-24, and complete a solution matrix similar to Table 16-1.

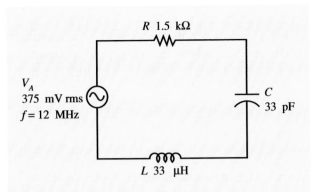

Figure 16-23. Analyze this *RLC* circuit.

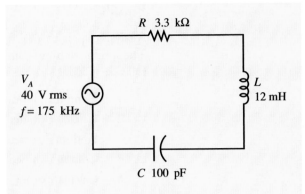

Figure 16-24. Analyze this *RLC* circuit.

Answers to Practice Problems

1.

CIRCUIT QUANTITY		RESISTOR	INDUCTOR	CAPACITOR	TOTAL
Current (rms)		145.9 µA	145.9 µA	145.9 µA	145.9 µA
Voltage	V_P	0.31 V	0.514 V	82.95 mV	0.53 V
	V_{PP}	0.62 V	1.03 V	165.9 mV	1.06 V
	V_{rms}	0.219 V	0.363 V	58.67 mV	0.375 V
Resistance/Reactance/Impedance		1.5 kΩ	2.49 kΩ	402.1 Ω	2.57 kΩ
Conductance/Susceptance/Admittance		666.7 µS	401.6 µS	2.49 mS	389.1 µS
Power		31.95 µW	52.96 µVAR	8.56 µVAR	54.7 µVA
Phase Angle (overall)		54.3°			
Power Factor (overall)		0.583 (lagging)			

2.

CIRCUIT QUANTITY		RESISTOR	INDUCTOR	CAPACITOR	TOTAL
Current (rms)		7.61 mA	7.61 mA	7.61 mA	7.61 mA
Voltage	V_P	35.5 V	142 V	97.92 V	56.56 V
	V_{PP}	71 V	284 V	195.8 V	113.1 V
	V_{rms}	25.1 V	100.5 V	69.25 V	40 V
Resistance/Reactance/Impedance		3.3 kΩ	13.2 kΩ	9.1 kΩ	5.26 kΩ
Conductance/Susceptance/Admittance		303 µS	75.76 µS	109.9 µS	190.1 µS
Power		191 mW	764.8 mVAR	527 mVAR	304.4 mVA
Phase Angle (overall)		51.2°			
Power Factor (overall)		0.627 (lagging)			

Parallel *RLC* Circuits

Analysis of parallel *RLC* circuits is similar to the analysis of equivalent *RC* or *RL* circuits. The specific steps, of course, vary with the specific problem, but the general sequence follows:

1. Compute all reactances.
2. Calculate branch currents.
3. Find total current.
4. Compute impedance.
5. Calculate other circuit parameters (e.g., power, phase angle, power factor).

EXAMPLE SOLUTION

Analyze the parallel *RLC* circuit shown in Figure 16-25, and complete the solution matrix provided in Table 16-3.

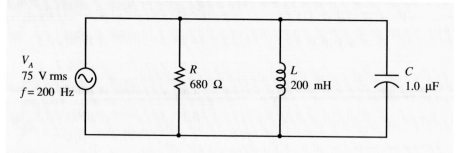

Figure 16-25. Analyze this parallel *RLC* circuit.

CIRCUIT QUANTITY		RESISTOR	INDUCTOR	CAPACITOR	TOTAL
Current (rms)					
Voltage	V_P				
	V_{PP}				
	V_{rms}				75 V
Resistance/Reactance/Impedance		680 Ω			
Conductance/Susceptance/Admittance					
Power					
Phase Angle (overall)					
Power Factor (overall)					

Table 16-3. Solution Matrix for the Circuit in Figure 16-25

First, we apply the basic reactance equations to compute inductive and capacitive reactance.

$$X_L = 2\pi fL = 6.28 \times 200 \text{ Hz} \times 200 \text{ mH} = 251.2 \ \Omega$$

$$X_C = \frac{1}{2\pi fC} = \frac{1}{6.28 \times 200 \text{ Hz} \times 1.0 \ \mu\text{F}} = 796 \ \Omega$$

We can now use Ohm's Law to compute the individual branch currents. The voltage is, of course, the same for all components.

$$I_R = \frac{V_R}{R} = \frac{75 \text{ V}}{680 \ \Omega} = 110.3 \text{ mA}$$

$$I_L = \frac{V_L}{X_L} = \frac{75 \text{ V}}{251.2 \ \Omega} = 298.6 \text{ mA}$$

$$I_C = \frac{V_C}{X_C} = \frac{75 \text{ V}}{796 \ \Omega} = 94.2 \text{ mA}$$

The branch currents can be combined to find total current. We use Equation 16-8 as follows:

$$I_T = \sqrt{(I_L - I_C)^2 + I_R^2}$$

$$= \sqrt{(298.6 \text{ mA} - 94.2 \text{ mA})^2 + (110.3 \text{ mA})^2} = 232.3 \text{ mA}$$

Application of Ohm's Law will give us the value of impedance in the circuit.

$$Z = \frac{V_A}{I_T} = \frac{75 \text{ V}}{232.3 \text{ mA}} \approx 322.9 \ \Omega$$

The remaining circuit quantities can be computed in most any sequence. Let's convert the rms voltages to equivalent peak and peak-to-peak values by applying the basic sine wave equations.

$$V_{R_P} = V_{R_{rms}} \times 1.414 = 75 \text{ V} \times 1.414 = 106.1 \text{ V}$$

$$V_{R_{PP}} = V_{R_P} \times 2 = 106.1 \text{ V} \times 2 = 212.2 \text{ V}$$

Since the voltage is the same across all components in a parallel circuit, this same value applies to V_A, V_C, and V_L.

The conductance, susceptance, and admittance is found by taking the reciprocal of resistance, reactance, and impedance, respectively.

$$G = \frac{1}{R} = \frac{1}{680 \ \Omega} = 1.47 \text{ mS}$$

$$B_L = \frac{1}{X_L} = \frac{1}{251.2 \ \Omega} = 3.98 \text{ mS}$$

$$B_C = \frac{1}{X_C} = \frac{1}{796 \ \Omega} = 1.26 \text{ mS}$$

$$Y = \frac{1}{Z} = \frac{1}{322.9 \ \Omega} = 3.1 \text{ mS}$$

We can use any of the basic power equations to compute power in the circuit. For purposes of illustration, let's use the basic form of $P = I^2R$.

$$P_T = I_R^2 R = (110.3 \text{ mA})^2 \times 680 \ \Omega = 8.27 \text{ W}$$

$$P_{R_L} = I_L^2 X_L = (298.6 \text{ mA})^2 \times 251.2 \ \Omega = 22.4 \text{ VAR}$$

$$P_{R_C} = I_C^2 X_C = (94.2 \text{ mA})^2 \times 796 \ \Omega = 7.06 \text{ VAR}$$

$$P_A = I_T^2 Z = (232.3 \text{ mA})^2 \times 322.9 \ \Omega = 17.4 \text{ VA}$$

We could just as easily have used Equation 16-6 to compute total or apparent power. Sometimes, it's good to use both calculations as a way to catch errors.

Before we calculate phase angle and power factor, let's sketch the phasor diagram to lessen the chance for error. We can use either a current or power phasor diagram. Let's choose the current phasor diagram. Because it is a parallel circuit, we will use voltage as the reference phasor. The resistive current phasor is always drawn in phase with voltage. The inductive current always lags voltage by 90°, while capacitive current always leads voltage by 90°. These phasors are sketched on the diagram in Figure 16-26.

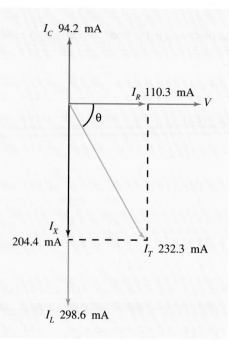

Figure 16-26. A current phasor diagram for the circuit in Figure 16-25.

Next, we algebraically combine the two reactive currents to find the net reactive current (I_X). We can use Equation 16-7.

$$I_X = I_L + I_C = -298.6 \text{ mA} + 94.2 \text{ mA} = -204.4 \text{ mA}$$

The minus sign tells us that the net current is inductive and should be drawn downward on the phasor diagram. If we complete the parallelogram between net reactive current (I_X) and resistive current (I_R), we can locate the phasor for total current (I_T). This is sketched in Figure 16-26.

The phase angle is always measured between total voltage and total current, as marked on the diagram in Figure 16-26. We can compute its value with any of the basic right-triangle equations. If we use the cosine function, then we will also find the value of the power factor.

$$pf = \cos\theta = \frac{\text{adjacent}}{\text{hypotenuse}} = \frac{I_R}{I_T}$$

$$= \frac{110.3\text{ mA}}{232.2\text{ mA}} = 0.475$$

$$\theta = \arccos 0.475 = 61.6°$$

The circuit has a lagging power factor, since total current is lagging total voltage. You will recall that an *RL* circuit exhibits a similar characteristic. In effect, the high value of inductive current (298.6 mA) has cancelled the lesser value of capacitive current (94.2 mA). The remaining reactive current ($I_X = 204.4$ mA) combines with resistive current (I_R) to produce a total current (I_T) that lags the total voltage, just as would occur in a simple *RL* circuit. The completed solution matrix is given in Table 16-4.

CIRCUIT QUANTITY		RESISTOR	INDUCTOR	CAPACITOR	TOTAL
Current (rms)		110.3 mA	298.6 mA	94.2 mA	232.3 mA
Voltage	V_P	106.1 V	106.1 V	106.1 V	106.1 V
	V_{PP}	212.2 V	212.2 V	212.2 V	212.2 V
	V_{rms}	75 V	75 V	75 V	75 V
Resistance/Reactance/Impedance		680 Ω	251.2 Ω	796 Ω	322.9 Ω
Conductance/Susceptance/Admittance		1.47 mS	3.98 mS	1.26 mS	3.1 mS
Power		8.27 W	22.4 VAR	7.06 VAR	17.4 VA
Phase Angle (overall)		61.6°			
Power Factor (overall)		0.475 (lagging)			

Table 16-4. Completed Solution Matrix for the Circuit in Figure 16-25

Practice Problems

1. Analyze the circuit shown in Figure 16-27, and complete a solution matrix similar to Table 16-3.

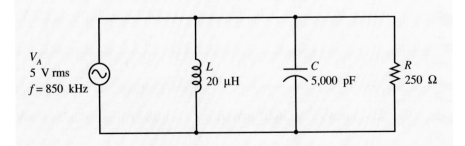

V_A
5 V rms
$f = 850$ kHz

L
20 μH

C
5,000 pF

R
250 Ω

Figure 16-27. Analyze this circuit.

2. Analyze the circuit shown in Figure 16-28, and complete a solution matrix similar to Table 16-3.

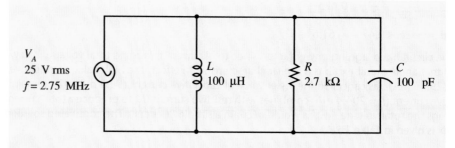

V_A
25 V rms
$f = 2.75$ MHz

L
100 µH

R
2.7 kΩ

C
100 pF

Figure 16-28. Analyze this circuit.

Answers to Practice Problems

1.

CIRCUIT QUANTITY		RESISTOR	INDUCTOR	CAPACITOR	TOTAL
Current (rms)		20 mA	46.82 mA	133.4 mA	88.9 mA
Voltage	V_P	7.07 V	7.07 V	7.07 V	7.07 V
	V_{PP}	14.14 V	14.14 V	14.14 V	14.14 V
	V_{rms}	5 V	5 V	5 V	5 V
Resistance/Reactance/Impedance		250 Ω	106.8 Ω	37.47 Ω	56.24 Ω
Conductance/Susceptance/Admittance		4 mS	9.37 mS	26.7 mS	17.8 mS
Power		100 mW	234.1 mVAR	667 mVAR	444.5 mVA
Phase Angle (overall)		77°			
Power Factor (overall)		0.225 (leading)			

2.

CIRCUIT QUANTITY		RESISTOR	INDUCTOR	CAPACITOR	TOTAL
Current (rms)		9.26 mA	14.5 mA	43.2 mA	30.16 mA
Voltage	V_P	35.35 V	35.35 V	35.35 V	35.35 V
	V_{PP}	70.7 V	70.7 V	70.7 V	70.7 V
	V_{rms}	25 V	25 V	25 V	25 V
Resistance/Reactance/Impedance		2.7 kΩ	1.73 kΩ	579 Ω	828.9 Ω
Conductance/Susceptance/Admittance		370.4 µS	578 µS	1.73 mS	1.21 mS
Power		231.5 mW	362.5 mVAR	1.08 VAR	754.0 mVA
Phase Angle (overall)		72.1°			
Power Factor (overall)		0.307 (leading)			

Series-Parallel *RLC* Circuits

The analysis of series-parallel *RLC* circuits follows the same basic procedure as analysis of resistive series-parallel circuits. We simplify the circuit by replacing sets of series or parallel components with equivalent components. If we encounter a series or parallel combination of similar components (i.e., all resistors, all inductors, or all capacitors), we replace them with an equivalent value. If the series or parallel components are dissimilar, then we represent the impedances with rectangular or polar notation and simplify them into an equivalent network. In general, rectangular and polar notation ensure that we account for the effects of phase differences. At a minimum, we will use rectangular or polar notation as we work toward finding total impedance. When we work back through the circuit to find individual currents and voltages, we may elect to omit the complex notation if we do not need to know the phase relationships at intermediate points in the circuit. Although it is impractical to describe a sequential procedure that is optimum for every type of series-parallel *RLC* circuit, the following will provide some general guidance.

1. Compute individual reactances.
2. Simplify the circuit to find total impedance.
3. Compute total current.
4. Compute individual voltages and currents.
5. Compute all other desired quantities.

DIRECT ANALYSIS OF SERIES-PARALLEL *RLC* CIRCUITS

We will emphasize the direct solution of *RLC* circuit analysis problems using techniques and procedures that are consistent with previously studied circuit analysis methods. Later, we will briefly examine an alternative method that can be used to simplify certain types of series-parallel problems.

EXAMPLE SOLUTION

Analyze the series-parallel *RLC* circuit shown in Figure 16-29, and complete the solution matrix shown in Table 16-5.

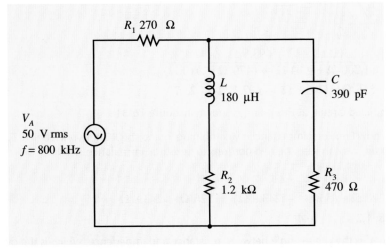

Figure 16-29. Analyze this circuit.

CIRCUIT QUANTITY	R_1	R_2	R_3	C	L	TOTAL
Voltage (rms)						50 V
Current (rms)						
Resistance/Reactance/Impedance	270 Ω	1.2 kΩ	470 Ω			
Conductance/Susceptance/Admittance						
Power						
Phase Angle (overall)						
Power Factor (overall)						

Table 16-5. A Solution Matrix for the Circuit in Figure 16-29

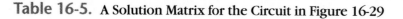

First, we find the reactance of the inductor and the capacitor by applying the basic reactance equations.

$$X_L = 2\pi fL = 6.28 \times 800 \text{ kHz} \times 180 \text{ μH} = 904 \text{ Ω}$$

$$X_C = \frac{1}{2\pi fC} = \frac{1}{6.28 \times 800 \text{ kHz} \times 390 \text{ pF}} = 510 \text{ Ω}$$

Next, let's combine the two parallel branches consisting of L, R_2, C, and R_3. For ease of notation, we will label these two branches as Z_A and Z_B as shown in Figure 16-30. We can express these two impedances as follows:

$$Z_A = 1{,}200 \text{ Ω} + j904 \text{ Ω, or}$$

$$Z_A = 1{,}502 \text{ Ω} \angle 37°$$

$$Z_B = 470 \text{ Ω} - j510 \text{ Ω, or}$$

$$Z_B = 693.5 \text{ Ω} \angle{-}47.4°$$

These two parallel branches (Z_A and Z_B) can be combined with the reciprocal formula for parallel circuits or the product-over-the-sum equation. Let's use the latter method to find the equivalent impedance $Z_{A,B}$.

$$Z_{A,B} = \frac{Z_A Z_B}{Z_A + Z_B}$$

$$= \frac{(1{,}502 \text{ Ω} \angle 37°)(693.5 \text{ Ω} \angle{-}47.4°)}{(1{,}200 \text{ Ω} + j904 \text{ Ω}) + (470 \text{ Ω} - j510 \text{ Ω})}$$

$$= 556 \text{ Ω} - j243.8 \text{ Ω} = 607.1 \text{ Ω} \angle{-}23.7°$$

The simplified circuit, at this point, is shown in Figure 16-31.

We can now find total impedance by combining R_1 and the RC network labeled $Z_{A,B}$. Since it is a series circuit, we can sum the two portions to find total impedance. That is,

$$Z_T = R_1 + Z_{A,B}$$

$$= 270 \text{ Ω} + (556 \text{ Ω} - j243.8 \text{ Ω}) = 826 \text{ Ω} - j243.8 \text{ Ω}$$

$$= 861.2 \text{ Ω} \angle{-}16.4°$$

The −16.4° is the phase angle between resistance and impedence, which is the overall phase angle (θ) of the circuit. The resulting simplified circuit is shown in Figure 16-32.

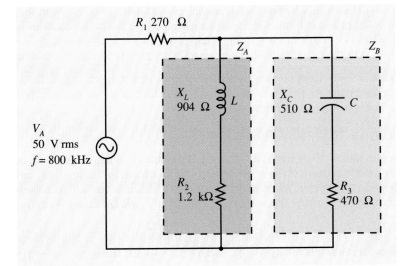

Figure 16-30. A simplification step in the analysis of the circuit shown in Figure 16-29.

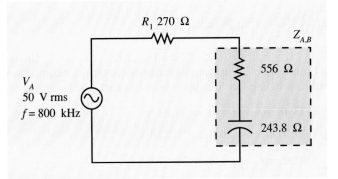

Figure 16-31. A partially simplified version of the circuit shown in Figure 16-29.

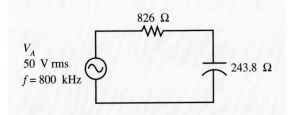

Figure 16-32. The simplified equivalent for the circuit shown in Figure 16-29.

Ohm's Law can now be used to compute total current flow.

$$I_T = \frac{V_A}{Z_T} = \frac{50 \text{ V}}{861.2 \ \Omega \ \angle{-16.4°}} = 58.1 \text{ mA} \ \angle{16.4°}$$

Because we have no apparent need to know the phase relationships between the individual component voltages and currents, we will no longer represent the circuit quantities as complex numbers. If we did want to know the intermediate phase angles, then we would simply perform all calculations with the circuit quantities expressed in rectangular and polar notation.

We are now ready to work our way back through the circuit to compute individual component voltages and currents. First, we know by inspection that total current flows through R_1. We compute its voltage drop with Ohm's Law.

$$V_{R_1} = I_{R_1}R_1 = 58.1 \text{ mA} \times 270 \ \Omega = 15.69 \text{ V}$$

According to Kirchhoff's Voltage Law, the rest of the supply voltage must be dropped across $Z_{A,B}$ in Figure 16-31. Because of the phase relationships, however, we cannot do a simple arithmetic subtraction of voltages. We must either perform the subtraction with complex numbers, or simply compute the voltage drop across $Z_{A,B}$ with Ohm's Law. Let's use the latter approach.

$$V_{A,B} = I_{A,B} \times Z_{A,B} = 58.1 \text{ mA} \times 607.1 \ \Omega = 35.27 \text{ V}$$

We can now transfer this voltage ($V_{A,B}$) back to Figure 16-30. This is redrawn in Figure 16-33.

The current through Z_A and Z_B can be found with Ohm's Law as follows.

$$I_A = \frac{V_{A,B}}{Z_A} = \frac{35.27 \text{ V}}{1,502 \ \Omega} = 23.48 \text{ mA}$$

$$I_B = \frac{V_{A,B}}{Z_B} = \frac{35.27 \text{ V}}{693.5 \ \Omega} = 50.86 \text{ mA}$$

Since L and R_2 are in series, they will both have the same current as Z_A. Similarly, the Z_B current will flow through both C and R_3. This completes our calculations for component currents. We can now use Ohm's Law to find the voltage drops across each component in branches Z_A and Z_B.

$$V_L = I_A X_L = 23.48 \text{ mA} \times 904 \ \Omega = 21.23 \text{ V}$$

$$V_{R_2} = I_A R_2 = 23.48 \text{ mA} \times 1,200 \ \Omega = 28.18 \text{ V}$$

$$V_C = I_B X_C = 50.86 \text{ mA} \times 510 \ \Omega = 25.94 \text{ V}$$

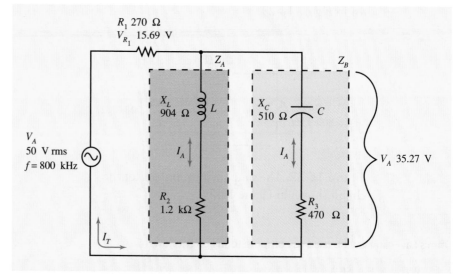

Figure 16-33. $V_{A,B}$ appears across parallel networks Z_A and Z_B.

$$V_{R_3} = I_B R_3 = 50.86 \text{ mA} \times 470 \text{ } \Omega = 23.9 \text{ V}$$

The various conductances, susceptances, and admittances can be found by taking the reciprocal of the resistance, reactance, and impedance, respectively.

$$G_1 = \frac{1}{R_1} = \frac{1}{270 \text{ } \Omega} = 3.7 \text{ mS}$$

$$G_2 = \frac{1}{R_2} = \frac{1}{1,200 \text{ } \Omega} = 833.3 \text{ } \mu\text{S}$$

$$G_3 = \frac{1}{R_3} = \frac{1}{470 \text{ } \Omega} = 2.13 \text{ mS}$$

$$B_L = \frac{1}{X_L} = \frac{1}{904 \text{ } \Omega} = 1.11 \text{ mS}$$

$$B_C = \frac{1}{X_C} = \frac{1}{510 \text{ } \Omega} = 1.96 \text{ mS}$$

$$Y = \frac{1}{Z_T} = \frac{1}{861.2 \text{ } \Omega} = 1.16 \text{ mS}$$

We can use our choice of the basic power equations to compute the circuit power. Let's choose the basic form of $P = VI$.

$$P_{T_1} = V_{R_1} I_{R_1} = 15.69 \text{ V} \times 58.1 \text{ mA} = 911.6 \text{ mW}$$

$$P_{T_2} = V_{R_2} I_{R_2} = 28.18 \text{ V} \times 23.48 \text{ mA} = 661.7 \text{ mW}$$

$$P_{T_3} = V_{R_3} I_{R_3} = 23.9 \text{ V} \times 50.86 \text{ mA} = 1.22 \text{ W}$$

$$P_{R_L} = V_L I_L = 21.23 \text{ V} \times 23.48 \text{ mA} = 498.5 \text{ mVAR}$$

$$P_{R_C} = V_C I_C = 25.94 \text{ V} \times 50.86 \text{ mA} = 1.32 \text{ VAR}$$

$$P_A = V_A I_T = 50 \text{ V} \times 58.1 \text{ mA} = 2.91 \text{ VA}$$

Power factor is the only remaining circuit quantity to be computed. Power factor is always equal to the cosine of the overall phase angle (θ).

$$pf = \cos\theta = \cos -16.4° = 0.959 \text{ (leading)}$$

We know the power factor is leading, since the overall circuit simplifies to an *RC* circuit (Figure 16-32), and we know that current always leads voltage in an *RC* circuit. The completed solution matrix is shown in Table 16-6.

CIRCUIT QUANTITY	R_1	R_2	R_3	C	L	TOTAL
Voltage (rms)	15.69 V	28.18 V	23.9 V	25.94 V	21.23 V	50 V
Current (rms)	58.1 mA	23.48 mA	50.86 mA	50.86 mA	23.48 mA	58.1 mA
Resistance/Reactance/Impedance	270 Ω	1.2 kΩ	470 Ω	510 Ω	904 Ω	861.2 Ω
Conductance/Susceptance/Admittance	3.7 mS	833.3 µS	2.13 mS	1.96 mS	1.11 mS	1.16 mS
Power	911.6 mW	661.7 mW	1.22 W	1.32 VAR	498.5 mVAR	2.91 VA
Phase Angle (overall)	−16.4°					
Power Factor (overall)	0.959 (leading)					

Table 16-6. A Completed Solution Matrix for the Circuit in Figure 16-29

Practice Problems

1. Analyze the circuit shown in Figure 16-34, and complete a solution matrix similar to Table 16-5.

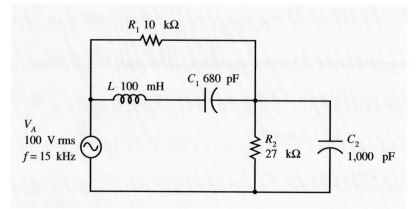

Figure 16-34. Analyze this circuit.

2. Analyze the circuit shown in Figure 16-35, and complete a solution matrix similar to Table 16-5.

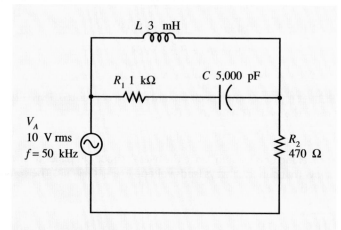

Figure 16-35. Analyze this circuit.

Answers to Practice Problems

1.

CIRCUIT QUANTITY	R_1	R_2	C_1	C_2	L	TOTAL
Voltage (rms)	34.88 V	65.52 V	87.96 V	65.52 V	53.08 V	100 V
Current (rms)	3.49 mA	2.43 mA	5.64 mA	6.17 mA	5.64 mA	6.63 mA
Resistance/Reactance/Impedance	10 kΩ	27 kΩ	15.61 kΩ	10.62 kΩ	9.42 kΩ	15.09 kΩ
Conductance/Susceptance/Admittance	100 μS	37 μS	64.1 μS	94.2 μS	106.2 μS	66.3 μS
Power	121.7 mW	159.2 mW	496.1 mVAR	404.3 mVAR	299.4 mVAR	663 mVA
Phase Angle (overall)	–64.96°					
Power Factor (overall)	0.423 (leading)					

2.

CIRCUIT QUANTITY	R_1	R_2	C	L	TOTAL
Voltage (rms)	6.17 V	3.22 V	3.93 V	7.32 V	10 V
Current (rms)	6.17 mA	6.85 mA	6.17 mA	7.77 mA	6.85 mA
Resistance/Reactance/Impedance	1 kΩ	470 Ω	636.9 Ω	942 Ω	1.46 kΩ
Conductance/Susceptance/Admittance	1 mS	2.13 mS	1.57 mS	1.06 mS	684.9 μS
Power	38.1 mW	22.1 mW	24.3 mVAR	56.9 mVAR	68.5 mVA
Phase Angle (overall)	28.4°				
Power Factor (overall)	0.880 (lagging)				

TRANSFORMATION OF SERIES-PARALLEL *RLC* CIRCUITS

The previously discussed method for analyzing series-parallel *RLC* circuits is applicable to all types of series-parallel *RLC* configurations. There is one common series-parallel configuration that deserves special mention. Figure 16-36 shows a parallel *LC* circuit. The resistance of the coil appears as a resistance in series with the coil inductance. Thus, the apparently parallel circuit must be analyzed as a series-parallel circuit.

Some technicians prefer to convert the series-parallel configuration (shown in the left portion of Figure 16-36) to an equivalent parallel *RLC* circuit (shown in the right portion of Figure 16-36). The primary motivation for this conversion is to avoid the use of complex numbers. If your engineering calculator manipulates complex numbers directly, then there is little advantage to the conversion process.

As long as the Q of the coil (i.e., Equation 12-14 where $Q = X_L/\text{ESR}$) is greater than 10 (the usual case), then Equation 16-9 can be used to transform the series resistance (ESR) into an equivalent parallel resistance (R_p).

$$R_P = \text{ESR} \times Q^2 \qquad (16\text{-}9)$$

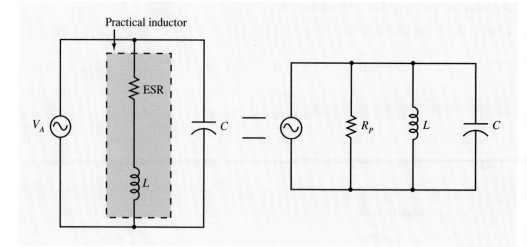

Figure 16-36. Transformation of a series-parallel *RLC* circuit into an equivalent parallel *RLC* circuit.

EXAMPLE SOLUTION

A parallel (ideally) *LC* circuit consists of a 1,000-pF capacitor and a 120-μH coil that has an equivalent series resistance of 18 Ω. The circuit is being operated at 600 kHz. Convert the circuit to an equivalent parallel circuit.

EXAMPLE **SOLUTION**

The basic conversion process is illustrated in Figure 16-36 and works for coils with Q factors greater than 10. Let's first determine the Q of the coil.

$$X_L = 2\pi fL = 6.28 \times 600 \text{ kHz} \times 120 \text{ μH} = 452.2 \text{ Ω}$$

$$Q_{(COIL)} = \frac{X_L}{ESR} = \frac{452.2 \text{ Ω}}{18 \text{ Ω}} = 25$$

Since this qualifies for our conversion method, we can apply Equation 16-9.

$$R_P = R_S Q^2 = 18 \text{ Ω} \times 25^2 = 11.3 \text{ kΩ}$$

Complex *RLC* Circuits

Complex *RLC* circuits can be analyzed by applying the same techniques and same network theorems that were used to analyze complex resistive circuits. The primary difference is that circuit quantities in the complex *RLC* circuit must be represented in polar or rectangular notation to account for the effects of differing phase angles. Ohm's and Kirchhoff's Laws remain your two most important analytical tools.

Exercise Problems 16.2

Refer to Figure 16-37 for Problems 1–10. All values are rms unless otherwise stated.

    1. What is the value of inductive reactance?

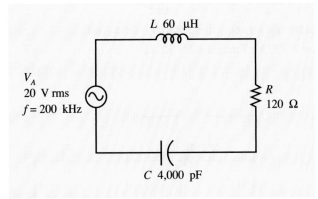

Figure 16-37. Analyze this circuit.

2. What is the value of capacitive reactance?
3. What is the impedance of the circuit?
4. How much total current flows through the circuit?
5. How much current flows through C?
6. What is the voltage drop across L?
7. What is the net reactive voltage?
8. What is the admittance of the circuit?
9. What is the overall phase angle of the circuit?
10. What is the circuit's power factor?

Refer to Figure 16-38 for Problems 11–20. All values are rms unless otherwise stated.

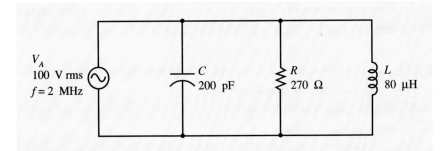

Figure 16-38. Analyze this circuit.

11. What is the value of inductive reactance in the circuit?
12. What is the rms voltage across C?
13. How much peak voltage is dropped across R?
14. How much current flows through L?
15. How much current flows through C?
16. What is the net reactive current?
17. What is the total current in the circuit?
18. What is the impedance of the circuit?

19. What is the phase angle of the circuit?

20. How much true power is dissipated by the circuit?

Refer to Figure 16-39 for Problems 21–30. All values are rms unless otherwise stated.

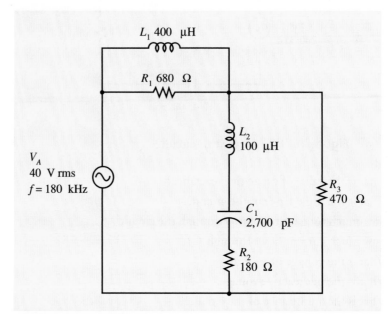

Figure 16-39. Analyze this circuit.

21. What is the reactance of L_2?

22. What is the reactance of C_1?

23. Express the impedance of the branch consisting of L_2, C_1, and R_2 in rectangular form.

24. Express the impedance of the parallel combination of L_1 and R_1 in polar notation.

25. What is the total impedance of the circuit?

26. What is the phase angle between total voltage and total current in the circuit?

27. How much current flows in the circuit?

28. What is the peak current through R_3?

29. What is the reactive power in L_2?

30. What is the voltage drop across R_2?

16.3 Resonance

The concept of resonance is very important to an electronics technician, since it plays such a central role in the operation of many electronic devices. Although we will address the subject of resonance as a separate section, it is very important for you to realize that resonance is nothing more than a description of the circuit characteristics of an *RLC* circuit at a particular operating frequency. That is, every *RLC* circuit that we have previously discussed and analyzed has a resonant frequency and exhibits the characteristics of resonance that are detailed in this section. A resonant *RLC* circuit is exactly like any other *RLC* circuit, except it is operating at a particular frequency called the resonant frequency.

Mechanical Resonance

Before we begin our discussion of resonant *RLC* circuits, let's briefly consider the more familiar aspects of mechanical resonance. Figure 16-40 shows the motion associated with a common pendulum. In Figure 16-40(a), the pendulum has been forcibly pulled to one side of its center or rest position. Once it is released, it accelerates toward its rest position as illustrated in Figure 16-40(b). When it reaches the center or rest position, as indicated in Figure 16-40(c), it has gained substantial momentum and continues to swing beyond its rest position. Its movement slows as it moves farther past the rest position. Eventually, as shown in Figure 16-40(d), it stops and begins to move back toward its rest position. Again, it accelerates toward the rest position, as shown in Figure 16-40(e), so that it has substantial momentum when it reaches the rest position, as shown in Figure 16-40(f). Finally, it begins to slow and eventually reaches its initial position, as represented in Figure 16-40(a).

Although the basic movement of the pendulum is familiar, there are other characteristics that are important. First, the rate (i.e., number of swings or cycles per second) at which the pendulum swings is solely determined by the length of the pendulum (assuming the force of gravity is a constant). That is, the frequency at which the pendulum oscillates is determined by the physical characteristic of length. Second, as the pendulum swings, it will lose energy as a result of air resistance, friction at the pivot point, bending of the pendulum arm, and so on. This means that each time the pendulum tries to return to its initial position, as represented in Figure 16-40(a), it will fall a little short. Unless additional energy is added to overcome the energy losses (e.g., we give it another push), the pendulum will continue to lose energy and will eventually stop in its rest position.

Now let's consider what would have to be done to keep the pendulum in motion indefinitely. Can you see that at the end of each cycle, we only need to add the amount of energy that was lost by the pendulum? If we add this tiny amount of energy each cycle, the pendulum will continue to make full swings.

Now consider when this external energy must be added. You know intuitively that for maximum efficiency, we would want to push the pendulum exactly as it reaches its maximum deflection. This is comparable to pushing a child in a swing. If we try to push the pendulum at the wrong time or in the wrong direction, we will actually interfere with the natural rhythm of the pendulum. If we try to make it swing at any frequency other than its natural frequency, we will have to add substantial energy. If, by contrast, we add

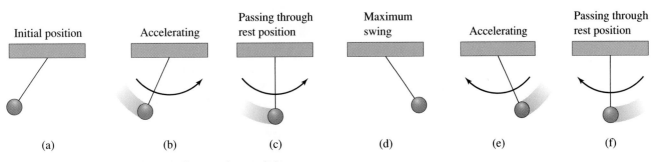

Figure 16-40. The movement of a simple pendulum.

the energy at the correct time, we aid the natural frequency and very minimal energy is required. Electrical resonance exhibits similar effects, as we will soon see.

Many readers will be familiar with yet another example of mechanical resonance that is illustrated in Figure 16-41. Here, we have a crystal goblet with only a small amount of liquid. If a finger is rubbed smoothly and lightly around the rim of the glass, the glass will begin to vibrate at a very definite frequency. Once it has started to oscillate, you can sustain the oscillation with only the slightest movement of your finger along the rim. Like the pendulum, the crystal goblet is exhibiting mechanical resonance. If we add energy at the right time each cycle, we need only add enough energy to compensate for losses. In Figure 16-41, we are adding the energy from a sliding finger. Some singers can add the energy with their voice (excessive energy can shatter the glass). The frequency of oscillation is determined by the physical characteristics of the glass (e.g., size, thickness, amount of liquid). Unless we change these physical characteristics, we cannot easily alter the frequency of oscillation. This natural frequency of oscillation that is exhibited by the pendulum and by the crystal goblet is called the resonant frequency.

Parallel Resonance

The similarities between electrical and mechanical resonance are easier to understand when considering a parallel RLC circuit, so let's begin by studying the characteristics of a parallel resonant circuit.

KEY POINTS

A parallel RLC circuit above the resonant frequency acts capacitive ($I_C > I_L$). A parallel RLC circuit below the resonant frequency acts inductive ($I_L > I_C$).

Figure 16-42 shows a parallel RLC circuit being operated at three frequencies. In Figure 16-42(a), the circuit is operated below the resonant frequency. At low frequencies, X_L, which decreases with decreasing frequencies, will be lower than X_C, which increases with decreasing frequencies. Since both L and C have the same voltage (i.e., they are in parallel), we know that I_L will be greater than I_C (Ohm's Law). The phasor diagram in Figure 16-42(a) illustrates the relationships in the circuit.

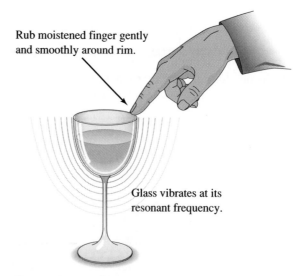

Rub moistened finger gently and smoothly around rim.

Glass vibrates at its resonant frequency.

Figure 16-41. An interesting demonstration of resonance.

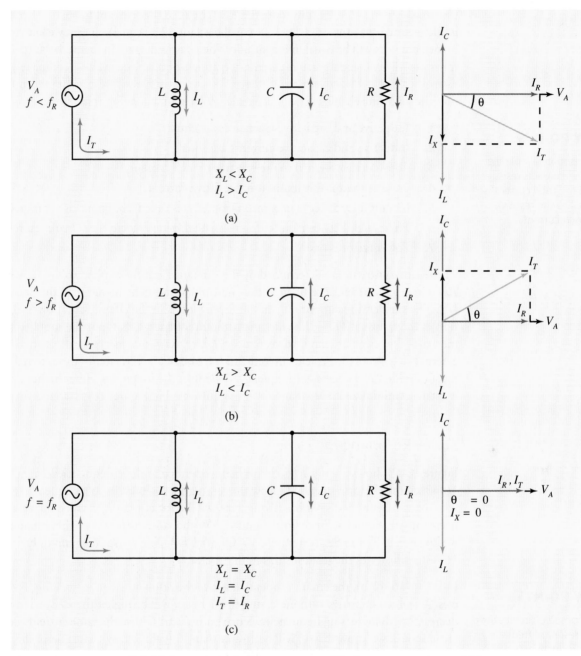

Figure 16-42. A parallel *RLC* circuit (a) below resonance, (b) above resonance, and (c) at resonance.

In Figure 16-42(b), the circuit is operated above the resonant frequency. At high frequencies, X_L, which increases with increasing frequencies, will be higher than X_C, which decreases with increasing frequencies. Since both L and C have the same voltage (i.e., they are in parallel), we know that I_C will be greater than I_L (Ohm's Law). The phasor diagram in Figure 16-42(b) illustrates the relationships in the circuit.

Now let's consider the circuit conditions if the input frequency is adjusted such that the inductive reactance and the capacitive reactance are equal. This is the **resonant frequency** of the circuit. Figure 16-42(c) illustrates the *RLC* circuit at the resonant frequency. Because the inductive and capacitive branches have equal reactances and equal voltages, we know the two branch currents will be equal in magnitude. The phasor diagram in Figure 16-42(c) illustrates that the two equal reactive currents (regardless of their exact values) completely cancel each other (i.e., net reactive current is zero). This leaves only resistive current to form I_T. We note the following characteristics of a parallel *RLC* circuit operating at its resonant frequency:

KEY POINTS

At resonance a parallel *RLC* circuit acts resistive and the total current is equal to the resistive branch current.

1. Inductive and capacitive reactances are equal.
2. Inductive and capacitive currents are equal.
3. Total current is equal to the resistive branch current.
4. Total current is minimum (only resistive current).
5. Circuit impedance is maximum (sometimes called a resonant rise of impedance).
6. Phase angle between total current and total voltage is zero (i.e., circuit acts resistive).
7. Power factor is one.

The reactive currents are determined by the reactance and the applied voltage as with any *RLC* circuit. However, at resonance, they may be substantially higher than the line current (I_T). The smaller line current only has to supply losses in the circuit (e.g., power dissipation in the resistor). This is like the small amount of energy that must be supplied to a mechanically resonant circuit to keep it oscillating. As with a mechanical system, the external energy must be timed correctly. In the case of an *RLC* circuit, the external energy must be added at the resonant frequency. If we shift the frequency, either higher or lower, we start to minimize the resonance effect as illustrated in Figures 16-42(a) and (b).

Series Resonance

Figure 16-43 shows a series *RLC* circuit being operated at three frequencies. In Figure 16-43(a), the circuit is operated below the resonant frequency. At low frequencies, X_L, which decreases with decreasing frequencies, will be lower than X_C, which increases with decreasing frequencies. Since both L and C have the same current (i.e., they are in series), we know that V_C will be greater than V_L (Ohm's Law). The phasor diagram in Figure 16-43(a) illustrates the relationships in the circuit.

KEY POINTS

A series *RLC* circuit above the resonant frequency acts inductive ($V_L > V_C$). A series *RLC* circuit below the resonant frequency acts capacitive ($V_C > V_L$).

In Figure 16-43(b), the circuit is operated above the resonant frequency. At high frequencies, X_L, which increases with increasing frequencies, will be higher than X_C, which decreases with increasing frequencies. Since both L and C have the same current (i.e., they are in series), we know that V_L will be greater than V_C (Ohm's Law). The phasor diagram in Figure 16-43(b) illustrates the relationships in the circuit.

Now let's consider the circuit conditions if the input frequency is adjusted such that the inductive reactance and the capacitive reactance are equal. This is the resonant frequency of the circuit. Figure 16-43(c) illustrates the *RLC* circuit at the resonant frequency. Because the inductive and capacitive reactances are equal, we know the two voltage drops will be equal. The phasor diagram in Figure 16-43(c) illustrates that the two equal reactive voltages (regardless of their exact values) completely cancel each other (i.e., net reactive voltage is zero). This means that the resistance will drop the entire applied voltage. We note the following characteristics of a series *RLC* circuit operating at its resonant frequency:

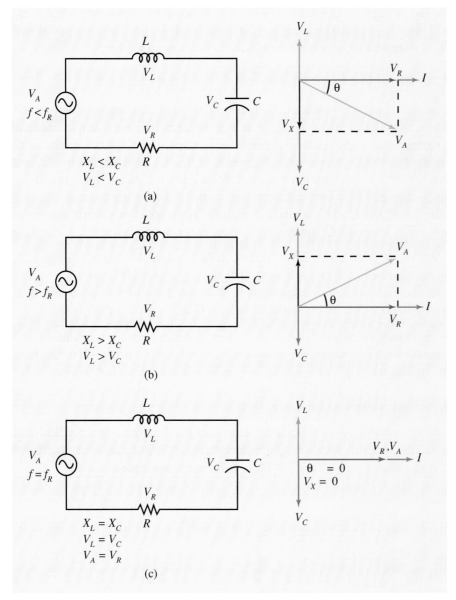

Figure 16-43. A series *RLC* circuit (a) below resonance, (b) above resonance, and (c) at resonance.

1. Inductive and capacitive reactances are equal.
2. Inductive and capacitive voltage drops are equal.
3. The resistive voltage drop is equal to the applied voltage.
4. Circuit impedance is minimum (reactances cancel).
5. Current is maximum (limited only by the resistance).
6. Phase angle between total current and total voltage is zero (i.e., circuit acts resistive).
7. Power factor is one.

KEY POINTS

At resonance, a series *RLC* circuit acts resistive, and the total impedance is equal to the resistance.

The reactive voltages are determined by the reactance and the current as with any *RLC* circuit. However, at resonance, they may be substantially higher than the applied voltage (V_A). This increase in voltage is often called a resonant rise in voltage.

Q of a Resonant Circuit

The degree to which the resonance effects are evident in an *RLC* circuit is determined by the quality, or Q, of the circuit. **Q** has no units and is a ratio between the resistance and the inductive reactance in the circuit at the resonant frequency. The higher the value of Q, the more marked the effects of resonance. Figure 16-44 shows a graph of current as a function of frequency for a series resonant circuit (recall that current is maximum at resonance in a series *RLC* circuit). There are three cases plotted on the graph representing low-, moderate-, and high-Q *RLC* circuits. The highest Q produces a very sharp response at resonance. The lower the Q, the less pronounced the resonance effect.

Values of Q range from less than 10 to over 100 for standard *RLC* circuits. In general, we classify circuits whose Q factor is less than 10 as low-Q circuits. By contrast, circuits with Q factors over 100 are considered to be high-Q circuits. Later in your electronics education, you will study circuits and devices that have Q factors greater than 1,000.

Figure 16-45 shows a graph of current as a function of frequency for a parallel *RLC* circuit (recall that current is minimum at resonance in a parallel *RLC* circuit). There are three cases plotted on the graph representing low-, moderate-, and high-Q *RLC* circuits. As with series *RLC* circuits, the highest Q produces a very sharp response at resonance. The lower the Q, the less pronounced the resonance effect.

Increased resistance in a series circuit decreases the Q of the circuit. In a parallel circuit, higher parallel resistance increases Q. We can compute the Q of a series or parallel *RLC* circuit with Equations 16-10 and 16-11, respectively. These equations are

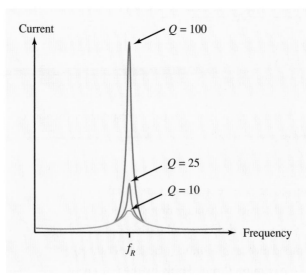

Figure 16-44. Current as a function of frequency for a series *RLC* circuit. The sharpness of the resonance response is determined by the Q of the circuit.

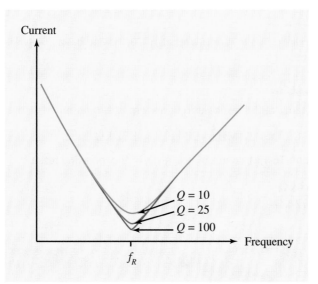

Current

Q = 10
Q = 25
Q = 100

Frequency

f_R

Figure 16-45. Current as a function of frequency for a parallel *RLC* circuit. The sharpness of the resonance response is determined by the *Q* of the circuit.

$$Q = \frac{X_L}{R_S} \qquad (16\text{-}10)$$

where R_S is the series resistance and X_L is the inductive reactance at the resonant frequency, and

$$Q = \frac{R_P}{X_L} \qquad (16\text{-}11)$$

where R_P is the resistance of the parallel resistive branch and X_L is the inductive reactance at the resonant frequency.

EXAMPLE SOLUTION

What is the *Q* of a series circuit with a resonant frequency of 3.11 MHz and a 1.75-μH coil, a 1,500-pF capacitor, and a 2.2-Ω resistor?

EXAMPLE **SOLUTION**

First, we compute the inductive reactance at the resonant frequency.

$X_L = 2\pi f L = 6.28 \times 3.11 \text{ MHz} \times 1.75 \text{ μH} \approx 34.18 \text{ Ω}$

Now we can apply Equation 16-10 to determine the *Q* of the circuit.

$Q = \dfrac{X_L}{R_S} = \dfrac{34.18 \text{ Ω}}{2.2 \text{ Ω}} = 15.5$

EXAMPLE SOLUTION

Find the Q of a parallel circuit that resonates at 1.37 MHz and has a 200-μH coil, a 68-pF capacitor, and a 68-kΩ resistor.

EXAMPLE **SOLUTION**

The inductive reactance at the resonant frequency must be computed first.

$$X_L = 2\pi f L = 6.28 \times 1.37 \text{ MHz} \times 200 \text{ μH} = 1.72 \text{ kΩ}$$

Applying Equation 16-11 to determine Q gives us the following result.

$$Q = \frac{R_P}{X_L} = \frac{68 \text{ kΩ}}{1.72 \text{ kΩ}} = 39.5$$

Practice Problems

1. If a series *RLC* circuit consisting of a 10-μH coil, a 100-pF capacitor, and a 7-Ω resistor resonates at 5 MHz, what is the *Q* of the circuit?

2. What is the *Q* of a parallel *RLC* circuit that consists of a 250-μH coil, a 150-pF capacitor, and a 24-kΩ resistor, and has a resonant frequency of 822.3 kHz?

Answers to Practice Problems

1. 44.9   2. 18.6

Selectivity, Bandwidth, and Bandpass of a Resonant Circuit

SELECTIVITY

Selectivity of an *RLC* circuit describes how sharply the circuit distinguishes between the resonant frequency and frequencies on either side of the resonant frequency. Frequencies that cause a response that is 70.7% of the maximum (voltage, current, or impedance) response or greater are considered to be passed or selected by the circuit. The frequencies that cause a response of less than 70.7% of the maximum (voltage, current, or impedance) response are considered to be rejected (i.e., not selected) by the circuit.

> **KEY POINTS**
>
> Since the lower (70.7%) response at these frequencies produces only one-half of the power (in the case of a series *RLC* circuit) produced at the resonant frequency, these points are also called the half-power points. In decibel measurements, this corresponds to a 3-dB reduction in power.

Figure 16-46 shows the response of three *RLC* circuits with different *Q* factors. Their 100% responses have been adjusted to be equal. Regardless of the *Q* factor, all frequencies with responses above 70.7% of the maximum voltage, current, or impedance are considered to be selected or passed by the circuit. Clearly, there is a band or range of frequencies that are above the 70.7% level. The greater the selectivity (i.e., the higher the *Q*) of the circuit, the narrower the range of frequencies that produces a response of greater than 70.7% of the maximum.

In the case of parallel *RLC* circuits, we measure the response in terms of impedance. That is, the impedance is maximum at the resonant frequency (f_R) and decreases on either side of f_R. In the case of series *RLC* circuits, it is common to use resistive voltage, power, or circuit current as the indicator. All of these are maximum at the resonant frequency and decrease for frequencies on either side of f_R. In the case of current or voltage responses, we use 70.7% as the dividing line between selection and rejection. Since power is equal to the

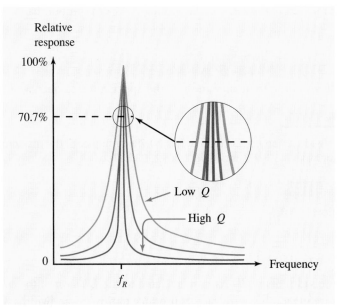

Figure 16-46. The Q factor determines the selectivity and bandwidth of an *RLC* circuit.

product of voltage and current, the dividing line for a power response is 70.7% × 70.7% or 50%. For this reason, the points at which the response falls below 70.7% of the maximum voltage or current in a series *RLC* circuit are called the **half-power points.** Power is often measured in decibels, so these same points are also called 3-dB points (technically −3-dB points), since a −3-dB power loss corresponds to a 50% power reduction.

BANDPASS

The band of frequencies that causes a response that is above the half-power points is called the **bandpass** of the *RLC* circuit. Bandpass (also called passband) is expressed as a range of frequencies. The lowest frequency that still produces a response above the half-power point is called the lower **cutoff frequency** (f_L). The upper cutoff frequency (f_H) is the highest frequency that still produces a response above the half-power point. The bandpass of an *RLC* circuit is the range of frequencies between the lower and upper cutoff frequencies.

EXAMPLE SOLUTION

What is the bandpass of an *RLC* circuit that has 70.7% or higher of the maximum response for frequencies higher than 150 kHz and lower than 250 kHz?

EXAMPLE **SOLUTION**

The bandpass is simply the range of frequencies that cause a 70.7% or more of the maximum response. In the present example, the bandpass would be stated as the range of 150 kHz to 250 kHz.

BANDWIDTH

The width (measured in hertz) of the bandpass of an *RLC* circuit is called the **bandwidth** of the circuit. The bandwidth is not a measure of specific frequencies like the bandpass,

but rather it is a measure of the width of the bandpass. We can compute bandwidth with Equation 16-12.

$$BW = f_H - f_L \qquad (16\text{-}12)$$

where f_L is the lower cutoff frequency and f_H is the upper cutoff frequency of the *RLC* circuit.

EXAMPLE SOLUTION

What is the bandwidth of an *RLC* circuit that has 70.7% or higher of the maximum response for frequencies higher than 150 kHz and lower than 250 kHz?

EXAMPLE **SOLUTION**

We apply Equation 16-12.

$$BW = f_H - f_L$$
$$= 250 \text{ kHz} - 150 \text{ kHz} = 100 \text{ kHz}$$

Clearly, the bandwidth of an *RLC* circuit is related to the *Q* factor of the circuit. For a given resonant frequency, higher *Q* factors produce narrower bandwidths. Conversely, lower *Q* factors produce wider bandwidths for a given center frequency (f_R). We can express the relationship of Q, f_R, and bandwidth with Equation 16-13.

$$BW = \frac{f_R}{Q} \qquad (16\text{-}13)$$

EXAMPLE SOLUTION

What is the bandwidth of an *RLC* circuit that has a resonant frequency of 2.5 MHz and a Q of 20?

EXAMPLE **SOLUTION**

We apply Equation 16-13.

$$BW = \frac{f_R}{Q} = \frac{2.5 \text{ MHz}}{20} = 125 \text{ kHz}$$

Figure 16-47 further clarifies the definitions and relationships affecting the bandwidth of an *RLC* circuit.

Calculations for a Resonant *RLC* Circuit

Now that we have an overall view of the characteristics of series and parallel *RLC* circuits, we can analyze them. It is very important for you to realize that literally all of the techniques you used to analyze series and parallel *RLC* circuits also apply to resonant *RLC* circuits. The resonant frequency is just a specific frequency where X_L and X_C are equal. We will learn a few new equations used by technicians to simplify calculations.

CALCULATION OF THE RESONANT FREQUENCY

We know that resonance occurs when the inductive and capacitive reactances are equal. It is very useful to be able to quickly and directly determine this frequency for a particular *RLC* circuit. We can evolve such an equation by setting the two reactance equations equal to each other and solving for frequency as follows:

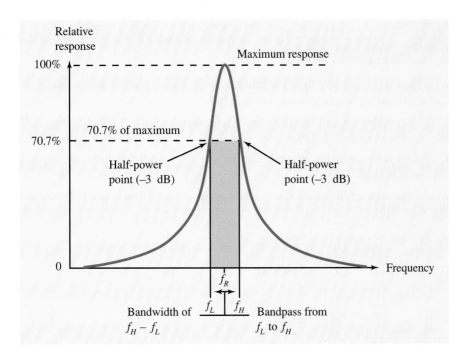

Figure 16-47. The relationship of bandpass and bandwidth to the 70.7% response level.

$$X_L = X_C$$

$$2\pi f L = \frac{1}{2\pi f C}$$

$$4\pi^2 f^2 LC = 1$$

$$f^2 = \frac{1}{4\pi^2 LC}$$

Finally, taking the square root of both sides gives us Equation 16-14.

$$f_R = \frac{1}{2\pi\sqrt{LC}} \qquad (16\text{-}14)$$

This equation applies to either series or parallel *RLC* circuits.

EXAMPLE SOLUTION

What is the resonant frequency of a series circuit consisting of a 200-μH inductor, a 1,000-pF capacitor, and a 5-Ω resistor?

EXAMPLE **SOLUTION**

We apply Equation 16-14.

$$f_R = \frac{1}{2\pi\sqrt{LC}}$$

$$= \frac{1}{6.28 \times \sqrt{200 \text{ μH} \times 1,000 \text{ pF}}}$$

$$= 356.1 \text{ kHz}$$

Practice Problems

1. If a 10-μH coil, a 250-pF capacitor, and a 1.2-MΩ resistor are in parallel, what is the resonant frequency of the circuit?
2. What is the resonant frequency of a series circuit with a 1.5-mH coil, a 2,200-pF capacitor, and a 7.5-Ω resistor?
3. What value capacitor is needed in parallel with a 200-μH inductor to produce resonance at 1.13 MHz?
4. What value of inductor is needed in series with a 270-pF capacitor to resonate at 8.85 MHz?

Answers to Practice Problems

1. 3.18 MHz   2. 87.66 kHz   3. 99.3 pF   4. 1.2 μH

SERIES RESONANCE CALCULATIONS

Most of the calculations for a series resonant *RLC* circuit are based on Ohm's and Kirchhoff's Laws and basic series circuit rules. We will introduce other more specific equations as they are needed.

EXAMPLE SOLUTION

Analyze the series *RLC* circuit shown in Figure 16-48, and complete the solution matrix shown in Table 16-7. Assume that the circuit is operating at the resonant frequency.

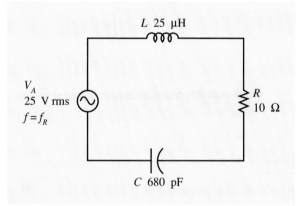

Figure 16-48. A series resonant *RLC* circuit.

EXAMPLE **SOLUTION**

First, we need to compute the resonant frequency with Equation 16-14.

$$f_R = \frac{1}{2\pi\sqrt{LC}} = \frac{1}{6.28 \times \sqrt{25\ \mu H \times 680\ pF}} = 1.22\ \text{MHz}$$

The two reactances can now be computed at the resonant frequency.

CIRCUIT QUANTITY	RESISTOR	INDUCTOR	CAPACITOR	TOTAL
Current (rms)				
Voltage (rms)				25 V
Resistance/Reactance/Impedance	10 Ω			
Resonant Frequency				
Q				
Bandwidth				
Phase Angle				
Power Factor				

Table 16-7. Solution Matrix for the Circuit in Figure 16-48

$$X_L = 2\pi fL = 6.28 \times 1.22 \text{ MHz} \times 25 \text{ μH} \approx 192 \text{ Ω}$$

$$X_C = \frac{1}{2\pi fC} = \frac{1}{6.28 \times 1.22 \text{ MHz} \times 680 \text{ pF}} \approx 192 \text{ Ω}$$

We need only compute one of the reactances, since we know they are equal at the resonant frequency. Computation of both values, however, is a convenient way to check your work.

The impedance of a series *RLC* circuit at the resonant frequency is equal to the resistance in the circuit (i.e., the reactances cancel). Nevertheless, we can compute the impedance of a series *RLC* circuit at any frequency with Equation 16-3.

$$Z = \sqrt{(X_L - X_C)^2 + R^2}$$
$$= \sqrt{(192 \text{ Ω} - 192 \text{ Ω})^2 + (10 \text{ Ω})^2}$$
$$= \sqrt{0 + 100} = \sqrt{100} = 10 \text{ Ω}$$

Ohm's Law can now be used to find the total current in the circuit.

$$I_T = \frac{V_A}{Z} = \frac{25 \text{ V}}{10 \text{ Ω}} = 2.5 \text{ A}$$

Again, we can apply Ohm's Law to determine the individual component voltage drops.

$$V_R = I_R R = 2.5 \text{ A} \times 10 \text{ Ω} = 25 \text{ V}$$
$$V_L = I_L X_L = 2.5 \text{ A} \times 192 \text{ Ω} = 480 \text{ V}$$
$$V_C = I_C X_C = 2.5 \text{ A} \times 192 \text{ Ω} = 480 \text{ V}$$

Note that the two reactive voltages are greater than the applied voltage and are equal in magnitude. You will recall that they are 180° out of phase with each other and effectively cancel each other. This is also confirmed by the observation that the resistive voltage drop is equal to the applied voltage.

Since this is a series *RLC* circuit, we can use Equation 16-10 to determine the Q of the circuit.

$$Q = \frac{X_L}{R_S} = \frac{192 \text{ Ω}}{10 \text{ Ω}} = 19.2$$

You will recall that the voltages across the reactances in a series resonant circuit exceed the value of applied voltage. We computed the exact values with Ohm's Law. This voltage increase as the circuit nears resonance is called a resonant rise or Q rise in voltage. It can also be computed with Equation 16-15.

$$V_L = V_C = QV_A \qquad (16\text{-}15)$$

This equation only applies to a series *RLC* circuit at the resonant frequency. It is also useful in a transposed version for computing the Q of the circuit when the component voltages are known (or measured in the laboratory).

We can use Equation 16-13 to determine the bandwidth of the circuit.

$$BW = \frac{f_R}{Q} = \frac{1.22\ \text{MHz}}{19.2} = 63.5\ \text{kHz}$$

The phase angle and power factor for a resonant *RLC* circuit are always zero and one, respectively, since the circuit acts resistive. If you forget this relationship, you can always compute the values as with any other *RLC* circuit.

This completes the analysis of the series resonant circuit shown in Figure 16-48. The completed solution matrix is provided in Table 16-8.

CIRCUIT QUANTITY	RESISTOR	INDUCTOR	CAPACITOR	TOTAL
Current (rms)	2.5 A			
Voltage (rms)	25 V	480 V	480 V	25 V
Resistance/Reactance/Impedance	10 Ω	192 Ω	192 Ω	10 Ω
Resonant Frequency	1.22 MHz			
Q	19.2			
Bandwidth	63.5 kHz			
Phase Angle	0°			
Power Factor	Unity (1)			

Table 16-8. Completed Solution Matrix for the Circuit in Figure 16-48

Practice Problems

1. Complete a solution matrix similar to Table 16-7 for the circuit shown in Figure 16-49.

2. A series *RLC* circuit has the following values: 2.5 mH, 82 pF, 68 Ω, and an 18-V rms voltage source. Complete a solution matrix similar to Table 16-7 for this circuit.

3. Complete a solution matrix similar to Table 16-7 for a series *RLC* circuit having the following values: 27 μH, 270 pF, 10 Ω, and a 5-V rms voltage source.

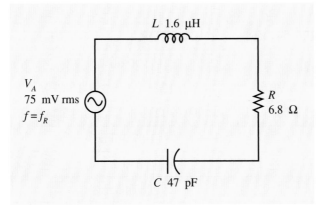

Figure 16-49. A series *RLC* circuit.

Answers to Practice Problems

1.

CIRCUIT QUANTITY	RESISTOR	INDUCTOR	CAPACITOR	TOTAL
Current (rms)	11.03 mA			
Voltage (rms)	75 mV	2.04 V	2.04 V	75 mV
Resistance/Reactance/Impedance	6.8 Ω	184.5 Ω	184.5 Ω	6.8 Ω
Resonant Frequency	18.36 MHz			
Q	27.13			
Bandwidth	676.7 kHz			
Phase Angle	0°			
Power Factor	Unity (1)			

2.

CIRCUIT QUANTITY	RESISTOR	INDUCTOR	CAPACITOR	TOTAL
Current (rms)	264.7 mA			
Voltage (rms)	18 V	1.46 kV	1.46 kV	18 V
Resistance/Reactance/Impedance	68 Ω	5.52 kΩ	5.52 kΩ	68 Ω
Resonant Frequency	351.7 kHz			
Q	81.18			
Bandwidth	4.33 kHz			
Phase Angle	0°			
Power Factor	Unity (1)			

3.

CIRCUIT QUANTITY	RESISTOR	INDUCTOR	CAPACITOR	TOTAL
Current (rms)	500 mA			
Voltage (rms)	5 V	158.1 V	158.1 V	5 V
Resistance/Reactance/Impedance	10 Ω	316.2 Ω	316.2 Ω	10 Ω
Resonant Frequency	1.87 MHz			
Q	31.62			
Bandwidth	59.14 kHz			
Phase Angle	0°			
Power Factor	Unity (1)			

PARALLEL RESONANCE CALCULATIONS

For the most part, analysis of parallel *RLC* circuits at resonance is no different than the analysis of the same circuit at some other frequency. We will, however, introduce alternate equations that can streamline your work in some cases.

EXAMPLE SOLUTION

Analyze the parallel *RLC* circuit shown in Figure 16-50, and complete the solution matrix given in Table 16-9. Assume that the circuit is operating at the resonant frequency.

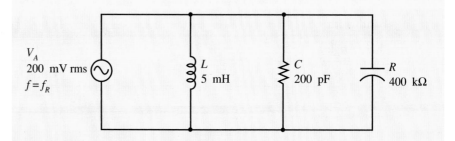

Figure 16-50. Analyze this parallel *RLC* circuit.

EXAMPLE SOLUTION

Finding the resonant frequency is a good place to start solving a problem like this. We apply Equation 16-14.

$$f_R = \frac{1}{2\pi\sqrt{LC}} = \frac{1}{6.28 \times \sqrt{(5\ \text{mH}) \times (200\ \text{pF})}} = 159.2\ \text{kHz}$$

Now, we can compute the reactance of the inductive and capacitive branches.

$$X_L = 2\pi fL = 6.28 \times 159.2\ \text{kHz} \times 5\ \text{mH} = 5\ \text{k}\Omega$$

$$X_C = \frac{1}{2\pi fC} = \frac{1}{6.28 \times 159.2\ \text{kHz} \times 200\ \text{pF}} = 5\ \text{k}\Omega$$

CIRCUIT QUANTITY	RESISTOR	INDUCTOR	CAPACITOR	TOTAL
Voltage (rms)	200 mV			
Current (rms)				
Resistance/Reactance/Impedance	400 kΩ			
Resonant Frequency				
Q				
Bandwidth				
Phase Angle				
Power Factor				

Table 16-9. Solution Matrix for the Circuit in Figure 16-50

The second calculation is not essential, since we know that the inductive and capacitive reactances are always equal at the resonant frequency.

Application of Ohm's Law will provide the value of current through each of the parallel branches.

$$I_R = \frac{V_R}{R} = \frac{200 \text{ mV}}{400 \text{ k}\Omega} = 500 \text{ nA}$$

$$I_L = \frac{V_L}{X_L} = \frac{200 \text{ mV}}{5 \text{ k}\Omega} = 40 \text{ }\mu\text{A}$$

$$I_C = \frac{V_C}{X_C} = \frac{200 \text{ mV}}{5 \text{ k}\Omega} = 40 \text{ }\mu\text{A}$$

Kirchhoff's Current Law can be used to determine the total current. We will sum the branch currents with phasor addition (Equation 16-8), since they are out of phase.

$$I_T = \sqrt{(I_L - I_C)^2 + I_R^2}$$
$$= \sqrt{(40 \text{ }\mu\text{A} - 40 \text{ }\mu\text{A})^2 + (500 \text{ nA})^2} = 500 \text{ nA}$$

We can now apply Ohm's Law to calculate the total impedance of the circuit.

$$Z = \frac{V_A}{I_T} = \frac{200 \text{ mV}}{500 \text{ nA}} = 400 \text{ k}\Omega$$

This calculation could have been avoided, since we know that the total impedance of a parallel *RLC* circuit at the resonant frequency is equal to the value of the resistive branch.

The Q of the circuit can be found with Equation 16-11.

$$Q = \frac{R_P}{X_L} = \frac{400 \text{ k}\Omega}{5 \text{ k}\Omega} = 80$$

You will recall that the impedance of a parallel resonant circuit is maximum at the resonant frequency. We computed the exact value with Ohm's Law. This impedance increase as the circuit nears resonance is called a resonant rise or Q rise in impedance. It can also be computed with Equation 16-16.

$$Z = QX_L \qquad (16\text{-}16)$$

This equation only applies to a parallel *RLC* circuit at the resonant frequency. It is simply a transposed version of Equation 16-11.

We can now use the computed value of Q and the previously computed resonant frequency to find the bandwidth of the circuit (Equation 16-13).

$$BW = \frac{f_R}{Q} = \frac{159.2 \text{ kHz}}{80} = 2 \text{ kHz}$$

We can draw a phasor diagram and compute the values of phase angle and power factor as with any other parallel *RLC* circuit, or we can simply remember that the phase angle is always zero and the power factor is always unity at the resonant frequency. The completed solution matrix for this analysis problem is given in Table 16-10.

CIRCUIT QUANTITY	RESISTOR	INDUCTOR	CAPACITOR	TOTAL
Voltage (rms)	200 mV			
Current (rms)	500 nA	40 μA	40 μA	500 nA
Resistance/Reactance/Impedance	400 kΩ	5 kΩ	5 kΩ	400 kΩ
Resonant Frequency	159.2 kHz			
Q	80			
Bandwidth	2 kHz			
Phase Angle	0°			
Power Factor	Unity (1)			

Table 16-10. Completed Solution Matrix for the Circuit in Figure 16-50

Practice Problems

1. Complete a solution matrix similar to Table 16-9 for the circuit shown in Figure 16-51.

2. A parallel *RLC* circuit has the following values: 2.5 μH, 120 pF, 5.0 kΩ, and a 12-V rms voltage source. Complete a solution matrix similar to Table 16-9 for this circuit.

3. Complete a solution matrix similar to Table 16-9 for a parallel *RLC* circuit that has the following values: 270 μH, 27 pF, 200 kΩ, and a 500-mV rms voltage source.

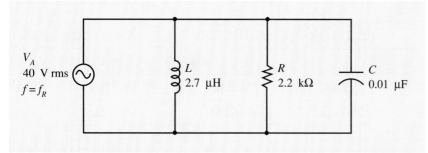

Figure 16-51. A parallel *RLC* circuit.

Answers to Practice Problems

1.

CIRCUIT QUANTITY	RESISTOR	INDUCTOR	CAPACITOR	TOTAL
Voltage (rms)	40 V			
Current (rms)	18.18 mA	2.44 A	2.44 A	18.18 mA
Resistance/Reactance/Impedance	2.2 kΩ	16.43 Ω	16.43 Ω	2.2 kΩ
Resonant Frequency	969.1 kHz			
Q	133.9			
Bandwidth	7.24 kHz			
Phase Angle	0°			
Power Factor	Unity (1)			

2.

CIRCUIT QUANTITY	RESISTOR	INDUCTOR	CAPACITOR	TOTAL
Voltage (rms)	12 V			
Current (rms)	2.4 mA	83.16 mA	83.16 mA	2.4 mA
Resistance/Reactance/Impedance	5 kΩ	144.3 Ω	144.3 Ω	5 kΩ
Resonant Frequency	9.19 MHz			
Q	34.65			
Bandwidth	265.2 kHz			
Phase Angle	0°			
Power Factor	Unity (1)			

3.

CIRCUIT QUANTITY	RESISTOR	INDUCTOR	CAPACITOR	TOTAL
Voltage (rms)	500 mV			
Current (rms)	2.5 µA	158.2 µA	158.2 µA	2.5 µA
Resistance/Reactance/Impedance	200 kΩ	3.16 kΩ	3.16 kΩ	200 kΩ
Resonant Frequency	1.865 MHz			
Q	63.29			
Bandwidth	29.47 kHz			
Phase Angle	0°			
Power Factor	Unity (1)			

Self-Resonance of Inductors and Capacitors

For many applications and analyses, we can assume that an inductor is purely inductive and that a capacitor is purely capacitive. In other cases (high-frequency circuits in particular), a technician must consider the nonideal effects of a practical inductor and a practical capacitor.

Figure 16-52 illustrates how a physical coil that is designed to have inductance also possesses capacitance. Recall that a capacitor is simply two conductors separated by an insulator. As shown in Figure 16-52(a), a practical coil has stray or parasitic capacitance that appears between adjacent turns on the coil. The stray capacitance appears electrically in parallel with the inductance. Additionally, the wire used to wind the coil has resistance. The wire resistance appears electrically in series with the inductance. Figure 16-52(b) shows the equivalent circuit for a physical coil.

For low frequencies, the stray capacitance can generally be ignored (i.e., the capacitive reactance is very high). At higher frequencies, however, the capacitance can play a significant role. In fact, since the coil begins to act like an *RLC* circuit at high frequencies, we can infer that it will also exhibit the characteristics of resonance at some frequency. This frequency is called the **self-resonant frequency** and is provided in the manufacturer's specification sheet for a given coil.

Practical capacitors also exhibit nonideal properties. They have inductance in the leads and resistive losses caused by the ESR of the capacitor (explained in Chapter 14). Figure 16-53 shows the equivalent circuit for a practical capacitor. The rated capacitance and the parasitic resistance and inductance all appear in series. Thus, the capacitor alone becomes a series resonant circuit at some high frequency.

At frequencies in the low kilohertz, the self-resonance of coils and capacitors can be safely ignored for most applications. As the frequency increases, the technician must be increasingly aware of the nonideal effects of capacitors and inductors in order to understand and explain the behavior of the circuits.

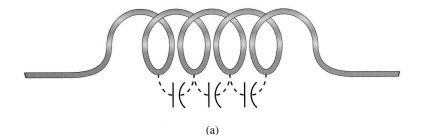

(a)

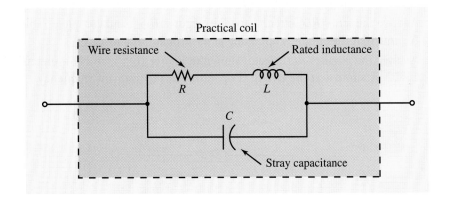

(b)

Figure 16-52. A physical coil also has resistance and capacitance.

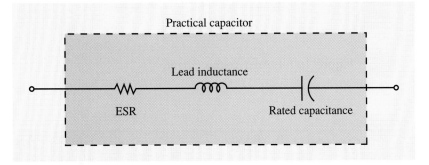

Figure 16-53. A practical capacitor acts like a series *RLC* circuit at high frequencies.

Exercise Problems 16.3

1. Describe two examples of mechanical resonance.

2. At frequencies above resonance in an *RLC* circuit, inductive reactance is (*greater than, less than, equal to*) capacitive reactance.

3. At resonance, the inductive reactance in an *RLC* circuit is (*greater than, less than, equal to*) the capacitive reactance.

4. The current in a series *RLC* circuit is maximum at resonance. (True or False)

5. The current through the resistive branch of a parallel *RLC* circuit is maximum at resonance and decreases at other frequencies. (True or False)

6. What is the phase angle between total voltage and total current in a parallel resonant circuit?

7. What is the power factor of a series resonant circuit?

8. What is meant by the phrase *Q rise in voltage* for a series *RLC* circuit?

9. Analyze the series *RLC* circuit shown in Figure 16-54, and complete Table 16-11. Assume that the circuit is operating at its resonant frequency.

10. Analyze the parallel *RLC* circuit shown in Figure 16-55, and complete Table 16-12. Assume that the circuit is operating at the resonant frequency.

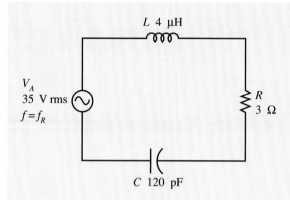

Figure 16-54. Analyze this circuit.

CIRCUIT QUANTITY	RESISTOR	INDUCTOR	CAPACITOR	TOTAL
Current (rms)				
Voltage (rms)				35 V
Resistance/Reactance/Impedance	3 Ω			
Resonant Frequency				
Q				
Bandwidth				
Phase Angle				
Power Factor				

Table 16-11. Solution Matrix for the Circuit in Figure 16-54

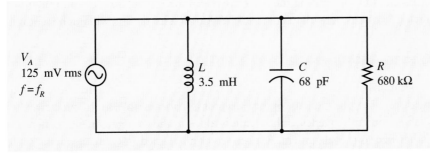

Figure 16-55. Analyze this circuit.

CIRCUIT QUANTITY	RESISTOR	INDUCTOR	CAPACITOR	TOTAL
Voltage (rms)	125 mV			
Current (rms)				
Resistance/Reactance/Impedance	680 kΩ			
Resonant Frequency				
Q				
Bandwidth				
Phase Angle				
Power Factor				

Table 16-12. Solution Matrix for the Circuit in Figure 16-55

16.4 Troubleshooting *RLC* Circuits

Malfunctions in *RLC* circuits can be categorized into two general classes: defective components and misalignment. We will consider these individually.

Defective Components in *RLC* Circuits

The list of possible defects in an *RLC* circuit is essentially a combination of the defects that may occur in *RL* and *RC* circuits. You will recall the following possibilities:

RESISTOR DEFECTS

- open
- shorted
- wrong value

CAPACITOR DEFECTS

- open
- shorted
- leaky (generally limited to electrolytics)
- wrong value

INDUCTOR DEFECTS

- open
- shorted turns
- coil-to-core short

> **KEY POINTS**
>
> In addition to defective components, an *RLC* circuit can malfunction due to misalignment.

The actual method for locating the defective component in an *RLC* circuit is identical to that previously discussed with reference to *RL* and *RC* circuits and will not be repeated here.

RLC Circuit Alignment

Most applications of *RLC* circuits require that the circuit be operated at its resonant frequency. In many cases, either the inductor or the capacitor is made variable, so the circuit can be tuned to a specific resonant frequency. If the circuit is tuned to the wrong resonant frequency, we say it is misaligned or out of alignment. A mistuned or misaligned *RLC* circuit will not perform as expected. It must be adjusted by a technician to obtain the desired performance.

TUNING PROCEDURES FOR A SERIES *RLC* CIRCUIT

Figure 16-56 shows a method that can be used to tune a series *RLC* circuit to the correct resonant frequency. The circuit is connected to a source voltage (typically a signal generator, which can be found in most electronic laboratories) that is operating at the desired resonant frequency. An oscilloscope is connected across the resistor and calibrated for a convenient display. The circuit is then tuned to resonance by adjusting *L* and/or *C* while monitoring the oscilloscope. As you know, series resonance will produce the maximum voltage across *R*. This, of course, is indicated by maximum amplitude on the oscilloscope display.

As a technician, you must be careful of multiple ground connections in circuits that you are testing. In the case of Figure 16-56, if one end of the resistor is connected to ground, then the ground side of the oscilloscope should be connected to this same point. If neither side of the resistor is connected to ground, then you can use a dual-channel oscilloscope to measure the voltage across the resistor. In this case, Channel A of the scope is connected to one end of the resistor and Channel B is connected to the other. The scope is set to measure the difference between the two channels (e.g., A–B on the vertical mode selector).

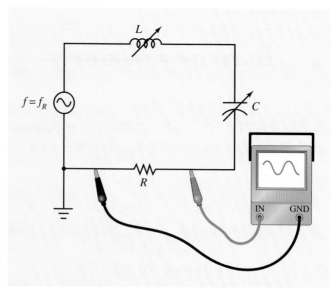

Figure 16-56. How to tune a series resonant circuit.

You may be tempted to insert a current meter in series with the *RLC* circuit and tune the circuit to obtain maximum current. While this is a valid approach in theory and in some practical cases, there is a potential problem; the current meter must be capable of measuring currents in the frequency range of the resonant circuit. Most common current meters are low-frequency measuring devices.

TUNING PROCEDURES FOR A PARALLEL *RLC* CIRCUIT

Figure 16-57 illustrates a procedure for tuning parallel *RLC* circuits to the correct frequency. Here again, a signal generator is used to provide a voltage at the correct frequency. A 1-Ω resistor (R_S) is connected in series with the *RLC* circuit. The oscilloscope measures the voltage across the series resistor. The circuit is tuned by adjusting the value of *L* and/or *C* and monitoring the scope display. At resonance, the *RLC* circuit will have maximum impedance and minimum current. Since the total line current flows through the series resistor, the voltage across it (and the scope display) will also be minimum when the circuit is tuned to the input frequency.

There are many other ways to calibrate an *RLC* circuit, but most require more specialized equipment that is not always available to the technician. Frequency counters, resonant dip meters, high-frequency voltmeters, high-frequency current meters, and absorption wave meters can also be used.

KEY POINTS

Resonance in a parallel circuit is indicated by a dipping of voltage across a small series resistor.

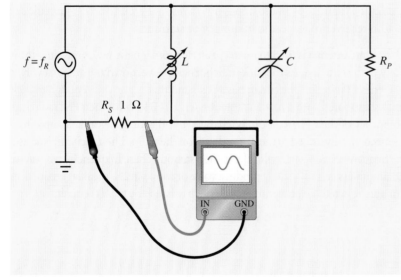

Figure 16-57. Procedure for tuning a parallel *RLC* circuit.

Exercise Problems 16.4

1. When a series *RLC* circuit is tuned to the same frequency as the source voltage, the voltage across the resistor will (*peak, dip*).

2. When a parallel *RLC* circuit is tuned to the same frequency as the source voltage, the line current will (*peak, dip*).

3. Based on your knowledge of series resonant circuits, think of a way to align it to a specific resonant frequency that was not described in this text.

4. Based on your knowledge of parallel resonant circuits, think of a way to align it to a specific resonant frequency that was not described in this text.

16.5 Applied Technology: *RLC* Circuits

RLC (often called *LC*) circuits have many uses in electronic circuits. In nearly all cases, their performance in a given application utilizes the characteristics of resonance.

Radio Frequency Selection

At any given point on earth (or anywhere else), there is a constant bombardment of electromagnetic waves of many different frequencies. For example, there are electromagnetic waves from many AM and FM radio stations, TV stations, police radios, business radios, cellular telephones, paging systems, portable telephones, satellite communications, microwave links, and a host of other sources such as motors, fluorescent lights, and computers, that unintentionally emit electromagnetic waves. Unintentional emissions are called interference or noise when detected by a radio receiver. In order to select a particular frequency or group of frequencies from among all of the existing signals, we rely on the use of resonant *RLC* circuits. Figure 16-58 illustrates how a resonant *LC* (or *RLC*) circuit can be used to tune a radio receiver to a specific frequency or station.

In Figure 16-58, an antenna is used to intercept all electromagnetic waves traveling through space in the vicinity of the antenna. As the various frequencies travel down the antenna wire, they encounter a series *LC* circuit. The circuit has a passband that is just wide enough to include all of the frequencies associated with a particular station (e.g., 150 kHz for each FM radio station). The resonant frequency of the *LC* circuit can be changed by adjusting the variable capacitor. The capacitor is mechanically linked to the tuning knob on the radio. The *LC* circuit is adjusted so that it passes the frequencies associated with the desired station. These frequencies pass on to the radio circuits and amplifiers and ultimately produce voice or music in the speaker. Frequencies from all other stations are rejected (i.e., they are outside the passband) by the *LC* circuit.

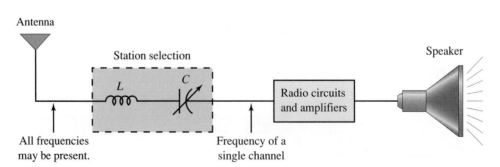
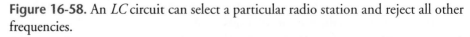

Figure 16-58. An *LC* circuit can select a particular radio station and reject all other frequencies.

Rejection of Interference

Figure 16-59 shows how an *RLC* circuit can be used to separate a desired frequency from another frequency, which would otherwise cause interference. As shown in Figure 16-59, the circuit is essentially a two-part voltage divider. The first part is the series resistance (*R*). The second part of the voltage divider is the series *LC* circuit. The *LC* circuit is tuned to the frequency of the interference.

Recall that a series *LC* circuit has minimum impedance at resonance (i.e., the net reactance is zero ohms). In the case of the circuit shown in Figure 16-59, there will be a zero-ohm (theoretically) impedance through the *LC* portion of the circuit to ground at the frequency of the interference. This means all of the interference voltage will be dropped across the series resistance and will not pass on to subsequent circuitry.

The desired frequency, on the other hand, is either higher or lower than the resonant frequency of the *LC* circuit. Recall that a series *LC* combination can have substantial reactance at frequencies on either side of the resonant frequency. In the case shown in Figure 16-59, the impedance of the *LC* circuit at the desired frequency is much greater than the value of series resistance. This means that nearly all of the desired signal voltage will be felt across the *LC* portion of the circuit and will be available for use in subsequent circuitry connected in parallel with the *LC* circuit.

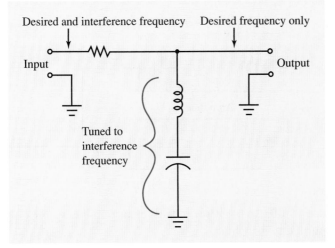

Figure 16-59. An *RLC* circuit can be used to eliminate interference.

Frequency Determination for Oscillators

An oscillator is an electronic circuit that can generate sine waves. It may be viewed as an amplifier that provides its own input. You have probably heard the shrill squeal that occurs when a microphone in a public address system is held too close to the speaker for the same system. Feedback occurs and you hear a loud squeal or oscillation. The output from the speaker provides its own input to the microphone.

Figure 16-60 illustrates how an *LC* circuit can be used to determine the frequency of an oscillator. All electronic circuits generate a wide range of electrical frequencies at very low levels (like the noise between stations on a television). In the case of the circuit illustrated in Figure 16-60, the random low-level noise from the oscillator is passed through a series LC circuit to the input of the amplifier. The LC circuit will offer opposition to off-resonance frequencies, but will offer low (ideally zero) opposition to signals at the resonant frequency. When the low-level signal at the resonant frequency returns to the input of the amplifier, it is amplified and appears even larger at the output. Now this stronger signal can make the feedback trip to the input of the amplifier and appear even larger at the output. This process continues until the circuit reaches its maximum amplitude. At that time, the circuit becomes stable, and the constant frequency, constant amplitude signal is available at the output of the amplifier. Since oscillation (self-generation of a signal) depends on feedback, and since the LC circuit only allows feedback at the resonant frequency, oscillation will occur at the frequency set by the LC network. Either L or C can be made variable to alter the frequency of oscillation.

When a portion of an amplifier's output is returned to its own input, the returned energy is called feedback. The phase of feedback relative to the original input can either aid (as described in the preceding discussion) or cancel. Feedback that aids the original input is called **positive (or regenerative) feedback.** If the feedback is out of phase with the input signal, it is called **negative (or degenerative) feedback.**

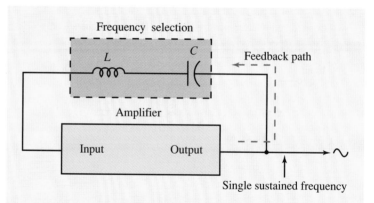

Figure 16-60. An oscillator consists of an amplifier whose output is returned to its own input.

Exercise Problems 16.5

1. Refer to Figure 16-58. With the circuit connected as shown, explain why a series LC circuit was used instead of a parallel LC circuit.
2. Refer to Figure 16-59. Explain what would happen to circuit operation if the series LC circuit were replaced with a parallel LC circuit.
3. Refer to Figure 16-60. If the value of C were made smaller, what would happen to the frequency of oscillation?

Chapter Summary

- This chapter introduced the characteristics of series and parallel *RLC* circuits. Many of the characteristics are similar to previously studied series and parallel circuits. For example, current is the same throughout a series circuit, the sum (phasor sum for reactive circuits) of the voltage drops in a series circuit always equals the supply voltage, the voltage is the same across all components in a parallel circuit, and the sum (phasor sum for reactive circuits) of the branch currents in a parallel circuit always equals the total supply current.

- *RLC* circuits also exhibit some interesting phenomena. For example, the voltage drop across the reactances in a series *RLC* circuit can individually exceed the value of supply voltage, the reactive branch currents in a parallel *RLC* circuit can exceed the supply current, and the total impedance of either a series or a parallel *RLC* circuit at resonance is equal to the value of the resistance in the circuit.

- Complete analysis of series, parallel, and series-parallel *RLC* circuits was presented. Analysis of complex *RLC* circuits was not formally presented, but is similar to the analytical procedures presented for other complex circuit configurations.

- All *RLC* circuits have a single frequency where the inductive and capacitive reactances are equal. We call this the resonant frequency of the circuit. The resonant frequency is strictly determined by the values of inductance and capacitance in the circuit. The characteristics of an *RLC* circuit at resonance are very important to a technician. In short, a series *RLC* circuit at resonance has minimum impedance, maximum current, and maximum component voltages. The power factor is unity, the phase angle is zero and the circuit acts purely resistive. In the case of a parallel *RLC* circuit at resonance, the circuit has maximum impedance, minimum line current, a unity power factor, and a phase angle of zero. It also acts purely resistive.

- On either side of the resonant frequency, a series or parallel circuit acts reactive. Series *RLC* circuits above and below resonance act inductive and capacitive, respectively. Parallel *RLC* circuits act capacitive and inductive, respectively, for frequencies above and below the resonant frequency.

- The *Q* factor of an *RLC* circuit determines how pronounced the effects of resonance will be in the vicinity of the resonant frequency. At frequencies on either side of the resonant frequency, circuit response diminishes. Frequencies on either side of the resonant frequency that cause a 70.7% or higher response relative to the maximum (100%) response at the resonant frequency are called the passband or bandpass of the circuit. The width of the passband is called the bandwidth of the circuit. Bandwidth and *Q* factor are inversely related. Higher *Q*s result in narrower bandwidths. The frequencies on the lower and upper edges of the passband are called the lower cutoff frequency and the upper cutoff frequency, respectively. In the case of series *RLC* circuits, these same points are also called the half-power or 3-dB points.

- The increase in reactive voltage (series *RLC* circuits) or impedance (parallel *RLC* circuits) is related to the *Q* factor. The voltage across the inductance or capacitance in a series *RLC* circuit at resonance is higher than the supply voltage by a factor of *Q*.

This is called a Q rise in voltage. Similarly, a Q rise in impedance occurs in a parallel *RLC* circuit and causes the total impedance to be higher than either reactance by a factor of Q.

- Analysis of *RLC* circuits at the resonant frequency is largely identical to the analysis at any other frequency. Computation of the resonant frequency and calculations involving Q and bandwidth are most easily accomplished using specialized equations.

- Troubleshooting an *RLC* circuit requires the same basic methods that are used to diagnose *RL* or *RC* circuits. In the case of an *RLC* circuit that is used for its resonance effects (the usual case), the circuit must be tuned for the correct resonant frequency. Either L or C may be made variable for the purpose of aligning or tuning the circuit.

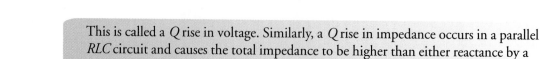

Review Questions

Section 16.1: Introduction to *RLC* Circuits

1. The current is the same through every component in a series *RLC* circuit. (True or False)

2. The voltage drop is the same across every component in a series *RLC* circuit. (True or False)

3. What is the phase relationship between total current and inductive voltage in a series *RLC* circuit?

4. What is the phase relationship between total current and capacitive voltage in a series *RLC* circuit?

5. What is the phase relationship between inductive current and capacitive current in a series *RLC* circuit?

6. What is the phase relationship between inductive voltage and capacitive voltage in a series *RLC* circuit?

7. If a series *RLC* circuit has an inductive voltage drop of 120 mV, a capacitive voltage drop of 80 mV, and a resistive voltage drop of 40 mV, what is the value of applied voltage?

8. What is the impedance of a series *RLC* circuit with the following values: $X_L = 10$ kΩ, $X_C = 4$ kΩ, and $R = 8.2$ kΩ?

9. How much current flows in a series *RLC* circuit with 10 V rms applied and consisting of the following values: $X_L = 7.5$ kΩ, $X_C = 22$ kΩ, and $R = 10$ kΩ?

10. The current is the same through every component in a parallel *RLC* circuit. (True or False)

11. The voltage drop is the same across every component in a parallel *RLC* circuit. (True or False)

12. What is the phase relationship between total voltage and inductive current in a parallel *RLC* circuit?

13. What is the phase relationship between total voltage and capacitive current in a parallel *RLC* circuit?

14. What is the phase relationship between inductive current and capacitive current in a parallel *RLC* circuit?

15. What is the phase relationship between inductive voltage and capacitive voltage in a parallel *RLC* circuit?

16. If a parallel *RLC* circuit has an inductive branch current of 3.5 A, a capacitive branch current of 5 A, and a resistive branch current of 1.2 A, what is the value of source current?

17. If an *RLC* circuit has reactive powers of 20 VAR (P_{R_L}) and 15 VAR (P_{R_C}), and has a true power dissipation of 10 W, determine the value of apparent power in the circuit.

Section 16.2: *RLC* Circuit Calculations

Refer to Figure 16-61 for Questions 18–30.

18. What is the value of inductive reactance?

19. What is the value of capacitive reactance?

20. What is the value of impedance in the circuit?

21. How much current flows through L?

22. How much current flows through R?

23. What is the voltage drop across C?

24. What is the voltage drop across L?

25. What is the voltage drop across R?

26. What is the phase angle between total voltage and total current in the circuit?

27. What is the power factor of the circuit?

28. Compute the value of true power.

29. Compute the value of apparent power.

30. What is the value of net reactive power?

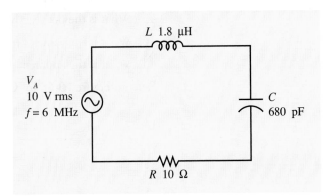

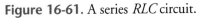

Figure 16-61. A series *RLC* circuit.

Refer to Figure 16-62 for Questions 31–45.

31. What is the value of inductive reactance?

32. What is the value of capacitive reactance?

33. How much current flows through the inductor?

34. How much current flows through the capacitor?

35. How much current flows through the resistor?

36. What is the value of source current?

37. What is the impedance of the circuit?

38. What is the admittance of the circuit?

39. What is the phase angle between total current and total voltage?

40. What is the power factor?

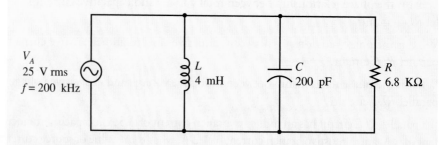

Figure 16-62. A parallel *RLC* circuit.

41. How much reactive power is due to the inductor?

42. How much reactive power is due to the capacitor?

43. What is the net reactive power?

44. What is the value of true power?

45. What is the apparent power in the circuit?

Refer to Figure 16-63 for Questions 46–60.

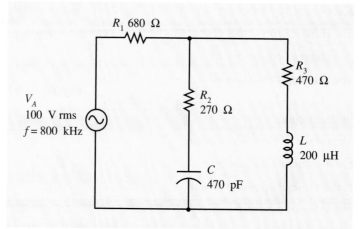

Figure 16-63. A series-parallel *RLC* circuit.

46. What is the capacitive reactance of *C*?

47. What is the inductive reactance of *L*?

48. Write the impedance of the R_3, *L* branch in polar and rectangular notation.

49. Write the impedance of the R_2, *C* branch in polar and rectangular notation.

50. What is the combined impedance of the R_2, *C* and the R_3, *L* branches?

51. What is the total impedance of the circuit?

52. What is the total current in the circuit?

53. How much current flows through R_1?

54. How much current flows through L?

55. What is the voltage drop across C?

56. What is the voltage drop across R_1?

57. What is the power factor of the circuit?

58. What is the value of apparent power for the circuit?

59. What is the phase angle between total voltage and total current in the circuit?

60. How much power is dissipated by R_3?

Section 16.3: Resonance

61. Only certain kinds of RLC circuits have a resonant frequency. (True or False)

62. What are the relative values of inductive and capacitive reactance in an RLC circuit that is operating at its resonant frequency?

63. A series RLC circuit that is operating below its resonant frequency will act (*resistive, inductive, capacitive*).

64. A series RLC circuit that is operating above its resonant frequency will act (*resistive, inductive, capacitive*).

65. A series RLC circuit that is operating at its resonant frequency will act (*resistive, inductive, capacitive*).

66. A parallel RLC circuit that is operating above its resonant frequency will act (*resistive, inductive, capacitive*).

67. A parallel RLC circuit that is operating below its resonant frequency will act (*resistive, inductive, capacitive*).

68. A parallel RLC circuit that is operating at its resonant frequency will act (*resistive, inductive, capacitive*).

69. The reactive voltage drops in a series resonant circuit are always equal. (True or False)

70. The impedance of a series RLC circuit at resonance is maximum. (True or False)

71. The current through a series RLC circuit at resonance is maximum. (True or False)

72. What is the phase angle between total current and total voltage in an RLC circuit that is operating at its resonant frequency?

73. The impedance of a parallel RLC circuit at resonance is maximum. (True or False)

74. The supply current for a parallel RLC circuit at resonance is minimum. (True or False)

75. An RLC circuit with a Q of greater than _____ is considered to have a high Q.

76. An RLC circuit with a Q of less than _____ is considered to have a low Q.

77. The higher the resistance in a series RLC circuit, the higher the Q. (True or False)

78. The Q of a parallel RLC circuit is directly proportional to the value of the resistive branch. (True or False)

79. For a given resonant frequency, high-Q circuits have wider bandwidths than low-Q circuits. (True or False)

80. What is the name given to the range of frequencies that extends between the lower cutoff frequency and the upper cutoff frequency of an *RLC* circuit?

81. Explain why the half-power point frequency in a series *RLC* circuit is also called the 3-dB frequency.

82. If the resonant frequency of an *RLC* circuit is 25 MHz, the lower cutoff frequency is 23.75 MHz, and the bandwidth is 2.5 MHz, what is the pass band of the circuit?

83. Refer to Question 82. What is the *Q* of the circuit?

84. Refer to Question 82. What is the upper cutoff frequency?

85. If the current in a series *RLC* circuit is 250 mA at resonance, what is the value of current at the lower cutoff frequency?

86. If the resistor voltage in a series *RLC* circuit is 5 V at the upper 3-dB frequency, what is the value of resistor voltage at the lower cutoff frequency?

87. Refer to Question 86. What is the value of resistor voltage at the resonant frequency?

88. What is the bandwidth of an *RLC* circuit that has a resonant frequency of 15 MHz and a *Q* of 35?

89. Compute the resonant frequency of a series *RLC* circuit that has a 175-µH inductor, an 860-pF capacitor, and a 3.5-Ω resistor.

90. Compute the resonant frequency of a parallel *RLC* circuit that has a 2-mH inductor, a 2,000-pF capacitor, and a 27-kΩ resistor.

91. Analyze the series resonant circuit shown in Figure 16-64, and complete the solution matrix provided in Table 16-13.

92. Analyze the parallel resonant circuit shown in Figure 16-65, and complete the solution matrix provided in Table 16-14.

93. Due to the nonideal effects of stray (interwinding) capacitance, a coil can exhibit the characteristics of a resonant circuit. The frequency at which this occurs is called the _____ frequency of the coil.

94. Due to the nonideal effects of lead inductance and resistance, a capacitor becomes a (*series, parallel*) resonant circuit at a frequency called the _____ frequency of the capacitor.

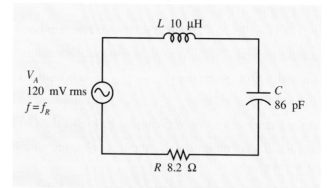

Figure 16-64. Analyze this circuit.

CIRCUIT QUANTITY	RESISTOR	INDUCTOR	CAPACITOR	TOTAL
Current (rms)				
Voltage (rms)				120 mV
Resistance/Reactance/Impedance	8.2 Ω			
Resonant Frequency				
Q				
Bandwidth				
Phase Angle				
Power Factor				

Table 16-13. Solution Matrix for the Circuit in Figure 16-64

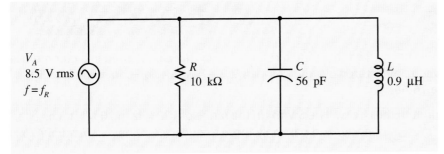

V_A
8.5 V rms
$f = f_R$

R
10 kΩ

C
56 pF

L
0.9 μH

Figure 16-65. Analyze this circuit.

CIRCUIT QUANTITY	RESISTOR	INDUCTOR	CAPACITOR	TOTAL
Voltage (rms)		8.5 V		
Current (rms)				
Resistance/Reactance/Impedance	10 kΩ			
Resonant Frequency				
Q				
Bandwidth				
Phase Angle				
Power Factor				

Table 16-14. Solution Matrix for the Circuit in Figure 16-65

Section 16.4: Troubleshooting *RLC* Circuits

95. Malfunctions in *RLC* circuits can be caused by defective components or _____ of the *LC* circuit.

96. List six possible defects that may occur in an *RLC* circuit.

97. If you monitor the line current in a parallel *RLC* circuit as you tune it to resonance, it will peak as you tune through the resonant frequency. (True or False)

98. If you monitor the resistor voltage in a series *RLC* circuit as you tune it to resonance, it will peak as you tune through the resonant frequency. (True or False)

Section 16.5: Applied Technology: *RLC* Circuits

99. Refer to Figure 16-58. If *L* were smaller, you would be tuning in a radio station that has a higher channel frequency. (True or False)

100. Refer to Figure 16-59. If the frequency of interference were higher than the resonant frequency of the *LC* circuit, how could you alter the *LC* circuit to eliminate the interference?

TECHNICIAN CHALLENGE

You have been asked to design a resonant filter that can be used in a communications receiver manufactured by your company. The basic design parameters are listed in Figure 16-66.

The input to the filter will be 5 Vrms in the range of 100 kHz to 10 MHz. The filter must reject most frequencies and pass only those frequencies in the passband of 475 kHz to

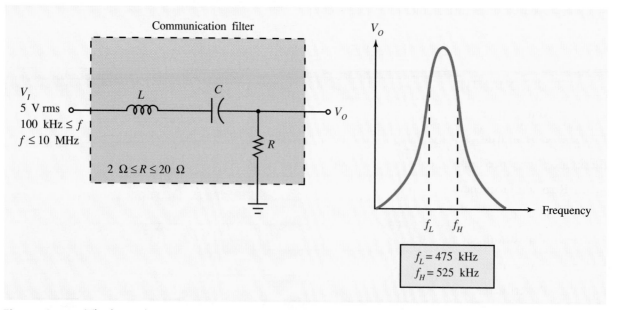

Figure 16-66. The basic design requirements for a communications filter.

525 kHz. For compatibility with existing circuitry, the resistance shown in Figure 16-66 must be in the range of 2 to 20 Ω.

Determine an acceptable set of values for L and C. After you complete your design, completely analyze the circuit to verify that the original design requirements have been satisfied. If you have access to the required materials, then measure the performance of your design in the laboratory.

Equation List

(16-1) $V_{REACTIVE} = V_L + V_C$

(16-2) $V_A = \sqrt{(V_L - V_C)^2 + V_R^2}$, or

$V_A = \sqrt{V_R^2 + (V_L - V_C)^2}$

(16-3) $Z = \sqrt{(X_L - X_C)^2 + R^2}$, or

$Z = \sqrt{R^2 + (X_L - X_C)^2}$

(16-4) $X_{NET} = X_L + X_C$

(16-5) $P_{R_{NET}} = P_{R_L} + P_{R_C}$

(16-6) $P_A = \sqrt{(P_{R_L} - R_{R_C})^2 + P_T^2}$, or

$P_A = \sqrt{P_T^2 + (P_{R_L} - P_{R_C})^2}$

(16-7) $I_X = I_L + I_C$

(16-8) $I_T = \sqrt{(I_L - I_C)^2 + I_R^2}$, or

$I_T = \sqrt{I_R^2 + (I_L - I_C)^2}$

(16-9) $R_P = ESR \times Q^2$

(16-10) $Q = \dfrac{X_L}{R_S}$

(16-11) $Q = \dfrac{R_P}{X_L}$

(16-12) $BW = f_H - f_L$

(16-13) $BW = \dfrac{f_R}{Q}$

(16-14) $f_R = \dfrac{1}{2\pi\sqrt{LC}}$

(16-15) $V_L = V_C = QV_A$

(16-16) $Z = QX_L$

key terms

coefficient of coupling
dot notation
Faraday shield
hot wire
leakage flux
leakage inductance

magnetizing current
mutual inductance
neutral
primary
reflected impedance
secondary

step-down transformer
step-up transformer
turns ratio

objectives

After completing this chapter, you should be able to:

1. Compute the total inductance of series- or parallel-connected coils that are magnetically coupled.

2. Analyze transformer circuits by applying the relationships between turns ratio, voltage ratio, current ratio, and impedance ratio between the primary and secondary windings.

3. Name and describe three types of transformer cores.

4. List and describe at least three types of transformer losses.

5. Solve problems relating to the efficiency of a transformer.

6. Test a transformer to locate defects.

7. Describe at least three applications for transformers.

8. Explain the terms step-up and step-down as applied to transformers.

9. Explain the operation of each of the following types of transformers: autotransformers, tapped transformers, and multiwinding transformers.

10. Describe the basic power distribution scheme used by commercial power companies.

11. Identify delta and wye transformer connections and state the relationship between leg and line currents and voltages.

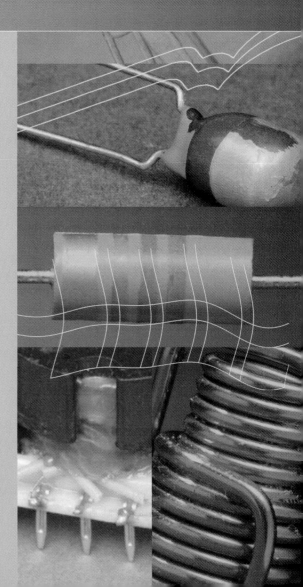

Mutual Inductance and Transformers

Transformers are basic circuit components like resistors, capacitors, and inductors. The operation of transformers may seem natural to you, since their operation is based on the same magnetic principles discussed with reference to inductors. Transformers are used in nearly every electronic system that operates from the ac power line and in most battery-operated circuits as well. A technician must understand the theory of operation of a transformer, know how to analyze transformer circuits, and be able to troubleshoot transformers to locate defects.

17.1 Mutual Inductance and Coupling

You already know that when current passes through an inductor, a magnetic field is produced around the inductor. The strength of the field is proportional to current and the physical properties of the coil (e.g., number of turns, type of core, and so on). You will also recall that a changing magnetic field can induce a voltage into the windings of an inductor. The amount of voltage induced is proportional to such things as the relative rate of movement of the field, strength of the field, and physical properties of the coil.

Figure 17-1 shows two coils that are physically close to each other. One coil is connected to an alternating voltage source, the other coil is connected to an ac voltmeter. The alternating current in L_1 will cause the surrounding flux (shown in Figure 17-1 as dashed lines) to continuously expand and contract. Because L_2 is nearby, some of the flux produced by L_1 cuts the windings of L_2 and induces a voltage into the L_2 coil. This is a measurable, useful voltage as indicated by the voltmeter in Figure 17-1. As indicated in Figure 17-1(a), not all of the flux lines produced by L_1 pass through L_2.

Now, if the two coils are brought closer together as shown in Figure 17-1(b), a greater percentage of the flux is shared by the two coils. Because more flux lines are cutting the L_2 turns, a higher voltage will be produced in L_2 as indicated by the voltmeter in Figure 17-1(b).

The percentage of flux from one coil that passes through a second coil is called the **coefficient of coupling.** The coefficient of coupling can range from zero (i.e., the two coils share no flux lines) to 100 (i.e., the two coils share 100% of the flux lines). Generally, the coefficient of coupling is expressed as a decimal, so the range is from zero to one. It is represented by the letter k.

When two coils are magnetically linked as represented in Figure 17-1, we say they have **mutual inductance.** You will recall that 1 H is the measure of inductance that causes 1 V to be induced when the current through it changes at the rate of 1 A/s. In the case of magnetically coupled coils, if the current through one coil changes at the rate of 1 A/s and a voltage of 1V is produced in the second coil, we say they have a mutual inductance of 1 H.

The value of mutual inductance (L_M) between two coils depends on the inductance of each winding (L_1 and L_2) and how closely they are coupled (k). We can express this formally with Equation 17-1.

$$L_M = k\sqrt{L_1 L_2} \qquad (17\text{-}1)$$

where k is the coefficient of coupling, and L_M, L_1, and L_2 are the inductance values in henrys of the mutual and coil inductances, respectively.

EXAMPLE SOLUTION

If two coils have a coefficient of coupling of 0.75 and have individual inductances of 100 mH and 250 mH, what is the value of mutual inductance?

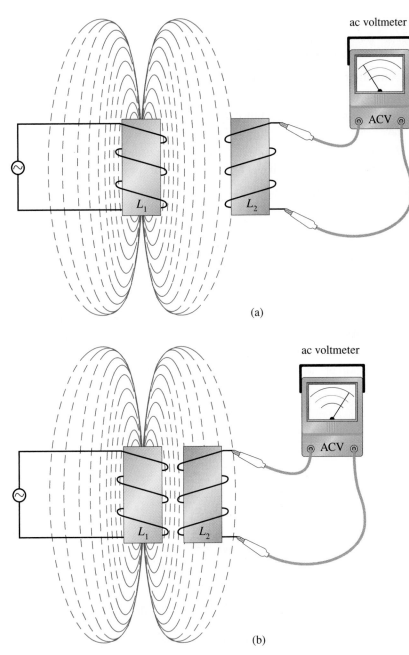

Figure 17-1. Two nearby coils can be magnetically linked.

EXAMPLE SOLUTION

We apply Equation 17-1.

$$L_M = k\sqrt{L_1 L_2}$$
$$= 0.75 \times \sqrt{(100 \text{ mH}) \times (250 \text{ mH})} = 118.6 \text{ mH}$$

Practice Problems

1. Compute the value of mutual inductance between two 50-mH coils that have a coefficient of coupling of 0.8.
2. What is the mutual inductance between a 50-µH coil and a 175-µH coil if they have a coefficient of coupling of 0.5?
3. When a 2.5-mH coil has a 0.9 coefficient of coupling to another coil, the mutual inductance is 4 mH. What is the inductance of the second coil?

Answers to Practice Problems

1. 40 mH   **2.** 46.77 µH   **3.** 7.9 mH

Effect of Mutual Inductance on Series Coils

KEY POINTS

When magnetically linked coils are connected in series, the total inductance is affected by the amount of mutual inductance in the coils.

You will recall that inductors in series combine like resistors in series (i.e., simple addition). You may also recall that this simple relationship requires that there be no magnetic flux linkage between the coils. We are now in a position to consider the effects of magnetic linkage between two coils (i.e., mutual inductance). Figure 17-2 shows two series coils that have some shared flux. That is, a portion of the flux from one inductor cuts the winding of the second inductor.

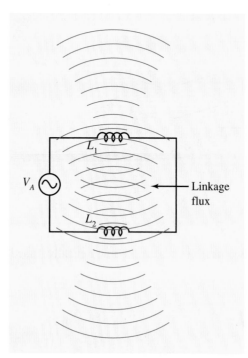

Figure 17-2. When two coils are magnetically linked, they have mutual inductance.

The total inductance of the two series coils is affected by the mutual inductance. Additionally, the mutual inductance may increase or decrease the total inductance, depending on the relative polarities of the two coils. Recall that the polarity of induced voltage is determined by the direction of magnetic flux motion and the direction of the coil winding (left-hand rule). If we change the direction of the winding for one of the coils, then we alter the additive or subtractive effects of the mutual inductance. This is illustrated in Figure 17-3.

In Figure 17-3(a), the magnetically linked coils are wound such that their magnetic fields are additive. This increases the total inductance in the circuit. If we change the direction of one of the coil windings, as shown in Figure 17-3(b), then the magnetic fields of the two coils oppose each other. This lessens the effective self-induced voltage and results in a lower total inductance.

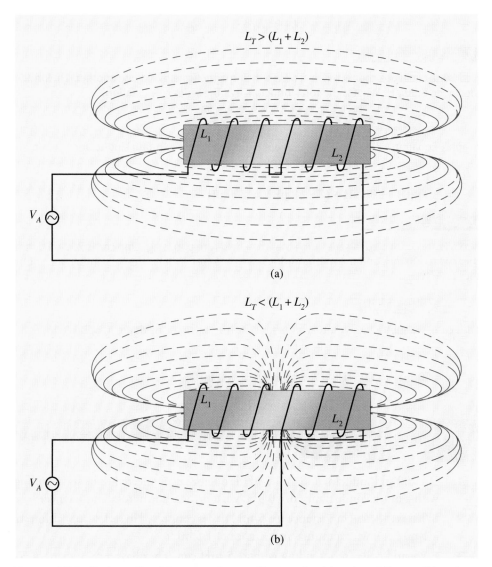

Figure 17-3. Series coils with magnetic coupling can be (a) series-aiding or (b) series-opposing.

The increase or decrease in total inductance as a result of aiding or opposing fields is expressed more formally in Equation 17-2, which computes the total inductance of two series coils.

$$L_T = L_1 + L_2 \pm 2L_M \qquad (17\text{-}2)$$

where L_1 and L_2 are the individual coil inductances, and L_M is the mutual inductance. The plus or minus ($\pm$) operator accounts for the two possible polarities of the coils. If the coil polarities aid, as shown in Figure 17-3(a), then the equation becomes

$$L_T = L_1 + L_2 + 2L_M$$

If, by contrast, the coil polarities are in opposition as illustrated in Figure 17-3(b), then Equation 17-2 becomes

$$L_T = L_1 + L_2 - 2L_M$$

EXAMPLE SOLUTION

Two 100-µH coils are connected in series so their magnetic fields aid one another. Their mutual inductance is 50 µH. What is the total inductance of the series combination?

EXAMPLE **SOLUTION**

We apply Equation 17-2. Since the fields are aiding, we add the mutual inductance factor.

$L_T = L_1 + L_2 + 2L_M$
$\quad = 100 \ \mu H + 100 \ \mu H + (2 \times 50 \ \mu H) = 300 \ \mu H$

EXAMPLE SOLUTION

Two coils are connected in series such that their fields are opposing. One coil is 250 mH, the other coil is 400 mH, and the mutual inductance is 75 mH. What is the total inductance of the series circuit?

EXAMPLE **SOLUTION**

In this case, we subtract the mutual inductance factor, since the fields are in opposition.

$L_T = L_1 + L_2 - 2L_M$
$\quad = 250 \ mH + 400 \ mH - (2 \times 75 \ mH) = 500 \ mH$

Practice Problems

1. If a 200-µH inductor and a 175-µH inductor are connected to be series-aiding with a mutual inductance of 50 µH, what is the value of total inductance?
2. What is the total inductance if a 5-mH coil is connected in series-opposition with a 2-mH coil with a mutual inductance of 1.5 mH?
3. A 25-mH coil is series-aiding with a 35-mH coil. They have a coefficient of coupling of 0.8. What is the total inductance of the series combination?

Answers to Practice Problems

1. 475 µH   **2.** 4 mH   **3.** 107.3 mH

Effect of Mutual Inductance on Parallel Coils

Magnetic flux linkage between parallel-connected inductors also affects the value of their combined inductance. Computation of total inductance is more involved, but it can be approximated with Equation 17-3.

$$L_T = \frac{L_1 L_2 - L_M^2}{L_1 + L_2 \pm 2L_M} \qquad (17\text{-}3)$$

The mutual inductance factor in the denominator $(2L_M)$ is positive when the magnetic fields of the two coils aid and negative when the fields oppose.

EXAMPLE SOLUTION

What is the approximate value of total inductance when two parallel coils (with aiding magnetic fields) have inductances of 400 µH and 300 µH, and a mutual inductance of 100 µH?

EXAMPLE SOLUTION

We apply Equation 17-3 directly.

$$L_T = \frac{L_1 L_2 - L_M^2}{L_1 + L_2 \pm 2L_M}$$

$$= \frac{(300 \text{ µH} \times 400 \text{ µH}) - (100 \text{ µH})^2}{300 \text{ µH} + 400 \text{ µH} + (2 \times 100 \text{ µH})}$$

$$= 122.2 \text{ µH}$$

> **KEY POINTS**
>
> When magnetically linked coils are connected in parallel, the total inductance is affected by the amount of mutual inductance in the coils.

Practice Problems

1. Calculate the approximate total inductance if two 150-mH coils are connected in parallel with their magnetic fields in opposition. The mutual inductance is 25 mH.

2. Two parallel coils have fields that are magnetically aiding. One coil is 6 mH, the other is 10 mH, and the mutual inductance is 0.8 mH. What is the approximate inductance of the parallel combination?

3. The magnetic fields of two parallel-connected coils are magnetically aiding and produce a mutual inductance of 5 µH. If each coil has an inductance of 35 µH, what is the total inductance of the parallel combination?

Answers to Practice Problems

1. 87.5 mH   **2.** 3.37 mH   **3.** 15 µH

Exercise Problems 17.1

1. If 100% of the flux lines generated by one coil also cut the windings of another coil, what is the coefficient of coupling between the two coils?

2. If 35% of the flux lines generated by one coil also cut the windings of another coil, what is the coefficient of coupling between the two coils?

3. If two coils have a coefficient of coupling of 0.85 and have individual inductances of 235 mH and 150 mH, what is the value of mutual inductance?

4. What is the mutual inductance between a 150-μH coil and a 75-μH coil if the coefficient of coupling is 0.6?

5. The presence of mutual inductance between two coils always increases the value of total inductance when the two coils are connected in series. (True or False)

6. Two 35-mH coils are connected in series, so their magnetic fields are additive. If their mutual inductance is 10 mH, what is the total inductance of the series combination?

7. Two coils are connected in series such that their fields are opposing. One coil is 200 μH, the other is 375 μH, and the mutual inductance is 50 μH. What is the total inductance of the series circuit?

8. If two 25-mH coils are connected in parallel with magnetically aiding fields, calculate the total inductance if the mutual inductance is 5 mH.

9. If connections to one of the coils described in Problem 8 were interchanged, what would be the value of total inductance?

17.2 Transformers

A transformer is a basic component whose operation depends on the magnetic linkage (mutual inductance) between two or more coils. The coils in the transformer are wound on a common core to increase the amount of flux linkage. In many cases, the coils are wound on overlapping layers to obtain the highest degree of coupling.

Basic Transformer Action

Figure 17-4 shows two coils wound on a common magnetic core. A sinusoidal voltage is applied to one of the windings. This winding is called the **primary** of the transformer. The inductive reactance of the primary winding limits the primary current. The magnetic flux in the core varies as the current in the primary varies. Because the core is permeable, much of the flux created by the primary passes through the secondary winding. The changing flux induces a voltage in the secondary winding. As illustrated in Figure 17-4, the secondary voltage is a measurable, usable voltage. As you might expect, the greater the coefficient of coupling, the higher the value of secondary voltage for a given primary voltage.

The polarity of the voltage in the secondary depends on the direction in which the secondary winding is wrapped. In certain applications, the primary and secondary windings must be connected into the circuit with proper phase relationships. Schematic

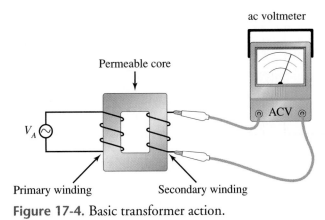

Figure 17-4. Basic transformer action.

diagrams often indicate the phase relationships in the transformer with **dot notation.** Figure 17-5 shows the schematic symbol for one type of transformer and illustrates the use of dot notation.

As shown in Figure 17-5, dots are added to both primary and secondary windings. The location of the dots indicates similar instantaneous polarity. As indicated by the sine wave outputs in Figure 17-5, the input/output phase relationship is indicated by the relative positioning of the primary and secondary phase dots.

Transformers can be constructed to provide secondary voltages that are different than the primary voltage. If the secondary voltage of a transformer is higher than its primary voltage, we call it a **step-up transformer.** Similarly, if the secondary voltage is lower than the primary voltage, we call it a **step-down transformer.** Figure 17-6 illustrates step-up and step-down transformers.

Transformer Types

There are several ways to categorize transformers. They can be classified according to their intended application, the type of core material, or the way their windings are configured.

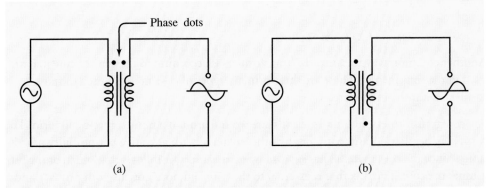

Figure 17-5. Schematic symbol for a basic transformer including the use of dots to indicate transformer phase.

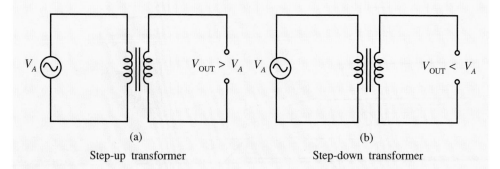

Step-up transformer   Step-down transformer

Figure 17-6. Illustration of step-up and step-down transformers.

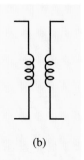

(a)

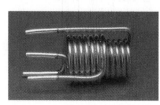

(b)

Figure 17-7.
A representative air-core transformer and its schematic symbol.

CLASSIFICATION BY APPLICATION

Transformer applications will be discussed later in this chapter, but let us briefly examine how transformers can be categorized based on their primary application. Some transformers are designed for connection to the power line and are used to provide power to electronic circuits. This type of transformer is generally called a power transformer. Power transformers can be used to increase or decrease the voltage applied to the primary. If the transformer does not increase or decrease the voltage, but is used strictly to provide isolation between the primary and secondary circuits, it is often called an isolation transformer.

Some transformers are specifically designed for operation throughout the audio range. They are, for example, used to connect audio amplifiers to speakers. In any case, these transformers are commonly called audio transformers.

Transformers that are constructed for operation at high radio frequencies are classified as r.f. (radio frequency) transformers. The internal circuits of a radio receiver utilize signals that are called intermediate frequencies. The transformers used in these circuits are called i.f. (intermediate frequency) transformers.

Many pulse (e.g., rectangular waveform) circuits utilize transformers for coupling signals from one point to another. These transformers are called pulse transformers and are optimized for coupling nonsinusoidal waveforms.

CLASSIFICATION BY CORE MATERIAL

Another common way to categorize transformers is according to the type of core material used in the transformer. There are three primary types of core material used in transformers: air, iron, and ferrite.

Air-core transformers, like air-core coils, are wound around a nonmagnetic coil form. The form may be plastic, cardboard, or any other material with a relative permeability near unity. Since the core material has such a low permeability, it follows that much of the flux escapes the core. The flux that is external to the core and does not cut both primary and secondary windings is called **leakage flux.** Leakage flux causes additional inductance to appear in series with the primary and secondary windings. This apparent inductance is called **leakage inductance.** Figure 17-7 shows an air-core transformer and its generic schematic symbol. These devices are generally used at high radio frequencies.

The primary and secondary windings in an iron-core transformer are wound on a common, high-permeability core. Because of the high permeability of the core, the coefficient of coupling approaches unity (i.e., there is minimal leakage flux). Iron-core transformers experience the same core losses as previously discussed for iron-core inductors. These losses increase with frequency. Iron-core transformers are generally limited to frequencies in the audio range. One of the most common applications for iron-core transformers is power transformers used to couple power from the ac power line. Figure 17-8 shows a typical iron-core transformer and its generic schematic symbol.

The third category of transformer cores is ferrite. Ferrite is a high-permeability ceramic material that is relatively brittle. Because the ferrite core has a fairly high dc resistance, it has less core losses at high frequencies than an equivalent iron-core transformer. Ferrite-core transformers are used for applications extending from audio well into the high-megahertz range.

The cores used in ferrite-core transformers come in many different shapes and sizes. Figure 17-9 shows some core shapes. The torroid core has a very low level of leakage flux; nearly all of the flux is contained within the continuous core material. Figure 17-10 shows a ferrite-core transformer and the generic schematic symbol.

CLASSIFICATION BY WINDING CONNECTION

Figure 17-11 shows a pictorial sketch and the schematic diagram for a transformer with multiple secondaries. The changing (i.e., sinusoidal) primary current causes corresponding changes in the magnetic flux. The high-permeability core material causes most of this changing flux to pass through the two secondary windings. Each of the secondary windings will have an induced voltage that can be used by subsequent circuits or devices. As you will see later in this chapter, the two (or more) secondary windings are essentially independent of each other.

(a)

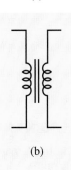

(b)

Figure 17-8. A typical iron-core transformer and its schematic symbol.

(a)

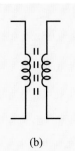

(b)

Figure 17-10. A representative ferrite-core transformer and its schematic symbol.

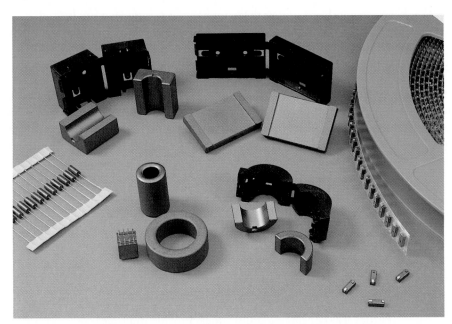

Figure 17-9. Ferrite cores are available in a variety of shapes and sizes. (Courtesy of Fair-Rite Products Corporation)

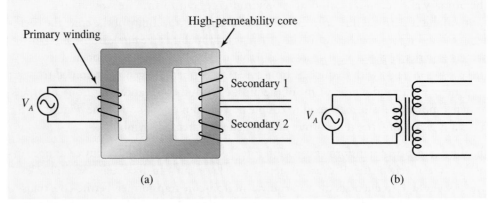

Figure 17-11. A transformer can have multiple secondary windings. Each secondary acts like a separate transformer.

Figure 17-12 shows another way to alter the connection of transformer windings. In the case shown in Figure 17-12(a), the secondary winding is tapped in the center. During manufacture, we can position the tap at any convenient point along the length of the winding. Although the winding is continuous, the tap allows us to access two different voltages (V_1 and V_2). As you would expect, the sum of V_1 and V_2 is equal to the voltage of the entire secondary. Figure 17-12(b) shows a secondary with multiple taps. We can obtain a useful voltage between any two of the connection points. Although not specifically pictured in Figure 17-12, we can also provide taps on the primary of the transformer. This option is often used when constructing transformers that can be operated from two different voltages (e.g., 120 Vac and 240 Vac). The voltage selection can be done by soldering to a different tap on the primary or, more commonly, by using a switch to change the primary connection.

Figure 17-13 shows yet another way that the windings of a transformer can be constructed. Here a single, tapped winding serves as both the primary and the secondary of the transformer. One end of the single coil serves as a common line for both primary and secondary windings. This configuration is called an *autotransformer.*

If the input voltage is applied between the two ends of the transformer winding, as illustrated in Figure 17-13(a), then the output voltage will be lower than the input voltage. By contrast, a step-up autotransformer can be constructed as shown in Figure 17-13(b) by connecting the primary voltage between the common and the tap. In either case, the amount of increase or

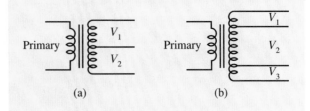

Figure 17-12. Tapped transformers provide multiple access points to the transformer winding.

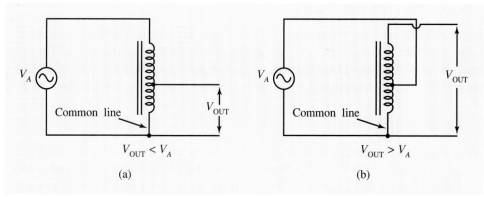

Figure 17-13. An autotransformer has a common primary and secondary winding.

decrease in primary voltage is determined by the relative location of the tap. Some manufacturers make autotransformers with the tap connected to a movable slider. The slider is connected to an external knob that can be used to adjust the position of the tap and, therefore, the amount of step-up or step-down provided by the transformer. Such a device is shown in Figure 17-14. Typically, autotransformers such as the one shown in Figure 17-14 can be used to adjust the 120-Vac power line voltage from 0 to about 150 V.

Autotransformers are also frequently used in high-voltage power supplies. A common example is the power supply in your television set, which generates voltages as high as 27,000 V.

Transformer Losses

A practical transformer has several nonideal losses that result in power dissipation. Some of the losses occur in the transformer windings, while others occur in the core of the transformer. Let's examine each of them individually.

Figure 17-14. A typical autotransformer that can be used to adjust the voltage provided by the power line. (Courtesy of Technipower)

LOSS DUE TO WIRE RESISTANCE

The copper wire used for the primary and secondary windings has a definite amount of ohmic resistance. The resistance of a wire is directly proportional to its length and inversely proportional to its cross-sectional area. Loss due to the resistance of the wire is called copper loss or I^2R loss. This is identical to the copper loss discussed with reference to inductors.

LOSS DUE TO SKIN EFFECT

When alternating current flows through a wire, each moving electron has an associated changing magnetic field. The fields from the various electrons interact with neighboring electrons and affect their movement. The result is that the electrons tend to flow near the surface of the wire. This phenomenon is called the skin effect and was introduced in Chapter 12. Skin-effect losses increase with frequency.

HYSTERESIS LOSS

You will recall from our study of basic magnetic theory that a magnetic material has domains that align with external magnetic fields. In the case of a magnetic-core transformer, the domains in the core must realign themselves every half-cycle. This requires energy, and the energy must come from the ac source. As the frequency is increased, the hysteresis loss also increases, since the domain-switching energy is being consumed more often.

EDDY-CURRENT LOSS

When a changing magnetic field intersects a conductor, it induces a voltage in the conductor. The induced voltage can cause current to flow. We know from our basic power formula ($P = VI$) that there must be an associated power dissipation.

When the changing magnetic fields of a transformer cut through its magnetic core, a voltage is induced in the core if the core is conductive. Many materials that are highly magnetic are also conductive. Since the core is relatively large, different potentials are induced into different regions of the core at any instant in time. This causes current to flow from one point in the core to another. However, since the flux pattern continually changes, so do the specific current paths within the core. Currents induced into the core of a transformer are called eddy currents. They are circulating currents whose paths are dynamic. They do draw energy from the power source and, therefore, represent a power loss. Eddy currents increase with higher frequencies, since the voltage induced into the core material increases.

We can reduce the power dissipation due to eddy currents by using a high-resistance core. This is one advantage of a ferrite-core or an air-core transformer over an iron-core transformer. An air-core transformer has no eddy-current loss. A ferrite-core transformer has a high ohmic resistance, which limits the magnitude of the eddy currents. Iron-core transformers use laminated cores to increase the ohmic resistance while maintaining a low permeability. The core consists of thin sheets of iron (actually silicon steel) separated by an insulative coating. This allows the core to provide the high permeability needed to obtain high values of inductance, but the insulative barriers keep the eddy-current losses to a minimum.

Faraday Shielding

Another nonideal characteristic of transformers is primary-to-secondary capacitance. Since the primary and secondary windings are conductors that are electrically separated, a capacitance is formed between them. Even in the case of an iron-core transformer, there is a capacitive path that extends from the primary winding to the core and from the core to the secondary winding. Although the value of primary-to-secondary capacitance may be only a few picofarads, it can cause problems at high frequencies, where the capacitive reactance becomes relatively low.

We can minimize the primary-to-secondary capacitance by separating the primary and secondary windings with a grounded, conductive barrier. This barrier is called a **Faraday shield** and is illustrated in Figure 17-15. Any energy that passes through the winding-to-shield capacitance is passed directly to ground and does not couple to the other winding.

Faraday shields are commonly used in high-frequency transformers to prevent the unwanted coupling of signals via the primary-to-secondary capacitance. Similar shields are sometimes used in communications line transformers to protect the electronic circuits from damage due to lightning, motor transients, and so on.

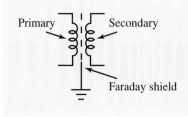

Figure 17-15. A Faraday shield reduces the primary-to-secondary capacitance.

Exercise Problems 17.2

1. Power is applied to the _____ winding of the transformer.
2. Power is supplied to external devices or circuits by the _____ winding of a transformer.
3. The relative phase relationship between primary and secondary voltages is indicated on a schematic diagram with _____ _____.
4. List three ways that transformers can be classified.
5. What is the name given to the magnetic flux that does not link the primary and secondary windings in a transformer?
6. List three types of material used for the cores in transformers.
7. What type of core material is a ceramic product?

8. If 24 Vac and 200 Vac were both required by a particular application, a transformer with multiple secondaries might be used. (True or False)

9. What is the name of the transformer that has a single winding that is common to both primary and secondary?

10. Explain the terms step-up and step-down as applied to transformers.

11. An autotransformer can be used to step-up or step-down the voltage applied to the primary. (True or False)

17.3 Analysis of Transformer Circuits

We shall limit our discussion to the analysis of iron-core transformer circuits. We will begin our analysis by assuming an ideal transformer that has unity coupling. This not only simplifies calculations, but it provides adequate accuracy for many applications encountered by a technician.

Turns Ratio

A given transformer has a certain number of turns in the primary and a certain number of turns in the secondary. The ratio of primary turns to secondary turns is called the **turns ratio** of the transformer. This ratio is the heart of many transformer calculations. We can express it formally with Equation 17-4.

$$k = \frac{N_P}{N_S} \qquad\qquad (17\text{-}4)$$

It should be noted that some textbooks define turns ratio as N_S/N_P. This is acceptable, provided the reciprocal of all other transformer ratios are used.

EXAMPLE SOLUTION

What is the turns ratio for a transformer that has 400 turns in the primary winding and 100 turns in the secondary winding?

EXAMPLE **SOLUTION**

The given transformer is illustrated in Figure 17-16. We compute the turns ratio by dividing the primary turns by the secondary turns (Equation 17-4). Rather than express the turns ratio as a single number (4 in this case), it is customary to express it as a reduced fraction (4/1 or simply 4:1 in this case).

EXAMPLE SOLUTION

What is the turns ratio of a transformer that has 225 turns on the primary and 300 turns on the secondary?

EXAMPLE **SOLUTION**

$$k = \frac{N_P}{N_S} = \frac{225 \text{ T}}{300 \text{ T}} = \frac{3}{4}, \text{ or } 3{:}4$$

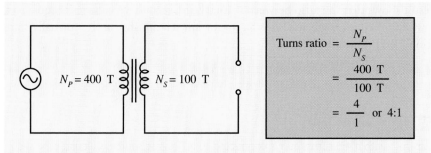

Figure 17-16. A transformer turns ratio example.

Practice Problems

1. If a transformer has 50 turns on the primary and 250 turns on the secondary, what is its turns ratio?

2. What is the turns ratio of a transformer with 800 turns on its primary and 80 turns on its secondary?

3. If a transformer with a 5:2 turns ratio has 100 turns on its primary, how many turns are on the secondary?

Answers to Practice Problems

1. 1:5   2. 10:1   3. 40

Voltage Ratio

For purposes of this discussion, we are assuming unity coupling. This means that exactly the same flux cuts both primary and secondary windings. Whatever voltage is induced into a single turn of the primary will also be induced into a single turn in the secondary. That is, the volts per turn are the same for both primary and secondary windings. This should seem reasonable, since the coils are wound on a common core and are cut by the same flux lines.

Now, we know from inspection (or Kirchhoff's Voltage Law) that the sum of the voltages induced into the various turns in the primary winding must equal the applied voltage. The voltage in the secondary, however, depends on the number of turns in the secondary (remember the volts per turn are the same as the primary). Let's examine this mathematically. First, we set the volts per turn ratios of the primary and secondary windings equal to each other, and then transpose the equation as follows:

$$\frac{V_P}{N_P} = \frac{V_S}{N_S}$$

$$V_P N_S = V_S N_P$$

$$\frac{N_P}{N_S} = \frac{V_P}{V_S}$$

The result shows that the ratio between primary and secondary voltages is equal to the turns ratio of the transformer. This is an important relationship and is formally stated as Equation 17-5.

$$\frac{N_P}{N_S} = \frac{V_P}{V_S} \qquad\qquad (17\text{-}5)$$

EXAMPLE SOLUTION

A transformer with a 4:3 turns ratio is connected to a 120-Vac source. Calculate the secondary voltage.

EXAMPLE **SOLUTION**

We apply Equation 17-5 as follows.

$$\frac{N_P}{N_S} = \frac{V_P}{V_S} \text{ or}$$

$$N_P V_S = N_S V_P \text{ or}$$

$$V_S = \frac{N_S V_P}{N_P}$$

$$V_S = \frac{3\ \text{T} \times 120\ \text{V}}{4\ \text{T}} = 90\ \text{V}$$

Practice Problems

1. A transformer has a 5:1 turns ratio and delivers a secondary voltage of 10 V. What is the value of the primary source voltage?
2. A transformer has a primary voltage of 120 V and a secondary voltage of 12 V. What is the turns ratio of the transformer?
3. If a transformer has 80 turns in its primary winding and provides 20 V in the secondary when its primary is connected to 5 V, how many turns are on the secondary winding?

Answers to Practice Problems

1. 50 V   **2.** 10:1   **3.** 320

Power Ratio

The power ratio for an ideal transformer is unity. That is, with 100% coupling and no transformer losses, the output power must be the same as the input power. In particular, power in the primary (i.e., power taken from the source) must always be equal to the power in the secondary (i.e., power delivered to devices or circuits connected to the secondary winding).

Practical transformers have losses and less than 100% coupling. Nevertheless, the ideal assumptions will satisfy our immediate needs.

Current Ratio

We know that power is the product of current and voltage (i.e., $P = VI$). We also know that the primary power must equal the secondary power. It follows, therefore, that if the secondary voltage is higher than the primary voltage, then the current in the secondary must be correspondingly smaller, so that the power will remain the same. This means that if the voltage is stepped up in a transformer, then current will always be stepped down.

Let's examine this relationship mathematically. We begin with the knowledge that primary and secondary powers are equal.

$$P_P = P_S; \text{ therefore}$$
$$V_P I_P = V_S I_S, \text{ or}$$
$$\frac{V_P}{V_S} = \frac{I_S}{I_P}$$

This shows us that the voltage ratio is equal to the inverse of the current ratio. We know the voltage ratio is equal to the turns ratio (Equation 17-5). It is common to express the current ratio in terms of the turns ratio as shown in Equation 17-6.

$$\frac{N_P}{N_S} = \frac{I_S}{I_P} \qquad \textbf{(17-6)}$$

KEY POINTS

The current ratio in a transformer is the inverse of the turns ratio or voltage ratio. This implies that a transformer that steps up the voltage between primary and secondary will also step down the current.

EXAMPLE SOLUTION

If the turns ratio of a transformer is 5:1 and the primary current is 100 mA, what is the value of secondary current?

EXAMPLE **SOLUTION**

We apply Equation 17-6 as follows:

$$\frac{N_P}{N_S} = \frac{I_S}{I_P}, \text{ or}$$

$$I_S = \frac{N_P I_P}{N_S}$$

$$I_S = \frac{5 \text{ T} \times 100 \text{ mA}}{1 \text{ T}} = 500 \text{ mA}$$

EXAMPLE SOLUTION

A transformer is connected to a 120-Vac source and supplies 12 Vac to a load. The load draws 1.5 A. What is the value of primary current?

EXAMPLE **SOLUTION**

We know that the voltage and turns ratios are equal (Equation 17-5). We use this relationship along with Equation 17-6 to solve for primary current.

$$\frac{V_P}{V_S} = \frac{N_P}{N_S} = \frac{I_S}{I_P}, \text{ so}$$

$$I_P = \frac{V_S I_S}{V_P}$$

$$I_P = \frac{12 \text{ V} \times 1.5 \text{ A}}{120 \text{ V}} = 150 \text{ mA}$$

Practice Problems

1. Calculate the secondary current in a transformer with a 4:1 turns ratio and a primary current of 2.75 A.
2. What is the turns ratio of a transformer that has a secondary current of 200 mA, with a primary current of 50 mA?
3. If a transformer has a primary voltage of 220 V, a secondary voltage of 25 V, and a primary current of 100 mA, what is the value of secondary current?

Answers to Practice Problems

1. 11 A **2.** 4:1 **3.** 880 mA

Impedance Ratio

KEY POINTS

Any impedance connected to the secondary of a transformer will be reflected through the transformer and appear as an impedance to the source.

We know that a transformer can alter both voltage and current levels between the primary and secondary. It should seem reasonable, then, that a transformer can also alter the impedance between primary and secondary.

REFLECTED IMPEDANCE

Consider the circuit shown in Figure 17-17. In Figure 17-17(a), the secondary is connected to a high-resistance load. The flux produced by the secondary tends to cancel (i.e., it is moving in the opposite relative direction) some of the induced voltage in the primary. This allows more current to flow in the primary.

Now, if the resistance in the secondary is made smaller as in Figure 17-17(b), then more secondary current flows. This causes more secondary flux to induce an opposite polarity voltage in the primary, which again allows even more primary current to flow. Finally, Figure 17-17(c) shows that if the secondary load resistance is made even smaller, more secondary current and, therefore, more primary current will flow.

Since changes in the resistance or, more universally the impedance of the secondary, cause current changes in the primary (with the source voltage held constant), it follows that the impedance changes in the secondary are transferred to the primary. The impedance in the primary that results from the secondary load is called the **reflected impedance.** Changes in secondary impedance are reflected to the primary.

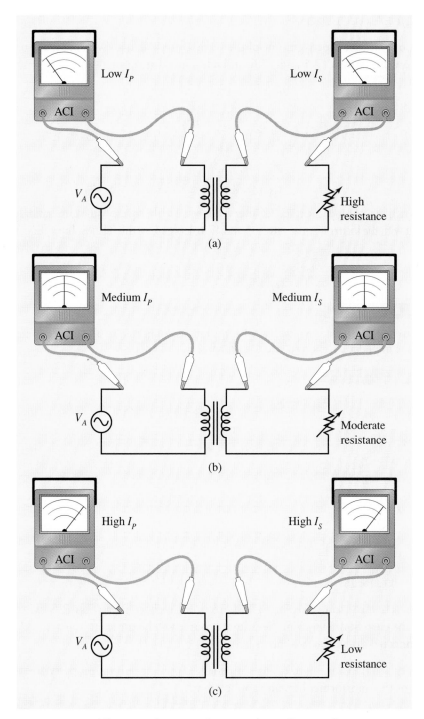

(a)

(b)

(c)

Figure 17-17. The impedance in the secondary of a transformer is reflected into the primary.

IMPEDANCE CALCULATIONS

Now, let us consider the magnitude of the reflected impedance. We shall make use of Ohm's Law, Equations 17-5 and 17-6, and relevant substitutions.

$$\frac{Z_P}{Z_S} = \frac{\dfrac{V_P}{I_P}}{\dfrac{V_S}{I_S}} = \frac{V_P I_S}{V_S I_P} \text{ , or}$$

$$\frac{Z_P}{Z_S} = \left(\frac{N_P}{N_S}\right)\left(\frac{N_P}{N_S}\right) = \left(\frac{N_P}{N_S}\right)^2$$

This tells us that the impedance ratio (Z_P over Z_S) is equal to the square of the turns ratio. To be more consistent with the form of Equations 17-5 and 17-6, let's express this relationship as Equation 17-7.

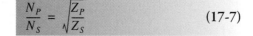

$$\frac{N_P}{N_S} = \sqrt{\frac{Z_P}{Z_S}} \qquad\qquad (17\text{-}7)$$

EXAMPLE SOLUTION

The secondary of a transformer with a 5:1 turns ratio is connected to a 100-Ω resistor. What is the value of impedance reflected into the primary?

EXAMPLE **SOLUTION**

We apply Equation 17-7 as follows.

$$\frac{N_P}{N_S} = \sqrt{\frac{Z_P}{Z_S}} \text{ , or}$$

$$\left(\frac{N_P}{N_S}\right)^2 = \frac{Z_P}{Z_S} \text{ , so}$$

$$Z_P = Z_S\left(\frac{N_P}{N_S}\right)^2$$

$$Z_P = 100 \ \Omega \times \left(\frac{5 \text{ T}}{1 \text{ T}}\right)^2$$

$$Z_P = 100 \ \Omega \times 25 = 2.5 \text{ k}\Omega$$

This means that the source sees the 100-Ω resistance reflected back as a 2.5-kΩ resistance. That is, the current drawn from the primary source will be the same as if a 2.5-kΩ resistor were connected directly across the source.

The ability of a transformer to change impedances is an important property and is the sole purpose of the transformer in many applications.

Practice Problems

1. A transformer with a 2:1 turns ratio has a 1,000-Ω resistor connected across the secondary. What impedance is reflected into the primary?

2. A transformer with 120 V across the primary produces 24 V in the secondary. If the secondary load is 10 Ω, what is the reflected impedance in the primary?

3. If a transformer has 200 turns in the primary, 300 turns in the secondary, and has a 50-Ω resistor connected across the secondary, what is the impedance reflected into the primary?

4. What is the impedance ratio of a transformer that has 100 turns in the primary and 250 turns in the secondary?

Answers to Practice Problems

1. 4,000 Ω   2. 250   3. 22.22   4. 4:25

Transformer Efficiency

The transformers referenced in the preceding calculations had an assumed efficiency of 100%. This means that no power was lost in the transformer. Practical transformers do have winding and core losses that dissipate power in the form of heat. The efficiency (η) of a transformer is computed the same as for any other system (output power/input power). In the case of a transformer it is expressed as

$$\eta = \frac{P_{OUT}}{P_{IN}} = \frac{P_S}{P_P}$$

where P_S and P_P are the power dissipations in the secondary and primary, respectively. Primary power dissipation consists of three parts: power delivered to the secondary (P_S), power lost in the windings (copper and skin-effect losses), and power lost in the core (hysteresis and eddy currents). The expression for transformer efficiency is stated more completely by Equation 17-8.

$$\eta = \frac{P_S}{P_S + P_{WINDING} + P_{CORE}} \quad (17\text{-}8)$$

EXAMPLE SOLUTION

The secondary of a transformer provides 25 W to a resistive load. The combined core losses are 0.8 W. The copper and skin-effect losses total 1.5 W. What is the efficiency of the transformer?

EXAMPLE **SOLUTION**

We apply Equation 17-8.

$$\eta = \frac{P_S}{P_S + P_{WINDING} + P_{CORE}}$$

$$= \frac{25\ W}{25\ W + 1.5\ W + 0.8\ W} = 91.6\ \%$$

Practice Problems

1. The secondary power of a transformer is 150 W. The core and winding losses are 3.75 W and 6.5 W, respectively. What is the efficiency of the transformer?

2. A transformer draws 200 mA from a 120-V source. The secondary maintains 20 V across a 17.5-Ω resistor. What is the efficiency of the transformer?

3. If the primary winding of a transformer with 92% efficiency is connected to a 120-V source and the secondary supplies 12 V with a current of 2.5 A, what is the value of primary current?

Answers to Practice Problems

1. 93.6%   **2.** 95.2%   **3.** 271.7 mA

Practical Transformer Considerations

The calculations in the preceding section focused on the analysis of ideal iron-core transformers with limited discussion of nonideal characteristics (e.g., efficiency). We are now in a position to examine a practical iron-core transformer and all of its nonideal characteristics.

To avoid getting lost in details, it is important for you to realize that for a great many applications likely to be encountered by a technician, there are only minor differences between an ideal iron-core transformer and a practical one. The following discussion, however, will provide you with additional insights regarding transformer operation.

PRACTICAL TRANSFORMER EQUIVALENT

When analyzing a new or complex device, it is often helpful to represent the characteristics of the device in a more obvious way. In the case of the iron-core transformer, we can represent the effect of its nonideal characteristics with a simple equivalent circuit. Figure 17-18 shows the equivalent circuit that we will be using. This equivalent circuit omits the parasitic capacitances between the windings, between the windings and core, and between the turns on a winding. These capacitances have only minimal effect except at high frequencies. We will discuss each component in the equivalent circuit in the following paragraphs.

The model consists of an ideal transformer (T_1) surrounded by series and parallel resistances and inductances that represent nonideal quantities. Resistances R_{W_P} and R_{W_S} represent the winding losses (copper and skin-effect) for the primary and secondary, respectively. Similarly, R_{CORE} represents the core losses (hysteresis and eddy currents). All

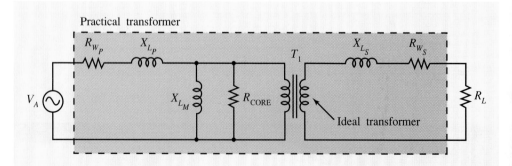

Figure 17-18. An equivalent circuit for a practical iron-core transformer.

of these resistances take power from the source that is never delivered to the load (R_L). They all reduce the efficiency to less than 100%.

Reactances X_{L_p} and X_{L_s} are equivalent reactances that represent the effects of leakage flux in the primary and secondary, respectively. The series reactances have the same effect on the overall circuit as flux that expands into the surrounding space without linking the primary and secondary. Finally, reactance X_{L_M} represents the reactance associated with the mutual inductance. The source "sees" this reactance as a parallel path.

UNLOADED SECONDARY

When the secondary of the transformer has no load (i.e., it is open-circuited), then none of the secondary components in Figure 17-18 are seen by the source. The primary current is largely limited by the inductive reactance of the primary winding. Only enough current flows to produce a self-induced voltage across the primary that is equal to the applied voltage. This small current is called the **magnetizing current.** Because the magnetizing current is small, the winding losses are also small ($P = I^2 R_{W_p}$ in Figure 17-18). The primary current then is composed of two components: magnetizing current (inductive) and current due to core losses (resistive current through R_{CORE} in Figure 17-18). Under no-load conditions, the core losses are low and the primary current is essentially inductive.

We can also express the transformer relationships with the aid of a phasor diagram. Figure 17-19 shows a phasor representation of the primary circuit under no-load conditions. I_M is the magnetizing current which, under no-load conditions, makes up the entire primary current. Note that θ is essentially 90° and the circuit appears to the source as a rather large inductor (i.e., voltage leads current by 90°).

FULLY LOADED SECONDARY

Now let's see what happens when a heavy load (i.e., small load resistance) is connected across the secondary. As you would expect, secondary current begins to flow. The increased secondary current creates corresponding magnetic flux, which cuts the primary winding. The voltage induced in the primary as a result of the secondary current is of a polarity to cancel a portion of the primary's self-induced voltage. Recall that it was the self-induced voltage in the primary that was limiting primary current. So, with some of the self-induced voltage cancelled, the primary current increases until the self-induced voltage is restored. Figure 17-20 shows a phasor representation of the primary circuit under full-load conditions.

In Figure 17-20, I'_p is the portion of the primary current that results from the flow of secondary current. Note that it is in phase with V_A, since the reflected load is resistive. I_M in Figure 17-20 is the magnetizing current. Finally, I_p is the phasor sum of the two primary current components. The resulting phase angle (measured between total voltage and total current) is a very small angle. If the load on a practical iron-core transformer is resistive and heavy, the primary current and primary voltage can be within a few degrees of each other. In summary, the phase relationship between primary current and voltage can range from near 90° to near 0° as the load varies from no load (infinite load resistance) to a heavy load (small load resistance). Reactive loads on the secondary reflect into the primary as reactive loads and cause corresponding phase shifts.

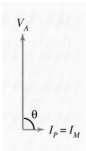

Figure 17-19.
Under no-load conditions, the primary current is inductive and limited by the reactance of the primary.

Figure 17-20.
Under full-load conditions (resistive load), the primary current is nearly resistive.

The reactance X_{L_s} and resistance R_{W_s} in Figure 17-18 introduce another important, but nonideal, behavior. We can see by inspection of Figure 17-18 that an increased secondary current will cause an increased voltage drop across the series elements X_{L_s} and R_{W_s}. This causes the output voltage (voltage across R_L) to decrease as secondary current is increased. The decrease in voltage depends on the design of the transformer and the extent of the loading, but it can be substantial. Transformers are generally designed such that their rated voltage is available when the secondary is supplying its rated current. At lesser currents, the secondary voltage may be higher.

Exercise Problems 17.3

1. What is the turns ratio of a transformer that has 665 turns in the primary and 95 turns in the secondary?

2. What is the turns ratio of a transformer with 500 turns in the primary and 625 turns in the secondary?

3. If a transformer with 200 turns in its primary has a 1:5 turns ratio, how many turns are in the secondary?

4. The primary of a transformer with a 5:2 turns ratio is connected across a 120-V source. What is the value of secondary voltage?

5. A transformer has a 4:1 turns ratio and delivers a secondary voltage of 25 V. What is the primary voltage?

6. If a transformer has 120 turns in its primary winding and provides 12 V in the secondary when its primary is connected to 10 V, how many turns are on the secondary winding?

7. If the turns ratio of a transformer is 3:1 and the primary current is 600 mA, what is the value of secondary current?

8. A transformer is connected to a 120-Vac source and supplies 50 V to a secondary load. The load draws 275 mA. What is the value of primary current?

9. Calculate the secondary current in a transformer that has a 5:2 turns ratio and a primary current of 150 mA.

10. What is the turns ratio of a transformer that has a secondary current of 2 A and a primary current of 25 mA?

11. The secondary of a transformer with a 2:1 turns ratio is connected to a 51-Ω resistor. What is the value of impedance (resistance in this case) reflected into the primary?

12. A transformer with a 1:4 turns ratio has a 1,500-Ω resistor connected across the secondary. What impedance is reflected into the primary?

13. A transformer has 200 turns in the primary and 50 turns in the secondary. The secondary load is reflected into the primary as a 1.2-kΩ resistance. What is the actual value of secondary load resistance?

14. The secondary power of a transformer is 100 W. The core and winding losses are 1.2 W and 4.5 W, respectively. What is the efficiency of the transformer?

15. A transformer draws 25 mA from a 120-V source. The secondary maintains 40 V across a 560-Ω resistor. What is the efficiency of the transformer?

16. With no load on the secondary of a transformer, the primary current is very low. (True or False)

17. If the secondary of a transformer is heavily loaded with a resistive load, the primary current will be nearly in phase with the primary voltage. (True or False)

18. A technician measures the secondary voltage of an unloaded transformer as 8.7 V. When the transformer is loaded, the technician measures the secondary voltage as 6.3 V. Explain the reason for these different measurements.

17.4 Applied Technology: Transformers

If one tries to think of all the electronic products in the world, it is far easier to name products that include a transformer than products without a transformer. We will briefly examine five specific applications that rely on the use of transformers.

Commercial Power Distribution

Power companies use many different kinds of transformers to effectively transfer electrical power from the generating plant to your home. Figure 17-21 illustrates a representative power distribution system. The exact voltage levels and sequence of voltage transformations vary greatly in different installations.

In the example shown in Figure 17-21, the power company alternators generate the initial power at 22 to 26 kV. The alternators actually generate three-phase power. That is, they generate three 60-Hz sine waves that are exactly 120° out of phase with each other. Many factories, farms, and businesses that have large motors or other high-power electrical equipment use all three phases. As indicated by Figure 17-21, only one of the three phases is generally brought to your door.

Immediately outside the generating plant, the voltage goes to a transformer which steps up the voltage to as high as 765 kV. Recall that when a transformer steps up the voltage, the current is reduced by a similar amount. The power companies use such high voltages to minimize the copper loss ($P = I^2R$) and voltage drop ($V = IR$) in the hundreds or thousands of miles of wire needed to reach your home. The wires for these extremely high voltages are supported by huge steel towers. Generally, you can see three large-diameter ($\approx$2 inches) wires and one smaller one. The three larger wires are the three phases and the smaller one is the neutral or ground wire. Less current flows in the neutral, so it can be smaller.

Some very large factories have step-down transformers that connect directly to the high-voltage transmission lines. Somewhere near your community, the high transmission voltage goes to another transformer, which steps down the voltage to the range of 12.5 to 138 kV. These are the transformers that are often referred to as substations. They are generally surrounded by high steel fences. The voltage is now routed on high wooden poles to smaller substations in your neighborhood. The voltage is still transferred as three-phase power. Some industrial plants have step-down transformers connected directly to the 12.5 to 138 kV lines.

KEY POINTS

The distribution of power throughout the country relies heavily on the use of transformers.

KEY POINTS

Transformers are used to step up the generated voltage for reduced loss during transmission.

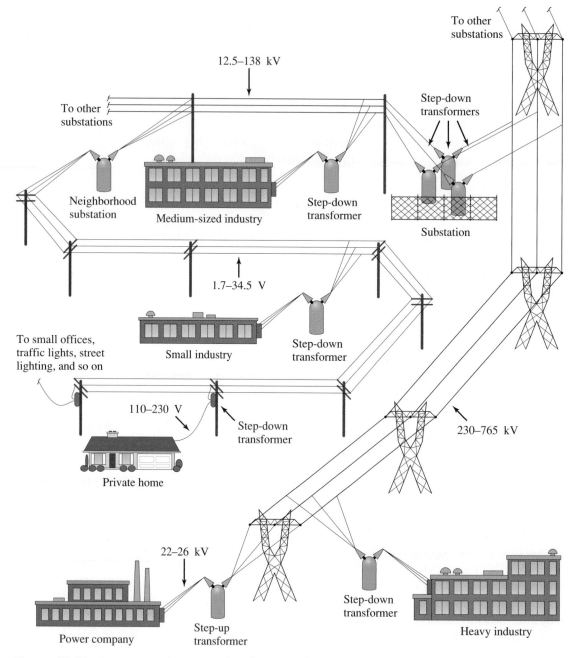

Figure 17-21. A representative power distribution scheme.

In the local substations, the voltage is reduced to a range of 1.7 to 34.5 kV by passing through another step-down transformer. All three phases of this lower-level voltage are connected to the step-down transformers of some smaller factories. Individual phases are used for streetlights and local businesses, each with its own step-down transformer. One of the phases of this power is routed to the power pole outside your home. Here, it passes through a step-down transformer with a center-tapped secondary. All three of the secondary wires are brought into the main electrical panel in your home. The transformer delivers a full secondary voltage of 220 to 240 V. Certain appliances like air conditioners and electric clothes dryers require 220 to 240 V and connect directly across the secondary of the transformer (via fuses or breakers). The lights and other smaller appliances in your home require 110 to 120 V. Some of them are connected between one side of the transformer secondary and the center tap. The rest are connected between the other side of the secondary and the center tap. The center tap of the secondary is physically connected to earth ground. Additional detail is provided later in this section.

Three-Phase Transformers

As previously mentioned, commercial power is generated as three-phase power. That is, three separate sets of coils are mounted on the alternator shaft. The coils are physically positioned 120° apart. Therefore, the sine waves of voltage that are produced in the coils are 120° out of phase with each other.

The primary and secondary windings of three-phase transformers can be connected in either of two ways: wye (tee) and delta (pi). In each of these cases, there are two measurements that are commonly used: leg and line. Figure 17-22 shows the two basic connections and definitions of leg and line voltage and current. Leg voltage and leg current are associated with a particular winding. Line voltage is measured between any two lines, and line current is the current flowing in a given line.

In a wye connection, we can see that line current and leg current are equal, since they are essentially the same current (see Figure 17-22a). This is expressed by Equation 17-9.

$$I_{line} = I_{leg} \text{ (wye connection)} \qquad \textbf{(17-9)}$$

Line voltage in a wye connection is actually the sum (according to Kirchhoff's Law) of two windings. However, since the voltages are 120° out of phase, the summation must account for the phase difference. Equation 17-10 describes this relationship:

$$V_{line} = \sqrt{3}V_{leg} \text{ (wye connection), or}$$
$$V_{line} = 1.732V_{leg} \text{ (wye connection)} \qquad \textbf{(17-10)}$$

By inspection of Figure 17-22(b), we can see that line current is actually the summation of two leg currents (Kirchhoff's Current Law). Again, we must remember that these currents are 120° out of phase. Equation 17-11 expresses the correct relationship.

$$I_{line} = \sqrt{3}I_{leg} \text{ (delta connection), or}$$
$$I_{line} = 1.732I_{leg} \text{ (delta connection)} \qquad \textbf{(17-11)}$$

Finally, we can see from Figure 17-22(b) that leg and line voltages in delta connections are essentially the same. We can express this relationship with Equation 17-12.

$$V_{line} = V_{leg} \text{ (delta connection)} \qquad \textbf{(17-12)}$$

Since both primary and secondary windings of a three-phase transformer can be either wye or delta connected, this leads to four possible combinations of primary/secondary configurations. Figure 17-23 illustrates all four connections.

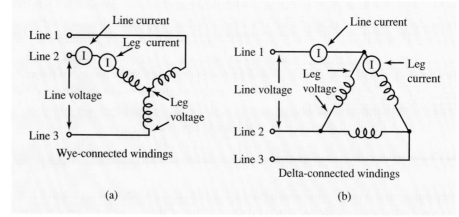

Figure 17-22. Three-phase transformer windings can be either (a) wye or (b) delta connected. In either case, both leg and line voltages and currents are useful measurements.

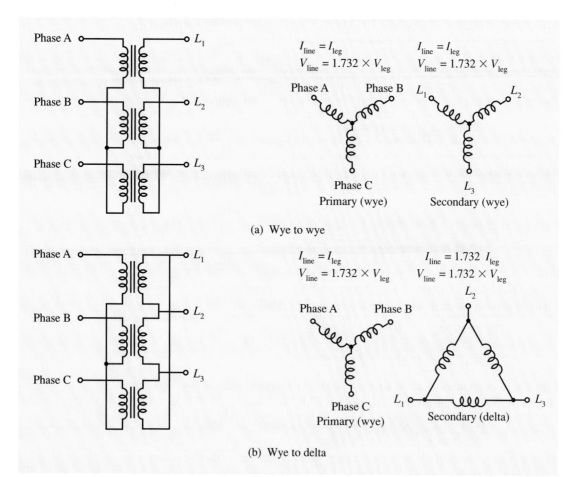

Figure 17-23. There are four combinations of wye and delta primary/secondary configurations.

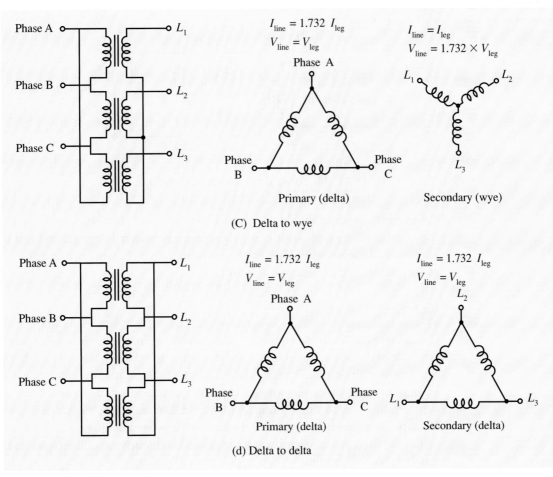

Figure 17-23. *(Continued)*

POWER DISTRIBUTION TERMINOLOGY

Figure 17-24 illustrates a portion of the power distribution system used to deliver 60-Hz power to your home. The transformer located on the pole near your house has its primary connected to one of the three phases provided by your power company. The secondary of the pole transformer is center tapped. The voltage across the entire secondary is nominally 240 Vac. From the center tap to either side is 120 Vac. Common electrician jargon labels the center tap as the **neutral.** The other two wires are often called the **hot** wires, since they are both "hot" (i.e., 120 Vac) with respect to the neutral.

As indicated in Figure 17-24, the neutral is connected to earth ground. For this reason, it is also referred to as ground by some electricians. By inspection of Figure 17-24, we can see that if we wanted to power a 120-Vac device (e.g., lamps, fans, electric blankets, and so on) in your home, we would connect it between the neutral and one of the hot wires. In practice, part of your 120-Vac house wiring is supplied from one hot line and the rest of your house is supplied by the other hot line. The electric clothes dryer or other appliance that requires 240 Vac would be connected between the two hot lines (the neutral also goes to the appliance). Electricians often say, "Pick up two hots to get 240 volts."

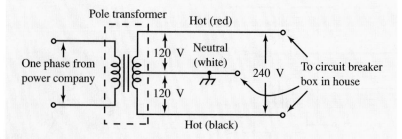

Figure 17-24. Power distribution terminology.

Electronic technicians should take note of the color codes indicated in Figure 17-24. For most house-wiring applications, the white wire is considered to be ground and the black wire is one of the hot wires. This can be confusing, since it is common practice to use black as the ground wire in electronic systems.

Isolation Transformers

Certain types of electronic equipment have no transformer in their internal power supply. One side of the power line is connected directly to the chassis. Now in use, this type of equipment is supposed to have a polarized plug, so there is only one way it can be plugged in. In practice, however, plugs do get inserted backwards (e.g., using an adapter to convert a three-prong plug to a two-prong plug). When this occurs, the chassis (and any exterior metal parts) becomes connected to the side of the power line that is 120 V with respect to earth ground. If you are standing on the ground and touch the cabinet, you will be shocked; possibly fatally.

Figure 17-25(a) illustrates the same basic problem, but in a situation likely to be experienced by a technician. Two electrical items (Equipment 1 and Equipment 2 in Figure 17-25) are being used or tested by a technician in a shop environment. One may be an oscilloscope and one may be a transformerless computer power supply, for example. In any case, there is a dangerous shock hazard for the technician. Additionally, if the technician attempts to connect the ground of Equipment 1 (e.g., the ground lead for an oscilloscope) to the chassis of Equipment 2 (e.g., the computer power supply), there will be fireworks. More specifically, the technician will essentially be placing a direct short across the 120-V power line. Trace the current path in Figure 17-25(a). At a minimum, the 120-V circuit breaker will blow, the equipment and test lead will have burn marks, and the technician will be worried about future employment opportunities.

Figure 17-25(b) shows how an isolation transformer can eliminate the problem. The figure shows a 1:1 transformer associated with each of the two equipment items. In practice, only one transformer is required and it can be on either power cord. The 1:1 isolation transformer has no effect on the voltage being supplied to the test equipment or the equipment being repaired, but it does remove or isolate the reference to earth ground. Now, either equipment can be plugged in either polarity without creating a difference in potential between the two cabinets. If it is your job to repair equipment that is internally referenced to earth ground, then be sure your shop is equipped with an isolation transformer.

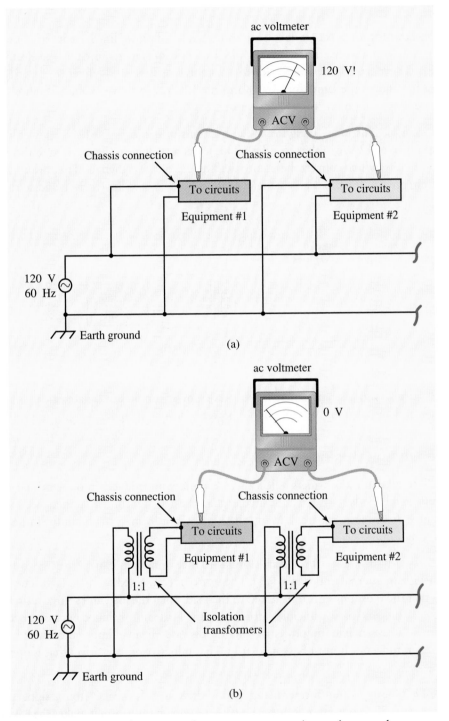

Figure 17-25. An isolation transformer can remove the earth-ground reference and eliminate a shock hazard for technicians.

dc Power Supplies

Most electronic products that operate from the standard power line have internal power supply circuits that convert the 120 Vac into lower dc voltages required by the electronic circuitry. Transformers are widely used to isolate the earth-ground reference (described previously) and, at the same time, transform the 120 Vac to a lower voltage. Figure 17-26 illustrates a typical power supply application.

In the example illustrated in Figure 17-26, the transformer steps the 120-V power line voltage down to 12 Vac in the secondary. This lower ac voltage is then routed to the power supply circuits, which convert the ac into dc. The dc voltage is then used to power the electronic circuitry in the product (e.g., television, computer, satellite receiver, and so forth).

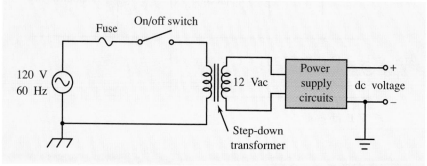

Figure 17-26. A transformer is used in dc power supplies to isolate earth ground and to transform the 120-V power to lower voltages.

Impedance Matching

You will recall that transformers reflect their secondary impedances into the primary. The reflected impedance is larger or smaller than the actual secondary impedance by a factor of k^2 (turns ratio squared). Many circuits use transformers to obtain the impedance transformation.

Figure 17-27 illustrates the importance of impedance transformation. A voltage source is shown with an internal impedance (R_S). The source is connected to a load (R_L). The graph shows that the most power is transferred to the load when the load and source resistances are equal. The same basic principle is true when the load and/or source has reactance associated with it. For maximum power transfer in this case, the load impedance must be the same magnitude, but it must have a polarity (i.e., inductive or capacitive) that is opposite the source.

Figure 17-28 shows a transformer being used to drive an 8-Ω speaker from a signal generator that has a 50-Ω output resistance. The 5:2 step-down transformer makes the 8-Ω load appear to be a 50-Ω resistance when it is reflected into the primary. The source acts as if it were connected to a 50-Ω load, and the load acts as if it were connected to an 8-Ω source. Maximum power is transferred because the source and load resistances are equal. It should be noted that a practical speaker will appear somewhat inductive, but the concept of impedance matching is still the same.

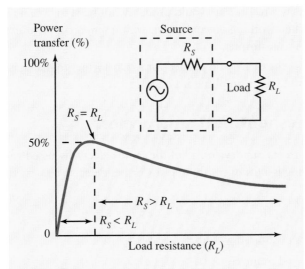

Figure 17-27. Maximum power transfer occurs when the source resistance is equal to the load resistance.

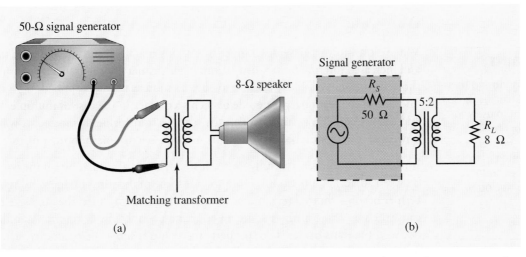

Figure 17-28. A transformer can match the 50-Ω output resistance of a signal generator to the 8-Ω resistance of a speaker.

Exercise Problems 17.4

1. Briefly explain why power companies use high voltages for transmission of power even though your home only requires 120 V.
2. Most power company substations utilize step-up transformers. (True or False)
3. What is the turns ratio of a typical isolation transformer?

4. Explain why a technician would probably not need to use an isolation transformer when working on equipment whose power supply utilizes an internal step-down transformer.

5. Determine the turns ratio needed for a transformer to match a preamplifier output of 250 Ω to an amplifier input of 25 kΩ.

17.5 Troubleshooting Transformers

In general, transformers can develop all of the same defects discussed with reference to inductors. Following is a list of common transformer defects:

- open primary
- open secondary(s)
- shorted turns or shorted winding
- winding shorted to the core
- short between primary and secondary

Most defective transformers can be detected through effective use of three things: technician observation, voltmeter checks, and ohmmeter checks.

Observation

When a transformer develops a short circuit, it generally results in increased current flow and increased internal power dissipation. If the primary of the transformer is fused, then a shorted winding will likely cause it to blow as soon as power is applied. If you disconnect one side of the secondary (one side of each secondary in the case of multiple windings), and the fuse still blows, then you can be sure the transformer is shorted. Always use your powers of observation before you begin an extensive troubleshooting process.

Iron-core transformers typically use varnish or shellac as insulation on the wires and between adjacent laminations in the core. If some of the turns in one winding of the transformer become shorted (e.g., the insulation breaks down), then the excessive heat will cause the shellac or varnish to emit an odor and possibly visible smoke. A similar symptom occurs if the transformer is not properly fused and is subjected to an excessive load in its secondary (e.g., a shorted component). In any case, the smell of an overheated transformer is very distinct. Once a technician has smelled the odor, it will be remembered forever. Be alert when troubleshooting. By detecting this aroma, you may be able to quickly locate a defective transformer and save a lot of troubleshooting time.

There may also be visible evidence indicating that a transformer has been overheated. The visible paper insulation may be discolored or the visible varnish may have a bubbled appearance. Use your powers of observation to help you quickly locate transformer defects.

Voltmeter Tests

If a winding on a transformer is open (either primary or secondary), there will be no voltage developed across the secondary winding. In the case of multiple secondaries, an open primary results in no voltage in any secondaries. An open secondary, on the other hand, results in no voltage across the defective secondary, but relatively normal voltages across all other secondaries.

Ohmmeter Tests

An ohmmeter can be used to absolutely confirm that a particular winding is open. Desolder one end of the suspected winding, and measure its resistance. An open winding will read infinite ohms. In many cases, the normal resistance of the transformer windings is so much lower than any parallel sneak paths that you can test for an open winding without desoldering one lead first. If it checks open, then it definitely is. If it checks good, then check carefully to be sure you are not measuring the resistance of a parallel sneak path.

An ohmmeter is also useful for detecting a winding-to-core short or a primary-to-secondary short. In either of these cases, the normal resistance is infinite ohms. If the measured resistance is very low or even zero, then you have located a short circuit.

Ohmmeters do not usually provide adequate resolution to reliably detect shorted turns in a transformer winding. That is, if the resistance of a normal winding were 2.8 Ω, then a few shorted turns might cause it to have a resistance of 2.75 Ω. Not only is this small change difficult to detect reliably, but it is well within the normal variation of different transformers (of the same type) and different ohmmeters (i.e., measurement error).

KEY POINTS

An open primary will prevent the generation of voltage across any secondaries. An open secondary will have zero volts across it, but normal voltage across any other secondaries.

KEY POINTS

Final confirmation of an open winding is best done with an ohmmeter.

Exercise Problems 17.5

1. While troubleshooting a transformer circuit, you measure infinite ohms across one of the secondary windings. What does this indicate?
2. If the primary winding measures infinite resistance, what would a voltmeter across the secondary measure with the transformer connected to power?
3. What is a normal resistance reading between the primary and secondary windings?
4. What is a normal resistance reading between one of the secondary windings and the core of the transformer?
5. Explain why observation can play an important role in the troubleshooting of transformer circuits.

Chapter Summary

- When two or more inductors have flux in common, we say they are magnetically linked. The portion of the total flux that does not link the coils is called leakage flux and gives rise to leakage inductance. The portion of the total flux that is common to the coils produces mutual inductance. The amount of mutual inductance is determined by the value of the inductances and by the coefficient of coupling (i.e., the percentage of total flux that links the coils).

- When magnetically linked coils are connected in series, the total inductance may be higher or lower (by a factor of two times the mutual inductance) than if the coils had no common flux. Whether total inductance is higher or lower depends on whether the magnetic polarities of the two coils aid or oppose. Similarly, when parallel-connected coils have mutual inductance, the total inductance may be higher or lower than the same two coils without mutual inductance.

- A transformer consists of two or more coils that are magnetically coupled. The coil to which power is applied is called the primary winding. All other coils are called secondary windings. The phase relationship between the primary and any given secondary is indicated on a schematic diagram with dot notation. The phase dots indicate points of similar instantaneous polarity.

- Transformers may be classified many ways, including by their application, by the type of core material, or by how their windings are constructed. There may be a single or multiple secondaries, and the primary and/or the secondary(s) may be tapped. An autotransformer has a special winding configuration, where the primary and secondary share a common, tapped winding.

- Practical transformers have winding losses and core losses. Winding losses include copper loss and losses due to skin effect. Core losses include hysteresis loss and loss due to eddy currents. Practical transformers have parasitic capacitance between adjacent turns and between the primary and secondary windings. This latter capacitance can be eliminated by using a Faraday shield between the primary and secondary windings.

- The ratio of the number of turns in the primary to the number of turns in the secondary is called the transformer turns ratio. The primary-to-secondary voltage ratio is equal to the turns ratio, because the volts per turn must be the same in both primary and secondary. The current ratio is equal to the inverse of the turns ratio. Primary and secondary power are the same with the exception of transformer losses. The ratio of secondary power to primary power is called the transformer efficiency. Iron-core transformers can have efficiencies on the order of 95%.

- Any impedance connected to the secondary of a transformer is reflected into the primary. The value of the reflected impedance is related to the actual secondary impedance by the square of the turns ratio.

- The primary of an unloaded transformer has a very small magnetizing current that is nearly 90° behind the primary voltage. The transformer acts inductive. Under conditions of heavy resistive loads, the primary current is largely resistive and the primary current and voltage are nearly in phase. The secondary voltage of a transformer generally decreases as more secondary current is drawn. This is due to the voltage drop across the nonideal secondary impedance consisting of the secondary leakage inductance and the resistance of the secondary winding.

- Transformers play a key role in the distribution of commercial power. They are used to step up (increase) and step down (decrease) the voltage at various points in the distribution network. Other transformer applications include isolation transformers, step-down transformers for low-voltage dc power supplies, and transformers used for impedance matching to attain maximum transfer of power between two circuits.

- Transformer defects include open or shorted windings and windings that are shorted to the core or to each other. Many defective transformers can be detected by smelling burned insulation or by visually locating indications of overheating. A voltmeter can be used to detect open windings, but results should be verified with an ohmmeter.

Review Questions

Section 17.1: Mutual Inductance and Coupling

1. If two magnetically linked coils are moved closer to each other, the coefficient of coupling will increase. (True or False)

2. If all of the flux produced by one coil cut through the windings of a second coil, what would be the coefficient of coupling for the two coils?

3. Mutual inductance can only exist if two or more coils have common flux. (True or False)

4. If two coils have a coefficient of coupling of 0.85 and have individual inductances of 2.5 µH and 4.8 µH, what is the value of mutual inductance?

5. Calculate the mutual inductance for two 175-mH coils that have a 0.5 coefficient of coupling.

6. What is the mutual inductance between a 75-mH coil and a 225-mH coil if they have a coefficient of coupling of 0.6?

7. When a 200-µH coil has a 0.9 coefficient of coupling to another coil, the mutual inductance is 350 µH. What is the inductance of the second coil?

8. When a 1.75-mH coil has a 0.75 coefficient of coupling with another coil, the mutual inductance is 750 µH. What is the inductance of the second coil?

9. When two magnetically linked coils are connected in series, the total inductance is always higher than if the coils were not magnetically linked. (True or False)

10. Compute the total inductance of two series coils having values of 25 mH and 75 mH if they have a mutual inductance of 10 mH and are connected to be series-aiding.

11. Two 225-mH coils are connected in series so that their magnetic fields are in opposition. The mutual inductance is 75 mH. What is the total inductance of the series circuit?

12. What is the total inductance if a 35-µH coil is connected series-aiding with a 10-µH coil with a mutual inductance of 8 µH?

13. What is the approximate value of total inductance when two parallel coils (with opposing magnetic fields) have inductances of 175 mH and 250 mH and a mutual inductance of 100 mH?

14. Two parallel coils have fields that are magnetically aiding. One coil is 650 µH, the other is 470 µH, and the mutual inductance is 450 µH. What is the approximate inductance of the parallel combination?

Section 17.2: Transformers

15. Transformers always have mutual inductance. (True or False)

16. The winding of a transformer where input power is connected is called the _____ winding.

17. How is the phase relationship between primary voltage and secondary voltage indicated on a schematic diagram?

18. A transformer whose secondary voltage is higher than its primary voltage is called a step-_____ transformer.

19. The secondary voltage in a step-down transformer is (*higher, lower*) than the primary voltage.

20. Transformers used in power supplies are often classified as _____ transformers.

21. Transformers intended for use in the audio frequency range are classified as _____ transformers.

22. Name the three types of material commonly used for cores in transformers.

23. What type of core material has the lowest permeability?

24. What type of core material would be used in a transformer designed for use at 60 Hz?

25. What type of material is generally used as the core material in a toroid-core transformer?

26. If the full secondary voltage of a center-tapped transformer is 30 V, how much voltage will be measured between either end of the transformer and the center tap?

27. When a transformer has multiple secondaries, each secondary can have its own turns ratio. (True or False)

28. How many windings are there in an autotransformer?

29. Is it possible to connect an autotransformer as a step-up transformer?

30. Can an autotransformer be used as a step-down transformer?

31. The power loss due to the resistance of the transformer windings is called _____.

32. What is the name of the phenomenon that causes high-frequency currents to flow only near the surface of a conductor?

33. Hysteresis loss can be classified as a loss due to winding resistance. (True or False)

34. The core of an iron-core transformer is laminated to reduce the losses due to hysteresis. (True or False)

35. What is done in the construction of an iron-core transformer to reduce losses due to eddy currents?

36. An ideal transformer core would have very high resistance and very high permeability. (True or False)

37. What is the primary purpose of a Faraday shield?

38. To be effective, the material used in a Faraday shield must have a high resistance. (True or False)

Section 17.3: Analysis of Transformer Circuits

39. What is the turns ratio of a transformer that has 350 turns in the primary and 1,750 turns in the secondary?

40. What is the turns ratio of a transformer that has 500 turns in the primary and 750 turns in the secondary?

41. What is the turns ratio of a transformer that has 700 turns in the primary and 525 turns in the secondary?

42. What is the turns ratio of a transformer that has 250 turns in the primary and 500 turns in the secondary?

43. If a transformer with a 2:1 turns ratio has 275 turns on its primary, how many turns are on the secondary?

44. If a transformer with a 4:3 turns ratio has 900 turns on its secondary, how many turns are on the primary?

45. If the volts per turn on the primary of a transformer is 1.75 V/T, what is the volts per turn on the secondary of the transformer?

46. A transformer with a 2:1 turns ratio has a secondary voltage of 6.3 V. What is the primary voltage?

47. A transformer with a 4:3 turns ratio has a primary voltage of 220 V. What is the secondary voltage?

48. A transformer has a turns ratio of 5:1 and delivers a secondary voltage of 100 V. What is the primary voltage?

49. A transformer has a 1:5 turns ratio and delivers a secondary voltage of 100 V. What is the primary voltage?

50. If the turns ratio of a transformer is 3:1 and the primary current is 250 mA, what is the value of secondary current?

51. A transformer is connected to a 120-V source and supplies 24 V to a load that draws 800 mA. What is the value of primary current?

52. If a transformer has a primary voltage of 100 V, a secondary voltage of 20 V, and a primary current of 1.2 A, what is the value of secondary current?

53. When the secondary current in a transformer increases due to a lower resistance load, the primary current will (*increase, decrease*).

54. In your own words, explain what is meant by the term *reflected impedance.*

55. Reflected impedance is always higher than the actual secondary impedance. (True or False)

56. The secondary of a transformer with a turns ratio of 4:1 is connected to a 250-Ω resistor. What is the value of impedance reflected into the primary?

57. A transformer with 220 V across the primary produces 10 V in the secondary. If the secondary load is 1.25 Ω, what is the current in the primary?

58. A transformer produces 12 V in the secondary when 120 V are connected to the primary. If the secondary has 100 mA of current, what is the impedance seen by the source?

59. The secondary of a transformer provides 100 W to a resistive load. The combined core losses are 3 W and the winding losses are 5 W. What is the efficiency of the transformer?

60. A transformer draws 2 A from a 120-V source. The secondary supplies 10 V to a 0.5-Ω resistance. What is the efficiency of the transformer?

61. If the secondary of a transformer is unloaded, the primary current is very small. (True or False)

62. Under no-load conditions, the primary current and voltage of a transformer are nearly 90° out of phase. (True or False)

63. When the secondary of a transformer is fully loaded with a resistive load, the primary acts almost purely inductive. (True or False)

64. What causes the secondary voltage of a transformer to decrease as more current is drawn from the secondary?

Section 17.4: Applied Technology: Transformers

65. The transformers that are located between a power generating plant and a high-voltage transmission line are step-up transformers. (True or False)

66. The transformer whose secondary supplies power to your home is a step-up transformer. (True or False)

67. What is the name of a transformer with a 1:1 turns ratio?

68. An autotransformer is used to eliminate the earth-ground reference from the power line. (True or False)

69. Explain why impedance matching is such an important consideration in electronic circuits.

Section 17.5: Troubleshooting Transformers

70. An open secondary will develop a higher-than-normal voltage. (True or False)

71. An open primary will cause the voltage across all secondaries to increase. (True or False)

72. Name two ways that some defective transformers can be identified without making any electrical tests.

73. What is the normal resistance between the primary and secondary windings of a transformer?

74. If a center-tapped secondary measures 10 V from the tap to one end, but measures 0 V from the tap to the other end, what is the most probable trouble?

75. One indication of an open transformer winding is a blown fuse in the primary. (True or False)

TECHNICIAN CHALLENGE

You are working as a computer technician and have just located a defective transformer in a video monitor. The monitor is old, and the manufacturer has gone out of business. You decide to have a local transformer manufacturer wind a new transformer for you, but you must provide the needed specifications. Here is what you know:

The transformer operates from 120 Vac. It has three secondary windings with voltages of 6.3 V, 12.6 V, and 48 V. The 6.3-V, 12.6-V, and 48-V secondaries have 2.5-A, 1.0-A, and 0.125-A fuses, respectively. The primary is also fused, but the fuse was physically burned so badly it could not be interpreted. You don't know what size fuse to use in the primary.

Take the technician challenge and determine the following information:

- required turns ratios
- required power ratings for each secondary
- required fuse size for the primary (assume 100% efficiency)

Equation List

$$(17\text{-}1) \quad L_M = k\sqrt{L_1 L_2}$$

$$(17\text{-}2) \quad L_T = L_1 + L_2 \pm 2L_M$$

$$(17\text{-}3) \quad L_T = \frac{L_1 L_2 - L_M{}^2}{L_1 + L_2 \pm 2L_M}$$

$$(17\text{-}4) \quad k = \frac{N_P}{N_S}$$

$$(17\text{-}5) \quad \frac{N_P}{N_S} = \frac{V_P}{V_S}$$

$$(17\text{-}6) \quad \frac{N_P}{N_S} = \frac{I_S}{I_P}$$

$$(17\text{-}7) \quad \frac{N_P}{N_S} = \sqrt{\frac{Z_P}{Z_S}}$$

$$(17\text{-}8) \quad \eta = \frac{P_S}{P_S + P_{\text{WINDING}} + P_{\text{CORE}}}$$

$$(17\text{-}9) \quad I_{\text{line}} = I_{\text{leg}} \ (\text{wye connection})$$

$$(17\text{-}10) \quad \begin{aligned} V_{\text{line}} &= \sqrt{3}V_{\text{leg}} \ (\text{wye connection}), \text{ or} \\ V_{\text{line}} &= 1.732V_{\text{leg}} \ (\text{wye connection}) \end{aligned}$$

$$(17\text{-}11) \quad \begin{aligned} I_{\text{line}} &= \sqrt{3}I_{\text{leg}} \ (\text{delta connection}), \text{ or} \\ I_{\text{line}} &= 1.732I_{\text{leg}} \ (\text{delta connection}) \end{aligned}$$

$$(17\text{-}12) \quad V_{\text{line}} = V_{\text{leg}} \ (\text{delta connection})$$

coupling circuits   passband
cutoff frequency   peaking
decoupling circuit Q factor
frequency response   roll-off
half-power point   stopband
notch filter

objectives

After completing this chapter, you should be able to:

1. Name the five general classes of passive filters.

2. Sketch the generic frequency response curve for each of the following filter types:

   a. low-pass
   b. high-pass
   c. bandpass
   d. bandstop
   e. notch

3. Compute the cutoff frequency for a given low-pass or high-pass RC or RL filter.

4. Distinguish between coupling and decoupling circuits.

5. Troubleshoot passive filter circuits.

18

Passive Filter Circuits

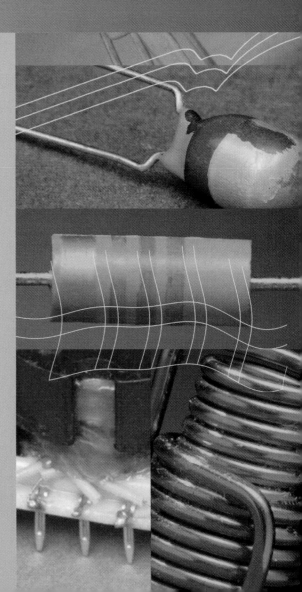

Filter circuits are used extensively in many types of electronic circuits. A filter, be it an air filter, a lint filter, an oil filter, or a passive electronic filter, accepts a broad range of inputs but only allows certain of these inputs to pass through to the output. Some filters are designed to let the "good stuff" pass through the filter while the filter catches or stops the "bad stuff." A lint filter in a washing machine and an air filter in a car are examples of this type of filter action. A filter can also be designed to catch the "good stuff" and let the "bad stuff" pass through the filter. A gold prospector's sieve is an example of this type of filter action.

*All of the filters given as examples in the preceding discussion are mechanical filters and discriminate between "good" and "bad" on the basis of physical size (e.g., size of a dust particle relative to an air molecule for an air filter). In the case of the passive filters described in this chapter, "good" and "bad" signals will be classified on the basis of their frequencies. The input to the filter circuits can be a broad range of frequencies, but the filter circuit will only allow a certain range of these frequencies to pass. All other frequencies will be rejected or attenuated (reduced in amplitude). The frequency (or frequencies) that separates the range of allowed frequencies from the range of rejected frequencies is called the **cutoff frequency** of the filter. As discussed in Chapter 16, signal voltages at the cutoff frequency are attenuated to 70.7% of the input voltage. This point is also called the **half-power point** as detailed in Chapter 16. You will also recall that the 70.7% response also corresponds to the −3-dB point. That is,*

$$dB = 20 \log \frac{V_{OUT}}{V_{IN}}$$
$$= 20 \log 0.707 = -3 \text{ dB}$$

*We will examine the performance of five basic filter classes: low-pass, high-pass, bandpass, bandstop, and notch. It is important for a technician to be able to recognize and identify the schematic diagram for each of these circuits and to be able to determine the **frequency response** of each circuit (i.e., determine which frequencies are passed and which ones are rejected).*

18.1 Low-Pass Filters

Low-pass filters, as the name implies, are designed to pass low frequencies and to reject higher frequencies. Figure 18-1 shows the basic frequency response of a low-pass filter.

There are several ways to obtain a frequency response similar to that shown in Figure 18-1. Figure 18-2 illustrates the fundamental requirements for low-pass filter action. As shown in Figure 18-2(a), low-frequency signals (i.e., frequencies below the cutoff frequency) must see a low series impedance and a high shunt impedance. Under these conditions,

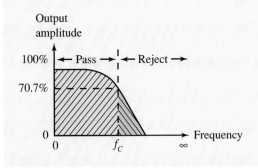

Figure 18-1. A low-pass filter allows frequencies below the cutoff frequency (f_C) to pass, but rejects or attenuates all higher frequencies.

basic voltage divider action will cause the output voltage (V_O) to be nearly the same amplitude as the input voltage (V_I). Figure 18-2(b) shows the condition that must exist for high-frequency signals (i.e., frequencies higher than the cutoff frequency). The high frequencies must see a high series impedance and a low shunt impedance. Voltage divider action, in this case, causes a severe attenuation of the input signals. That is, the high-frequency signals are not passed through the filter.

There are numerous ways to achieve the requirements outlined in Figure 18-2. We shall examine two common methods using *RC* and *RL* circuits.

KEY POINTS

Low-pass filters can be constructed as *RC* or *RL* circuits, where:

- The reactance (inductive or capacitive) is equal to the resistance at the cutoff frequency.
- The series element has a lower resistance or reactance than the shunt element at frequencies below the cutoff frequency.
- The series element has a higher resistance or reactance than the shunt element at frequencies above the cutoff frequency.

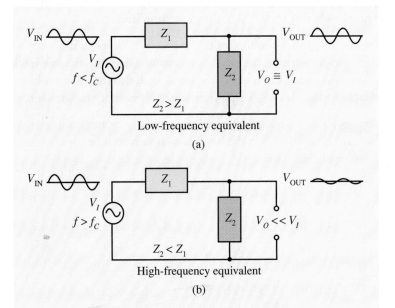

Figure 18-2. Basic requirements for a low-pass filter circuit.

RC Filters

Figure 18-3 shows a basic *RC* low-pass filter circuit. The range of input frequencies is shown to be from dc to infinity (i.e., all frequencies). The output frequency range, by contrast, will only consist of those frequencies that are below the cutoff frequency.

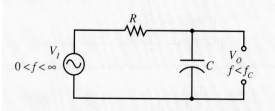

Figure 18-3. A basic *RC* low-pass filter circuit.

Figure 18-4 illustrates the relative behavior of the *RC* low-pass filter at three key frequencies: below the cutoff frequency, at the cutoff frequency, and above the cutoff frequency. In Figure 18-4(a), the input frequency is below the cutoff frequency. You will recall that capacitive reactance is inversely proportional to frequency. So as frequency goes down, capacitive reactance goes up. As shown in Figure 18-4(a), the voltage divider action caused by a capacitive reactance that is greater than the series resistance results in an output voltage (i.e., the voltage across the capacitor) that is nearly the same as the input voltage. That is, the frequencies below the cutoff frequency are passed through the filter and appear in the output with amplitudes that are at least 70.7% of the input amplitude (i.e., $V_O \cong V_I$).

As shown in Figure 18-4(b), the capacitive reactance in the circuit is equal to the resistance at the cutoff frequency. Voltage divider action (detailed in Chapter 15) causes equal voltage drops across *R* and *C*. Due to the phase shift in the circuit (45°), the output voltage will have an amplitude that is 70.7% of the input amplitude.

Finally, Figure 18-4(c) shows the equivalent circuit seen by frequencies above the cutoff frequency. Throughout this range, the capacitive reactance is less than the series resistance. Therefore, voltage divider action attenuates the signals such that the output voltage is less than 70.7% of the input voltage (i.e., $V_O \ll V_I$). The higher the frequency, the greater the attenuation.

As stated previously, the capacitive reactance is equal to the series resistance at the cutoff frequency. We can use this fact and the basic capacitive reactance equation to develop an important relationship as follows:

$$R = X_C$$

$$R = \frac{1}{2\pi f_C C}$$

$$f_C = \frac{1}{2\pi RC}$$

This result is expressed formally as Equation 18-1.

$$f_C = \frac{1}{2\pi RC} \qquad \text{(18-1)}$$

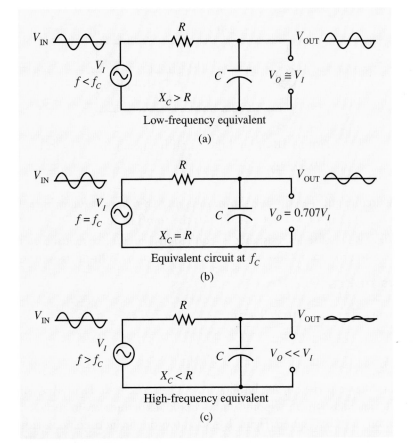

Figure 18-4. The equivalent circuits for an *RC* low-pass filter at three key frequencies.

EXAMPLE SOLUTION

Determine the cutoff frequency for the filter circuit shown in Figure 18-5.

EXAMPLE SOLUTION

We apply Equation 18-1.

$$f_C = \frac{1}{2\pi RC}$$

$$= \frac{1}{6.28 \times 10 \times 10^3 \times 0.01 \times 10^{-6}}$$

$$= 1.59 \text{ kHz}$$

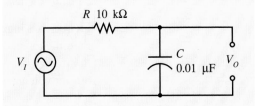

Figure 18-5. Determine the cutoff frequency for this filter circuit.

Practice Problems

1. Calculate the cutoff frequency for the circuit shown in Figure 18-6.

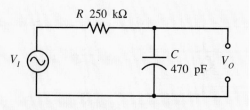

Figure 18-6. Find the cutoff frequency for this circuit.

2. A circuit similar to the one shown in Figure 18-6 has the following values: $R = 250\ \Omega$ and $C = 1,000$ pF. What is the cutoff frequency?

3. What value of series resistance is required in a circuit like that shown in Figure 18-6 to produce a 250-kHz cutoff frequency with a 500-pF capacitor?

Answers to Practice Problems

1. 1.36 kHz   **2.** 639.9 kHz   **3.** 1.27 kΩ

RL Filters

The low-pass filter response can also be obtained with an *RL* circuit. Figure 18-7 shows an *RL* low-pass filter and illustrates its response under conditions of three key frequencies: below cutoff, at cutoff, and above cutoff. Figure 18-7(a) shows the circuit conditions with an input frequency lower than the cutoff frequency (i.e., within the passband of the filter). The reactance of the inductor is less than the value of resistance. This means that voltage divider action will cause most of the voltage to be dropped across *R*. Since the output voltage is taken across *R*, then V_O will nearly equal V_I. That is, the lower frequencies are allowed to pass through the filter.

Figure 18-7(b) illustrates the *RL* low-pass filter circuit at cutoff. The inductive reactance is equal to the resistance. The two components drop equal voltages (70.7% of V_I).

Frequencies higher than the cutoff frequency cause the inductive reactance to be larger than the resistance as reflected in Figure 18-7(c). Voltage divider action results in most of the voltage being dropped across the inductive reactance and very little across *R*. Since the output voltage is taken across *R*, the output is greatly attenuated.

Because $X_L = R$ at the cutoff frequency, we can substitute the inductive reactance equation and obtain an expression for the cutoff frequency.

$$X_L = R$$
$$2\pi f_c L = R$$
$$f_c = \frac{R}{2\pi L}$$

This latter expression is given as Equation 18-2.

$$f_c = \frac{R}{2\pi L} \qquad\qquad (18\text{-}2)$$

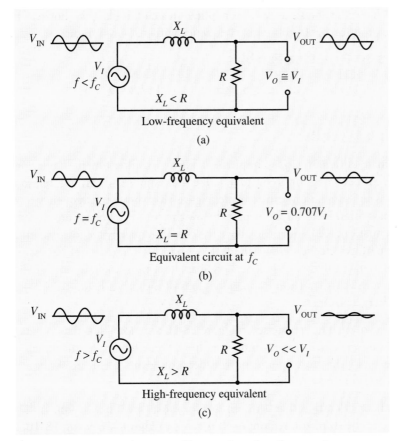

Figure 18-7. An *RL* low-pass filter at three key frequencies.

Determine the cutoff frequency for the low-pass filter circuit shown in Figure 18-8.

We apply Equation 18-2 as follows.

$$f_C = \frac{R}{2\pi L} = \frac{27 \text{ k}\Omega}{6.28 \times 200 \text{ }\mu\text{H}} = 21.5 \text{ MHz}$$

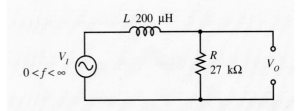

Figure 18-8. Find the cutoff frequency for this circuit.

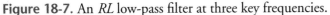

Practice Problems

1. Compute the cutoff frequency for a circuit like the one shown in Figure 18-8 if it has the following component values: $R = 33$ kΩ and $L = 375$ μH.

2. A circuit similar to the one shown in Figure 18-8 has the following values: $R = 250$ Ω and $L = 1.75$ mH. What is the cutoff frequency?

3. What value of resistance (R) is required in a circuit like that shown in Figure 18-8 to produce a 750-kHz cutoff frequency with a 25-mH inductor?

Answers to Practice Problems

1. 14.01 MHz   **2.** 22.75 kHz   **3.** 117.8 kΩ

Describing Filter Response

There are many different ways to implement a low-pass filter function, but not all work equally well. It becomes important to describe the response of a given filter, so that comparisons and evaluations can be made. Figure 18-9 shows the frequency response of an ideal low-pass filter. Here, all frequencies below the cutoff frequency are passed with virtually no attenuation. All frequencies above the cutoff frequency are totally eliminated. While this performance represents an ideal low-pass filter, it does not represent the response of a practical filter. A practical low-pass filter must make a more gradual transition between the passband and stopband regions of the curve. Figure 18-10 shows several practical filter responses.

Clearly, some of the filter responses in Figure 18-10 are more ideal than others. Several factors can be considered when comparing filters. We will consider three major ones. The first and generally the most significant consideration is the actual cutoff frequency. This is given as a certain number of hertz.

The second consideration that is important for most filter applications is the steepness of the slope in the stopband region. As illustrated in Figures 18-9 and 18-10, the steeper the slope, the more ideal the filter. The steepness of the slope (also called **roll-off**) is generally specified in units of decibels (dB) per decade or decibels per octave. A decade represents a frequency change factor of ten. For example, 100 Hz, 1,000 Hz, and 10 kHz represent three frequencies that are one decade apart. If a filter were specified as having a −60 dB/decade slope between 1.0 kHz and 10.0 kHz, then the output signal would be 60 dB lower at 10.0 kHz than it is at 1.0 kHz.

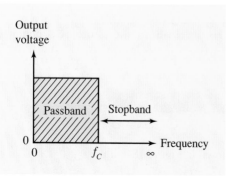

Figure 18-9. The frequency response of an ideal low-pass filter.

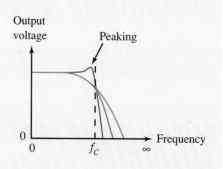

Figure 18-10. The frequency response of practical low-pass filters makes a more gradual transition between the passband and stopband regions.

Filter roll-off is sometimes stated in terms of dB/octave. An octave represents a frequency change of two (or one-half). Thus, 6.0 kHz is one octave higher than 3.0 kHz. If a filter has a −12 dB/octave slope between 3.0 kHz and 6.0 kHz, then the output voltage will be 12 dB lower at 6.0 kHz than at 3.0 kHz.

All of the *RC* and *RL* filters presented in this section have theoretical slopes of 20 dB/decade or 6 dB/octave. Steeper slopes can be obtained by cascading (connecting the output of one filter to the input of a second filter) filter sections. Even greater slopes can be realized by adding other circuitry (e.g., amplifiers with feedback).

The third factor that is important when contrasting the performance of filters is **peaking.** As illustrated in Figure 18-10, the response of some filter circuits peaks just before the edge of the passband. The degree of peaking for a low-pass filter is indicated by its **Q factor.** A Q of 1 has only slight peaking. Q values less than 1 have no peaking, and Q values more than 1 have more pronounced peaking. In most cases, there is a tradeoff between peaking (generally undesired) and steepness (generally desired) of the slope. None of the passive low-pass filters presented in this chapter have any degree of peaking.

KEY POINTS

A steep slope with minimal peaking is generally a desired response since it more closely approximates the response of an ideal low-pass filter.

Exercise Problems 18.1

1. Which of the circuits shown in Figure 18-11 will function as low-pass filters?
2. Which of the frequency response curves shown in Figure 18-12 represent the performance of a low-pass filter?
3. Calculate the cutoff frequency for the low-pass filter shown in Figure 18-13.
4. If the values in Figure 18-13 are changed to $R = 39$ kΩ and $C = 1,800$ pF, what is the new cutoff frequency?
5. What value of C must be used in a circuit like Figure 18-13 to provide a 100-kHz cutoff frequency when the resistor value is 200 kΩ?

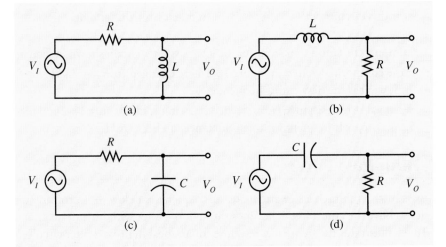

Figure 18-11. Which of these circuits are low-pass filters?

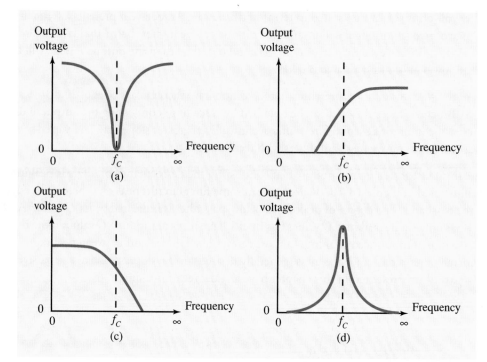

Figure 18-12. Which of these graphs represent the response of a low-pass filter?

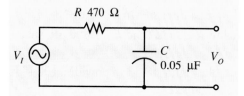

Figure 18-13. What is the cutoff frequency for this circuit?

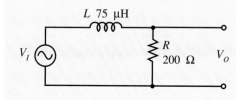

Figure 18-14. Calculate the cutoff frequency for this circuit.

6. Compute the cutoff frequency for the low-pass filter circuit shown in Figure 18-14.

7. If the component values in Figure 18-14 are changed to $R = 4.7$ kΩ and $L = 6.8$ mH, what is the new cutoff frequency?

8. What value of resistance (R) is needed in a circuit like Figure 18-14 to provide a 5.8-kHz cutoff frequency if the inductance (L) is 2.5 mH?

KEY POINTS

Filter circuits that pass frequencies above a certain frequency—called the cutoff frequency—with little or no loss but attenuate frequencies lower than the cutoff frequency are called high-pass filters.

18.2 High-Pass Filters

A high-pass filter circuit rejects or attenuates all frequencies below the cutoff frequency. Frequencies above the cutoff frequency pass through the filter with little or no attenuation. Figure 18-15 illustrates the frequency response for an ideal high-pass filter circuit. Practical filters have a more gradual roll-off below the cutoff frequency.

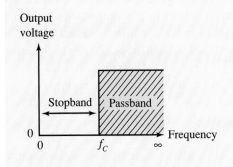

Figure 18-15. The frequency response of an ideal high-pass filter makes a step transition at the cutoff frequency.

There are many ways to achieve a high-pass filter response, but the illustrations in Figure 18-16 show the basic requirements. Figure 18-16(a) shows that for frequencies below the cutoff frequency, the series impedance (Z_1) must be greater than the shunt impedance

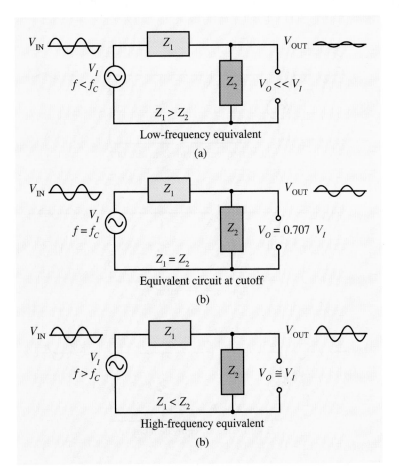

Figure 18-16. Basic requirements for a high-pass filter circuit.

(Z_2). Under these conditions, voltage divider action will cause most of the voltage to be dropped across Z_1, leaving very little for the output voltage (voltage across Z_2). Figure 18-16(b) shows that the series and shunt impedances are equal at the cutoff frequency. The two impedances will have equal voltage drops (70.7% of the input voltage). Finally, as shown in Figure 18-16(c), frequencies above the cutoff frequency must see Z_1 as a lower impedance than Z_2. This causes most of the input voltage to be dropped across Z_2. Since the output voltage is taken across Z_2, we know that the output voltage will nearly equal the input voltage under these conditions.

RC Filters

Figure 18-17 shows how to construct a high-pass RC filter circuit. Figure 18-17(a) shows that the capacitive reactance is higher than the resistance for frequencies below the cutoff frequency. Voltage divider action will drop most of the input voltage across C, leaving very little for the output voltage (voltage across R). At the cutoff frequency, shown in Figure 18-17(b), the capacitive reactance and the resistance values are equal and drop equal voltages (70.7% of the input voltage). For frequencies higher than the cutoff frequency, the capacitive reactance is lower than the shunt resistance as shown in Figure 18-17(c). Voltage divider action results in most of the input voltage being dropped across the resistance and

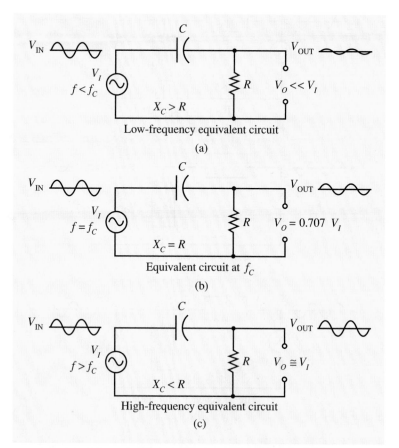

Figure 18-17. An RC circuit can provide a high-pass filter response.

appearing as output voltage. That is, frequencies above the cutoff frequency are passed through with minimal attenuation.

Since the reactance and resistance values for a high-pass filter are equal at the cutoff frequency, as they were in a low-pass filter, we can use Equation 18-1 to compute the cutoff frequency.

EXAMPLE SOLUTION

Determine the cutoff frequency for the high-pass filter circuit shown in Figure 18-18.

EXAMPLE **SOLUTION**

We apply Equation 18-1 as follows:

$$f_C = \frac{1}{2\pi RC}$$

$$= \frac{1}{6.28 \times 10 \text{ k}\Omega \times 0.05 \text{ }\mu\text{F}} = 318.5 \text{ Hz}$$

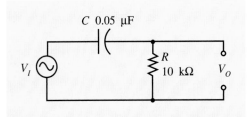

Figure 18-18. What is the cutoff frequency for this circuit?

Practice Problems

1. Determine the cutoff frequency for the *RC* high-pass filter circuit shown in Figure 18-19.
2. If the capacitor in Figure 18-19 were changed to 1.5 µF and the resistor was left as 18 kΩ, what would be the value of cutoff frequency?
3. What value of resistor would be required for a circuit like that shown in Figure 18-19 to produce a cutoff frequency of 250 Hz if the capacitor is 0.05 µF?

Answers to Practice Problems

1. 4.02 kHz   **2.** 5.9 Hz   **3.** 12.74 kΩ

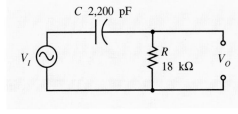

Figure 18-19. Calculate the cutoff frequency for this circuit.

RL Filters

Figure 18-20 shows how an *RL* circuit can provide the response of a high-pass filter. Figure 18-20(a) shows the circuit's response to frequencies below the cutoff frequency (stopband frequencies). In this range, the inductive reactance is less than the resistance, so most of the input voltage is dropped across the resistance; very little voltage appears in the output (across X_L). Figure 18-20(b) shows the circuit response at the cutoff frequency. Since the inductive reactance and the resistance are equal, they will have equal voltage drops (70.7% of the input voltage). Frequencies higher than the cutoff frequency cause the inductive reactance to be higher than the resistance as shown in Figure 18-20(c). In this range (the passband), most of the input voltage is dropped across the inductive reactance, which means that the output voltage nearly equals the input voltage.

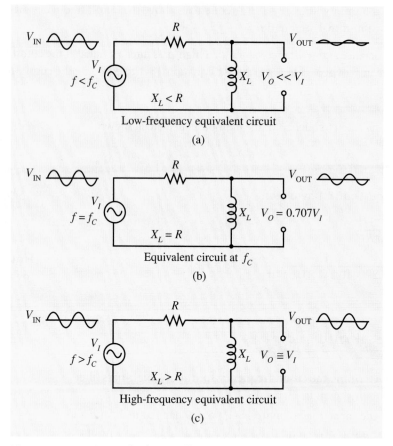

Figure 18-20. An *RL* high-pass filter passes all frequencies above the cutoff frequency.

As with *RL* low-pass filters, the value of inductive reactance is equal to the resistance at the cutoff frequency. This means that we can find the cutoff frequency for an *RL* high-pass filter by applying Equation 18-2.

EXAMPLE SOLUTION

Calculate the cutoff frequency for the *RL* high-pass filter shown in Figure 18-21.

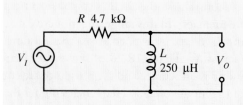

EXAMPLE SOLUTION

We apply Equation 18-2 as follows:

$$f_C = \frac{R}{2\pi L} = \frac{4.7 \text{ k}\Omega}{6.28 \times 250 \text{ }\mu\text{H}} \approx 3 \text{ MHz}$$

Figure 18-21. Calculate the cutoff frequency for this circuit.

Practice Problems

1. Find the cutoff frequency for the high-pass circuit shown in Figure 18-22.
2. If the inductor in Figure 18-22 was changed to 50 µH, what would be the new cutoff frequency?
3. What value of resistance is needed with a 5-mH coil to obtain a 100-kHz cutoff frequency in a filter circuit like the one shown in Figure 18-22?

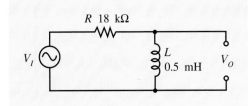

Figure 18-22. Calculate the cutoff frequency for this circuit.

Answers to Practice Problems

1. 5.73 MHz   2. 57.3 MHz   3. 3.14 kΩ

Exercise Problems 18.2

1. Which of the circuits shown in Figure 18-23 will function as high-pass filters?
2. Which of the frequency response curves shown in Figure 18-24 represent the performance of a high-pass filter?
3. Calculate the cutoff frequency for the high-pass filter shown in Figure 18-25.
4. If the values in Figure 18-25 are changed to $R = 47$ kΩ and $C = 1,500$ pF, what is the new cutoff frequency?
5. What value of C must be used in a circuit like Figure 18-25 to provide a 500-kHz cutoff frequency when the resistor value is 270 kΩ?
6. Compute the cutoff frequency for the high-pass filter circuit shown in Figure 18-26.

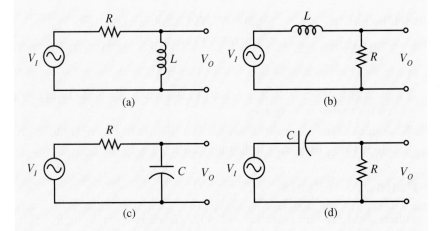

Figure 18-23. Which of these circuits are high-pass filters?

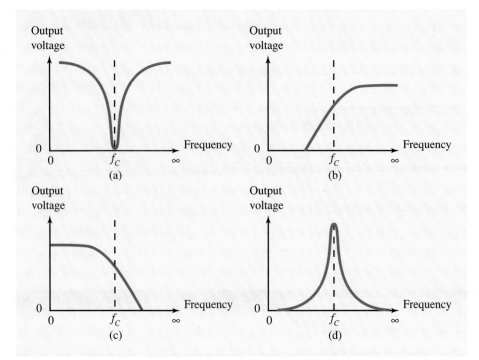

Figure 18-24. Which of these graphs represent the response of a high-pass filter?

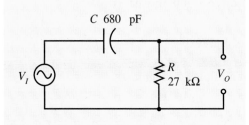

Figure 18-25. What is the cutoff frequency for this circuit?

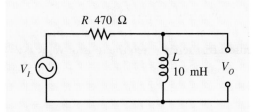

Figure 18-26. Calculate the cutoff frequency for this circuit.

7. If the component values in Figure 18-26 are changed to $R = 6.8\ k\Omega$ and $L = 250\ \mu H$, what is the new cutoff frequency?

8. What value of resistance (R) is needed in a circuit like Figure 18-26 to provide a 12.5-kHz cutoff frequency, if the inductance (L) is 25 mH?

18.3 Bandpass Filters

Bandpass filters allow a certain range or band of frequencies to pass through the filter with minimal attenuation. Frequencies either higher or lower than the passband are attenuated by the filter. Figure 18-27 shows the frequency response curves for an ideal and a practical

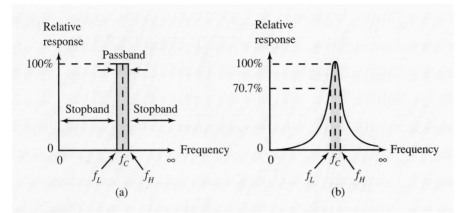

Figure 18-27. The frequency response curves for (a) an ideal and (b) a practical bandpass filter.

bandpass filter. Figure 18-27(a) shows the ideal response to have two cutoff frequencies (f_L and f_H). Input voltages at frequencies lower than f_L are completely eliminated (i.e., they do not appear in the output). Similarly, all frequencies higher than f_H are attenuated and do not appear in the output. By contrast, frequencies within the passband (i.e., higher than f_L and lower than f_H) are passed through the filter with no attenuation.

Figure 18-27(b) shows the frequency response of a practical bandpass filter. Again, there are two cutoff frequencies that set the limits for the passband. However, there is a more gradual transition between the stopband and the passband regions. The edges of the passband are defined as the points where the relative response has fallen to 70.7% of the maximum response. You will recall from Chapter 16 that these points are also called half-power points.

Figure 18-28 illustrates the basic requirements of a bandpass filter circuit. As reflected in Figures 18-28(a) and (c), the series impedance (Z_1) must be greater than the shunt impedance (Z_2) for frequencies outside the passband of the filter. Under these conditions, voltage divider action causes most of the input voltage to be dropped across Z_1. This leaves very little voltage across Z_2 (V_O).

Figure 18-28(b) shows the circuit conditions for frequencies that are within the passband of the filter. Here, the series impedance (Z_1) must be lower than the shunt impedance (Z_2). Voltage divider action causes most of the input voltage to be dropped across Z_2, where it appears as V_O. Ideally, there is no attenuation of input voltages for frequencies in the passband. In practice, there will always be a small voltage drop across Z_1 even in the passband.

Resonant Filters

A bandpass filter can be realized with a series- or parallel-resonant RLC circuit. A more complete mathematical analysis of series-resonant RLC circuits was presented in Chapter 16 and will not be repeated here. Rather, let us concentrate on the general behavior of RLC circuits as it applies to filter applications.

KEY POINTS

Ideally, the transitions between stopband and passband regions are abrupt. Practical filters, however, have more gradual transitions.

KEY POINTS

Bandpass filters can be made with series or parallel RLC circuits.

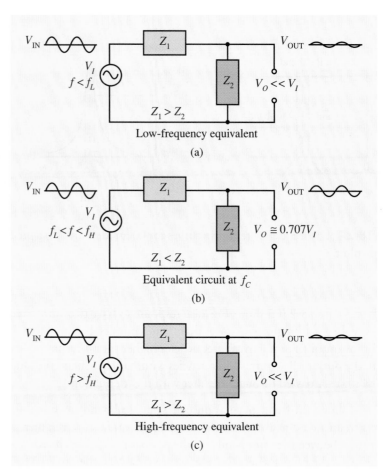

Figure 18-28. The basic requirements for a bandpass filter circuit.

SERIES-RESONANT BANDPASS FILTER

Figure 18-29 shows a series-resonant circuit being used as a bandpass filter. Recall the following important characteristics about a series LC circuit:

- At resonance, the inductive and capacitive reactances are equal and essentially cancel each other. Current is limited only by the resistance in the circuit. The LC portion of the circuit acts like a short circuit.

- Below resonance, the reactance of the capacitor is the dominant factor in determining impedance. As the operating frequency approaches dc, the capacitive reactance approaches infinity. The LC portion of the circuit acts like an open circuit.

- Above resonance, the reactance of the inductor is the dominant factor in determining impedance. As the operating frequency increases, so does the inductive reactance. At sufficiently high frequencies, the inductor and, therefore, the LC portion of the circuit begin to act like an open circuit.

Figure 18-30 illustrates the relative impedances in the RLC circuit at three key frequencies: below resonance, at resonance, and above resonance. At frequencies far below the lower

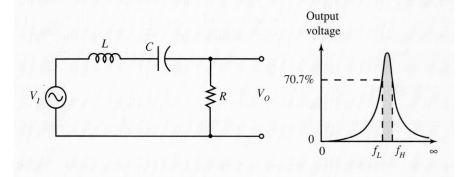

Figure 18-29. A bandpass filter using a series-resonant circuit.

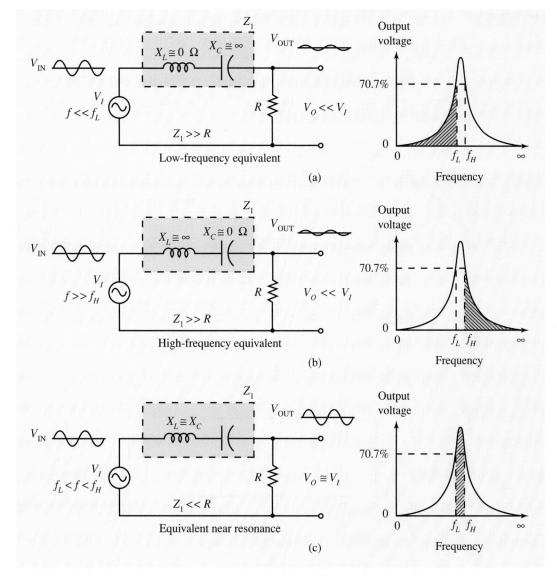

Figure 18-30. Circuit conditions in an *RLC* bandpass filter at three key frequencies.

cutoff frequency, X_C is so high (relative to R) that the net reactance of the LC portion of the circuit is essentially open (i.e., it drops nearly all of the applied voltage). This condition is represented in Figure 18-30(a). A similar condition occurs when the operating frequency is far above the upper cutoff frequency. In this case, as shown in Figure 18-30(b), X_L is so high (relative to R) that the net reactance of the LC portion of the circuit is essentially open and drops nearly all of the input voltage. So, for frequencies outside of the passband, the net reactance of the LC portion of the circuit (Z_1) is high relative to R. Voltage divider action causes most of the input voltage to be dropped across the LC network, leaving near zero to be dropped across R (output voltage).

Figure 18-30(c) shows the circuit conditions for frequencies in the passband of the filter (i.e., above the lower cutoff frequency and below the upper cutoff frequency). In this range, X_L is nearly the same value as X_C. These two reactances effectively cancel each other, leaving a near-zero net reactance for Z_1. Voltage divider action will cause most of the input voltage to be dropped across R. That is, the output voltage is nearly the same as the input voltage for frequencies in the passband. More specifically, as discussed in Chapter 16, the output voltage will be at least 70.7% of the input voltage for frequencies in the passband.

All of the calculations presented in Chapter 16 for series RLC circuits apply to filter circuits like the one shown in Figure 18-29. The output voltage is simply taken across the resistive portion of the circuit.

PARALLEL-RESONANT BANDPASS FILTER

Figure 18-31 shows how a parallel-resonant circuit can be used to implement a bandpass filter. Recall the following important characteristics about a parallel LC network:

- At resonance, the inductive and capacitive currents are equal in magnitude, but they are 180° out of phase. The net reactive current is zero. That is, the LC portion of the circuit acts like an open circuit.

- Below resonance, the inductive reactance is lower than the capacitive reactance and dominates the circuit behavior. At frequencies far below resonance, the LC circuit begins to act as a short circuit due to the relatively low reactance of the inductor.

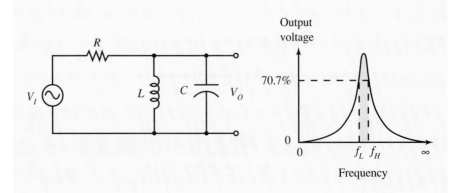

Figure 18-31. A parallel resonant circuit can serve as a bandpass filter.

- Above resonance, the capacitive reactance is lower than the inductive reactance and dominates the circuit characteristics. At frequencies far above resonance, the *LC* circuit begins to act like a short circuit due to the relatively low reactance of the capacitor.

Figure 18-32 shows a bandpass filter circuit at three key frequencies: below resonance, above resonance, and at resonance. At frequencies well below the lower cutoff frequency as shown in Figure 18-32(a), the low value of inductive reactance makes the *LC* portion of the circuit act as a short (i.e., low impedance relative to *R*). Voltage divider action causes most of the input voltage to be dropped across *R*, leaving very little across the *LC* circuit (V_O).

Figure 18-32(b) shows the circuit conditions at frequencies far above the upper cutoff frequency. In this range, the low value of capacitive reactance makes the *LC* portion of the circuit act as a short circuit (relative to *R*). Again, voltage divider action drops most of the input voltage across *R*, and produces an output voltage (V_O) that is greatly attenuated.

Figure 18-32(c) shows the response of the circuit for frequencies within the passband of the filter. In this case, X_L is nearly equal to X_C, and the two reactive currents effectively

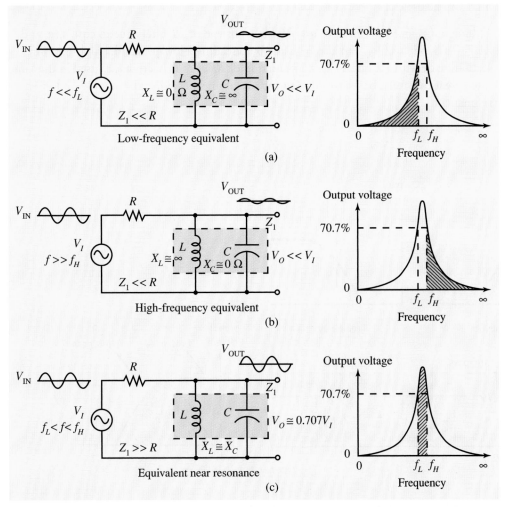

Figure 18-32. Circuit conditions in an RLC circuit at three key frequencies.

KEY POINTS

The cutoff frequency of the low-pass section determines the upper cut-off frequency of the over-all bandpass filter, while the cutoff frequency of the high-pass filter deter-mines the lower cutoff frequency for the overall bandpass filter.

KEY POINTS

The low- and high-pass fil-ter sections can be either RC or RL types, but gener-ally not a combination of the two types, since this could cause undesired res-onant effects.

cancel each other. This means the LC portion of the circuit is acting like an open circuit (i.e., a high impedance relative to R). Voltage divider action causes most of the input voltage to be dropped across the high-impedance LC circuit and very little across R. The output voltage is very near the same as the input voltage. That is, frequencies in the pass-band receive minimal attenuation. By definition, all passband frequencies pass through the filter with an amplitude of at least 70.7% of the input voltage.

RC Bandpass Filters

Since a low-pass filter passes all frequencies below its cutoff frequency and a high-pass filter passes all frequencies above its cutoff frequency, we can cascade a low-pass and a high-pass filter to obtain the frequency response of a bandpass filter. This technique is illustrated in Figure 18-33. The cutoff frequency for the low-pass filter section establishes the upper cutoff frequency (f_H) for the overall bandpass filter. Likewise, the cutoff frequency for the high-pass filter section establishes the lower cutoff frequency (f_L) for the overall filter. Clearly, if the cutoff frequency of the low-pass section is lower than the cutoff frequency of the high-pass section, then all frequencies will be attenuated and the filter will be useless.

Although it is more common to use RC filters instead of RL filters due to cost, size, and weight, a bandpass filter can also be made by cascading a low-pass and a high-pass filter section made with RL filters. If a combination of RL and RC sections are used in the same filter, great care must be used due to the effects of unexpected, and generally undesired, resonances.

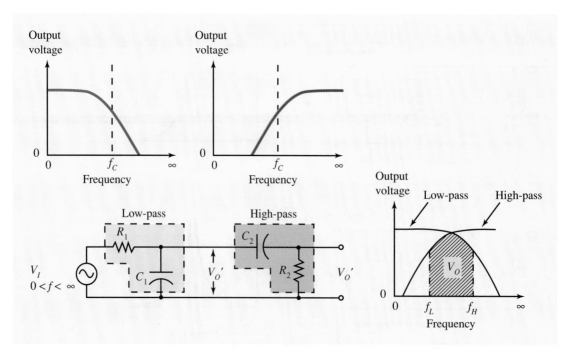

Figure 18-33. A bandpass filter formed by cascading low-pass and high-pass filter sections.

Exercise Problems 18.3

1. Which of the frequency response curves shown in Figure 18-34 represents the performance of a bandpass filter?

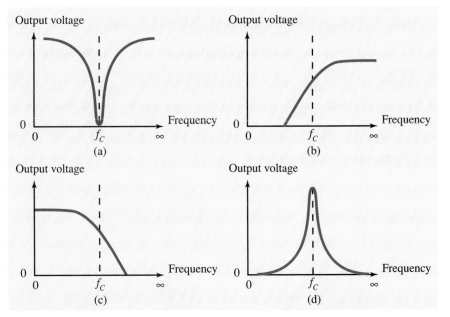

Figure 18-34. Which is the frequency response of a bandpass filter?

2. Which of the circuits shown in Figure 18-35 are bandpass filters?

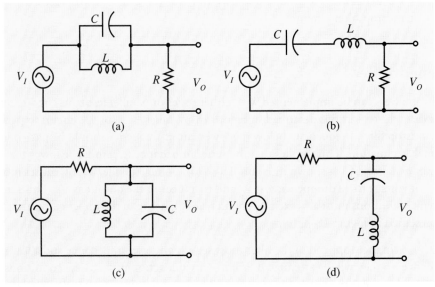

Figure 18-35. Which of these circuits are bandpass filters?

3. If high-pass and low-pass filter sections are cascaded to form a bandpass filter, the cutoff frequency of the high-pass section must be lower than the cutoff frequency of the low-pass section. (True or False)

4. All input frequencies within the passband of a bandpass filter have an amplitude that is at least _____% of the maximum response.

18.4 Bandstop or Band-Reject Filters

A bandstop—also called a band-reject—filter attenuates all frequencies within the stopband of the filter. Frequencies that are lower or higher than the stopband pass through the filter with minimal attenuation. Figure 18-36 shows the frequency responses of both ideal and practical bandstop filters. The ideal filter, represented in Figure 18-36(a), makes an abrupt transition at the cutoff frequencies. Passband signals are passed with no attenuation, whereas stopband signals are reduced to zero. Practical filters, as shown in Figure 18-36(b), have more gradual transitions.

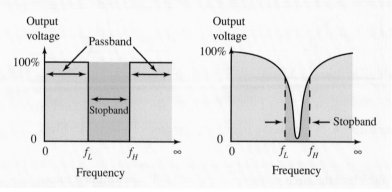

Figure 18-36. Frequency response curves for (a) ideal and (b) practical bandstop filter circuits.

Resonant Filters

Bandstop filters can be implemented with either series or parallel resonant circuits. In either case, the conditions described in Figure 18-37 must exist for the circuit to perform as a bandstop filter. Frequencies below the lower cutoff frequency should be passed with minimal attenuation. This implies that the series impedance (Z_1) must be lower than the shunt impedance (Z_2) as shown in Figure 18-37(a). Voltage divider action causes most of the input voltage to be dropped across Z_2 and to appear in the output as V_O. This same set of circuit conditions must also exist for frequencies higher than the upper cutoff frequency as represented in Figure 18-37(c).

Frequencies in the stopband of the filter must see a high series impedance and a low shunt impedance, so they will be attenuated. Voltage divider action under these conditions causes most of the input voltage to be dropped across Z_1, leaving very little to be dropped across Z_2. The stopband conditions are illustrated in Figure 18-37(b).

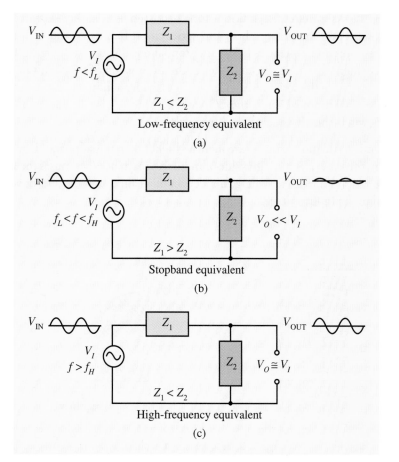

Figure 18-37. Conditions required for a bandstop filter circuit.

SERIES-RESONANT BANDSTOP FILTERS

Figure 18-38 shows a series-resonant circuit configured as a bandstop filter. You will recall that a series LC circuit has a low impedance at resonance and a higher impedance on either side of resonance. This characteristic satisfies the requirements of the shunt impedance (Z_2) in Figure 18-37.

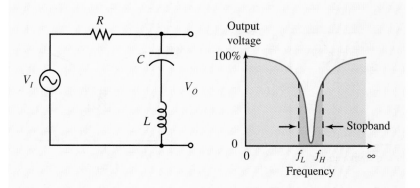

Figure 18-38. A series-resonant circuit can provide a bandstop filter response.

Figure 18-39 shows the circuit conditions for a bandstop filter at three key frequencies: below the lower cutoff frequency, above the upper cutoff frequency, and within the stopband. The response to frequencies below the stopband is illustrated in Figure 18-39(a). The relatively high capacitive reactance causes the LC portion of the circuit to have a high impedance relative to the series resistance. Voltage divider action will cause most of the input voltage to be dropped across the LC network. Since V_O is taken across the LC network, V_O will be nearly equal to the input voltage.

A nearly identical situation exists for frequencies higher than the stopband. Figure 18-39(b) shows that in this case, it is the high value of inductive reactance that causes the LC network (Z_2) to have a high impedance. Voltage divider action again causes the output voltage to be nearly equal to the input voltage.

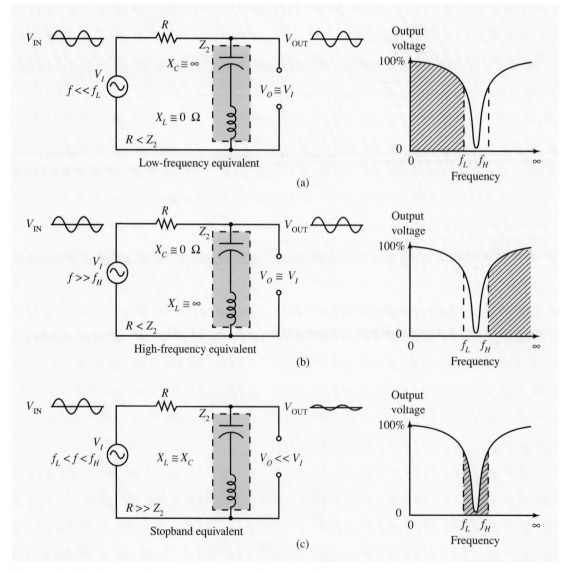

Figure 18-39. The conditions in a bandstop filter at three key frequencies.

Frequencies within the stopband cause nearly equal values for inductive and capacitive reactance. These out-of-phase components tend to cancel each other, which produces an overall low impedance for the LC network (Z_2). The LC network approximates a short circuit. This condition is represented in Figure 18-39(c). Voltage divider action in this case causes most of the input voltage to be dropped across the series resistance, which greatly attenuates the output voltage. Output voltages within the stopband will be reduced to 70.7% or less of the maximum response.

All of the calculations presented in Chapter 16 for series RLC circuits apply to filter circuits like the one shown in Figure 18-38. The output voltage is simply taken across the LC portion of the circuit.

PARALLEL-RESONANT BANDSTOP FILTERS

Figure 18-40 shows how a parallel-resonant circuit can be used to implement a bandstop filter. You will recall that a parallel LC circuit has a high impedance at resonance and a lower impedance on either side of resonance. This characteristic satisfies the requirements of the series impedance (Z_1) in Figure 18-37.

Figure 18-41 shows the circuit conditions for a bandstop filter at three key frequencies: below the lower cutoff frequency, above the upper cutoff frequency, and within the stopband. The response to frequencies below the stopband is illustrated in Figure 18-41(a). The relatively low inductive reactance causes the LC portion of the circuit to have a low impedance relative to the resistance (R). Voltage divider action will cause most of the input voltage to be dropped across the resistance. Since V_O is taken across the resistor, V_O will be nearly equal to the input voltage.

A nearly identical situation exists for frequencies higher than the stopband. Figure 18-41(b) shows that in this case, it is the low value of capacitive reactance that causes the LC network to have a low impedance. Voltage divider action again causes the output voltage to be nearly equal to the input voltage.

Frequencies within the stopband cause nearly equal values for inductive and capacitive reactance. The currents through these two reactances tend to cancel each other, which

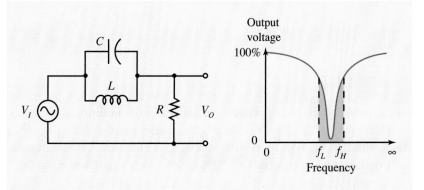

Figure 18-40. A parallel-resonant circuit can provide a bandstop filter response.

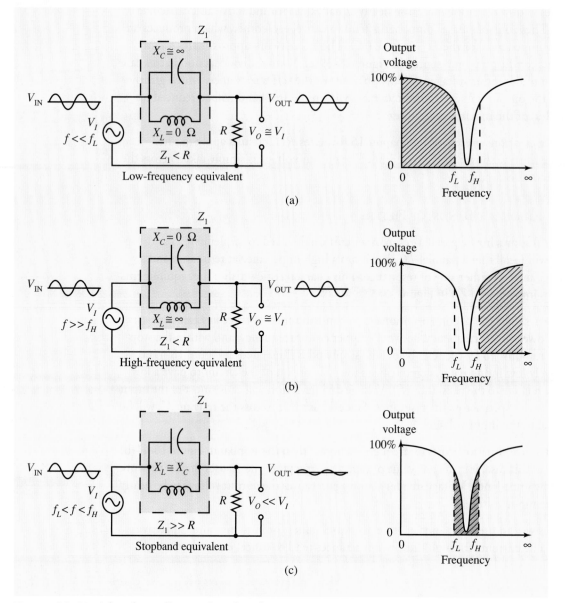

Figure 18-41. A bandstop filter at three key frequencies.

means the *LC* network acts much like an open circuit. This condition is represented in Figure 18-41(c). Voltage divider action in this case causes most of the input voltage to be dropped across the *LC* network. Very little voltage is available as V_O. Output voltages within the stopband will be reduced to 70.7% or less of the maximum response.

All of the calculations presented in Chapter 16 for series-parallel *RLC* circuits apply to filter circuits like the one shown in Figure 18-40. The output voltage is simply taken across the resistive portion of the circuit.

RC Bandstop Filters

In a previous section, we saw that an *RC* bandpass filter could be constructed by cascading low-pass and high-pass filter sections. In a similar manner, an *RC* bandstop filter can be constructed by connecting low-pass and high-pass filter sections in parallel. In this way, frequencies lower or higher than the stopband can pass easily through the low-pass or high-pass filter section, respectively. Those frequencies that are stopped by both filter sections will not appear in the output. Figure 18-42 shows the schematic diagram of an *RC* bandstop filter. This particular configuration is called a twin-tee network. It gets its name from the two *RC* tee networks. A similar filter function can be realized with *RL* circuits, but it is not normally done due to cost, weight, and physical size.

● **KEY POINTS**

A twin-tee filter is an *RC* circuit that provides a notch filter frequency response.

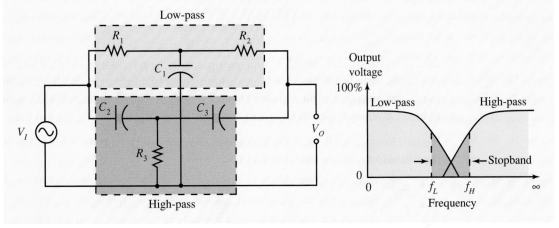

Figure 18-42. A notch filter attenuates a very narrow band of frequencies.

In Figure 18-42, the network consisting of R_1, R_2, and C_1 is, by itself, a low-pass filter. C_1 has a high reactance to low frequencies and allows the signal to pass. High-frequencies, by contrast, are shorted to ground by C_1.

The C_2, C_3, and R_3 network is, by itself, a high-pass filter. The low reactances of C_2 and C_3 pass high frequencies through to the output with minimal attenuation. These same capacitors are effective open circuits for low frequencies and prevent the passage of low-frequency signals.

The actual operation of the circuit is somewhat more complex and nearly achieves total attenuation of one particular frequency. Because the circuit is so selective, it is sometimes called a **notch filter**. The frequency at the center of the notch receives the most attenuation.

At the notch frequency, the reactance of C_1 is equal to the resistance of R_3, and the reactances of C_2 and C_3 are equal to the resistances of R_1 and R_2. This means that the high-pass and low-pass networks will provide equal attenuation to input voltages at the notch frequency. Additionally, notch-frequency input voltage will receive equal but opposite phase shifts from the two networks. The net result is that notch-frequency input voltages are almost completely cancelled at the output of the filter. For frequencies on either side of the notch frequency, attenuation is less. Figure 18-43 shows the frequency response curve

● **KEY POINTS**

A notch filter is essentially a bandstop filter, but it has a very narrow bandwidth (high *Q*).

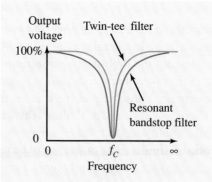

Figure 18-43. The frequency response of a twin-tee notch filter has a very narrow bandwidth.

for a practical twin-tee notch filter as compared to the response of a typical resonant band-stop filter. Both filters have the same center frequency, but the notch filter clearly has a narrower bandwidth. You will recall from Chapter 16 that the narrow bandwidth of the twin-tee filter corresponds to a relatively high Q ($Q = f_R/BW$).

Figure 18-44 shows the schematic diagram of a twin-tee notch filter. For proper operation, the following relationships must exist:

- $R_1 = R_2$
- $R_1 = 2R_3$
- $C_2 = C_3$
- $C_1 = 2C_2$

With these circuit relationships, the center frequency of the filter may be computed with Equation 18-3.

$$f_N = \frac{1}{2\pi R_1 C_2} \qquad (18\text{-}3)$$

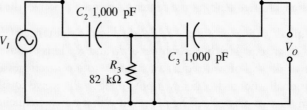

Figure 18-44. The schematic diagram of a twin-tee notch filter.

EXAMPLE SOLUTION

Determine the notch frequency for the twin-tee filter shown in Figure 18-44.

EXAMPLE **SOLUTION**

Since the component relationships satisfy the previously stated requirements, we can apply Equation 18-3 to compute the notch frequency.

$$f_N = \frac{1}{2\pi R_1 C_2}$$

$$= \frac{1}{6.28 \times 164 \text{ k}\Omega \times 1,000 \text{ pF}} = 971 \text{ Hz}$$

Practice Problems

1. Compute the notch frequency for a circuit like the one shown in Figure 18-44, if the circuit has the following component values: $R_1 = R_2 = 300 \text{ k}\Omega$, $R_3 = 150 \text{ k}\Omega$, $C_1 = 470 \text{ pF}$, $C_2 = C_3 = 235 \text{ pF}$.
2. If a twin-tee filter like the one shown in Figure 18-44 has a value of 75 Ω for R_3, what is the value of R_1?
3. What is the notch frequency of a circuit like that shown in Figure 18-44 if it has the following component values: $R_1 = R_2 = 1.5 \text{ k}\Omega$, $R_3 = 750 \text{ }\Omega$, $C_1 = 2.0 \text{ }\mu\text{F}$, $C_2 = C_3 = 1.0 \text{ }\mu\text{F}$?

Answers to Practice Problems

1. 2.26 kHz   2. 150 Ω 3. 106.2 Hz

Exercise Problems 18.4

1. Which of the frequency response curves shown in Figure 18-45 represents the performance of a bandstop filter?
2. Which of the circuits shown in Figure 18-46 are bandstop filters?
3. All input frequencies within the stopband of a bandstop filter have an amplitude that is at least 70.7% of the maximum response. (True or False)
4. A notch filter is generally characterized by a wide bandwidth. (True or False)
5. A twin-tee notch filter passes a narrow band of frequencies, but attenuates frequencies either higher or lower than the passband. (True or False)

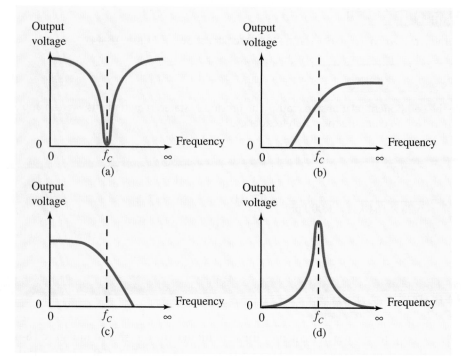

Figure 18-45. Which is the frequency response of a bandstop filter?

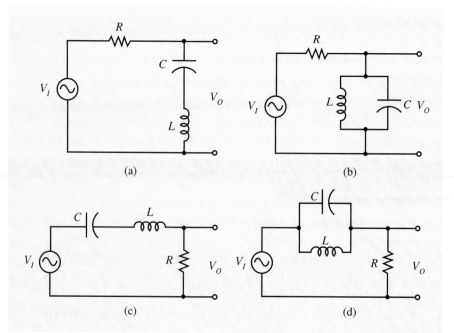

Figure 18-46. Which of these circuits are bandstop filters?

18.5 Applied Technology: Coupling and Decoupling Circuits

For proper operation of an electronic system, signal voltages must be routed to specified parts of the circuit and excluded from other parts. The routing of the signal voltages is often based on the frequency of the signal. In these cases, the routing can be done with filter circuits. We will now examine two common forms of signal routing: coupling and decoupling. Both of these techniques are used in nearly all nontrivial electronic systems.

Coupling Circuits

Coupling circuits provide a path for signal voltages to go between two points in the circuit, *neither of which is ground*. Figure 18-47 illustrates the basic function of a coupling circuit.

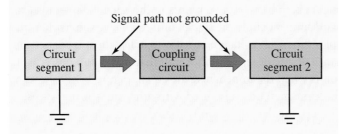

Figure 18-47. A coupling circuit provides passage for signal voltages between two nonground points.

KEY POINTS

Coupling circuits provide a low-impedance path between two points, neither of which is grounded.

CAPACITIVE COUPLING

One of the most common type of coupling circuit is capacitive coupling. It consists simply of connecting a capacitor between the two points to be coupled. Figure 18-48 illustrates capacitive coupling.

Examination of Figure 18-48 will show that signal voltages will be readily coupled from circuit segment 1 to circuit segment 2 as long as the capacitor has a low reactance

KEY POINTS

Capacitive coupling circuits are essentially high-pass filters.

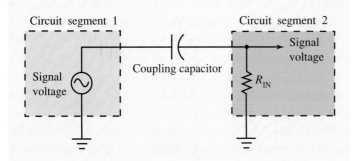

Figure 18-48. Capacitive coupling provides a signal path between two ungrounded points in a circuit.

compared to the resistance value of R_{IN}. R_{IN} is the effective resistance of circuit segment 2. Under these conditions, voltage divider action will cause most of the signal voltage to be developed across R_{IN}. You will recognize the *RC* portion of Figure 18-48 as a high-pass filter. That is, as the signal frequency decreases, the reactance of the coupling capacitor will increase. When the capacitive reactance is larger than the resistance (R_{IN}), then the circuit no longer serves as a good coupling circuit. Most of the signal voltage will be dropped across the coupling capacitor. Proper operation of a capacitive coupling circuit is assured by selecting a value of capacitor that will effectively couple the lowest frequency that is expected. If it couples adequately at the lowest frequency, then it will couple even better at higher frequencies where the capacitive reactance is even lower.

TRANSFORMER COUPLING

Another popular coupling circuit is illustrated in Figure 18-49. Here, a transformer is used to provide the signal path between two points in the circuit. The transformer may have a 1:1 turns ratio and simply couple the signal, or it may have some other turns ratio, so that it not only couples the signal voltages, but also matches the impedance of circuit segment 1 to the impedance of circuit segment 2. Recall that maximum power is transferred between two points when the impedances are equal. Figure 18-49 shows an iron-core transformer. The same method is also used with other transformer types. The best transformer choice for a particular application is based on frequency.

Regardless of the specific transformer type selected, the coupling circuit will be frequency selective (i.e., it acts like a filter circuit). The most obvious frequency selectivity of a transformer occurs as the frequency decreases. Recall that transformer operation is based on magnetic coupling. The voltage in the secondary exists because the winding is being cut by the magnetic flux lines of the primary. If the frequency is too low, then the voltage in the secondary falls off. At 0 Hz (i.e., dc), there is no relative movement of the magnetic flux and virtually no coupling between the primary and secondary. In this regard, the transformer acts like a high-pass filter.

If we study the circuit even more closely, we will recall that stray capacitance exists between the primary and secondary windings and between the turns on a given winding. The primary-to-secondary capacitance tends to bypass the transformer at high frequencies. The capacitance between adjacent turns on a given winding can cause the transformer to

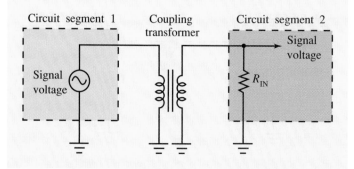

Figure 18-49. A transformer can couple a signal between two ungrounded points in a circuit.

become resonant at some frequency. The effects of parasitic capacitance cause the frequency response of the transformer to deviate from a normal low-pass filter curve. The exact response is highly dependent on the type of transformer. In noncritical applications, the effects of winding capacitance can often be ignored.

Decoupling Circuits

A **decoupling circuit** provides a low-impedance path between an ungrounded point and a grounded point in a circuit. Figure 18-50 illustrates a capacitive decoupling circuit. You will recognize the circuit in Figure 18-50 as a low-pass filter. As long as the signal frequencies are higher than the cutoff frequency of the filter, then minimal voltage (ideally zero) will be dropped across the decoupling capacitor. Since the voltage for circuit segment 2 is taken across the decoupling capacitor (i.e., parallel networks have equal voltage drops), there will be minimal signal voltage available at circuit segment 2. For proper operation, the decoupling capacitor must be selected such that it provides a low-impedance path to the lowest frequency that is to be decoupled. Higher frequencies will be attenuated even more.

The preceding discussion is based on the behavior of an ideal capacitor. You will recall that a practical capacitor has parasitic inductance (ESL) and resistance (ESR) associated with it. These parasitic components appear to be in series with the capacitor. Thus, the capacitor actually behaves like a series *RLC* circuit and exhibits resonance at some specific frequency. Above this self-resonant frequency, the capacitor behaves more like an inductor than a capacitor. It loses its value as a decoupling circuit for frequencies higher than the self-resonant frequency. For this reason, it is important to use the shortest possible leads on decoupling capacitors, since less lead inductance makes the resonant frequency higher.

Many digital circuits contain literally hundreds of integrated circuit packages. It is common design practice to provide a decoupling capacitor immediately adjacent to the power lead of each integrated circuit. The capacitor permits the dc supply voltage (i.e., low frequency) to pass with no attenuation. High-frequency switching noise generated within the integrated circuit, however, finds a low-reactance path through the decoupling capacitor to ground. This keeps the high-frequency noise from traveling to other portions of the circuit and interfering with proper operation.

● **KEY POINTS**

Decoupling circuits provide a low-impedance point between ground and an ungrounded point in the circuit.

● **KEY POINTS**

Capacitive decoupling circuits are essentially low-pass filters.

● **KEY POINTS**

Effectiveness of decoupling capacitors is improved by using the shortest possible leads to minimize parasitic inductance.

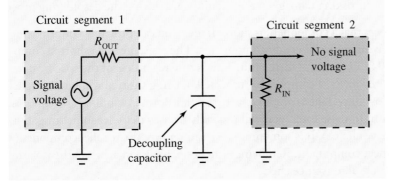

Figure 18-50. A decoupling circuit provides a low-impedance connection between an ungrounded and a ground point in a circuit.

1. Coupling circuits provide a low-impedance path between two ungrounded points in a circuit. (True or False)

2. Decoupling circuits provide a low-impedance path between two grounded points in a circuit. (True or False)

3. A coupling capacitor is selected to have a low reactance at the (*lowest, highest*) expected frequency. This ensures effective coupling at all other signal frequencies.

4. A capacitive coupling circuit is essentially a _____-pass filter.

5. A capacitive decoupling circuit is essentially a _____-pass filter.

18.6 Troubleshooting Passive Filter Circuits

Filter circuits are simply applications of *RLC*, *RL*, and *RC* circuits. Therefore, troubleshooting filter circuits is identical to troubleshooting any other comparable *RLC*, *RL*, or *RC* circuit. Filter-circuit defects include the following possibilities:

- open coil, capacitor, or resistor
- shorted coil, capacitor, or resistor
- wrong value coil, capacitor, or resistor
- intermittent or deteriorated component (e.g., leaky capacitor, poor solder joint).

Diagnosis of each of these defects has been discussed in preceding chapters and will not be repeated here. Rather, we shall provide you some technician troubleshooting tips that can speed your troubleshooting procedure.

○ **KEY POINTS**

Confirmation of suspected opens can be readily accomplished without desoldering by bridging the suspected component with a good component.

First, if you suspect an open component, then simply bridge across the suspected component with a known good one *without removing the "bad" component*. If the suspected device is actually defective, then the bridging will correct the problem. You can then spend the time necessary for desoldering and resoldering the components. If the problem still exists with the bridged component in place, then the suspected component is good (or there are multiple defects in the circuit). Bridging provides a quick way to diagnose this type of defect without risking damage to the circuit board during the desoldering process.

If you suspect that a component is shorted, then you can probably confirm your suspicions without having to desolder any components. The resistance of a shorted component will read near 0 Ω in or out of the circuit. This is true regardless of the specific circuit being tested. Occasionally, a component suspected of being shorted will be in parallel with a normally low impedance component (e.g., a transformer winding), which causes a sneak current path. In these cases, you will probably have to desolder something, but remember that you have choices. It is sometimes easier to remove the parallel component than the actual suspect component. Removing either one, however, achieves the isolation needed for a meaningful resistance check.

○ **KEY POINTS**

Shorted components can generally be detected in the circuit without desoldering.

Intermittent connections or poor solder joints are sometimes very difficult to locate in any circuit. They are often susceptible to mechanical shock or movement. Your goal is to move or vibrate individual joints while keeping all others still. This can be physically hard to do. One method used by many technicians is to use a pencil with a rubber eraser. By gently tapping or pressing with the eraser on various connections, you can stress one joint or area of the circuit board without stressing or jarring nearby areas. You must be particularly careful not to use a conductive probe to press on the board. It can slip, cause a short, and ultimately damage the circuit even more. Even a pencil may have a metal band near the eraser that demands care in use to avoid unexpected shorts.

Exercise Problems 18.6

1. Diagnosis of filter circuit defects requires specialized test equipment. (True or False)
2. Which of the following filter defects can be located by component bridging?
   a. open coil
   b. shorted capacitor
   c. incorrect resistor value
   d. open resistor
   e. leaky capacitor
   f. open capacitor
   g. primary-to-secondary transformer short
3. When stressing printed-circuit-board connections to reveal a loose or intermittent connection, why is it important to use localized force to stress the connection?

Chapter Summary

- Filter circuits are used to selectively pass (passband) or reject (stopband) signal voltages based on their relative frequencies. Frequencies in the passband of a filter produce an output response that is at least 70.7% of the maximum response (ideally 100%). Frequencies in the stopband, by contrast, produce output responses less than 70.7% of the maximum response (ideally zero). The point between the passband(s) and stopband(s) is called the half-power point. It occurs at the cutoff frequency of the filter. The cutoff frequency produces an output response that is 70.7% of the maximum response.

- Low-pass filter circuits pass all frequencies below the cutoff frequency of the filter. Frequencies higher than the cutoff frequency are attenuated. The stopband for high-pass filters is defined as all frequencies below the cutoff frequency. The passband for high-pass filters consists of all frequencies above the cutoff frequency. High- and low-pass filters can be constructed from either RC or RL circuits.

- Bandpass filters have two stopbands separated by a passband. This type of filter passes those frequencies that lie between the upper and lower cutoff frequency, but attenuates frequencies outside of this passband. Bandstop filters reject (i.e., attenuate) all frequencies that lie between the upper and lower cutoff frequency. Frequencies lower than the lower cutoff frequency or higher than the upper cutoff frequency are passed with minimal attenuation. Bandstop filters can utilize series- or parallel-resonant circuits. They can also be realized with RC or RL networks.

- A special subclass of bandstop filters called notch filters have very narrow bandwidths. A narrow band of frequencies receives maximum attenuation, but frequencies on either side of this stopband have minimal attenuation.

• Coupling and decoupling of signal voltages are two important filter applications. A coupling circuit provides a low-impedance path between two ungrounded points in a circuit. A decoupling circuit provides a low-impedance path between a grounded point and an ungrounded point in a circuit. Capacitive coupling circuits are high-pass filters. Capacitive decoupling circuits are low-pass filters.

• Troubleshooting of passive filter circuits can be accomplished using the same techniques used for other *RC*, *RL*, and *RLC* circuits. Component bridging can help confirm an open component without desoldering. Localized board flexing can be used to identify loose connections or bad solder joints.

Review Questions

Section 18.1: Low-Pass Filters

1. Low-pass filters have two cutoff frequencies. (True or False)

2. The output response is 70.7% or more of the maximum response for frequencies higher than the cutoff frequency in a low-pass filter. (True or False)

3. The passband of a low-pass filter ideally extends to dc. (True or False)

4. The stopband of a low-pass filter ideally extends to an infinite frequency. (True or False)

5. The output response of a low-pass filter is 3 dB lower than the maximum response at the cutoff frequency. (True or False)

6. In most cases, a steeper slope on the frequency response curve is desired for a low-pass filter. (True or False)

7. In order for the circuit represented in Figure 18-51 to function as a low-pass filter, Z_1 must be (*less than, greater than, equal to*) Z_2 for all frequencies above the cutoff frequency.

8. In order for the circuit represented in Figure 18-51 to function as a low-pass filter, Z_1 must be (*less than, greater than, equal to*) Z_2 for all frequencies below the cutoff frequency.

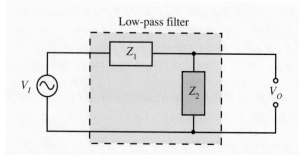

Figure 18-51. A low-pass filter diagram.

9. In order for the circuit represented in Figure 18-51 to function as a low-pass filter, Z_1 must be (*less than, greater than, equal to*) Z_2 at the cutoff frequency.

10. Figure 18-52 shows the frequency response curve for a low-pass filter. Match the following terms to the correct labeled point in Figure 18-52:
    Cutoff frequency_____
    Stopband_____
    Passband_____
    Half-power point_____

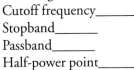

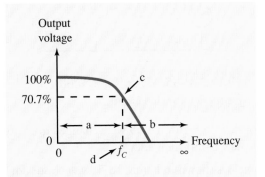

Figure 18-52. Identify the labeled points.

11. The circuit shown in Figure 18-53 is a low-pass filter. (True or False)

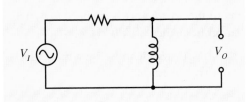

Figure 18-53. Is this a low-pass filter circuit?

12. Calculate the cutoff frequency for the circuit shown in Figure 18-54.

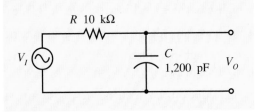

Figure 18-54. What is the cutoff frequency for this circuit?

13. If the component values in Figure 18-54 were changed to $R = 270$ kΩ and $C = 470$ pF, what would be the new cutoff frequency?

14. If the component values shown in Figure 18-54 were both doubled, the cutoff frequency would (*increase, decrease, remain the same*).

15. At frequencies above the cutoff frequency, the resistance in Figure 18-54 is greater than the capacitive reactance. (True or False)

16. Calculate the cutoff frequency for the circuit shown in Figure 18-55.

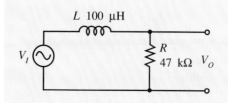

Figure 18-55. What is the cutoff frequency for this circuit?

17. If the component values in Figure 18-55 were changed to $R = 680\ \Omega$ and $L = 25$ mH, what would be the new cutoff frequency?

18. If the component values shown in Figure 18-55 were both doubled, the cutoff frequency would (*increase, decrease, remain the same*).

19. At frequencies below the cutoff frequency, the reactance of the coil in Figure 18-55 is less than the value of the resistor. (True or False)

20. Refer to Figure 18-55. If the resistance is changed to 12 kΩ, what value inductance is required to have a cutoff frequency of 50 kHz?

21. Refer to Figure 18-54. If the capacitance is changed to 470 pF, what value resistance is required to have a cutoff frequency of 780 kHz?

22. A low-pass filter with a 10-dB/decade roll-off is a more ideal filter than one that has a 40-dB/decade roll-off. (True or False)

Section 18.2: High-Pass Filters

23. High-pass filters have two cutoff frequencies. (True or False)

24. The output response is 70.7% or more of the maximum response for frequencies higher than the cutoff frequency in a high-pass filter. (True or False)

25. The passband of a high-pass filter ideally extends to dc. (True or False)

26. The stopband of a high-pass filter ideally extends to an infinite frequency. (True or False)

27. The output response of a high-pass filter is 3 dB lower than the maximum response at the cutoff frequency. (True or False)

28. In most cases, a steeper slope on the frequency response curve is desired for a high-pass filter. (True or False)

29. In order for the circuit represented in Figure 18-56 to function as a high-pass filter, Z_1 must be (*less than, greater than, equal to*) Z_2 for all frequencies above the cutoff frequency.

30. In order for the circuit represented in Figure 18-56 to function as a high-pass filter, Z_1 must be (*less than, greater than, equal to*) Z_2 for all frequencies below the cutoff frequency.

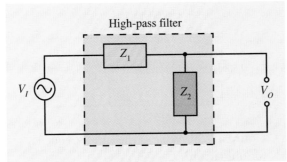

Figure 18-56. A high-pass filter diagram.

31. In order for the circuit represented in Figure 18-56 to function as a high-pass filter, Z_1 must be (*less than, greater than, equal to*) Z_2 at the cutoff frequency.

32. Figure 18-57 shows the frequency response curve for a high-pass filter. Match the following terms to the correct labeled point in Figure 18-57:
    Cutoff frequency   _____
    Stopband   _____
    Passband   _____
    Half-power point   _____

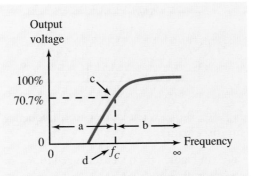

Figure 18-57. Identify the labeled points.

33. The circuit shown in Figure 18-58 is a high-pass filter. (True or False)

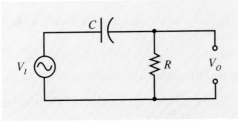

Figure 18-58. Is this a high-pass filter circuit?

34. Calculate the cutoff frequency for the circuit shown in Figure 18-59.

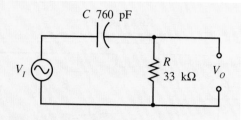

Figure 18-59. What is the cutoff frequency for this circuit?

35. If the component values in Figure 18-59 were changed to $R = 470$ kΩ and $C = 1,000$ pF, what would be the new cutoff frequency?

36. If the component values shown in Figure 18-59 were both doubled, the cutoff frequency would (*increase, decrease, remain the same*).

37. At frequencies above the cutoff frequency, the resistance in Figure 18-59 is greater than the capacitive reactance. (True or False)

38. Calculate the cutoff frequency for the circuit shown in Figure 18-60.

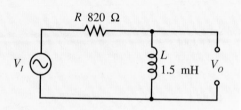

Figure 18-60. What is the cutoff frequency for this circuit?

39. If the component values in Figure 18-60 were changed to $R = 200$ kΩ and $L = 100$ mH, what would be the new cutoff frequency?

40. If the component values shown in Figure 18-60 were both doubled, the cutoff frequency would (*increase, decrease, remain the same*).

41. At frequencies below the cutoff frequency, the reactance of the coil in Figure 18-60 is less than the value of the resistor. (True or False)

42. Refer to Figure 18-60. If the resistance is changed to 47 kΩ, what value inductance is required to have a cutoff frequency of 75 kHz?

43. Refer to Figure 18-59. If the capacitance is changed to 470 pF, what value resistance is required to have a cutoff frequency of 2.5 kHz?

44. A high-pass filter with a 12-dB/octave roll-off is a more ideal filter than one that has a 6-dB/octave roll-off. (True or False)

Section 18.3: Bandpass Filters

45. Bandpass filters have two cutoff frequencies. (True or False)

46. Bandpass filters attenuate all frequencies above the upper cutoff frequency. (True or False)

47. Frequencies lower than the lower cutoff frequency pass through a bandpass filter with minimal attenuation. (True or False)

48. Bandpass filters provide minimal attenuation for frequencies within the passband. (True or False)

49. If the circuit in Figure 18-61 is a bandpass filter, then Z_1 must be greater than Z_2 for frequencies within the passband. (True or False)

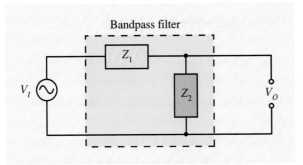

Figure 18-61. A bandpass filter diagram.

50. Z_1 must be greater than Z_2 in Figure 18-61 for frequencies in the stopband. (True or False)

51. If Z_1 and Z_2 in Figure 18-61 are equal, what can be said about the input frequency?

52. The circuit shown in Figure 18-62 is a bandpass filter. (True or False)

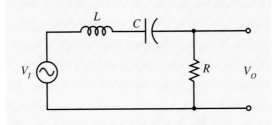

Figure 18-62. Is this a bandpass filter?

53. For frequencies below the lower cutoff frequency, the capacitive reactance in Figure 18-63 is greater than the inductive reactance. (True or False)

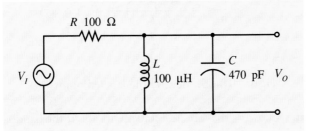

Figure 18-63. A bandpass filter.

54. The capacitive reactance in Figure 18-63 is equal to the inductive reactance at the center frequency of the passband. (True or False)

55. Compute the center frequency of the passband for the circuit shown in Figure 18-63.

56. If the series resistance (R) is doubled in value for the circuit shown in Figure 18-63, does the center frequency of the filter change?

57. Compute the center frequency for the circuit shown in Figure 18-64.

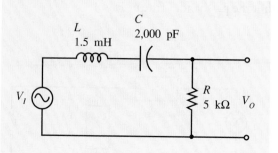

Figure 18-64. A filter circuit.

58. At frequencies in the passband of the circuit in Figure 18-64, the value of resistance is greater than the net reactance. (True or False)

59. At frequencies higher than the upper cutoff frequency in Figure 18-64, the combined reactance of L and C is greater than the value of resistance (R). (True or False)

60. Figure 18-65 shows the frequency response curve for a bandpass filter. Match the following terms to the correct labeled point in Figure 18-65:

    Cutoff frequencies_____

    Stopband_____

    Passband_____

    Half-power points_____

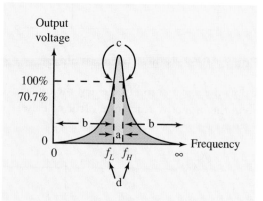

Figure 18-65. Identify the labeled points

61. Circle all of the following that are true statements about the bandpass filter shown in Figure 18-66.

    a. Resistor R_1 must be greater than resistor R_2

    b. Capacitor C_1 must be the same size as capacitor C_2.

c. The cutoff frequency of the R_1C_1 network must be the same as the cutoff frequency of the R_2C_2 network.

d. The cutoff frequency of the R_1C_1 network must be higher than the cutoff frequency of the R_2C_2 network.

e. This circuit cannot be used as a bandpass filter.

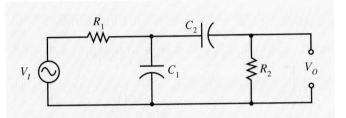

Figure 18-66. A possible filter circuit.

Section 18.4: Bandstop or Band-Reject Filters

62. Frequencies within the stopband of a bandstop filter receive minimal attenuation. (True or False)

63. Frequencies above the upper cutoff frequency receive minimal attenuation in a bandstop filter. (True or False)

64. Frequencies below the lower cutoff frequency receive minimal attenuation in a bandstop filter. (True or False)

65. A notch filter has a wider bandwidth than most bandstop filters.

66. An ideal bandstop filter would have a roll-off of 3 dB/decade. (True or False)

67. In order for the circuit shown in Figure 18-67 to function as a bandstop filter, Z_1 must be greater than Z_2 in the passband of the filter. (True or False)

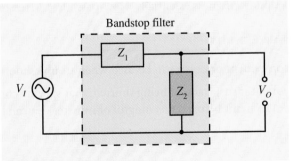

Figure 18-67. A bandstop filter.

68. Z_1 in Figure 18-67 must be greater than Z_2 for all frequencies higher than the lower cutoff frequency. (True or False)

69. Z_1 in Figure 18-67 must be greater than Z_2 for all frequencies higher than the upper cutoff frequency. (True or False)

70. If Z_1 has the same impedance as Z_2 in Figure 18-67, then the circuit is operating at a cutoff frequency. (True or False)

71. What is the name of the circuit configuration shown in Figure 18-68?

72. Calculate the center frequency of the circuit shown in Figure 18-68.

73. What value of resistance is required for R_2 in Figure 18-68 if the cutoff frequency is changed to 12 kHz? Assume the capacitor values remain unchanged.

74. The circuit shown in Figure 18-68 is characterized by a wide bandwidth. (True or False)

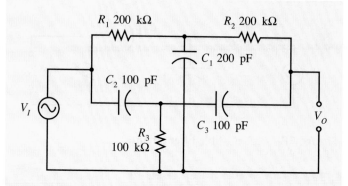

Figure 18-68. A filter circuit.

Section 18.5: Applied Technology: Coupling and Decoupling Circuits

75. A circuit that provides a low-impedance path between a grounded point and an ungrounded point in a circuit is called a coupling circuit. (True or False)

76. A typical decoupling circuit consists of a capacitor connected between ground and the point to be decoupled. (True or False)

77. Name an advantage of transformer coupling circuits over capacitive coupling circuits.

78. What is meant by the term *self-resonant frequency* with reference to capacitors?

79. Decoupling capacitors should always have the shortest possible leads. (True or False)

80. A capacitive coupling circuit is essentially a low-pass filter. (True or False)

Section 18.6: Troubleshooting Passive Filter Circuits

81. Discuss how component bridging can be used when troubleshooting a filter circuit.

82. When a component is suspected of being shorted, that specific component must be removed from the circuit before a meaningful ohmmeter test can be done. (True or False)

TECHNICIAN CHALLENGE

Following is a brief description of several filter applications. Based on the descriptions and your knowledge of filter circuits, select the type of circuit that should be used for each application. You may choose from any of the following filter types:

- low-pass
- high-pass
- bandpass
- bandstop
- notch

APPLICATION 1   The electrical system on an automobile is generating high-frequency noise that is interfering with radio reception. You have determined that the noise is getting to the radio circuit via the +12-Vdc power wire. What type of filter circuit can you put in the dc power wire to attenuate the interference?

APPLICATION 2   Individual stages in a multistage transistor audio-frequency amplifier circuit require dc voltages to operate, but the dc voltages in one stage are often different from the dc voltages in a subsequent stage. What type of filter could be used between successive stages to pass the audio signal but block the dc voltages?

APPLICATION 3   A composite television signal has both picture and sound information, but they are at different frequencies. The sound and picture information in the received signal must be split apart and processed by separate circuits. If the sound information is allowed to travel to the picture circuits, then picture distortion results. The sound information is contained in a well-defined band of frequencies. What kind of filter could be placed at the input of the picture circuits that would eliminate the sound information, but would allow information at all other frequencies to pass?

APPLICATION 4   The audio amplifier circuitry for a magnetic tape player is very sensitive, since it must respond to very small signals. Unfortunately, this high sensitivity can lead to problems if the 60-Hz power-line noise is allowed to get into the input amplifier circuitry. Normal audio signals range from 20 Hz to at least 15 kHz. Unfortunately, 60 Hz is in this band of desired frequencies. What type of filter could be used to attenuate 60-Hz noise and still pass most of the desired signals with minimal attenuation?

APPLICATION 5   You have an inexpensive transistor radio that has a "tinny" sound. You believe the radio would sound less annoying if the higher audio frequencies were prevented from reaching the speaker. What type of filter could be connected in line with the speaker to solve this problem?

Equation List

(18-1) $f_C = \dfrac{1}{2\pi RC}$

(18-2) $f_C = \dfrac{R}{2\pi L}$

(18-3) $f_N = \dfrac{1}{2\pi R_1 C_2}$

appendix A

PShooter Measurement Values

1. 54.4 k	33. 51.7 k	65. 4.7 k	97. 4.7 k
2. 50	34. 0.5 μ	66. 120	98. low
3. 245 m	35. 10	67. zero	99. ∞
4. 470	36. ∞	68. 0.5 μ	100. 4.7 k
5. ∞	37. 7.56	69. 16.41	101. 8.2 k
6. 8.65	38. −25	70. 25	102. −12.8
7. 8.6	39. 6.8 k	71. 7.39	103. 25
8. 39 k	40. 5.48	72. zero	104. 10
9. 3.5	41. zero	73. 39 k	105. zero
10. 1.2	42. 2.99 k	74. normal	106. 17.3
11. 150	43. 1.0 k	75. 59.4	107. 49 k
12. 4.7 k	44. 1.69	76. −12.8	108. 2.99 k
13. 1.8 k	45. 27 k	77. 8.6 k	109. 11.9
14. 3.6 k	46. 24.5	78. 25	110. −16.1
15. 10 k	47. 3.8	79. indeterminate	111. 50
16. 4.7 k	48. 11.3 k	80. ∞	112. 470
17. 8.2 k	49. 10	81. 9.26 m	113. ∞
18. 2.2	50. 943 μ	82. $0 \rightarrow \infty$	114. 27
19. 50	51. 25	83. 3.29	115. 1.5 p
20. 7.56	52. 38	84. 2.7 k	116. 6.8 k
21. 25	53. 4.7 k	85. 16.41	117. 22.9
22. zero	54. 6.6	86. 39 k	118. 0.5 μ
23. 2.99 k	55. 47 k	87. normal	119. ∞
24. 10 k	56. 100	88. zero	120. −12.8
25. 5.48	57. zero	89. 39 k	121. 470
26. 4.7 k	58. ∞	90. 50	122. 42.2
27. zero	59. 1.8 k	91. 2.7 k	123. 4.5 k
28. 75	60. 3.8	92. 24.5	124. 38.4
29. 5.6	61. zero	93. 57 k	125. 59.4
30. 2.2 μ	62. 470	94. 0.7	126. 6.6
31. 61.2 k	63. 50	95. −25	127. 25
32. $0 \rightarrow \infty$	64. 590	96. 8.2 k	128. 15

appendix
A

129. 23.83	161. normal	193. 24.5	225. 20
130. −50	162. 11.3 k	194. 2.2 μ	226. 2 k
131. 67 k	163. 25	195. 1,000	227. 200
132. zero	164. 8.2 k	196. ∞	228. 20
133. 50	165. 20.8	197. 10	229. 500
134. 470	166. 3.9 k	198. 9.07 m	230. 20
135. 18 k	167. 6.28 m	199. 0.6	231. −18.54
136. 75	168. 7.56	200. zero	232. 31.46
137. zero	169. zero	201. 275	233. 560
138. ∞	170. normal	202. high	234. 330
139. 31.7 m	171. 2.99 k	203. 0.65	235. −50
140. 0 → ∞	172. −12.6	204. ∞	236. −18.54
141. zero	173. −6	205. 76 k	237. 330
142. 13.9 m	174. 24.5	206. −6	238. 890
143. 8.2 k	175. 275	207. normal	239. 330
144. zero	176. zero	208. 10	240. −18.54
145. high	177. ∞	209. 16.41	241. 9
146. 10	178. 7.56	210. −12	242. 11
147. 20.8	179. 5.5	211. 8.6 k	243. 2.89 k
148. 8.65	180. 25	212. 24.5	244. 11
149. 39 k	181. ∞	213. 1.15	245. 2.89 k
150. 120	182. 13.6 m	214. 2.7 k	246. 820
151. zero	183. 274 m	215. normal	247. 1.07 k
152. 16.41	184. 10	216. 18.86	248. 9
153. 3.9 k	185. 2.99 k	217. 25	249. 11
154. 25	186. 4.6 k	218. 200	250. 684
155. 5.48	187. 470	219. 50	251. 1.8 k
156. 44.4	188. zero	220. 8.88	252. 26
157. 7.58 m	189. 22.9	221. 20	253. 1.53 k
158. 50	190. 25	222. 900	254. 4.41 k
159. 8.2 k	191. 0 → ∞	223. 20	255. 37.6
160. 50	192. 171 k	224. 100	256. 2.21 k

appendix

A

257. 26	277. 3.99	297. 1.77	317. 520
258. 1.53 k	278. 680	298. 5.6 k	318. 0.6
259. 20.4	279. 1.2 k	299. 2.2 k	319. 23.3
260. 1.6 k	280. 5.6	300. 150	320. 150
261. 37.5	281. 3.13	301. 389	321. 35
262. 75	282. 680	302. 2.14 k	322. 150
263. 12 k	283. 9.1 k	303. 910	323. 1.2
264. 1,200	284. 13.5	304. 150	324. 5.97
265. 3.13	285. 1.39 k	305. 1.68	325. 879.7
266. 7.39 k	286. 150	306. 6.53	326. 29
267. 1.53 k	287. 23.3	307. 6.53	327. 52
268. 17.5	288. 12 k	308. 1.49 k	328. 150
269. 11.6	289. 1.39 k	309. 150	329. 5.97
270. 1,200	290. 330	310. 16.8	330. 1 k
271. 20.4	291. 150	311. 389	331. 35
272. 2.2 k	292. 13.5	312. 3.9 k	332. 100
273. 19.3	293. 1,200	313. 910	333. 35
274. 5.74	294. 150	314. 1,000	334. zero
275. 6.71 k	295. 0.86	315. 22 k	335. 879.7
276. 9.59 k	296. 6.53	316. 29	

appendix
B

Table of Standard Resistor Values

Note: All values are available in 5% tolerance. Values set in **bold-face** type are available in 10% tolerance.

1.0 Ω	**15 Ω**	**220 Ω**	**3.3 kΩ**
1.1 Ω	16 Ω	240 Ω	3.6 kΩ
1.2 Ω	**18 Ω**	**270 Ω**	**3.9 kΩ**
1.3 Ω	20 Ω	300 Ω	4.3 kΩ
1.5 Ω	**22 Ω**	**330 Ω**	**4.7 kΩ**
1.6 Ω	24 Ω	360 Ω	5.1 kΩ
1.8 Ω	**27 Ω**	**390 Ω**	**5.6 kΩ**
2.0 Ω	30 Ω	430 Ω	6.2 kΩ
2.2 Ω	**33 Ω**	**470 Ω**	**6.8 kΩ**
2.4 Ω	36 Ω	510 Ω	7.5 kΩ
2.7 Ω	**39 Ω**	**560 Ω**	**8.2 kΩ**
3.0 Ω	43 Ω	620 Ω	9.1 kΩ
3.3 Ω	**47 Ω**	**680 Ω**	**10 kΩ**
3.6 Ω	51 Ω	750 Ω	11 kΩ
3.9 Ω	**56 Ω**	**820 Ω**	**12 kΩ**
4.3 Ω	62 Ω	910 Ω	13 kΩ
4.7 Ω	**68 Ω**	**1.0 kΩ**	**15 kΩ**
5.1 Ω	75 Ω	1.1 kΩ	16 kΩ
5.6 Ω	**82 Ω**	**1.2 kΩ**	**18 kΩ**
6.2 Ω	91 Ω	1.3 kΩ	20 kΩ
6.8 Ω	**100 Ω**	**1.5 kΩ**	**22 kΩ**
7.5 Ω	110 Ω	1.6 kΩ	24 kΩ
8.2 Ω	**120 Ω**	**1.8 kΩ**	**27 kΩ**
9.1 Ω	130 Ω	2.0 kΩ	30 kΩ
10 Ω	**150 Ω**	**2.2 kΩ**	**33 kΩ**
11 Ω	160 Ω	2.4 kΩ	36 kΩ
12 Ω	**180 Ω**	**2.7 kΩ**	**39 kΩ**
13 Ω	200 Ω	3.0 kΩ	43 kΩ

appendix
B

47 kΩ	240 kΩ	**1.2 MΩ**	6.2 MΩ
51 kΩ	**270 kΩ**	1.3 MΩ	**6.8 MΩ**
56 kΩ	300 kΩ	**1.5 MΩ**	7.5 MΩ
62 kΩ	**330 kΩ**	1.6 MΩ	**8.2 MΩ**
68 kΩ	360 kΩ	**1.8 MΩ**	9.1 MΩ
75 kΩ	**390 kΩ**	2.0 MΩ	**10 MΩ**
82 kΩ	430 kΩ	**2.2 MΩ**	11 MΩ
91 kΩ	**470 kΩ**	2.4 MΩ	**12 MΩ**
100 kΩ	510 kΩ	**2.7 MΩ**	13 MΩ
110 kΩ	**560 kΩ**	3.0 MΩ	**15 MΩ**
120 kΩ	620 kΩ	**3.3 MΩ**	16 MΩ
130 kΩ	**680 kΩ**	3.6 MΩ	**18 MΩ**
150 kΩ	750 kΩ	**3.9 MΩ**	20 MΩ
160 kΩ	**820 kΩ**	4.3 MΩ	**22 MΩ**
180 kΩ	910 kΩ	**4.7 MΩ**	
200 kΩ	**1.0 MΩ**	5.1 MΩ	
220 kΩ	1.1 MΩ	**5.6 MΩ**	

appendix
C

Conversion Table for Magnetic Units

QUANTITY	SYMBOL OR ABBREVIATION	TO CONVERT FROM	TO	MULTIPLY BY
Flux	Φ	webers	maxwells	1×10^8
		maxwells	webers	1×10^{-8}
Flux density	B	tesla	gauss	1×10^4
		gauss	tesla	1×10^{-4}
Magnetizing force	H	ampere-turns per meter	oersteds	0.01256
		oersteds	ampere-turns per meter	79.577
Magnetomotive force	$\mathcal{F}$	ampere-turns	gilberts	1.257
		gilberts	ampere-turns	0.796
Absolute permeability	μ	webers per ampere-turn-meter	gauss per oersted	795.7×10^3
		gauss per oersted	webers per ampere-turn-meter	1.257×10^{-6}
Relative permeability		No units		
Permeance	$\mathcal{P}$	webers per ampere-turn	maxwells per gilbert	79.6×10^6
		maxwells per gilbert	webers per ampere-turn	1.257×10^{-8}
Reluctance	$\mathfrak{R}$	ampere-turns per weber	gilberts per maxwell	1.257×10^{-8}
		gilberts per maxwell	ampere-turns per weber	79.6×10^6

Shaded entries identify SI (MKS) units. Unshaded entries are CGS units.

glossary

ac resistance The effective resistance of a component or device to alternating current. Also called dynamic resistance.

Accuracy A meter specification that indicates the largest difference between actual and indicated values.

Admittance (Y) The reciprocal of impedance. The ability of *RC*, *RL*, and *RLC* circuits to pass alternating current. Measured in siemens.

Air gap Any portion of a magnetic circuit where the magnetic flux passes through air.

Alphanumeric Consisting of both digits (0–9) and letters (A–Z), and often including special characters (e.g., !, ~, &, %, and so on).

Alternating current (ac) Current that periodically changes direction.

Alternator A device that converts mechanical energy into alternating voltage and current.

Amalgamation Used in the manufacture of carbon-zinc cells to reduce local action by coating the zinc electrode with mercury.

Ammeter A device used to measure current.

Ampere (A) The unit of measure for current.

Ampere-hour (A · h) The unit of measure for the capacity of a cell or battery.

Ampere-turn (A · t) The unit of measure for magnetomotive force.

Amplification The process of converting a small changing signal into a larger, but corresponding, signal.

Amplitude The maximum (unless otherwise stated) value of a waveform.

Analog A class of devices or systems that utilize a continuous range of values.

Anode The negative terminal of a cell. Also the more positive terminal of a conducting diode.

Apparent power (P_A) The phasor sum of true power and reactive power.

Armature The movable part of a motor or relay. Also refers to the winding of an alternator or generator where the voltage is induced.

Asymmetrical Not symmetrical. Generally refers to a waveform with dissimilar half-cycles.

Atom The smallest part of an element that still has the properties of the element.

Attenuation A reduction or loss of signal amplitude.

Autotransformer A transformer with a single tapped winding that serves as both primary and secondary.

Average value The sum of several instantaneous values of an electrical quantity divided by the number of values. In the case of a sinusoidal waveform, the average value is zero for a full cycle and $0.636 \, V_{PEAK}$ for a half-cycle.

AWG An abbreviation for American wire gage.

Ayrton shunt *See* Universal Shunt.

Backoff scale An ohmmeter scale that reads from right to left. The nonlinear scale has zero ohms on the far right and infinite ohms on the far left of the scale.

Balanced bridge A condition in a bridge circuit where the two legs have equal

glossary

resistance ratios and the voltage across the middle of the bridge is zero.

Band-reject filter A filter circuit that attenuates a band of frequencies, but allows higher and lower frequencies to pass with minimal attenuation. Also called a bandstop filter.

Bandstop filter *See* Band-reject Filter.

Bandpass The band of frequencies that pass through a circuit with at least 70.7% of the maximum amplitude.

Bandpass filter A filter circuit that passes a band of frequencies with minimal attenuation, but attenuates all frequencies lower or higher than the passband.

Bandwidth The width (in hertz) of the range between the half-power points of a resonant circuit or a filter circuit.

Battery A series and/or parallel connection of two or more cells.

***BH* curve** A graph showing the relationship between flux density (B) and magnetizing force (H) for a given material.

Bimetallic strip A structure consisting of two dissimilar metals that bends in response to temperature changes due to the unequal coefficients of expansion.

Bleeder current The current in a voltage divider that flows with or without a load connected.

Block diagram A generalized sketch that represents the functional components of a system with graphic boxes. The boxes are interconnected with lines to show the flow (generally signal flow in block diagrams of electronic systems).

Branch A current path in a circuit that is in parallel with one or more other paths.

Break frequency The frequency where the output of a circuit falls to 70.7% of its maximum voltage or current response. This also corresponds to the half-power (–3 dB) point(s) on the frequency response curve.

Bridge circuit A special series-parallel circuit consisting of two parallel branches with two series resistors in each branch. The output is taken between the midpoints of the two parallel branches. Bridge circuits are widely used in instrumentation circuits.

Brush A graphite block that provides sliding contact to a slip ring (alternator or ac motor) or commutator (dc motor or generator).

Cable Two or more individually insulated wires bound in a common sheath.

Capacitance (C) The electrical property that allows a capacitor to store energy in an electrostatic field. Measured in farads.

Capacitive reactance (X_C) The opposition to alternating current flow offered by capacitance. It is measured in ohms.

Capacitor An electrical component consisting of two or more conductive plates separated by insulation and used to store energy in an electrostatic field.

Cathode The positive terminal of a cell. Also the more negative terminal of a conducting diode.

Cell A single, stand-alone source of electrical energy (e.g., electrochemical cell, fuel cell, solar cell).

Cemf The voltage induced in a conductor or inductor by a changing current. The

glossary

induced voltage opposes the changing current.

Center tap A coil or transformer winding that has a connection in the middle of the winding.

CGS An older system of measurement based on the centimeter, gram, and second.

Charge A term used to describe the condition that exists when a material or region has unequal numbers of electrons and protons.

Chassis The metal frame or cabinet used to house an electronic system. The chassis is frequently, but not always, connected to ground.

Chattering The audible noise that results when a normally closed contact of a relay is connected in series with its own coil.

Chip Refers to the physical semiconductor material used to make integrated circuits and other solid-state devices.

Choke A name given to an inductor when its primary purpose is to attenuate high frequencies.

Circuit Any configuration of electrical and/or electronic devices interconnected with conductors.

Circuit breaker A protective device that mechanically opens a circuit if the current through the circuit exceeds the trip current of the breaker.

Circular mil (cmil) A unit of measure for wire area. One circular mil is the cross-sectional area of a round wire that has a diameter of one mil (1/1,000th of an inch).

Closed circuit A circuit that has a complete path for current.

Coaxial cable A shielded, two-conductor cable where the braided outer conductor completely surrounds the insulated inner conductor.

Coefficient of coupling (k) A dimensionless number that represents the percentage of total flux that is common between two coils or circuits.

Coercive force The amount of magnetizing force needed to overcome or cancel the residual magnetism in a magnetic material.

Coil An inductor or other device formed by winding multiple turns of wire on a core (even an air core).

Coil resistance The dc resistance (measured with an ohmmeter) of a coil.

Color code A standardized scheme that uses colored markings to identify component values or part numbers. Also used to identify leads on transformers.

Commutator A segmented conductor that is mounted on the rotor of a dc generator or motor and makes sliding contact with the brushes. Allows power to be applied (or removed) from a rotating coil.

Complex circuit A circuit configuration that cannot be simplified by replacing sets of series and parallel components with equivalent components.

Complex number A number composed of both real (resistive) and imaginary (reactive) parts used to describe a phasor.

Complex voltage source A circuit with both series-aiding and series-opposing cells or voltage sources.

glossary

Compound A material that consists of two or more elements that are chemically bonded.

Conductance (*G*) The reciprocal of resistance. It describes the ability of a circuit to allow current flow. It is measured in siemens.

Conductor A material with a very low resistance that readily permits current flow.

Constant current A source of current that is constant at all times and is unaffected by changes in circuit resistance.

Constant voltage A source of voltage that is constant at all times and is unaffected by changes in circuit resistance.

Contact bounce The series of momentary opens and closures that occurs when mechanical switch or relay contacts are moved.

Continuity A term used to indicate the presence of a complete path for current.

Conventional current A convention that conceptualizes current as flowing in a direction opposite that of electron flow. Conventional current moves from positive to negative through a complete circuit.

Copper loss The energy converted to heat by the resistance in the windings of a transformer or other electromagnetic device.

Core The material used as the central part of an inductor. It concentrates the magnetic flux and physically supports the coil windings.

Core loss The energy converted to heat in the core material of an electromagnetic device. Core loss consists primarily of losses due to hysteresis and eddy currents.

Cosine A trigonometric function of an angle in a right triangle that is equal to the length of the adjacent side divided by the length of the hypotenuse.

Coulomb (C) The SI unit of measure for charge. One coulomb is the amount of charge of 6.25×10^{18} electrons.

Coulomb's Law The law that relates the force between two charged bodies as a function of the strength of the two charges and the distance between them.

Counter emf *See* Cemf.

CRT An abbreviation for cathode-ray tube. It is the display tube used in most oscilloscopes, televisions, and radars.

Cryogenics The study of the behavior of materials as they approach absolute zero (−273.2°C).

Crystal A material whose atoms form a consistent lattice pattern throughout the bulk of the material.

Current The movement of charged particles. Generally used to describe the movement of electrons.

Current divider A circuit that consists of two or more parallel branches. It is used to divide the total current into two or more components.

Current probe An ammeter attachment that can sense the value of current flow in a circuit *without* breaking the circuit.

Current source *See* Constant Current.

Cutoff frequency *See* Break Frequency.

Cycle One complete repetition of a periodic waveform consisting of two alternations.

glossary

D'Arsonval movement A common meter movement consisting of a moving coil attached to a pointer and suspended in the field of a permanent magnet.

Damping A technique used to prevent dramatic overswings in pointer movement on analog meters.

dc resistance The ohmic resistance as measured by an ohmmeter.

Decade A tenfold (i.e., 10:1 or 1:10) change in the value of a quantity.

Decibel (dB) The logarithmic unit of measure for a ratio.

Degauss Demagnetize.

Degenerative feedback *See* Negative Feedback.

Degree An angular measure equal to 1/360th of a full circle.

Delta configuration A configuration where three components are connected in a loop with connection made at each node. Also called a pi configuration. One of two common connections for three-phase transformer windings.

Diamagnetic A material with a relative permeability of less than one.

Dielectric An insulator.

Dielectric constant (k) A measure of the ability of a material (relative to air) to concentrate an electric field.

Dielectric strength A measure of a dielectric material's ability to withstand high voltage.

Digital A device or system that utilizes discrete (noncontinuous) values.

Diode A two-terminal electronic component that permits current flow in only one direction.

Direct current (dc) Current that flows in only one direction and generally has a constant value.

Directly proportional Two quantities are directly proportional when increases in one quantity cause corresponding increases in the second.

DMM Digital multimeter. The digital equivalent of an analog VOM.

Domain A region within a magnetic material that behaves like a small bar magnet. Alignment of the domains in a material results in the material being magnetized.

Dot notation A method used on schematics to identify in-phase points on a multiple-winding transformer.

Drop-out current The value of coil current that permits the contacts of a relay to return to their normal state after the relay has been energized.

Drop-out voltage The value of coil voltage that permits the contacts of a relay to return to their normal state after the relay has been energized.

Dropping resistor A name given to a resistor that is placed in series with another circuit and whose primary purpose is to drop a portion of the total voltage.

DVM Digital voltmeter. A digital meter that measures voltage.

Dynamic resistance *See* ac Resistance.

Eddy current A circulating current in the core of an electromagnetic device that results from the conductive core material

glossary

being cut by changing magnetic flux. Eddy currents produce a heat loss in the core.

Effective value *See* Root-mean-square.

Efficiency The ratio of output power to input power. Ideally 100%, but always less in practice.

Electrode An electrical terminal of a cell or other electrical device that permits current to enter/exit the device.

Electrolyte A liquid or paste with mobile ions that reacts with the electrodes in an electrochemical cell and permits current flow between the anode and cathode of the cell.

Electromagnet A magnet produced by the flow of current through a coil. The magnetic field is present only so long as the current is flowing.

Electromagnetic field A magnetic field produced by current flow through a conductor.

Electromagnetic induction The process that causes a voltage to be produced in a wire as it is intercepted by moving magnetic flux.

Electromechanical A device whose operation is both electrical and mechanical.

Electromotive force (emf) A voltage source or potential difference that is sustained as charges are moved through the circuit. The electrical pressure that causes sustained current to flow in an electrical circuit. Measured in volts.

Electron A negatively charged atomic particle that orbits the nucleus of all atoms.

Electron current flow A convention that conceptualizes current as the movement of electrons. Electron current flows from negative to positive through a complete circuit.

Electronic Components or devices that control or regulate the flow of electrons with active devices (e.g., transistors).

Electrostatic field The region around a charged body where another charged body would experience a force of attraction or repulsion.

Element A material whose atoms are all identical. An element cannot be subdivided by chemical means.

Emf *See* Electromotive Force.

Energy The ability to do work.

Energy level Used to describe the energy content of an orbiting electron. Higher energy levels correspond to orbits that are farther from the nucleus.

Equivalent circuit A simplified circuit that provides similar performance to a more complex circuit under a given set of conditions.

Equivalent series inductance (ESL) The parasitic inductance of a capacitor caused primarily by the capacitor lead wires.

Equivalent series resistance (ESR) The effective resistance (i.e., equivalent power loss) of a capacitor caused primarily by dielectric losses.

EVM Electronic voltmeter. An analog VOM that has electronic circuitry, which makes the meter appear more ideal.

Farad (F) The unit of measure for capacitance.

Faraday shield A grounded conductive shield used to separate the primary and

glossary

secondary windings of a transformer to reduce coupling via the interwinding capacitance.

Fast-blo A type of fuse that is designed to open quickly.

Feedback The portion of a signal in an electronic system that is returned to a prior stage of the same system.

Ferrite A magnetic ceramic material used as a core material for transformers and coils. Also used in the form of a bead or clamp to attenuate high frequencies.

Ferromagnetic A material with a relative permeability much greater than one.

Field winding A coil in a motor, generator, or alternator that is used to create a steady magnetic field.

Filter A circuit designed to pass certain frequencies and reject (i.e., attenuate) other frequencies.

Firing voltage The minimum voltage required to ionize the gas in a neon lamp.

Flux Magnetic or electric lines of force

Flux density (B) The number of magnetic lines of force per unit area.

Flux leakage Magnetic flux that is intended to but does not link two circuits (e.g., primary and secondary of a transformer).

Free electron An electron that has been disassociated from its parent atom and is no longer in orbit.

Frequency (F) The number of complete cycles of a periodic waveform per unit time.

Fringing A phenomenon that causes magnetic flux lines to "bulge" when they

pass between two high-permeability materials that are separated by a low-permeability material (e.g., an air gap in a magnetic core).

Fuel cell A special type of electrochemical cell that must have a continuous supply of external fuel (e.g., hydrogen and oxygen).

Full-scale current The amount of current required to fully deflect an analog meter movement.

Full-scale voltage The amount of voltage required to fully deflect an analog meter movement.

Fully-specified circuit A circuit with all component values given on the schematic diagram.

Function generator An electronic instrument that generates periodic waveforms such as sine waves, rectangular waves, and triangular waves.

Fuse A protective device that burns open to protect a circuit if the current through the circuit exceeds the rating of the fuse.

Ganged The mechanical connecting together of two or more adjustable components (e.g., switches or potentiometers) such that they operate simultaneously.

Gauss (G) The CGS unit of measure for magnetic flux density.

Generator An electromechanical device that converts mechanical energy into electrical energy in the form of direct voltage and current.

Giga (G) A prefix used to represent 10^9.

Gilbert The CGS unit of measure for magnetomotive force.

Graticule A grid on the face of an oscilloscope CRT used to increase reading accuracy.

Ground The point in a circuit to which all voltage measurements are referenced. Sometimes used to refer to earth ground.

Ground plane A metallic plane having zero potential with reference to circuit ground.

Half-digit A digital indicator capable of displaying ±1.

Half-power frequency *See* Break Frequency.

Harmonics Any whole multiple of a base frequency called the fundamental frequency.

Henry (H) The SI unit of measure for inductance.

Hertz (Hz) The SI unit of measure for frequency.

High-pass filter A filter circuit that passes all frequencies above the cutoff frequency with minimal attenuation, but attenuates all frequencies below the cutoff frequency.

Horsepower A unit of mechanical power. One horsepower is equivalent to 746 watts.

Hot Electrician's jargon for any wire that is 120 Vac with respect to earth ground.

Hydrometer A device used to measure the specific gravity of a liquid.

Hypotenuse The longest side of a right triangle and opposite the right angle.

Hysteresis The characteristic that causes the flux changes in a magnetic material to lag behind the changes in magnetizing force.

Hysteresis loss A heat loss in a magnetic material caused by the rapid switching of the magnetic domains.

Impedance (Z) Total opposition to current flow in a circuit containing both resistance and reactance. Measured in ohms.

Induced voltage A voltage that is created in a conductor as a result of being intercepted by a moving magnetic field.

Inductance (L) The electrical property that allows a coil to store energy in a magnetic field. It is a characteristic or property that tends to oppose any change in current. Measured in henries.

Induction The process of producing an induced voltage.

Inductive reactance (X_L) The opposition to alternating current flow offered by an inductance. It is measured in ohms.

Inductor A component (coil) that is specifically designed to have inductance.

Input The voltage, current, or power applied to an electrical circuit.

Inrush current A transient current that is higher than normal, but occurs only when power is initially applied to a device or circuit.

Instantaneous value The value of a changing electrical quantity at a specific point in time.

Insulator A material that has a very high resistance and allows no practical current flow.

Integrated circuit A semiconductor device that consists of thousands of transis-

glossary

tors, resistors, and so on integrated into a single wafer of silicon.

Internal resistance An effective resistance that appears to be internal to a device or component. Although it is not generally a physical resistance, it behaves like a series resistance.

Interpolate A process used to estimate the indicated value when the pointer of an analog meter comes to rest between scale markings.

Inversely proportional Two quantities are inversely proportional when increases in one quantity produce corresponding decreases in the second.

Ion A charged particle. An atom that has unequal numbers of electrons and protons.

Ionization The process of creating ions by adding or removing electrons from an otherwise neutral atom.

Ionization voltage The voltage required to ionize the gas in a neon bulb and cause the indicator to emit light.

Isolation transformer A 1:1 transformer used to isolate circuit grounds from earth grounds.

_J_ operator A mathematical prefix or operation that indicates a 90° phase shift.

Joule The SI unit of measure for energy or work.

Junction A point in the circuit where two or more components are joined.

Kilo (k) A prefix representing 10^3.

Kilowatt-hour (kWh) The unit of energy commonly used by electrical power companies.

Kirchhoff's Current Law A fundamental law that says the current entering any point in a circuit must be equal to the current leaving that same point.

Kirchhoff's Voltage Law A fundamental law that states the sum of the voltage drops and voltage sources in any closed loop must be equal to zero.

_L/R_ time constant The time required in an _RL_ circuit for the current to increase or decrease by 63% of the total possible change. Measured in seconds.

Lag To be behind. Generally refers to one sine wave that occurs later in time (out of phase) than a second sine wave.

Laminated Built up from several layers. Material is usually different on adjacent layers.

Lead To be ahead of. Generally refers to one sine wave that occurs earlier in time (out of phase) than a second sine wave.

Leakage current A small (ideally zero) current that flows through an insulator.

Leakage flux _See_ Flux Leakage.

Leakage inductance An apparent inductance caused by leakage flux.

LED _See_ Light-Emitting Diode.

Lenz's Law The law that states the polarity of an induced voltage will oppose the current change that caused it.

Light-emitting diode (LED) A semiconductor device that emits light. LEDs are used for indicators and digital displays.

Linear Describes a relationship between two quantities that are directly proportional to each other.

glossary

Lines of flux Imaginary lines that indicate strength and direction of a magnetic field.

Lissajous pattern A pattern formed on an oscilloscope by applying a sinusoidal waveform to both vertical and horizontal channels. Lissajous patterns can be used to measure frequency and phase.

Load A device or component that draws current from a circuit.

Load current The current that flows through a load connected to a circuit.

Load resistor A resistor connected across the output of a circuit (e.g., a loaded voltage divider).

Loaded voltage divider A voltage divider that supplies power to other circuits or devices.

Loading The changing of a circuit quantity by the connection of another component, circuit, or device.

Local action A localized chemical activity in an electrochemical cell that destroys the electrodes and eventually ruins the cell. Local action can lessen the shelf life of a cell.

Long time constant A time constant (RC or L/R) that is at least ten times greater than the period of the input pulse waveform.

Loop Any closed path for current.

Low-pass filter A filter circuit that passes all frequencies below the cutoff frequency with minimal attenuation, but attenuates all frequencies above the cutoff frequency.

Magnet A material that possesses magnetism.

Magnetic domain *See* Domain.

Magnetic field The region around a magnet where another magnet would experience a force of attraction or repulsion.

Magnetic field intensity *See* Magnetizing Force.

Magnetic flux *See* Lines of Flux.

Magnetic polarity The relative direction of a magnet's field with respect to the earth's magnetic field. The north (actually north-seeking) pole of a magnet is attracted by the earth's north pole.

Magnetizing current The current that flows in the primary of a transformer with no load on the secondary. Power supplied by the magnetizing current is consumed as transformer core and winding losses.

Magnetizing force (H) The magnetomotive force per unit length.

Magnetomotive force ($\mathscr{F}$) The magnetic force produced by current flowing through a coil.

Magnitude The value of a circuit quantity without consideration of phase angle.

Make before break A type of switching contact where the movable part of the contact connects to the new position before contact is broken with the original position.

Matter Anything that occupies space and has weight.

Maximum power transfer theorem A theorem that states that maximum power (50%) can be transferred between two circuits when their resistances are equal.

Maxwell (Mx) A CGS unit of measure for magnetic flux.

Mega (M) A prefix representing 10^6.

glossary

Memory effect A characteristic of certain electrochemical cells (e.g., NiCad cells) that causes them to lose their ability to supply large amounts of power after an extended period of time with only modest loads.

Mesh analysis A technique used to analyze complex circuit configurations.

Meter shunt A resistance connected in parallel with a meter movement that bypasses part of the total current, thus extending the effective range of the movement to a value greater than full-scale current value of the meter movement itself.

Micro (μ) A prefix representing 10^{-6}.

Milli (m) A prefix representing 10^{-3}.

Millman's theorem A simplification technique that is particularly well-suited to circuits having several parallel (nonideal) voltage sources.

Mixture A material composed of more than one element or compound, but whose dissimilar atoms or molecules are not chemically bound together.

MKS *See* SI.

mmf *See* Magnetomotive Force.

Molecule The smallest part of a compound that still exhibits the properties of the compound.

Momentary-contact switch A switch whose contacts change from their normal position when activated (e.g., a button is pressed) but return to their normal position as soon as the mechanical activation force is removed.

Motor A device that converts electrical energy into rotating mechanical energy.

Multimeter A measuring instrument (e.g., VOM, EVM, DVM) capable of measuring resistance, voltage, and current.

Multiplier resistor A resistance connected in series with a meter movement to increase the effective value of voltage required for full-scale deflection.

Mutual inductance Inductance that is common to two magnetically linked coils.

Negative (–) The polarity of charge represented by an excess of electrons.

Negative feedback Feedback that is out of phase with the original signal and causes a decrease in amplitude. Also called degenerative feedback.

Negative ion An atom with fewer protons than electrons.

Network A configuration of electrical components; a circuit.

Neutral Electrician's terminology for the side of the 120-Vac power that is also connected to earth ground.

Neutron An atomic particle located in the nucleus of an atom and having no charge. Its mass is equivalent to that of a proton.

Nodal analysis A circuit analysis technique applicable to complex circuits.

Node Any point in a circuit where the current divides.

Nominal The ideal or expected value of a component or circuit quantity.

Nonlinear Describes a relationship between two quantities that are not directly proportional to each other. Uniform changes in one quantity cause corresponding changes in the second, but the resulting changes are not uniform.

glossary

Normally closed The contacts of a switch or relay that are closed without activating the switch or relay.

Normally open The contacts of a switch or relay that are open without activating the switch or relay.

Norton's theorem A simplification technique that converts a network into an equivalent circuit consisting of a current source and a parallel resistance.

Octave An eightfold (i.e., 8:1 or 1:8) change in the value of a quantity.

Oersted (Oe) The CGS unit of measure for magnetizing force.

Ohm (Ω) The unit of measure for resistance.

Ohm's Law A fundamental law that describes the relationship between current, voltage, and resistance in an electrical circuit.

Ohms per volt *See* Voltmeter Sensitivity.

Ohmic resistance *See* dc Resistance.

Ohmmeter An instrument used to measure resistance.

Open circuit A circuit that has no complete path for current flow; no continuity.

Oscillator A circuit that produces alternating voltage waveforms when a dc voltage is applied.

Oscilloscope An instrument used to display a graph of instantaneous circuit quantities as functions of time.

Output The voltage, current, or power taken from a circuit.

Parallax error An interpretation error on an analog meter movement caused by viewing the pointer and scale marks at an angle.

Parallel A method of connecting circuit components such that all components connect between the same two points.

Paramagnetic Materials with a relative permeability slightly greater than one.

Parameter Any electrical quantity or circuit characteristic.

Partially-specified circuit A circuit where one or more component values are unknown.

Passband The band of frequencies that are passed with minimal attenuation by a filter circuit.

Passive component An electrical component that cannot amplify or rectify. Resistors, inductors, and capacitors are passive components, whereas transistors and other solid-state devices are active components.

Peak value The maximum instantaneous value of a waveform.

Peak-to-peak value The measure of an alternating circuit quantity that describes the difference between the minimum and maximum levels.

Period (T) The time required for one complete cycle of a periodic waveform.

Periodic A waveform that repeats at regular intervals.

Permanent magnet A magnet that does not lose its magnetism when the magnetizing force is removed.

glossary

Permeability (μ) The ability of a material to concentrate magnetic flux. Often expressed as a dimensionless ratio of the permeability of the material relative to air.

Permeance (𝒫) A measure of the ease with which a magnetic field may be established in a material. Analogous to conductance in an electrical circuit.

Permittivity (∈) The ability of a dielectric material to concentrate an electric field.

Phase The timing of a waveform relative to another waveform that has an identical frequency.

Phasor A graphical or numerical representation of the magnitude and phase of an electrical quantity.

Pi configuration *See* Delta Configuration.

Pick-up voltage The coil voltage required to energize a relay.

Pico (p) A prefix representing 10^{-12}.

Piezoelectric effect A phenomenon that causes certain materials to generate a voltage when mechanically stressed.

Point of simplification The point in a circuit that separates components to be replaced by an equivalent circuit from those that will remain.

Polar notation A method of expressing a complex circuit quantity that includes both magnitude and phase information (e.g., $50 \angle 45°$).

Polarity A term used to describe the direction of the relative potential between two points in a circuit. Also used to describe the direction of a magnetic field.

Polarization A buildup of hydrogen gas on the positive electrode of an electro-chemical cell that degrades the cell's operation.

Pole The movable contact of a relay or switch; also the area of maximum flux density in a magnet.

Positive (+) The polarity of charge represented by a deficiency of electrons.

Positive feedback Feedback that is in phase with the original signal and causes an increased amplitude. Also called regenerative feedback.

Positive ion An atom with fewer electrons than protons.

Potential The ability of an electrical charge to do work by moving electrons.

Potential difference Voltage.

Potentiometer A three-terminal variable resistor. The end-to-end resistance remains constant, but the resistance from either end to the wiper varies as the wiper is moved.

Power (P) The rate of energy consumption; the rate of doing work.

Power factor (pf) The ratio of true power to apparent power in a circuit.

Power supply A device or circuit used to supply electrical energy. In most cases, the power supply delivers direct current and voltage.

Powers of ten A method used to express large or small numbers as a modest number times a power of ten (i.e., ten raised to some exponent).

Primary The winding on a transformer where power is applied.

glossary

Primary cell An electrochemical cell that is not designed to be recharged. The chemical processes are not generally reversible (practically).

Proton A positively charged particle in the nucleus of an atom.

Pull-in current The coil current required to energize a relay.

Pythagorean theorem A fundamental theorem that describes the relationship between the sides of a right triangle ($c^2 = a^2 + b^2$).

Quality factor (Q) A dimensionless figure of merit for inductors, capacitors, and resonant circuits. Higher Q values correspond to less losses and more ideal performance.

Radian (rad) An angular measure equal to 57.3°.

RC time constant The time required for the capacitor voltage in an RC circuit to change by 63% of the total possible change.

Reactive power (P_R) A measure of the power that is taken from and subsequently returned to a circuit by the inductance and capacitance in a circuit.

Real number Any rational or irrational number.

Real power *See* True Power.

Rectangular notation A method of representing complex circuit quantities that includes both real (resistive) and imaginary (reactive) portions (e.g., $25 + j10$).

Recurrent sweep A type of sweep circuit in an oscilloscope that causes the horizontal sweep to occur automatically (i.e., without a trigger).

Reflected impedance The apparent impedance in the primary of a transformer that results from a load in the secondary.

Regenerative feedback *See* Positive Feedback.

Relative permeability (μ_r) A dimensionless measurement of the permeability of a material relative to the permeability of air (or vacuum).

Relay An electromechanical device that consists of an electromagnet and switching contacts. The switch contacts are activated by energizing the electromagnet.

Reluctance ($\mathfrak{R}$) A measure of a material's opposition (magnetic resistance) to magnetic flux.

Residual magnetism The level of magnetism remaining in a material after the magnetizing force has been removed.

Resistance (R) Opposition to current flow in a circuit; measured in ohms.

Resistivity (ρ) The resistance of a given volume (e.g., one cubic meter) of a material.

Resistor An electrical component designed to provide a given opposition to current flow.

Resistor tolerance The maximum amount of deviation due to manufacturing tolerances between the nominal and actual values of a resistor.

Resolution The smallest change in a measured value that can be resolved or displayed by a measuring instrument.

glossary

Resonance A condition in an *LC* or *RLC* circuit where $X_L = X_C$ and the impedance of the network is maximum (parallel circuit) or minimum (series circuit).

Resonant circuit An *LC* or *RLC* circuit that is operating at its resonant frequency.

Resonant frequency The frequency in an *LC* or *RLC* circuit that causes the inductive reactance to be equal to the capacitive reactance.

Response time The time required for a fuse to open in response to an overcurrent condition.

Retentivity The property of a magnetic material that causes it to have residual magnetism.

Rheostat A two-terminal variable resistor.

Right angle A 90° angle; an angle of $\pi/2$ radians.

Roll-off The slope of the frequency response curve of a filter circuit beyond the cutoff frequency.

Root-mean-square (rms) A unit of measure for alternating voltage or current that is an amount that produces the same heating effect in a resistance as a similar value of dc. It is numerically equal to 70.7% of the peak value in a sinusoidal circuit.

Rotor The rotating coil of a motor, generator, or alternator.

Schematic A diagram that depicts the various components and interconnections in an electrical circuit.

Secondary A winding on a transformer from which power is removed.

Secondary cell An electrochemical cell that is designed to be recharged. The chemical processes are reversible.

Selectivity The ability of a circuit to pass certain frequencies and reject others.

Self-holding contacts A relay circuit configuration where a normally open set of contacts is in parallel with the switch used to activate the relay. Once energized, the relay remains energized or latched.

Self-inductance The property of a conductor or coil that opposes any change in current.

Self-resonant frequency The frequency at which the parasitic components in a coil or capacitor resonate with the intended quantity.

Sensitivity *See* Voltmeter Sensitivity.

Series A circuit configuration that results in a single path for current flow.

Series-aiding Voltage sources connected in series with similar polarities are series-aiding. The net voltage is the sum of the individual sources.

Series-opposing Voltage sources connected in series with opposite polarities are series-opposing. The net voltage is equal to the difference between the two source voltages.

Series-parallel A circuit configuration that consists of groups of parallel and series components.

Seven-segment display A digital display consisting of seven illuminated segments. Selective illumination of the segments allows display of the numbers 0–9.

glossary

Shelf life The length of time that an electrochemical cell can remain inactive and still be expected to deliver its rated characteristics.

Shells Orbital levels of electrons in an atom. Each shell is a discrete region.

Shield A conductive or permeable sheet or enclosure that provides electromagnetic isolation between two circuits.

Short circuit A low-resistance path that essentially bypasses the shorted component(s).

Short time constant An *RC* or *L/R* time constant that is less than one-tenth the period of the input pulse.

Shorting switch *See* Make Before Break.

Shunt Parallel; also a resistor used to extend the current range of an ammeter.

SI Système International. A system of measurement based on the meter, kilogram, and second. Sometimes called the modern MKS system.

Siemens (S) The SI unit of measure for conductance, admitance, and susceptance.

Signal A current or voltage that is present in a circuit. Frequently refers to an ac waveform.

Sine A trigonometric function of an angle in a right triangle that is equal to the length of the opposite side divided by the length of the hypotenuse.

Sine wave A periodic waveform whose amplitude-versus-time graph is the same shape as a graph of the trigonometric sine function versus degrees.

Sinusoidal Any waveform (regardless of phase) that is generally shaped like a sine wave.

Skin effect A phenomenon that causes high-frequency currents to flow near the surface of a conductor, which reduces the effective cross-sectional area of the wire and increases the effective (ac) resistance of the wire.

Slip rings Metal rings on the rotor of an alternator or ac motor that make sliding contact with the brushes and provide a means of connecting or removing power from a rotating coil.

Slo-Blo A type of fuse that can withstand currents greater than its rating as long as the excessive current is only momentary.

Solar cell A solid-state device that converts light energy into electricity.

Solder A tin and lead alloy with a low melting point that is used to permanently bond electrical connections.

Solenoid In general, any coil wound on a long coil form. Also refers to an electromagnetic device that converts electrical energy into a pushing, pulling, or twisting motion.

Specific gravity The ratio of the weights of equal quantities of some liquid and water.

Spiraling A manufacturing process used to trim film resistors to the correct value.

Stator The stationary or nonrotating part of a motor, alternator, or generator.

Step-down transformer A transformer whose secondary voltage is lower than its primary voltage.

glossary

Step-up transformer A transformer whose secondary voltage is higher than its primary voltage.

Substrate The insulating base material used as the core of film resistors. Also the base semiconductor layer in a transistor or integrated circuit.

Superconductivity A characteristic of certain materials that causes their effective resistance to drop to zero as their temperature approaches absolute zero.

Superposition A simplification procedure for multiple-source linear circuits.

Surge A short-duration transient or current burst.

Susceptance (*B*) The ease with which current flows through a reactive component; the reciprocal of reactance; measured in siemens.

Switch An electrical component used to open and close a current path in a circuit.

Symmetrical A waveform whose positive and negative alternations are equal in amplitude, duration, and shape.

Tangent A trigonometric function of an angle in a right triangle that is equal to the length of the opposite side divided by the length of the adjacent side.

Tank circuit A parallel *LC* circuit.

Taper Describes the relationship (linear or logarithmic) between the resistance and the angle of rotation of a variable resistor.

Tee configuration A circuit configuration where one end of each of three components connects to a common point. Also called a wye configuration. One of two common connections for three-phase transformer windings.

Temperature coefficient Describes the relationship between a circuit parameter and its temperature. May be positive, negative, or zero.

Temporary magnets A magnetic material with minimal residual magnetism.

Tesla The SI unit of measure for flux density.

Thermistor An electrical device whose resistance varies with temperature in a specific way.

Thermocouple A bimetallic junction that converts heat energy into electrical energy.

Thermopile A series connection of several thermocouples.

Thevenin's theorem A simplification technique that converts a network into an equivalent circuit consisting of a voltage source and a series resistance.

Throw Identifies the number of circuits that are opened or closed by each pole of a switch.

Time constant A fixed time interval determined by the *RC* or *RL* values in an *RC* or *RL* circuit that specifies the time required for the voltage and current to change by 63% of the total possible change.

Tolerance The maximum amount of deviation due to manufacturing tolerances between the nominal and actual values of a component.

Toroid A donut-shaped object. Usually refers to a toroidal-shaped core used for a transformer or coil.

glossary

Transformer A device that couples electrical energy from one circuit (primary winding) to another (secondary winding) via magnetic flux linkage.

Transient A momentary, short-duration voltage or current surge.

Triggered sweep A type of sweep circuit used in oscilloscopes that produces no horizontal sweep until a specific set of conditions exists (such as the input voltage is at a given level).

Trimmer A variable component used to adjust a circuit parameter to a precise value. Generally provides a very limited range of adjustment (fine tuning).

Tripped A term used to describe the condition of a circuit breaker after it has opened the circuit.

Troubleshooting The process of locating the defective components in an electrical circuit.

True power (P_T) The power, measured in watts, that is dissipated by the resistance in a circuit.

Turns ratio The ratio of primary-to-secondary turns in a transformer.

Universal shunt A method of connecting and switching an ammeter shunt to provide multiple ranges.

Unloaded voltage divider A voltage divider that does not provide power to other circuits or devices.

Valence electrons Electrons in the outermost orbit of an atom.

VAR Abbreviation for volt-ampere-reactive. The unit of measure for reactive power.

Vector A graphical representation of the magnitude and phase of an electrical quantity or the magnitude and direction of a mechanical force.

Volt (V) The SI unit of measure for electromotive force.

Voltage (V) The amount of potential difference between two points that can be used to cause current flow.

Voltage breakdown The condition that exists when an insulator material is subjected to a sufficiently high voltage to destroy the high-resistance characteristics of the insulator. Breakdown results in a high current that may or may not permanently damage the insulator.

Voltage divider A series circuit used to reduce a supply voltage to one or more lower voltages.

Voltage drop (V) The voltage developed across a component as a result of the current flowing through it.

Voltage regulation The process of maintaining a relatively constant output from a voltage source even when the load current or power-line voltage varies.

Voltage source A circuit or device that provides a relatively constant voltage to other circuits or devices.

Voltmeter An instrument used to measure voltage.

Voltmeter loading Occurs when the internal resistance of a voltmeter causes the measured voltage to be less than the actual (unloaded) voltage in the circuit. The higher the internal resistance of a voltmeter, the less it disrupts or loads the circuit.

glossary

Voltmeter sensitivity The ohms-per-volt rating of a voltmeter.

VOM Volt-ohm-milliammeter. An analog meter that measures voltage, current, and resistance.

Watt (W) The SI unit of measure for power.

Watt's Law A fundamental law that describes the relationships between power, current, voltage, and resistance.

Wattmeter An instrument used to measure true power.

Waveform A graph of voltage, current, or other circuit parameter versus time.

Wavelength The physical distance that an acoustical or electromagnetic wave travels in the time required for one complete cycle of the waveform.

Weber (Wb) The SI unit of measure for magnetic flux.

Wheatstone bridge *See* Bridge Circuit.

Winding The turns of wire on an electro-magnetic device such as a coil, transformer, relay, or motor.

Wiper A movable, sliding contact; the center terminal of a potentiometer.

Work The expenditure of energy.

Wye configuration *See* Tee Configuration.

Z-axis Refers to intensity control of the CRT display in an oscilloscope.

Zeroed The condition of an ohmmeter that has been calibrated such that when the leads are shorted together, the pointer indicates zero ohms.

index

Answers to Odd-Numbered Exercise Problems and Review Questions

CHAPTER 11

Exercise Problems

Section 11.1:

1. • positive alternation: a   • time axis: c
   • negative alternation: d   • voltage or current axis: b
   • period: e

Section 11.2:

1. 10 μs

3. 100 kHz

5. 90

7. 95.5 A

9. 141.4 V

11. 50 V

13. 81.92 V

15. 2.62

Section 11.3:

1. 75 V

7. a. 53.13°
   b. 5.16°
   c. 84.81°

3. hypotenuse
   d. 65.51°
   e. 24.49°
   f. 88.09°

5. opposite side; hypotenuse

9. 46.66°

Section 11.4:

1.

	VOLTAGE				CURRENT			
	V (V)	V (V)	V (V)	V (V)	I (mA)	I (mA)	I (mA)	I (mA)
R	42.92	85.85	30.35	27.32	35.77	71.54	25.29	22.77
R	57.08	114.16	40.36	36.33	21.14	42.28	14.95	13.45
R	57.08	114.16	40.36	36.33	14.64	29.27	10.35	9.31
Total	100	200	70.7	63.7	35.77	71.54	25.29	22.77

Section 11.5:

1. No

3. False

Section 11.6:

1. **a.** 10 V

   b. 3.18 V

   c. 3.54 V

   d. 10 kHz

   e. 100 μs

3. **a.** 72 mV

   b. 22.91 mV

   c. 25.46 mV

   d. 3.125 Hz

   e. 320 ms

Review Questions

Section 11.1:

1. period

3. symmetrical

5. alternator

7. to maintain contact to the rotating slip ring

9. peak

Section 11.2:

11. seconds

13. Hertz

15. 13.33 MHz

17. 200 ns

19. 16.67 ms

21. twice

23. True

25. zero

27. 15.9 V

29. False

31. 166.5 mV

33. 20 V

35. radians; degrees

37. 70.71 V

39. 0.61 radians

41. 286.48°

43. 136.6 V

45. 1.7 kV

47. third

Section 11.3:

49. False

51. hypotenuse

53. opposite side; adjacent side

55. find the arccos

57. −0.0584

59. −0.0292

61. 1.34 radians

63. 68.40

65. 15.62

67. 154.87 V

69. 64.16°

71. 53.13°

Section 11.4:

73. 26.19 mA

75. V = 45 V

77. 20.06 mA

79. 3.55 mA

81. 2.15 mA

83. 3.55 mA

85. zero

87. 2.39 mA

Section 11.5:

89. False

91. True

93. speaker

95. 300×10

97. True

Section 11.6:

99. t = 5.3 div × 5 ms/div = 26.5 ms

101. 1.47 MHz

CHAPTER 12

Exercise Problems

Section 12.1:

1. electromagnetic induction

3. False

5. True

7. L

9. increase; 9

11. increase to five times the original value

13. increases by a factor of 30

Section 12.2:

1.

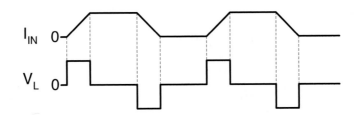

3. 90°; 270°

Section 12.3:

1. False

3. The purpose is to distinguish the inductor from a resistor.

5. 2.2 µH ± 10%

Section 12.4:

1. 500 µH

3. 13.64 mH

5. 43.33 mH

Section 12.5:

1. rate of change of current

Section 12.6:

1. 11 kΩ
3. 100 mH
5. directly
7. 5.86 kV
9. 240°

Section 12.7:

1. low
3. False
5. False
7. 20.9
9. 14.7

Section 12.8:

1. open
3. infinity

Review Questions

Section 12.1:

1. directly
3. minimum
5. increases
7. True
9. opposes
11. change
13. increases four times
15. increases
17. increases by a factor of three
19. True

Section 12.2:

21. zero volts (flat)
23. 0; 180

Section 12.3:

25.
27. air
29. higher
31. False
33. True
35. 82 μH ± 10%
37. small size

Section 12.4:

39. 75 μH
41. 370 mH
43. smaller
45. 20 mH
47. 100 mH

Section 12.5:

49. True
51. True

Section 12.6:

53. False
55. 70.7 kΩ
57. 703.4 kΩ
59. 900.8 nA
61. 4.34 kΩ
63. 79.6 mV
65. 10 kΩ
67. 180°
69. leads; 90

Section 12.7:

71. resistance

73. equivalent series resistance or effective series resistance

75. 75.4

77. No

79. skin effect

81. True

Section 12.8:

83. No

CHAPTER 13

Exercise Problems

Section 13.1:

1. same value in all components

3. 2.75 A

5. phasor addition

7. out of phase

9. 14.53 kΩ

11.

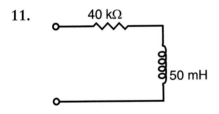

15.

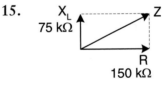

13.

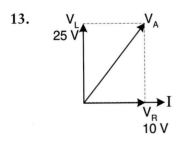

17. 17.35 V

19. watts (W)

21. siemens

23. 40 μS

Section 13.2:

1. 10 V

3. 25 V

5. 90° (voltage leading current)

7. 255 mA

9. 4 A

11. smaller

13.

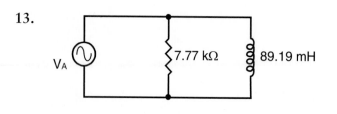

15. False

17.

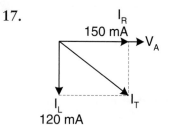

19.

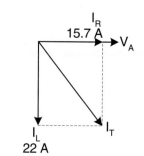

Section 13.3:

No problems

Section 13.4:

1. 785 Ω

3. 892.2 μS

5. 3.5 V

17. 127.39 μS

7. 44.46°

9. 4.46 mA

11. 18 V

19. 0.508

13. 3.6 mA

15. 7.09 mA

21. $100 + j100.48$ Ω $(141.76$ Ω $\angle 45.14°)$

23. $60.66 + j67.53$ Ω $(90.78$ Ω $\angle 48.1°)$

25. 11.02 mS

27. 120.2 V

29. 0.668

Section 13.5:

1. 60°

3. 48°

Section 13.6:

1. 166.67 μs

3. 54 mA

5. 1.75 kV

Section 13.7:

1. An inductor won't allow sudden changes in current, so the magnitude of the variations is reduced by passing the pulsating current through an inductor.

3. The circuit would pass 2 MHz through to the "100 kHz" output, but would allow very little voltage on the "1 kHz" output.

Section 13.8:

1. *L* is open

3. *L* is shorted

Review Questions

Section 13.1:

1. True

3. inductor

5. 90° (current lagging)

7. False

9. siemens

11. ohms

13.

15.

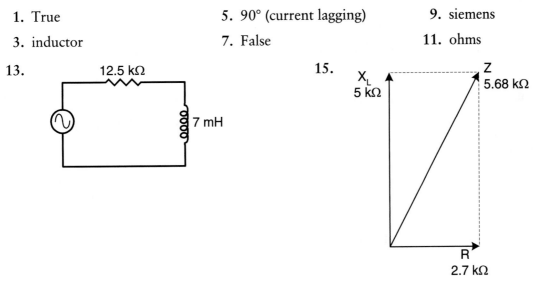

17. resistance

19. Apparent power; It is the phasor sum of true power and reactive power.

Section 13.2:

21. False

23. True

25. 2.92 A

27. 357.1 μA

29. 100 V

31. 196.42 μA

33. 51.32 kΩ

35.

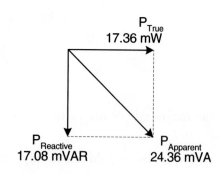

P_{True}
17.36 mW

$P_{Reactive}$
17.08 mVAR

$P_{Apparent}$
24.36 mVA

Section 13.3:

37. $I = 20\text{ A} + j25\text{ A}$
$I = -60\text{ A} - j60\text{ A}$
$I = 40\text{ A} - j25\text{ A}$

39. $93.97\ \Omega + j34.2\ \Omega$ **41.** $38.82\text{ mA} + j144.89\text{ mA}$ **43.** $36.8\text{ mA} \angle 42.8°$

Section 13.4:

45. $4.396\text{ k}\Omega$ **57.** 100 V   **67.** $10.94\text{ k}\Omega$

47. 2.47 mA   **59.** 12.25 mA   **69.** 1.71 mA

49. 10.86 V   **61.** $4.07\text{ k}\Omega$ **71.** 18.69 V

51. 41.49 mW   **63.** 2.13 W   **73.** 31.33 mW

53. 49.4 mVA   **65.** 0.867 (lagging)   **75.** 0.367 (lagging)

55. 0.84 (lagging)

Section 13.5:

77. 36°   **81.** 63.2   **85.** 72 kV

79. tau (τ)   **83.** 18.75 μs

Section 13.6:

87. Output 1

Section 13.7:

89. applied voltage   **91.** b

CHAPTER 14

Exercise Problems

Section 14.1:

1. electrostatic

3. False

5. False

7. farads

9. area of the plates, distance between the plates, and the type of material used for the dielectric (dielectric constant)

11. 354 pF

Section 14.2:

1. axial

3. SMD capacitors have no leads.

5. Capacitance exists between any two conductors that are separated by an insulator. If this capacitance is unintentional, it is called stray or parasitic capacitance.

7. zero

9. increases abruptly

11. 2,562.5 µF

13. variable

Section 14.3:

1. decreases

3. 6 µF

5. 800 pF

7. 20 pF

9. 7.14 µF

Section 14.4:

1. Capacitive reactance

3. increases

5. inversely

7. 63.7 pF

9. 133.56 Ω

Section 14.5:

1. None

3. low

5. low

7. 0.01

9. 0.005

Section 14.6:

1. It is a positive identification method. Capacitors are generally very inexpensive (particularly SMD), and risk of damage to the circuit board and/or capacitor is lessened.

3. shorted

Review Questions

Section 14.1:

1. False

3. dielectric

5. farads

7. 17 nC

9. dielectric constant

11. directly

13. directly

Section 14.2:

15. axial

17. surface-mount

19. If connected backwards, the capacitor may explode.

21. The dielectric will break down, and the capacitor effectively shorts.

23. It has a negative temperature coefficient of 750 ppm.

25. 570.5 pF

27. 651.95 pF

29. True

31. The polarity is marked (e.g., plus or minus signs, colored dots, etc.).

Section 14.3:

33. decreased

35. parallel

37. 1080 pF

39. 2500 pF

41. False

43. 1070 pF

45. 375 pF

Section 14.4:

47. True

49. decreases

51. 0.236 Ω

53. 60.1 Hz

55. 35 kΩ

57. series

59. 333.33 Ω

61. 14 kΩ

63. 150 pF

Section 14.5:

65. True

67. zero

69. dielectric dissipation resistance; plate and wire resistance

71. decreases

73. 0.01

Section 14.6:

75. The substitution method is replacing a suspected component with a component known to be good.

77. Yes

79. probably good

CHAPTER 15

Exercise Problems

Section 15.1:

1. 225 mA

3. Sum (phasoral) of the voltage drops equals the applied voltage.

5. True   **7.** impedance   **9.** 147.05 kΩ

11.

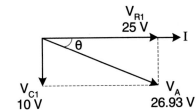

13. True

Section 15.2:

1. False

3. 90° (current leads)

5. True

7. 173.2 μA

9.

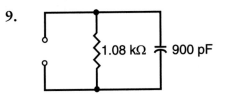

11. 24 kΩ   **13.** 41.67 μS

Section 15.3:

1. 53.08 kΩ   **3.** 15.18 μS   **5.** 303.63 μA

7. 16.12 V

9. 0.592 (leading)

11. 120.19 V

13. 31.48 mA

15. 34.84 mA

17. 314 μS

19. –60.28°

21. 924.56 Ω

23. 514.79 Ω

25. 1.94 mS

27. 254.3 mV

29. 0.822

Section 15.4:

1. 2.7 ms

3. 2.2 μF

5. short

Section 15.5:

1. The pulsating waveform is applied to a series *RC* circuit, and the output is taken across *C*. If the time constant is long, then *C* cannot charge or discharge fast enough to follow the input voltage changes. Therefore, the output is smooth.

3. charging

Section 15.6:

1. *C* open

3. *R* open

Review Questions

Section 15.1:

1. True

3. 10 mA; 10 mA

5. False

7. 0° (in phase)

9. True

11. 6.09 kΩ

13. 2.2 pF

15.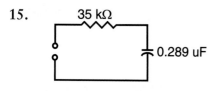

17.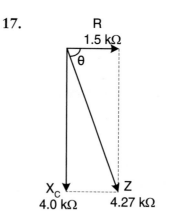

19. False

Section 15.2:

21. False

23. 90° (current leading)

25. True

27. 425.74 mA

29. True

31.

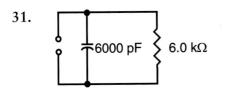

33.

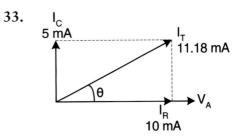

Section 15.3:

35. 454.96 Ω

37. 83.44 mA

39. 32.54 V

41. −49.39°

43. 2.72 W

45.

CIRCUIT QUANTITY		RESISTOR	CAPACITOR	TOTAL
Current		10.1 mA	10.1 mA	10.1 mA
Voltage	V	6.7 V	9.1 V	11.3 V
	V	13.4 V	18.2 V	22.6 V
	V	4.75 V	6.43 V	8 V
Resistance/Reactance/Impedance		470 Ω	636.9 Ω	791.5 Ω
Conductance/Susceptance/Admittance		2.13 mS	1.57 mS	1.26 mS
Power		47.98 mW	64.94 mVAR	80.8 mVA
Phase Angle			−53.6°	
Power Factor			0.593	

47. 636.9 Ω

49. 7.85 mA

51. 9.58 mA

53. 1.92 mS

55. 0.574

57. 27.47 mW

59.

CIRCUIT QUANTITY		RESISTOR	CAPACITOR	TOTAL
Current		9.26 mA	4.71 mA	10.39 mA
Voltage	V	353.5 V	353.5 V	353.5 V
	V	707 V	707 V	707 V
	V	250 V	250 V	250 V
Resistance/Reactance/Impedance		27 kΩ	53.08 kΩ	24.06 kΩ
Conductance/Susceptance/Admittance		37 μS	18.8 μS	41.6 μS
Power		2.32 W	1.18 VAR	2.6 VA
Phase Angle			−27°	
Power Factor			0.891	

61. 1.59 kΩ

63. 5.57 kΩ (–45.58°)

65. 5.11 kΩ (–56.49°)

67. 31.11 V

69. 5.95 mA

71. 1.96 VA

73. 0° (in phase)

75. 0.552

Section 15.4:

77. True

79. 12.5 seconds

81. 100 kΩ

83. short

85. 500 mA

87. 10 μA

89. 3.45 seconds

Section 15.5:

91. longer delay; longer delay

93. shorted, open, and leaky

95. C is shorted

CHAPTER 16

Exercise Problems

Section 16.1:

1. False

3. 25.1 kΩ

5. net reactive power

7. True

9. False

Section 16.2:

1. 75.36 Ω

3. 172.3 Ω

5. 116.1 mA

7. 14.35 V

9. –45.86°

11. 1.0 kΩ

13. 141.4 V

15. 251.2 mA

17. 400 mA

19. –22.2°

21. 113 Ω

23. 180 Ω – j214.6 Ω

25. 428.3 Ω

27. 93.39 mA

29. 464.6 mA

Section 16.3:

1. pendulum and crystal goblet (see text for details)

3. equal to

5. False

7. 1.0 (unity)

9.

CIRCUIT QUANTITY	RESISTOR	INDUCTOR	CAPACITOR	TOTAL
Current (rms)	11.67 A	11.67 A	11.67 A	11.67 A
Voltage (rms)	35 V	2.13 kV	2.13 kV	35 V
Resistance/Reactance/Impedance	3 Ω	182.6 Ω	182.6 Ω	3 Ω
Resonant Frequency	7.27 MHz			
Q	60.9			
Bandwidth	119.4 kHz			
Phase Angle	0°			
Power Factor	1.0			

Section 16.4:

1. peak

3. Your instructor will evaluate your response.

Section 16.5:

1. A series LC circuit acts like a short at resonance.

3. increase

Review Questions

Section 16.1:

1. True

3. 90° (current lags)

5. 0° (in phase)

7. 56.57 mV

9. 567.7 µA

11. True

13. 90° (current leads)

15. 0° (in phase)

17. 11.18 VA

Section 16.2:

19. 39 Ω

21. 327.8 mA

23. 12.78 V

25. 3.28 V

27. 0.328 (lagging)

29. 3.28 VA

31. 5.0 kΩ

33. 5 mA

35. 3.68 mA

37. 6.4 kΩ

39. 19.22°

41. 125 mVAR

43. 32 mVAR

45. 97.4 mVA

47. 1.0 kΩ

49. 270 Ω – j423.5 Ω; 502.2 Ω ∠ –57.48°

51. 1.23 kΩ   **55.** 40.66 V   **59.** 14.2°

53. 81.5 mA   **57.** 0.969

Section 16.3:

61. False   **67.** inductive   **73.** True

63. capacitive   **69.** True   **75.** 100

65. resistive   **71.** True   **77.** False

79. False

81. A 50% reduction in power corresponds to a 3 dB loss.

83. 10   **87.** 7.07 V

85. 176.8 mA   **89.** 410.5 kHz

91.

CIRCUIT QUANTITY	RESISTOR	INDUCTOR	CAPACITOR	TOTAL
Current (rms)	14.63 mA	14.63 mA	14.63 mA	14.63 mA
Voltage (rms)	120 mV	4.99 V	4.99 V	120 mV
Resistance/Reactance/Impedance	8.2 Ω	341 Ω	341 Ω	8.2 Ω
Resonant Frequency	5.43 MHz			
Q	41.6			
Bandwidth	130.6 kHz			
Phase Angle	0°			
Power Factor	1.0			

93. self-resonant

Section 16.4:

95. misalignment (improper tuning)

97. False

Section 16.5:

99. True

CHAPTER 17

Exercise Problems

Section 17.1:

1. 1.0

3. 159.6 mH

5. False

7. 475 μH

9. 15 mH

Section 17.2:

1. primary

3. dot notation

5. leakage flux

7. ferrite

9. autotransformer

11. True

Section 17.3:

1. 7:1

3. 1000

5. 100 V

7. 1.8 A

9. 375 mA

11. 204 Ω

13. 75 Ω

15. 95.2%

17. True

Section 17.4:

1. High voltages are used to reduce copper loss and voltage drop associated with higher currents.

3. 1:1

5. 1:10

Section 17.5:

1. open winding

3. infinity

5. Many transformer defects cause visible evidence and/or a pungent smell.

Review Questions

Section 17.1:

1. True

3. True

5. 87.5 mH

7. 756.2 μH

9. False

11. 300 mH

13. 150 mH

Section 17.2:

15. True	**23.** air	**31.** copper loss
17. dot notation	**25.** ferrite	**33.** False
19. lower	**27.** True	**35.** The core is laminated.
21. audio	**29.** Yes	

37. The purpose of a Faraday shield is to eliminate the effects of primary-to-secondary capacitance.

Section 17.3:

39. 1:5	**49.** 20 V	**57.** 363.6 mA
41. 4:3	**51.** 160 mA	**59.** 92.6%
43. 137.5	**53.** increase	**61.** True
45. 1.75	**55.** False	**63.** False
47. 165 V		

Section 17.4:

65. True

67. isolation transformer

69. Source and load impedance must be equal (matched) to have maximum power transferred to the load.

Section 17.5:

71. False	**73.** infinite	**75.** False

CHAPTER 18

Exercise Problems

Section 18.1:

1. b, c	**5.** 7.96 pF
3. 6.78 kHz	**7.** 110.1 kHz

Section 18.2:

1. a, d	**5.** 1.18 pF
3. 8.67 kHz	**7.** 4.33 MHz

Section 18.3:

1. d

3. True

Section 18.4:

1. a

3. False

5. False

Section 18.5:

1. True

3. lowest

5. low

Section 18.6:

1. False

3. If the force is spread over a large area, then the list of suspect connections is also large.

Review Questions

Section 18.1:

1. False	9. equal to	17. 4.33 kHz
3. True	11. False	19. True
5. True	13. 1.26 kHz	21. 434.4 Ω
7. greater than	15. True	

Section 18.2:

23. False	31. equal to	39. 318.5 kHz
25. False	33. Yes	41. True
27. True	35. 338.8 Hz	43. 135.5 kΩ
29. less than	37. True	

Section 18.3:

45. True	47. False	49. False

51. The input frequency is equal to one of the cutoff frequencies.

53. True	57. 91.9 kHz	61. d
55. 734.5 kHz	59. True	

Section 18.4:

63. True	67. False	71. twin-tee notch filter
65. False	69. False	73. 132.7 kΩ

Section 18.5:

75. False

77. They can also provide impedance matching.

79. True

Section 18.6:

81. Bridging can be used to identify an open component.